THE POPULATION CRISIS
AND THE USE
OF WORLD RESOURCES

WORLD ACADEMY OF ART AND SCIENCE

2

THE POPULATION CRISIS
AND THE USE
OF WORLD RESOURCES

edited by
STUART MUDD

Associate Editors

HUGO BOYKO, ROBERT C. COOK, LARRY NG, W. TAYLOR THOM JR.

INDIANA UNIVERSITY PRESS

BLOOMINGTON & LONDON

28468

THIRD PRINTING 1966

COPYRIGHT 1964 BY UITGEVERY DR. W. JUNK, THE HAGUE
ORIGINALLY PUBLISHED BY DR. W. JUNK IN THE NETHERLANDS
FIRST PUBLISHED IN THE UNITED STATES 1964
LIBRARY OF CONGRESS CATALOG CARD NUMBER 64-63015
MANUFACTURED IN THE UNITED STATES OF AMERICA

Contents

PART II. THE USE OF WORLD RESOURCES

APPENDIX

Preface

Among the dramatic changes in human ecology which have been brought about by the unprecedented and accelerating growth of the sciences and technology, two stand out as presenting problems of peculiar scope and urgency. First, of course, are those resulting from the liberation of fission and fusion energies of the atom; these are the subjects of daily discussion, anxiety and hope, and will not be further considered here beyond pointing out that they are intimately, if subtly, interwoven with the second great category of change. This category comprises the profound ecologica disequilibrium brought about by the world-wide application of scientific medicine and public health to reduction of death rates without corresponding reduction of birth rates. The resulting explosive increase in populations, in particular in the developing regions of the world, which is outpacing any practicable increase of resources, is a cause of grave concern to every thoughtful observer of human ecology. The two categories are interwoven because the pressure of population growth on natural resources has throughout history been an exciting cause of aggressive and often military expansion and warfare.

The choice of the population crisis and the use of world resources as the subject of Volume II of the World Academy of Art and Science was by vote of the charter members of the Academy. The student participation is explained in the second preface by Mr. NG. We are well aware that much has been said and written both on population and on natural resources. We offer no royal road out of the wilderness. However, we do dare hope that a balanced discussion of both facets of the question by authors of highest experience and competence may offer some useful guide lines toward rational policies.

It is a curious fact that the profound ecological disequilibrium we are facing is in large measure an unforeseen consequence of the very triumphs of the sciences and of their application to human welfare by the great international agencies such as WHO and UNICEF, the philanthropic foundations and progressive governments. Must we suppose that these same beneficent agencies and persons will pass by this crisis of our time with averted eyes? The editors refuse to accept so defeatist a view. There is hope if we will openly face the problems.

STUART MUDD, Editor
HUGO BOYKO
ROBERT C. COOK
LARRY NG
W. TAYLOR THOM, Jr., Associate Editors

Preface

This book represents the culmination of two separate efforts. The World Academy of Art and Science more than two years ago decided that the topic of their second volume should be the global population problem, considering it as "the most critical subject with which we could deal." It was probably no coincidence that at about the same time a group of undergraduate students at Stanford University, during an informal discussion, expressed concern over the world's population situation. It was certainly not expertise that led us to our expression of concern. Rather, it was prompted by a somewhat reluctant realization that our generation will be the one which will experience the effects of the population explosion, and any action that has to be taken must ultimately come from this particular generation. But intelligent action presumes knowledge and understanding of the situation, both of which we found to be conspicuously lacking. Clearly something should be done about this, but what?

Individual research and consultation with faculty members at Stanford convinced us that the most effective action would be to publish a collection of articles, written by leading authorities. In publishing such a collection, an unique effort will have been realized. In its idealistic aspect, such a book should represent the collaborative efforts of both the expert and the beginner working together on a common human problem. In its more pragmatic aspect, the book should serve to acquaint the student with the situation and hopefully to stimulate intelligent thought on the subject.

Such are the separate beginnings of both the World Academy of Art and Science and student projects. One soon came to learn of the other's undertaking. A meeting clearly disclosed the wisdom of pooling our assets. Our conclusion was that in so doing we would be using the manuscripts that we have to the best possible advantage. In this joint effort, we hope that the original purpose underlying our endeavour will not be forgotten: namely, that the younger generation is indeed concerned with the rapid expansion of population, and that this generation is doing something about it.

A subsequent paperback volume will be addressed primarily to a student audience, and will contain those articles from this volume which are appropriate, plus some additions which are not included here.

LARRY NG (Stanford '61)
JAMES E. McLENNAN (Stanford '62)
FRANK J. DITTER (Stanford '63)

Extract from an Address by Ambassador Adlai E. Stevenson at the Annual Banquet of Planned Parenthood-World Population, Tuesday evening, October 15, 1963, The Plaza Hotel, New York City

Within the very recent past, discovery of some of the secrets of the atom has put such destructive force into the hands of the great powers that the whole purpose of armed struggle is becoming meaningless. The conventional wisdom about national security which has instructed the leaders of all states in all times past, has suddenly become obsolete. And so it is that the unconventional wisdom of a national security based on developing means and procedures for the peaceful settlement, or at least, the containment of vital differences among states has suddenly become even more urgent – if that is possible – than ever before.

And this, not at all strangely, is linked directly with the reason we meet here. For within the very recent past, too, scientific discoveries have so extended the average span of life that population growth threatens to frustrate all our costly efforts to achieve significant improvements in living standards. So it is not only in the attainment of peace that conventional wisdoms must give way to the unconventional wisdoms.

To say the obvious, ours is a world of multiple revolutions, of vast ferment, of pervasive change, of political turmoil. OLIVER WENDELL HOLMES once said: "We need education in the obvious more than in investigation of the obscure." This observation seems to me particularly apt with regard to the work that brings you together here tonight.

Last year, RICHARD GARDNER, Deputy Assistant Secretary of State, told the General Assembly on behalf of the United States Government that world population growth was "a matter of transcendent importance for the United Nations." "Transcendent" is a word to use most sparingly, but since Mr. GARDNER's statement ten months ago, the population of the world has gone up even more swiftly so that there are now 45 million more people than when he spoke. In the next decade, man's numbers will swell by a full half billion and probably 100 million more.

So I would like to endorse the word "transcendent." Whether or not any one nation at the moment can be said to have a "population problem," mankind's runaway growth in the Twentieth Century must concern every nation. And within the family of nations we must do our utmost to help each other understand and deal with it. As Professor GEORGE ZEEGERS, the eminent Catholic sociologist of Geneva, said recently, "the expected growth of world population ... puts before humanity great problems, the like of which it has never known before."

A more informal way of stating it would be to say, "this thing is bigger than all of us." But it need not be if we become concerned with the quantity of life as well as with the quality of life. This depends to some extent on the quality of people; for I think our own estimate of ourselves, the human species, is somehow amiss these troubled days, in a way that bears obliquely but deeply on our approach to population.

Sometime ago I came across a comment that the major problems confronting the world today could be summarized as bombs, babies and bulldozers: Nuclear bombs and missiles which might destroy civilization overnight; an excess of babies which could frustrate efforts at economic development; and bulldozers which are well on their way to leveling the world's countryside to make way for a chaotic urban sprawl.

In short, the more we learn about our expanding universe, the more we must be impressed with the minuteness of our planet, and of our species, in the infinity of space. We are learning to master the physical universe faster than we learn to control ourselves. Surely man's view of himself has been rudely shaken and diminished since those quaint pre-Copernican days, brief centuries ago, when he looked upon himself as the hub around which all else turned. And yet, for all our new knowledge and for all our peering even farther into space, we have yet to discover anything like man – indeed, any inklings of sentient life – or any other place than this earth where he could live.

Our reason tells us that the galactic vastness of space may contain other creatures, some other organic intelligence. But our most advanced instruments have yet to find it: The satellite Mariner II confirmed, in the first space probes of another planet, that the temperature of Venus is 800°; reports about the moon, meanwhile, indicate an equally unlivable temperature at the other extreme – around zero minus 500. So our own mother earth, and our own species, should again begin to seem uniquely precious.

For practical purposes in our time, therefore – and perhaps absolutely and forever – man is alone. Will he recognize, in God's wisdom, that his needs for his fellow men far outweigh his arguments with them? Can he grasp and act wisely on the simple truth that we are living on a small jewel of a star which is our only habitat and hope, and that its God-given resources must therefore be nurtured and cherished for the benefit of all mankind, rather than plundered and fought over? There may be a special irony that the so-called population crisis – calling attention to a potential excess of humanity in relation to resources – may finally drive home this fact. Perhaps the necessity of confronting the population dilemma will finally usher in the brotherhood of man.

I

I need not dwell further on the importance of population problems, nor on the spreading awareness of the implications of population trends evident throughout the world and our own country. Nor do I need to read the lengthening roster of diplomats and statesmen of many countries who have spoken out on this subject – including Senator GRUENING of Alaska. But I do want to say a few words about the role of leadership in this field, and the special contributions of the United Nations.

If we look behind the words of diplomats and statesmen, we find that their leadership often lies in discerning and articulating the existing balance of forces which moves beneath the surface of popular opinion. There are not many areas in which governments and international organizations move creatively to lead public opinion in new directions. Yet I believe that population problems provide one of the rare opportunities.

For in this field, marked by deep differences of conviction, by slogans, by emotion, it may be possible for statesmen to discern underlying principles not fully apparent to the intense partisan. In this field we need not fear differences of conviction. In this field, so intimately intertwined with the most basic facts of human life and existence, we *must* fear ignorance, inattention, easy solutions.

We know only too well, that there is no one, simple solution to this many-faceted population problem. And even with respect to the most important aspect, responsible parenthood, the obstacle is not the intransigence of one group of another.

The obstacle is not political timidity; it is not lack of consensus. The true obstacle is the long neglect of population problems, only now beginning to be remedied by scientists, by theologians, by administrators, by social scientists, and by statesmen. The simple, shocking, fact is that we know very little about human behavior in this vital area.

Our ignorance would be even greater if it were not for the work of the United Nations. With remarkable foresight the pioneers of the UN provided for a special organ on population problems – the Population Commission of the Economic and Social Council. They also provided a corresponding population section in the Secretariat which over the past seventeen years has patiently and tirelessly, assembled the basic data which have enabled us now to begin to chart the dimensions of world population problems.

And now their work is beginning to bear fruit:

Last December, for the first time in its history, the General Assembly debated the question of "Population Growth and Economic Development." As a consequence of that debate, the Secretary-General is conducting an inquiry among all the members of the United Nations and the Specialized Agencies which will, for the first time, assemble the views of all member governments.

This December there will convene in New Delhi under United Nations auspices an Asian Population Conference, the first formal conference of governments ever held in this field.

In April the Economic and Social Council adopted a comprehensive resolution on the intensification of the demographic work of the United Nations. I venture to predict that these first steps presage a lasting interest in population problems by the most important organs of the United Nations system.

Are there principles which should guide the United Nations and associated agencies as it moves to grapple with so complex a problem? I believe that there are. The greatest contribution which the United Nations can make is the encouragement of attention, of sound knowledge, and of careful analysis of problems deeply involving the most basic human values. Population problems are not an area in which drama contributes nearly so much as thought.

Last December the General Assembly found itself divided on the question of technical assistance for dealing with population problems. Yet a careful reader of the records of that debate will find little concrete specification of precisely what would be involved in a program of United Nations technical assistance. I believe that interest in technical assistance will be more nearly universal when we clarify what it is we are talking about.

The United Nations already possesses authority to lend technical assistance in all aspects of population problems. Quite apart from legal authority, however, there is no reason for the United Nations to supply particular birth control devices which are repugnant to many of its members. The limited resources of the United Nations are insufficient for this purpose. What is more important, such materials are already available from certain governments and through private channels. The less developed countries are perfectly capable of securing these materials without special provision for technical assistance or external financing.

With respect to population there are, however, several vital tasks which the United Nations should be equipped to perform in its technical assistance programs and related activities:

First, the United Nations should be able to help member countries to learn more about their own population trends, particularly in relation to the implications for economic and social development. The inquiry currently being undertaken by the Secretary-General may provide some information on the need for this kind of technical assistance.

Second, the United Nations should be prepared to extend technical assistance to member countries which desire to undertake surveys of the attitudes of their people toward marriage, child-rearing and family size. Surprisingly little is known about this important subject, even in the case of our own country.

Third, the United Nations, along with such agencies as UNESCO and the World Health Organization, can advise countries upon request on how to transmit information on family planning consistent with the cultural and religious values of their people – so that individual parents will have free access to the growing fund of knowledge in this field.

Fourth, our knowledge of the basic life processes involved in human reproduction needs to be enlarged, so that parents can have the knowledge they need to overcome both involuntary parenthood and involuntary childlessness. As President KENNEDY said last April, we need to "know more about the whole reproductive cycle," and this knowledge should then "be made more available to the world." The World Health Organization has been enabled to make a small start in this direction by the pledge of the United States last May of $500,000 to initiate research on human reproduction.

Fifth, the United Nations can help less developed countries build effective institutions for health and social services. These are not only desirable for their own sake – they are essential to the success of family planning policies at the village level.

The common element in all these activities is the development and dissemination of knowledge. It should be made unequivocally clear that in this field, as in others, the United Nations and its related agencies will not engage in propaganda, and will not seek to influence the policies of member countries. But the United Nations system can and must provide international mechanism for making knowledge available to all countries who desire it for the purpose of finding solutions to their population problems, and for expanding and deepening that knowledge. To this effort the United States has pledged its wholehearted support.

II

But the United Nations system, with its many instrumentalities and its rich fund of experience, still is but one of the resources available to the international community. What about our own government, with its resources for foreign assistance, its vast research laboratories, and its familiarity with the immense reservoir of experience gained by foundations and private firms?

We ourselves will help other countries, upon request, to find sources of information and assistance in dealing with problems of population growth.

Within limits of scientific feasibility – and the more prosaic and abrasive limits of the availability of trained personnel – the Government is well launched toward this objective. The National Institutes of Health have committed more than $3.4 million a year to reproductive studies – a figure that is destined to grow. Within the National Institutes of Health, the new Institute of Child Health and Human Development embraces research in human reproduction as one of its specific and important functions.

As this new institute becomes more firmly established, expansion of federally–supported research in this field may be expected – assuming that scientific institutions are ready and able to merit federal support.

For its part, the Agency for International Development, which is responsible for United States foreign assistance programs, is currently surveying the needs of developing countries for U.S. assistance in collecting and analyzing basic data on population trends needed for national development planning. This is an outgrowth of the long-standing AID program under which the United States had made skilled demographers and statisticians available to countries for census-taking and vital statistics.

AID is also in a position to refer requests for medical assistance in the population field to appropriate agencies of the U.S. Government, such as the Public Health Service, to private organizations, to universities, and to foundations. And AID is prepared to support scientifically meritorious research on the economic and social determinants and consequences of population trends.

Finally, let me say a few words about one of the most distinctive of American resources: the rich diversity of private organizations which American citizens so generously support through their own efforts, organizational and financial.

I do not need to tell you who are assembled here at the Annual Dinner of the Planned Parenthood Federation of America how much imagination, dedication, and practical idealism has gone into the programs of voluntary organizations such as this.

Your immense contribution is drawing attention to a problem which, as I have already said, is of transcendent importance not only to the United States but increasingly to the world.

I salute you particularly for your work during the many years during which few, even among the best informed, recognized the true importance of the looming population problem.

And I urge you now to continue your contributions to understanding on a problem which, together with the problem of building a peaceful world, will determine the success of all our efforts in this century to secure the future of the human race.

The work and vision of people like you all over this shrunken globe will, I am confident, hasten the day when men will no longer live as strangers, or war against each other as hostile neighbors, but learn to live together in the world, to respect each other's differences, to heal each other's wounds, to promote each other's progress, and to benefit from each other's knowledge.

Robert Frost wrote:

> *"Only where love and need are one,*
> *And the work is play for mortal stakes,*
> *Is the deed ever really done*
> *For Heaven and the future's sakes."*

Adlai Ewing Stevenson, LL.D., D.C.L., L.H.D., Litt. D. United States Representative to U.N. since 1961. Admitted to Illinois Bar, 1926. Asst. to Secretary of Navy, 1941–44. Chief Economic Mission to Italy, 1943; War Department Mission to Europe, 1944. Assistant to Secretary of State, 1945; U. S. Minister, Chief of U.S. Delegation to Preparatory Commission of U.N., 1945; U.S. Delegate to General Assembly of U.N., 1946, 1947. Governor of Illinois, 1949–53. Democratic candidate for President 1952, 1956. Recipient of many awards. Author: Major Compaign speeches, 1953; Call to Greatness, 1954; What I Think, 1956; The New America, 1957; Friends and Enemies, 1958; Putting First Things First, 1960, Looking Outward 1963.

Population Pressure and War

by

Earl BERTRAND RUSSELL

THE AWAKENING OF THE WEST

The World is faced at the present day with two antithetical dangers. There is the risk, which has begun to sink into popular consciousness, that the human race may put an end to itself by a too lavish use of H-bombs. There is an opposite risk, not nearly so widely appreciated, that the human population of our planet may increase to the point where only a starved and miserable existence is possible except for a small minority of powerful people. These risks, though diametrically opposed to each other, are nevertheless connected. Nothing is more likely to lead to an H-bomb war than the threat of universal destitution through over-population. It is with the nature of this threat and with the means for averting it that I shall be concerned in what follows.

Wars caused by pressure of population are no novelty. Four times – so the historians of antiquity assure us – the population of Arabia was led to overrun neighbouring countries by drought at home. The results were many, and of many kinds. They included Babylon and Nineveh, the Code of Hammurabi, the art of predicting eclipses, the Old Testament, and finally Islam. The barbarians who destroyed the Roman Empire did not keep accurate vital statistics, but there can be little doubt that population outgrew the resources of their northern forests and that this pressure precipitated them against the rich Mediterranean lands. During the last few centuries population pressure in Europe has been relieved by emigration to the Western hemisphere, and, as Red Indians do not write history, we have thought of this process as peaceable. The East, however, has enjoyed no such outlet. It was mainly population pressure that precipitated Japan's disastrous excursion into imperialism. In China, the Taiping Rebellion, civil war, and Japanese aggression for a time kept population in check. In India,

1. Reprinted from "The Human Sum," edited by C. H. ROLPH, William Heinemann Ltd., London, by kind permission.

the population grew, and grows unchecked, producing a downward plunge towards misery and starvation.

But, although population pressure has been a vital element in human affairs from time immemorial, there are several new factors which make the present situation different from anything that has preceded it. The first of these is the utter disastrousness of scientific warfare, which means that war makes the survival of anything doubtful and the survival of any good thing almost certainly impossible. The second is the absence of empty or nearly empty lands such as those into which the white man has overflowed from the time of Columbus to the present day. The third, which has an immense importance but has hardly begun to be recognized, is the success of medicine in diminishing the death rate. These three factors taken together have produced a situation which is new in human history. It must be coped with if utter disaster is to be avoided. The East has been awakening to this necessity; the West, largely for ideological reasons, has been more backward.

A few facts are necessary to make the situation clear. The population of the world, which at most periods has been very nearly stationary, began to grow with unprecedented rapidity about the year 1650. Since then the rate of growth has been not merely maintained but continually increased and is now much more rapid than it was even twenty years ago. The present rate of increase in the population of the world is, roughly, 150,000 a day or 50 million a year, and there is every reason to think that during the next decade the rate of population growth will become even greater. As a consequence of the growth in numbers during the last 20 years, human beings, on the average, are less well nourished than they were before the Second World War. To this process of deterioration no limit can be set except by a slowing-up of the increase in numbers. A careful survey of the world's resources in the matter of food leads to the conclusion that technical advances in agriculture cannot keep pace with the great army of new mouths to be fed. Moreover, technical advances can barely hold their own against the deterioration of the soil which results from a desire for quick returns. There is yet another matter of policy which has played a great part in the U.S.S.R. and is destined to play a great part in China as well as in various other countries. This is the determination, for reasons of national power and prestige, to industrialize very quickly and even at the expense of agriculture. In the existing state of the world, one can hardly blame countries for this policy. Before the First World War, Russia had little industry but was an exporter of grain. Before the Second World War, Russia had much industry and had ceased to export grain. Russia was defeated in the First World War and was victorious in the Second. In view of such facts, we cannot wonder at the race towards rapid industrialising on which many underdeveloped countries have embarked.

THE NEXT TWENTY YEARS

All these reasons make it nearly certain that poverty and undernourishment will increase in many of the most important parts of the world during at least the next 20 years, even if everything possible is done to prevent this result. The downward trend will continue until the growth of population has been slowed up. The deterioration in living conditions must be expected to produce increasing discontent and increasing envy of the more prosperous parts of the world. Such feelings tend to produce war even if, on a sane survey, war can bring no good to anybody.

In regard to the population problem there is an enormous difference between the white and non-white parts of the world. In most white countries there has been a continual decline in the birth rate during the last 80 years and, at the same time, such a rapid advance in technique that the growth in population has not been incompatible with a rise in the standard of life. But in the East, in Africa, and in tropical America the situation is very different. While the death rate has declined enormously, the birth rate has remained nearly stationary and the nations concerned have not enjoyed those outlets which enabled Western Europe to prosper during the nineteenth century. Let us consider the three most important countries of the East: India, China, and Japan. These three countries, between them, contain two-fifths of the population of the world. All these three countries, as well as the U.S.S.R., have recently undergone a change of policy in regard to populatoin. In India and Japan this change has been very notable. NEHRU inaugurated the change by a pronouncement which had no precedent among the leading statesmen of the world: "We should," he said, "be a far more advanced nation if our population were about half what it is." In pursuance of this policy, his Government inaugurated a birth control campaign. Unfortunately, so far, economic and ideological reasons combined have led to the adoption of ineffective methods, but there is every reason to hope that better methods will be adopted before long. The Japanese Government in an official bulletin, published in December 1940, just one year before Pearl Harbor, said: "If we think of the distant future of mutual prosperity in Asia, and if we give heed to the glorious mission of the Japanese race, the one thing of which we can never have enough is the number of superior people belonging to the Imperial nation." Defeat in war has changed the attitude of the Japanese Government, which is now doing everything in its power to lower the rate of population growth. In the absence of birth control information, abortions in Japan have become extremely prevalent. According to Dr. YASUAKI KOGUCHI there were between 1,800,000 and 2,300,000 induced abortions in the one year 1953. So desperate is the economic situation that large numbers of women have resorted to sterilisation. The Japanese Government, although it does not forbid abortion, is aware that contraception would be preferable, and does what it can to encourage it.

THEORY VERSUS PRACTICE IN THE WEST

Both China and Russia have been compelled by hard facts to take up an attitude not consistent with what Communists have hitherto regarded as Marxist orthodoxy. They have been in the habit hitherto of proclaiming that only under capitalism does a population problem exist and that under Communism over-population cannot occur in any foreseeable future. In Russia abortion, which STALIN had made illegal, was again made legal by a decree of November 23rd, 1955. China, during the past years, has permitted and even encouraged propaganda for scientific methods of contraception avowedly "at the general request of the masses" and in the hope of bringing about a steady fall in the Chinese birth rate.

It is a humiliating reflection for those who are inclined to feel complacent about what are called "Western Values" that on this supremely important question, upon which the whole future of mankind depends, the West is less enlightened than the East and less capable of rational adjustment to circumstances. This is due, no doubt, in large part to the fact that the most powerful Western countries, owing to their low birth rates, do not have a serious domestic population problem. Western practice at home is at variance with Western theory. What people do is right, but what they think they ought to do is wrong. What they think they ought to do has disastrous consequences, not at home, but wherever Western nations dominate less developed regions either directly or through financial and medical assistance. By their superstitious and benighted policy, they are breeding great areas of discontent and hostility.

It is difficult not to be filled with despair when one contemplates the blindness of statesmanship and of everyday popular thought on the issues with which modern man is faced. The leading Powers of the world spend enormous sums and devote their best brains to the production of methods of killing each other. Eminent moral leaders give their blessing to such efforts, and at the same time tell us that it is wicked to prevent the births which, by their excessive number, drive the nations on to the invention of H-Bombs. I could wish to see it generally recognized in the West, as it is coming to be recognized in the East, that the problem of over-population could probably be painlessly solved by the devotion to birth control of one-hundredth or even one-thousandth of the sum at present devoted to armament, The most urgent practical need is research into some method of birth control which could be easily and cheaply adopted by even very poor populations. There is, at present, only an infinitesimal research on this all-important matter, although it is in the highest degree probable that rather more research and rather more public encouragement could produce incalculably beneficial results.

Given a successful outcome to such research, there should be in every town and village of the more prolific countries centres of birth control information and public assistance as regards the supply of birth control apparatus. The Western nations have a special responsibility in this matter, for it is the discoveries of Western medicine that have so lowered the death rate as to produce a lack of balance that, on a global scale, is a wholly new phenomenon.

The desirable remedy does not lie in restoring the death rate to its former level. It does not lie in the promotion of new pestilences. Least of all does it lie in the vast destruction that a new war may bring. It lies in adapting births to deaths. The stern limits of the earth's fertility will see to it before long that the balance between births and deaths is restored. It will see to it with an arithmetical inevitability which is independent of human wisdom or folly. But if the balance is restored through human folly, immense suffering throughout the world will be involved; while, if it is restored in accordance with the dictates of good sense and humanity, there can be an end to poverty and an end to the vast hopelessness of female lives devoted to the production of children who ought not to exist and whose existence must almost inevitably be filled with misery.

THE ALTERNATIVES

During what remains of the present century, the world has to choose between two possible destinies. It can continue the reckless increase of population until war, more savage and more dreadful than any yet known, sweeps away not only the excess but probably all except a miserable remnant. Or, if the other course is chosen, there can be progress, rapid progress, towards the extinction of poverty, the end of war, and the establishment of a harmonious family of nations. It seems that the East is becoming alive to the problem, but the West, in its theories and in its external dealings, lags behind. Of all the long-run problems that face the world, this problem of population is the most important and fundamental, for, until it is solved, other measures of amelioration are futile. It is too late to escape from great hardship in the near future, but there is good reason to believe that, if war can be averted meanwhile, the pressing needs of the world will bring amelioration before it is too late.

Earl BERTRAND ARTHUR WILLIAM RUSSELL, O.M., M.A., F.R.S., mathematician, philosopher, militant champion of Peace. Earl RUSSELL has long been a leader in man's intellectual and spiritual striving to achieve the good life. His idea of a World University, first published in 1951, is one of the major aims of the World Academy of Art and Science. Earl RUSSELL was awarded the Nobel Prize for Literature in 1950, the UNESCO Kalinga Prize in 1957, the Sonning Prize in 1960. He is author, among other works, of Principia Mathematica (with Professor A. N. WHITEHEAD); Principles of Social Reconstruction (1917); The Prospects of Industrial Civilization (1923); History of Western Philosophy (1946); New Hopes for a Changing World (1951); Wisdom of the West (1959); Has Man a Future? (1961), and Unarmed Victory (1963).

The Impending Crisis

by

Sir JULIAN HUXLEY

I shall try to take the broad view of an evolutionary biologist, who must try to look at things in the light of the enduring process of evolution of which we all form a part. Seen in this light, the population crisis is part of a very critical period in the history of the world.

Thanks to the new vision which we have attained through the knowledge explosion which has gone on parallel with the population explosion in the last half-century, we have a new vision of our destiny. We may say that today evolution in the person of man is now becoming conscious of itself.

I do not want to amplify this at great length. I would remind you, however, that all reality is, in a perfectly genuine sense, evolution; that biological evolution on this planet has been going on for nearly three billion years, and that in the course of that period life has advanced (not only increased in variety, but advanced in organization) so that its highest forms, instead of being submicroscopic, tiny pre-amoebic units, became larger and more powerful, and after hundreds of millions of years vertebrates, and then land vertebrates; and eventually the final dominant type, now spreading over the world ... man.

And man is now, whether he likes it or not, and indeed whether he knows it or not (but it is important that he is beginning to know it), he is now the sole agent for the future of the whole evolutionary process on this earth. He is responsible for the future of this planet.

Now to come back to the present crisis. I would describe the present crisis as one in which quantity is threatening quality, and also, if you like, one in which the present is threatening the future. Before we make up our minds what we ought to do in the present crisis – it is no good just getting into a flap and saying that we ought to do something – we must try to find what our ultimate aim is as agent or leader of evolution here.

Surely, it isn't just power. Surely, it isn't just to eat, drink, and be merry, and say, "Well, what's posterity done for us? To hell with posterity!". It isn't just mere quantity of possessions or mere quantity of people. Nor is it just preparation for some rather shadowy after-life. I would assert that it must be to hold in trust, to conserve and to cultivate the resources of the earth and the resources of our own nature. And so our aim should be to increase the richness of life and enhance its quality.

"Fulfillment" is probably the embracing word; more fulfillment and less frustration for more human beings. We want more varied and fuller achievement in human societies, as against drabness and shrinkage. We want more variety as against monotony. We want more enjoyment and less suffering. We want more beauty and less ugliness. We want more adventure and disciplined freedom, as against routine and slavishness. We want more knowledge, more interest, more wonder, as against ignorance and apathy.

We want more sense of participation in something enduring and worthwhile, some embracing project, as against a competitive rat-race, whether with the Russians or our neighbours on the next street. In the most general terms, we want more transcendence of self in the fruitful development of personality, and more human dignity not only as against human degradation, but as against more self-imprisonment in the human ego or mere escapism.

If we look at the present scene in the light of some such vision as this, what do we see? I might begin by telling a little of what I have seen in Africa. I was sent there to report to UNESCO on the conservation of wildlife and natural habitats. And in the wonderful Queen Elisabeth National Park in Uganda the animals had been so well preserved that the hippos were over-multiplying and had trampled down the margins of the lakes and the channels; they had eaten up all the surplus food, and in fact were destroying their own habitat. The point I want to make is that man is now busy destroying his own habitat.

Man has been over-exploiting the natural resources of this planet and has been ruining its soils and doing all sorts of other unpleasant things to it. He was wasted enormous amounts of resources which he ought to have conserved. He has cut down the forests and caused floods and erosion. As FAIRFIELD OSBORN put it in the title of his book, he has plundered our planet. (Can we expect we might have another book from him, with the title *Our Blundered Planet?*). And so we are well on the way to ruining our own material habitat.

The further point I want to make is that we are beginning to ruin our own spiritual and mental habitat. Not content with destroying or squandering our resources of material things, we are beginning to destroy the resources of true enjoyment – spiritual, esthetic, intellectual, emotional. We are spreading great masses of human habitation over the face of the land, neither cities nor suburbs nor towns nor villages, just a vast mass of urban sprawl or subtopia. And to escape from this, people are spilling out further and further into the wilder parts and so destroying them. And we are making our cities so big as to be monstrous. They are growing to such a size that they are becoming impossible to live in. Just as there is a maximum possible size for an efficient land animal – you can't have a land animal more than about twice as large as an elephant – so there is a maximum possible efficient size for a city. I think that London, New York, and Tokyo have already got beyond that size.

Ambassador CHAGLA of India has said that civilization has already imposed a grievous burden on the future. I entirely agree. We have to try to lighten that burden and prevent its getting heavier. To take another metaphor, man is in danger of losing his claim to be the lord of creation, and of becoming the cancer of the whole planet: Not a very nice prospect, but a perfectly genuine one. In the message which Australian Scientists have prepared, they made a profound and depressing remark that unless we took some care, the people of all countries all over the world would soon become under-privileged.

To look at the crisis more specifically, first of all there are nearly three billion people on earth. Whatever happens, there will be about six billion people by the end of the century, well within the lifetime of many of our children already living. Even at the present moment, over half the world's population are under-fed, under-healthy, under-housed, under-wealthy, under-educated and in general under-privileged. There is an immense gap between the "haves" and the "have-nots," the privileged and the underprivileged; and the gap is widening instead of narrowing.

The world's present rate of population increase is something phenomenal. It is about fifty million a year, and increasing every year, both for simply arithmetical reasons and because the compound interest rate of increase is still itself increasing. That means the equivalent of one good-sized town every 24 hours – a hundred and forty thousand odd. If you like to think of it in terms of minutes, it is the equivalent of ten baseball teams complete with coach every minute. And yet there are people who have so little quantitative sense that they talk of getting rid of our surplus population by sending them off to other planets!

Then there is the other great myth of the present day, that this crisis can be solved by Science – "Science" with a "S", – a sort of mystical magician. "Science will find a way." Well, it's not finding its way very well at the moment; Japan, for instance, has done a wonderful job in bringing its rate of population increase down, but it is still increasing at nearly 1% per annum and is already bursting at the seams. Science is not finding a way to make our traffic problems in big cities much easier. And it is completely unable to cope with the appalling problems of health and housing in great over-large cities in under-privileged countries, such as Calcutta.

Then there is the point with reference to what Mr. EUGENE BLACK has recently said – the point that science cannot find a way of successfully industrializing an under-developed country if its birth-rate is too high.

That is one of the important points that has emerged from careful economic studies. In order to industrialize an under-developed country, you need a great deal of capital and you need a great deal of human skill and expertise. If you have too many human beings to feed, house, educate, service, and all the rest of it, that capital and skill will be used up in looking after the growing generation, and you won't be able to industrialize.

This came out very clearly in the study of possible industrialization in India by Professors COALE and HOOVER in which they pointed out that unless India got its birth-rate down by about 50% in the next 35 or 40 years, it would never be able to break through to a successful, advanced, industrialized economy.

The same sort of thing applies even to developed countries. You can't develop your educational system adequately if too many children are coming along. I have noticed that the classroom deficit in the United States had not been reduced but had actually increased in the last year of the last administration. I was once Director-General of UNESCO, and there we are all the time struggling to keep up with the enormous deficiencies of educational systems all over the world; how can we do this when floods of new children are coming along every year?

One thing that science *could* do would be to discover better methods of birth control. That is the key to the whole matter. Physiological and medical science has already brought about what we call "death-control," with the result that population is exploding; but it has not done the necessary converse of this – discovering what to do about birth-control. I would say categorically that the control of population, birth-control applied on a large scale, is a prerequisite for anything that you can call progress and advance in human evolution, even in the immediate future.

The time has now come to think seriously about population policy. We want every country to have a population policy, just as it has an economic policy or a foreign policy. We want the United Nations to have a population policy. We want all the international agencies of the UN to have a population policy.

When I say a population policy, I don't mean that anybody is going to tell every woman how many children she may have, any more than a country which has an economic policy will say how much money an individual businessman is going to make and exactly how he should do it. It means that you recognize population as a major problem of national life, that you have a general aim in regard to it, and that you try to devise methods for realizing this aim. And if you have an international population policy, again it doesn't mean dictating to backward countries or anything of that sort; it means not depriving them of the right (which I should assert is a fundamental human right) to scientific information on birth-control and help in regulating and controlling their increase and planning their families.

It is said that there are three countries which have already a population policy. I think it depends actually upon how you define a country, but if you include colonial territories or areas of similar scope, there are at least four: India, Pakistan, Barbados and Puerto Rico. They have official population policies, and in some cases they have been reasonably successful. It is most important that these countries should be given every aid in pursuing these policies. [Note July 1963: China is now a fifth.]

When it comes to United Nations agencies, one of the great scandals of the present century is that owing to pressure, mainly from Roman Catholic countries, the World Health Organization has not been allowed even to consider the effects of population density on health in its deliberations. This must be reversed.

There is great frustration in the minds of medical men all over the world, especially those interested in international affairs, who, thanks to their devoted labors, have succeeded in giving people information on how to control or avoid disease. Malaria is a striking example. As a result of all this wonderful science and goodwill, population has exploded, and new diseases, new frustrations, new miseries are arising. Meanwhile medical men are not allowed to try to cope with these new troubles on an international scale – and indeed sometimes not even on a national scale. I think I am correct in saying that even in an advanced and civilized country, the United States, there are two States in which the giving of birth-control information, even on medical grounds, is illegal.

I would say that it is essential that this whole question of population policy should be raised in the United Nations itself.[1] The UN Assembly should be a forum for airing this major problem of our times. It is already a forum for airing other problems – disarmament, atomic warfare, and so on. We must not, out of deference to religious or national or political prejudice, put our heads in the sand or pretend that the problem does not exist. We must get it discussed in the most public way in the world's greatest forums.

We must look at the whole question of population increase not merely as an immediate problem to be dealt with ad hoc, here and now. We must look at it in the light of the new vision of human destiny which human science and learning has revealed to us. We must look at it in the light of the glorious possibilities that are still latent in man, not merely in the light of the obvious fact that the world could be made a little better than it is. We must also look at it in the light of the appalling possibilities for evil and misery that still remain in human life.

I would say that this vision of the possibilities of fruitful fulfillment on the one hand as against frustration resembles the Christian view of salvation as against damnation. And I would indeed say that this new

1. In this connection see United Nations General Assembly Resolution 1838, adopted 18 December, 1962. Republished in this volume, Section VI, p. 344.

point of view that we are reaching, the vision of evolutionary humanity is essentially a religious one, and that we can and should devote ourselves with truly religious devotion to the cause of ensuring greater fulfillment for the human race in its future destiny. And this involves an all-out attack on the problem of population; for the control of population is, I am quite certain, a prerequisite for any radical improvement in the human lot.

Sir JULIAN SORELL HUXLEY, M.A., D. Sc., F.R.S., biologist, naturalist, humanist and writer. Sir JULIAN was Professor of Zoology at the Rice Institute, Houston Texas, from 1913 to 1916, and at Kings College, University of London, from 1925 to 1928, and served as Secretary of the Zoological Society of London from 1935 to 1942. He was Director General of UNESCO from 1946 to 1948. He was Darwin Medallist of the Royal Society in 1957 and winner of a Lasker Award in 1959. Sir JULIAN is an Honorary Member of the Académie des Sciences, Paris. He is author, among other works, of The Science of Life (with H. G. and G. P. WELLS); Religion Without Revelation (1927); Africa View (1931); Problems of Relative Growth (1932); Evolution: The Modern Synthesis (1943); Ethics and Evolution (1947); From an Antique Land (1954); Biological Aspects of Cancer (1957); The Story of Evolution (1958), and The Humanist Frame (Ed., 1961).

PART I. THE POPULATION CRISIS

The Facts of Population Growth

Geography and the World's Population

by

C. LANGDON WHITE

The world's population map is striking (*Fig.* 1). Anyone who looks at it and studies it notes particularly the spotty nature of the distribution of the world's more than 3 billion persons. Some areas literally swarm with humanity, others are empty or nearly so, while still others run the gamut between these two extremes. In brief, about one-half of the world's people are concentrated on a mere 5% of the earth's surface whereas 57% of the land supports only 5% of the people.

Why is it that human beings have not scattered themselves more widely and more evenly over the earth? Is this a matter of human preference or does the natural environment invite here and repel there? If man can make a living anywhere on earth and still if so much of it is virtually empty, is there any reason to be greatly concerned over the world's so-called population problem? The answer to the question – *where man is in what total numbers and why* – is undeniably the most important, the most significant in the field of human geography. In the long run, the limiting factor to population growth is the amount of arable land. Too many people forget that despite the fantastic contributions of science and technology *everything* man uses comes from the earth. The size of the arable area and the size and quality of the natural resources are more or less definite and limited. Man must begin here!

Hence human geography is vitally concerned with the problem of population. The purpose of this chapter is to 1) point out why certain areas support a disproportionate number of the world's total population, 2) explain why huge segments of the earth are empty or nearly so, and 3) suggest reasons why man will experience difficulty feeding his increasing numbers (150,000 per day) unless he does something about his birthrate. The startling increase in world population has resulted not from higher birthrates, but from falling deathrates, particularly since World War II.

A BRIEF LOOK AT THE LAND

The earth's land surface from the standpoint of terrain is divisible into four principal classes: *plains*, which comprise 41%, *plateaus*, which make up 33%, *hill country*, which constitutes 14%, and *mountains*, which cover 12%. If topography were the sole criterion of land use, we would have little to worry about, for two-thirds of the land area would be adapted to agriculture – 95% of the plains, 75% of the plateaus, 25% of the hill country, even 5% of the mountains. *But topography is not the sole determinant:* climate and soil must be considered also for they restrict significantly the land suitable for farming to a startling one-fourth of the earth's total land area (*Fig. 2*). Thus many plains are unable to support agriculture and hence any considerable number of people because of cold, aridity, inaccessibility, or swamps; while the hot humid lands cannot be regarded as non-food crop lands, large segments remain unproductive and sparsely populated, and they are regarded as "problem lands." Whereas the Philippines and Java are densely populated, interior Brazil and New Guinea are nearly empty. These notable contrasts invite inquiry into their causes and into the food crop potential of enormous areas now almost unpopulated but apparently well suited climatically to food crop production and capable of supporting dense populations.[1]

If crops are to do well, there must be at least 15 inches of precipitation in middle latitudes and 40 inches in the tropics, where evaporation is high. Length of the frostless season also definitely limits the areas of the earth suitable for crops. Even where topography and climate are favorable, enormous areas are sub-marginal for agriculture because of infertile soils: witness the vast reaches of podzol soils in the North American and Eurasian taiga, of the extensive lateritic soils in the rainy tropics, and of raw sand in the Sahara, in Arabia, and elsewhere.

THE POPULOUS LANDS

Man is most densely settled on lands below 1500 feet – that is, on expansive plains and flood plains and even on low plateaus and hills. These lands are to be found in middle latitudes, in the subtropics and in a few areas in the tropics. The lands that support the largest numbers of human beings are shown in *Fig. 1* – Asia, Africa and Latin America. These lands, which contain two-thirds of mankind, have very high birthrates, and the masses of the people have an extremely low level of living. In recent years as a result of medical science and sanitation, the death rates have fallen sharply. In fact this is the main reason for the world population explosion. Population is

1. BENNETT, M. K., "A World Map of Foodcrop Climates," *Food Research Institute Studies*, Stanford University, 1, November, 1960, *285–295*.

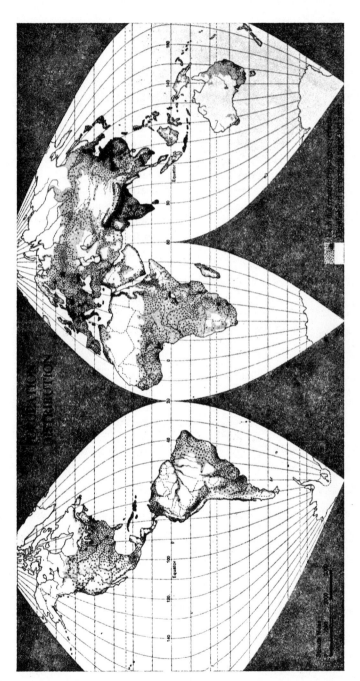

Fig. 1. Distribution of the world's population. Note the heavy concentration of people on the alluvial soils of Asia and in the industrialized areas of Europe and North America which, at the same time, have climates and terrain favorable for sustaining man, and crops. Note the emptiness of the cold, dry, mountainous, and to some degree of the wet tropical areas.
(From H. M. KENDALL, R. M. GLENDINNING, & C. H. MC-FADDEN, *Introduction to Geography*, Third Edition. New York. Copyright 1951 ©, 1958, 1962 by Harcourt, Brace and World, Inc. and reprinted with their permission.).

dense too in Western Europe and eastern North America and reasonably dense in parts of Australasia. Together these lands contain about one-fifth of the world's people. All have low death rates: birth rates, however, are high in some areas, but low in others. Nowhere is there concern currently regarding the ability of the people to produce the essentials of life. These are the lands where nature is kind and provides climatic, topographic, and soil conditions more directly suited to the production of food crops.

Comprising the third group are the countries of eastern and southeastern Europe, Spain, Japan, and several South American nations. They too contain about one-fifth of the world's population. They have moderate death rates but high enough birth rates to yield a rather high rate of in-

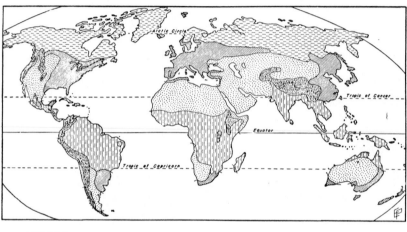

LEGEND

FAVORABLE

TOO COLD
Arctic & Subarctic

TOO DRY
Desert & Semi-desert

TOO HOT
Wet Tropics & Savanna

TOO HIGH
MT. Climates

Fig. 2. Areas of the world hospitable and hostile to man's occupance
(From R. H. FIFIELD & G. S. PEARCY, *Geopolitics in Principle and Practice*. Boston: Ginn and Company.)

crease. Recently Japan and Hungary, in this group, have ranked among those nations with the lowest human fertility.

THE SPARSELY SETTLED LANDS

Figures 1 and 3 show the parts of the world containing small numbers of human beings and the parts regarded as non-food-producing. With three

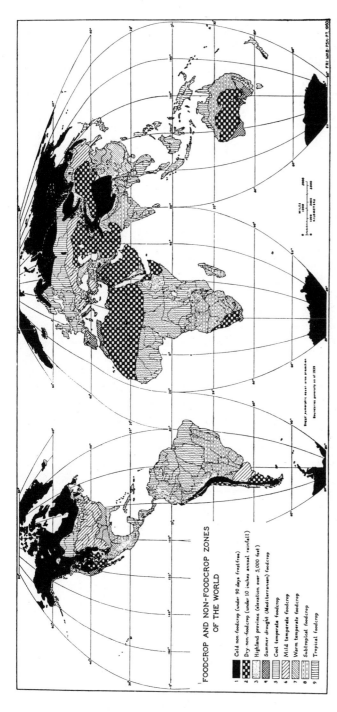

FOODCROP AND NON-FOODCROP ZONES
OF THE WORLD

1 Cold non-foodcrop (under 90 days frost-free)
2 Dry non-foodcrop (under 10 inches annual rainfall)
3 Highland province (elevation over 5,000 feet)
4 Summer drought (Mediterranean) foodcrop
5 Cool temperate foodcrop
6 Mild temperate foodcrop
7 Warm temperate foodcrop
8 Subtropical foodcrop
9 Tropical foodcrop

Fig. 3. Foodcrop and non-foodcrop zones of the world.

(Reprinted from "A *World Map of Food Crop Climates*," pp. 285–295. Food Research Institute Studies, Vol. I, No. 3, November 1960, with permission of the publishers Food Research Institute, Stanford University. © Copyright 1960 by the Board of Trustees of the Leland Stanford Junior University).

notable exceptions,[2] they are in the so-called restrictive environments –
high mountains, deserts, ice caps, and tundras. Any increase in population
(native and foreign) in these areas encounters serious obstacles, some at
present insuperable. For the most part, man has here only outposts.

High mountains. Rugged surfaces, shallow stony soils, and limited flat land,
conspire to restrict arable land in the mountain parts of the earth to 5%.
Inhospitable climate due to high altitude, keeps population to very small
numbers. The tropics are an exception, for there elevation lifts the people
into a temperate climate; e.g., mile-high Mexico City. Even in Peru's Sierra,
which man has occupied for centuries, the Indians are living mostly in
valleys and high plateaus rather than on high mountains; nowhere are the
Indians growing crops, even hardy ones, above 14,000 feet. Above this elevation, human beings live only by grazing sheep, llamas, and alpacas. The
highest permanent habitation on earth is in Peru at an altitude of 17,100
feet; and the farther man goes from the equator, the more inhospitable
high mountains become; in high latitudes they are wholly unoccupied.

Deserts. The world's deserts are presently among the most sparsely populated of all lands (*Figs.* 1 and 2). Only a minuscule portion of most deserts is
under cultivation, a situation that bids fair to persist, since water is scarce
and in the desert it is water that means life. So expansive are these lands
that food production is ruled out from about one-fifth of the land surfaces
of the globe. Even when the small "islands" made productive by irrigation
are added, the world's deserts probably have not more than 2 to 5% of their
total areas cultivable. It is estimated that deserts comprise 17% of the world's
land area and 2.6% of the world's population.

No one at this time really knows what the freshening of sea water may
mean to reclamation of the world desert lands; however, if such water is to be
utilized for irrigation, the price must be reduced from the present $1.25 per
1000 gallons to about 25 cents. In the United States even should the cost of
desalinated water be reduced to 25 cents per 1000 gallons, it would cost
farmers $80 an acre foot for irrigation against the current price (the highest
price) of about $5.

The Cold Lands. These comprise two categories, the ice caps and the tundras.
Together they cover about 29% of the world's land surface but have a mere
0.7% of the world's population.

The Ice Caps. Antarctica, most of Greenland, and several smaller ice-covered
areas are empty of population. Though Antarctica is almost twice the size
of the United States, it *has not one single permanent human inhabitant!* Since it is the

---

2. One notable exception is in parts of South America where enormous land holdings
are in the hands of the few and hence are held out of full settlement; a second is in
Inner Asia, where pastoral peoples, unwilling to farm, hold lands capable of agricultural
settlement. Under the communists, however, this system is breaking down in Mongolia,
Turkestan, and elsewhere. It is expected, too, that latifundia will begin to give way in
Latin America in the near future. The third exception is the Rainy Tropics.

coldest place on earth (the lowest surface temperature ever recorded was at the South Pole, —102 °F), and since it is covered with ice and snow, it is indeed difficult to see how any economic basis for settlement ever can be established there. Yet these ice caps make up one-fifth of the land surface thus ruling out food production there.

Tundras. Tundras cover millions of square miles in the Arctic, but human numbers are small. Agriculture is next to impossible, for the frostless season is too short for the majority of crops to reach the harvestable stage, most soils are infertile, drainage in summer is unbelievably bad, and isolation is appalling. The growing of crops is expected to inch slowly poleward into the southern fringe of the tundra but the intrusion will be small.

Up to the present time, neither the United States nor Canada has deemed it worthwhile to invest heavily in tundra agricultural enterprises. Their lands are in wilderness and are utilized by natives, chiefly Eskimos, for hunting and trapping. The widely scattered population, averaging less than one person to the square mile, is costly to maintain. In 1962 Canada announced that the most expensive citizens in the world were her Eskimos. In northern Fennoscandia the Lapps in small numbers live by grazing reindeer. The Soviet Union, conversely, makes spectacular claims regarding her achievements in the tundra at advanced agricultural experiment stations. Yet the *Great Soviet Atlas* shows no settlement of as many as 50,000 acres north of the northern limit of agriculture established in 1913. To be sure some farming is being carried on along the coasts of the Berents Sea and near the mouths of some of the larger rivers – the Ob and Yenesei and on areas once regarded as waste land north of the Arctic Circle on the Lena, the Kolyma, and the Indigarka. However, spots must be carefully selected by farmers thoroughly familiar with the vagaries of the climate so as to be protected from cold north winds. Moreover, only quick-ripening crops can be grown – cabbage, broccoli, turnips, spinach, radishes, lettuce, etc. In Finland and Sweden, farmers are plowing land that had lain under ice for centuries. In 1956, coastal Greenland began to experiment with the Inca cereal, quinua, which grows higher than any other grain in the Andes of Bolivia and Peru, and recently the United Nations announced that more than 1 million acres of Arctic lands are now producing food crops by scientific methods. Yet this is little more than a speck on the great tundra wilderness. In this habitat, man is primarily a hunter, trapper, or fisher, occupations that require much land – 70 to 200 square miles to sustain a single person. Because the pastures are poor and need resting, even graziers must be nomadic.

Wet Tropical Lowlands.[3] Enormous portions of these lands are empty or

3. There are two schools of thought regarding the tropical rain forest as a home for man. The devotees of one school are highly optimistic (they are known as the "Concuropia boys"). The other school is extremely pessimistic. Reputable scholars line up on both sides. No one knows positively whether the future is bright or dismal.

almost so. The Amazon Basin averages less than one person to the square mile; even this small population can scarcely feed itself. Java, on the other hand, is one of the most densely populated areas on earth. But it possesses volcanic soils of high nutrient status and the Dutch introduced scientific agriculture.

The sparsity of people over sizeable areas of the Wet Tropics results from many circumstances: disease, enervating climate, poor water supply, infertile soils, dense forest cover, poverty, dearth of implements, lack of incentive, and reluctance to change their ways.[4]

"Too poor to learn, too ignorant to improve, too frightened to try, a large mass of tropical peasantry is seemingly doomed to an endless round of inadequacy. Here and there a spark may be kindled, now and then an improvement made; but in spite of a growing awareness of the outside world, such people may still present a considerable drag to any progressive force." [5]

As the eminent French geographer and authority on the tropics, PIERRE GOUROU, has emphasized, it will not be easy for tropical natives to raise their level of living even if they obey nature's directions; it will be utterly impossible, however, for them to do so if they disregard them. In short, we do not yet know how to handle these lands.

For the most part, the hot wet lands have repelled the white man: perhaps he may win them in time but even this is problematical. Such lands are too hot and humid for comfort and progress; many of the same obstacles that impede the native populations are applicable also to the white population.

Many of the diseases are in the process of being conquered, however. Tropical medicine is making sensational progress. Since World War II the World Health Organization has treated and cured millions. It is attempting to stamp out 50 million cases of yaws from the world – half of them from Africa. It is also fighting a war against malaria – the world's costliest disease and its greatest cause of disablement. As a result of this war, the number of people who annually fall ill from malaria has dropped from 250 million to 140 million. WHO experts believe that within 10 years malaria can be eradicated from the earth (tropical Africa excepted for the time being). Along with several other agencies, WHO is slowly but surely driving the tsetse fly, slayer of cattle and killer of men, from the huge sweep of Africa where it has prevailed for ages – an area half as large again as the entire continent of Australia.

No great numbers of people are expected to migrate to the Rainy Tropics

4. This statement is a generalization and hence not applicable to many areas within the climatic realm. But insofar as broad generalizations are justifiable and reasonably accurate, the concept holds.

5. LEE, DOUGLAS H. K., Climate and Economic Development in the Tropics. New York: Harper and Brothers, 1957, pp. 157–158.

until life there can be much improved. Betterment involves progress in transport and communication, public health, food, water supply, and an overall improvement in level of living. Such progress would require capital of a size possessed by no tropical governments. The job is positively staggering and probably will continue to be so for decades, perhaps forever.

Much of the ill health results from poor food and contaminated water and ill health contributes to low economic status. When people are ill and weak from starvation or near-starvation, they cannot work and produce as they could if well and sustained by a satisfactory diet.

Probably the strongest argument against the wet tropics as a permanent home for white people is the current trend in pioneering. Even if science and medicine should be successful in banishing diseases that presently impede progress, white people *prefer* a cool climate to a hot one. What emigrants *desire* and not what they can or could do, determines the trend of population.

OVERPOPULATION AND UNDERPOPULATION

In discussions of population, much is heard regarding overpopulation and underpopulation. Persons who do not tunnel under the surface in their thinking tend to be of the opinion that the sparsely populated lands afford the safety valve for the densely populated ones and hence that there is no serious problem. Density *per se*, however, does not necessarily imply overpopulation nor does sparsity guarantee underpopulation. If the degree and skill in the sparsely populated country be low, that country possibly is overpopulated; conversely, if the skill be high and the natural resources base strong, very high densities may occur without overpopulation.

If *Figures* 1, 2, and 3 be superimposed, one upon another, it will be noted that they coincide very well indeed. The sparsely settled and virtually empty lands are those whose climates particularly make even subsistence agriculture highly speculative and often impossible.

INDUSTRIALIZATION: THE PANACEA?

The answer to population pressure by encroachment onto and development of new lands does not appear promising: all the best grasslands are already occupied. As already noted lands in restrictive environments show little promise at least for the immediate future (*Fig.* 2), and the lands already densely occupied may reach a saturation point – at least those in the underdeveloped category such as China, India, and Pakistan.

What then can be done? Many regard industrialization as the way out. The literature dealing with population and underdeveloped lands invariably preaches this credo. But is industrialization the magic wand? The writer does not think so. Modern industry cannot be superimposed upon the feudalistic society of underdeveloped lands. Many of these countries are limited by a lack, or at least a paucity, of fuel and power, by low wages, dearth of skilled workers, poorly developed transport, scarcity of capital, hostile or at least unfavorable climates, lean raw materials base, and all kinds of social obstacles and man-made economic difficulties. Neither undue ambition nor unbridled enthusiasm by political and social leaders can supply bases for industrialization if these are wanting. Many times underdeveloped nations have embarked on ambitious projects without adequate information, disregarding the bases operative in the scientific location of industry upon which success depends. The sporadic voices of caution invariably are ignored.[6] Those in power are extremely sensitive to any criticism of their programs. Undeniably the industrial fetish dies hard. However with the years, the weaknesses and strengths of hothouse industrialization are becoming more apparent.

Industrialization in nearly all underdeveloped countries faces five major difficulties:

1) The prevailing biting poverty and widespread illiteracy of the people which restrict the market for fabricated products and reduce the supply of skilled workers to man the plants.

2) Scarcity of local capital. Capital from the masses is an illusion; the majority of the people live too close to the level of bare subsistence to have funds for creating new real capital. Accordingly, for many years to come industrialization must depend to a very considerable degree upon foreign capital. However, for foreign capital to enter a given country, the investment climate must be good and the political situation must be reasonably stable. ELMER W. PEHRSON, authority on mineral economics, states that very few underdeveloped countries have realistic laws and regulations that encourage private capital to invest in the development of minerals.[7]

3) The prevalent concept of national self-sufficiency – that a country must have industrial plants and that these must make use of domestic raw materials even at high cost. It is difficult, for example, to understand how countries like Argentina and Egypt can justify from an economic standpoint, integrated iron and steel plants.

4) Inadequate transportation. With few exceptions railroads are so poorly integrated with the settlement pattern that the movement of goods is extremely costly. In some countries the railways may be of several gauges.

6. WHITE, C. LANGDON, "Industrialization: Panacea for Underdeveloped Nations?" Yearbook, Association of Pacific Coast Geographers, 17, 1955, 3–20.
7. PEHRSON, ELMER W., "Minerals in National and International Affairs," Chapter II, in Economics of the Mineral Industries, American Institute of Mining, Metallurgical and Petroleum Engineers, New York, 1959, p. 512.

5) The scarcity of technological know-how. In many countries this deficiency is being corrected. Hundreds of young men are learning skills in the United States, Western Europe, and the USSR. It must be remembered, however, that industrialization is not spontaneous but is a process of social change that takes place over a considerable period of time.

SUMMARY AND OUTLOOK

It has been pointed out that only about 25% of the earth's land surface possesses geographic conditions suitable for human life and for the production of food for human consumption. If it be true that human population will probably double by the year 2000 and if now two-thirds of the world's people are hungry, then the future points to trouble – deep trouble, for in the great world race food supply is no match for population. Even the foreign aid programs are threatened by the intolerable living standards of the two-thirds of humanity in large parts of Asia, Africa, and Latin America constantly in want. They are the product of a sharp decline in the death rate unaccompanied by a sharp decline in the birth rate.

The writer does not agree with the proponents of the cornucopia school that whenever mankind gets into trouble – even deep trouble – science and technology will rescue him. The major problem currently is to feed adequately, both in number of calories and nutritionally, all peoples on this earth. The intensity of production will increase and yet there is indisputably a maximum, measureable extent of the cultivable area. Geography's great contribution could be a world land-use survey. As L. DUDLEY STAMP has pointed out, the problem of the underdeveloped lands is not one to be solved by government decree; rather it is a problem that will persist for decades, generations, perhaps centuries.

There is no measurability available for man's multiplication. His numbers in the final analysis thus will depend upon the carrying capacity of the earth. Man must learn to get along with what nature has provided. He will be able to increase his numbers greatly but with a falling level of living. One of man's biggest jobs is to learn to control himself. Unless he can do this, all his accomplishments will be for naught. The path of life is strewn with the bones of those who failed to make the necessary adjustments to the times. We do know that man is capable of making the adjustments to his time. What we do not know is whether he will do so before it is too late.

SELECTED BIBLIOGRAPHY

BROWN, H., *The Challange of Man's Future*. New York: Viking Press, 1954.

GOUROU, P., *The Tropical World*. New York: John Wiley and Sons, Inc., 1961.

—, "The Quality of Land Use of Tropical Cultivators," in *Man's Role in Changing the Face of the Earth*. Chicago: University of Chicago Press, 1956, *336–349*.

GOULD, L. M., *The Polar Regions in Their Relation to Human Affairs*. New York: American Geographical Society, 1958.

GRAY, G. W., "*Life at High Altitudes*," *Scient. American*, 193, December 1955, *58–68*.

ISSAWI, CHARLES, *Egypt: An Economic and Social Analysis*. London: Oxford University Press, 1947.

KELLOGG, C. E., *The Soils that Support Us*. New York: The Macmillan Company, 1941.

MONGE, CARLOS, *Acclimatization in the Andes*. Baltimore: Johns Hopkins University Press, 1948.

KIMBLE, G. H. T., Editor, *Geography of the Northlands*. New York: John Wiley and Sons, 1955.

NOTESTEIN, F. W., "7 Billion People by the Year 2000," *Foreign Agric.*, 26, July, 1962, *3–4*; *22*.

PEHRSON, E. W., "Mineral Supply: There is Plenty of Everything We Need... If We Can Get It," *Int. Sci. and Technol.*, February, 1962, *23–27*.

President's Materials Policy Commission, *Resources for Freedom*, Washington, D.C., Government Printing Office, 1952. 5 Vols.

SPENGLER, J. J., "Population Threatens Prosperity," *Harvard Business Rev.*, 34 January–February, 1956, *85–94*.

STAMP, L. DUDLEY, *Lands for Tomorrow*. Bloomington, Indiana: Indiana University Press, 1952.

—, "The Measurement of Land Resources," *Geogr. Rev.*, 48, January, 1958, *1–15*.

"Symposium on World Food and Population," *Discovery*, 21, October, 1960, *419; 456–457*.

TAEUBER, I., *The Population of Japan*. Princeton: Princeton University Press, 1958.

United Nations, Department of Social Affairs, Population Division, *Population Growth and the Standard of Living in Underdeveloped Countries*, No. 20. New York: 1954.

WYLLIE, J., *Land Requirements for the Production of Human Food*. London: University of London Press, 1954.

CHARLES LANGDON WHITE, Ph. D., Sc. D., has been Professor of Geography at Stanford University since 1943. He has served as Visiting Professor at Columbia University, Ohio State, San Marcos University, Peru, University of Oregon, University of Guadalajara, Mexico, University of Hawaii, University of California in Los Angeles. He has directed field parties in Alaska, the Caribbean, the Mediterranean and Mexico, and has served on commissions of national and international scope. He is a contributor to technical journals and coauthor of books in his field, including a work on World Economic Geography, published in 1964.

How Many People Have Ever Lived on Earth?

by

ANNABELLE DESMOND *

How many people have ever been born since the beginning of the human race?

What percentage does the present world population of three billion represent of the total number of people who have ever lived?

These questions are frequently asked the Population Reference Bureau's Information Service. Because of the perennial interest and because of the credence sometimes given to what would seem to be unrealistic appraisals, this issue presents an estimate prepared by FLETCHER WELLEMEYER, Manpower, Education and Personnel Consultant, Washington, D.C., with FRANK LORIMER of American University, Washington, D. C., acting as advisor. This estimate, based on certain statistical, historic and demographic assumptions set forth in an appendix, should be regarded as no more than a reasonable guess. It assumes that man first appeared about 600,000 years ago, a date which has been proposed for the dawn of the prehistoric era. However, this date obviously is a compromise, anthropologically speaking, between varying extremes.

Since then, it is estimated that about 77 billion babies have been born. Thus, today's population of approximately three billion is about 4.0% of that number.

Absolutely no information exists as to the size and distribution of prehistoric populations. Presumably they were not large, nor very widely distributed. If the 600,000 B.C. date is accepted as a sound compromise, then only about 12 billion people – less than one sixth of the total number ever born – are estimated to have lived before 6,000 B.C.

Reprinted from February 1962 issue of the *Population Bulletin*, published by Population Reference Bureau, 1755 Massachusetts Ave, N.W., Washington 36, D.C.
* (This article was based on a research report prepared by FLETCHER WELLEMEYER with the technical assistance of FRANK LORIMER, and on supplemental research by GEORGINE OGDEN. The *Bulletin*, which represents a unique cooperative undertaking, makes available to the general reader various aspects of the world population crisis.)

Anthropologists and paleontologists differ by hundreds of thousands of years as to when man first walked this earth. Recent discoveries strongly suggest that the life-span of the human species might date back as much as two million years. However, this time-scale has not yet been accepted by all anthropologists.

If the "beginning" actually extended a million years prior to 600,000 B.C., the estimated number of births prior to 6,000 B.C. would be 32 billion, and the estimated total number, about 96 billion.

Prior to 1650, historical population data are very scanty for every part of the world. Despite this lack of knowledge, ancillary evidence exists which reveals the general pattern of human growth. Throughout the thousands of centuries which preceded the present technological age, human survival was such a touch-and-go affair that high fertility was essential to balance brutally high mortality. The human female – a relatively slow breeder, even among mammals – had to reproduce somewhere near her physiological limit in order for the family, the clan, the tribe and the nation to survive.

As human culture developed over the ages, the chances of survival tended to improve. When the invention of agriculture provided a more stable food supply, the base was laid for the maintenance of large populations and for their spread into new areas. However, high death rates continued to check population growth.

Until recently, at least a half of all babies born died before reaching maturity. Man's quest for some formula to avert death included magic, incantations and prayers, but none of these had shown any efficacy against the major killers. Then, with the advance of modern science, the mortality pattern of a million years was broken.

JENNER's dramatic discovery of vaccination for smallpox was the first of a multitude of discoveries destined to defer death, especially in infancy and childhood. This brilliant application of the scientific method to biology and medicine, together with improved agricultural technology, better transportation and the vast and complex nexus of an emerging industrial culture, set in motion forces which drastically lowered death rates and thereby greatly increased the efficiency of reproduction. In some countries, the birth rate declined also, although more slowly than the death rate. During the 19th century, the industrial countries of the West were the first to experience the transition from high to low birth and death rates. This transition took about 150 years.

These epochal changes profoundly altered the patterns of survival and population growth. In those countries of northern Europe and North America which were the first to exploit effectively the new medical discoveries, life expectancy at birth rose rapidly from 30 years to 40, then to 50, and, by 1960, to 70 years and more. Infant mortality declined drastically: now, 95 out of every 100 babies born in Western industrial countries live to reach adulthood.

Although the power to defer death is one of the greatest advances in man's long history, it has been the principal factor in the acceleration in the rate of population growth during the past century. Now, public health programs reach even the world's remote villages, and death rates in the less developed areas are falling rapidly. But the traditionally high birth rates – so essential to offset the high death rates of even the very recent past – remain high. Thus, population growth soars.

Therefore, over the long span of history, the rate of population growth has tended to accelerate – almost imperceptibly at first; then slowly; and recently, at a rapid clip. By the beginning of the Christian era, 200–300 million people are believed to have lived on earth. That number had grown to some 500 million by 1650. Then the growth curve took a sharp upward trend. By 1850, world population was more than 1 billion. Today, it is over 3 billion.

The quickening tempo of growth is even more dramatically expressed in doubling time. It took hundreds of thousands of years for world population to reach the quarter-billion mark, at about the beginning of the Christian era. Over 16 centuries more passed before that number reached an estimated half-billion. It took only 200 additional years to reach one billion, and only 80 more years – to about 1930 – to reach two billion. Population growth rates are still going up. During all of the eons of time – perhaps as long as two million years – the human race grew to its present total of three billion. But it will take only 40 years to add the next three billion, according to United Nations estimates. In certain nations and larger areas, populations will double in 25 years or even less, if growth rates remain unchanged.

This historical review traces the proliferation of the human species through three very broad time-spans: Period I extends from 600,000 B.C. to 6,000 B.C.; Period II extends to 1650 A.D.; and Period III, to 1962. These time periods are chosen because the dates mark important epochs in man's cultural development.

It should be emphasized, however, that not all portions of the globe experienced simultaneously the cultural and technological advances which mark these different stages of man's history. When the first European settlement was established in Australia in 1788, the aborigines there were in the Stone Age. Even today, some tribes living in New Guinea and elsewhere still remain at that level.

PERIOD I – THE OLD STONE AGE

Period I extends from 600,000 to 6,000 B.C. It begins early in the Paleolithic or Old Stone Age and continues to the beginning of the Neolithic or New Stone Age. It is estimated that during this period numbers grew to about five million, that man's birth rate was close to 50 per thousand, and that there was an approximate total of 12 billion births.

Little, if anything, is known about population size during this hunting and gathering stage of man's existence. The total land area of the earth is approximately 58 million square miles. It seems reasonable to assume that not more than 20 million square miles could have been used successfully by the relatively few who inhabited the earth at that time. The consensus of competent opinion indicates that, on moderately fertile soil in a temperate climate, about two square miles per person would be needed for a hunting and gathering economy.

It must be assumed that there were severe limitations on man's numbers during this period; and that his life cycle and average generation were much shorter than they are today. Man existed for the most part in wandering bands in order to survive. Our ancient ancestors were completely subject to all the vagaries of the weather and the ecological cycle of the game animals on which their existence depended. Food shortages were usually endemic, and the ravages of epidemics were routine – although the wide dispersal of the population tended to localize these hazards. Nevertheless, the picture that emerges is one in which births and deaths were roughly balanced, with births perhaps holding a narrow margin.

The Long Time-Span of Prehistory

Anthropologists and paleontologists are gradually putting together, piece by piece, the great jigsaw puzzle that is the history of early man. Dr. T. D. STEWART, Head Curator of the Department of Anthropology, National Museum in Washington, D.C., points out that only a few fossils of humans who lived in this period have been found. Nevertheless, man's long time-scale is known today with far greater accuracy than ever before, mainly because of the new radioactive dating techniques. According to Dr. STEWART, new discoveries demand new theories or that existing theories be adjusted.

The remains of *Zinjanthropus*, recently found in the Olduvai gorge of Tanganyika by L. S. B. LEAKEY, Curator of the Coryndon Museum, Nairobi, Kenya, which LEAKEY believes date back almost two million years, probably do not represent the beginning of the line. *Zinjanthropus* has been called man because he was a toolmaker, in the crudest sense. Since his physical form represents a very early stage of human evolution, it is not advisable to assume so early a beginning for purposes of estimating human population growth.

However, it is generally believed that "man" had reached the point of being able to make simple tools and to talk by a half million or even a million years ago. Though he presumably emerged much earlier, *Homo sapiens* first appeared with great force in Europe sometime between 25,000 and 30,000 years ago. Very little is known about where he came from or about his connection with the Neanderthal people who were one of many types of man to precede him. By 20,000 B.C., he had created the first great art in human history: the magnificent paintings and other artifacts found in certain caves in southern France and northern Spain. He engraved and carved bone and ivory with faithful representations of his women and of the animals he knew so well: the mammoth, the bison and others. These were believed to have had magic significance – to bring fertility to the clan and success to the hunter.

No birth rates or death rates have ever been found on the walls of the prehistoric caves. Thus, what is the puzzle of man to the anthropologist and the paleontologist becomes the enigma of man to the demographer. A United Nations Report, *The Determinants and Consequences of Population Trends*, published in 1953, presents a comprehensive survey of world population through the whole of man's history. Readers are referred to it for a more complete historical survey than this limited space permits. The Report states:

That men, using tools, have been living on this planet for at least one hundred thousand years, and possibly for over a million years, is proved by various types of evidence. For example, the definitely human skeletal remains found at Choukoutien, China, in association with artificial stone and bone implements and possible indications of the use of fire, were deposited during the second interglacial period, or earlier. There is evidence, also, that several divergent types of men emerged, some of whom had specialized characteristics which place them outside the ancestral line of all living races today. The Neanderthal people, who were dominant in Europe during the last (Würm) glaciation, were apparently such a divergent race.

PERIOD II – 6000 B.C. TO 1650 A.D.

Starting with the beginning of the New Stone Age, this period extends through the Bronze and Iron periods, through classical antiquity and the Dark Ages, the Renaissance and the Reformation. It is estimated that world population increased one hundredfold during the period, growing from five million to half a billion, and that about 42 billion births occurred.

It is believed that at the beginning of the era the earth was still very sparsely settled and population was widely dispersed. Vast areas of the globe were not inhabited, partly because the last glaciations had just receded.

It was during this period that man began to *produce* food instead of simply consuming what nature had laid before him. In the Near East, he had already passed the stage of the most primitive village-farming communities which grew out of the earliest agriculture with its domestication of animals. Some of these ancient communities developed into the earliest known urban settlements. The development of agriculture with its settled farming community spread to other areas of the earth during this period. Eventually, it was to change drastically man's pattern of survival and his way of life.

The earliest scene of settled village-farming communities appears to have

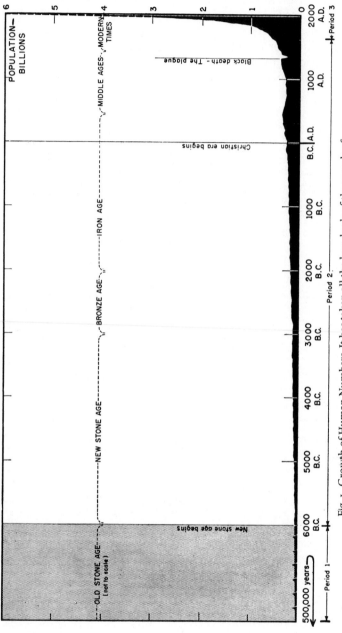

Fig. 1. Growth of Human Numbers. It has taken all the hundreds of thousands of years of man's existence on earth for his numbers to reach three billion. But in only 40 more years population will grow to six billion, if current growth rates remain unchanged. If the Old Stone Age were in scale, its base line would extend 35 feet to the left!

been in the Near East. ROBERT J. BRAIDWOOD, Professor of the Oriental Institute of Chicago, and Field Director of the Jarmo Project, a recently studied archeological site in Iraq, says: "It is probably very difficult for us now to conceptualize fully (or to exaggerate) the consequences of the first appearance of effective food production. The whole range of human existence, from the biological (including diet, demography, disease, and so on) through the cultural (social organization, politics, religion, esthetics, and so forth) bands of the spectrum took on completely new dimensions."

BRAIDWOOD described the hilly piedmont and intermontane regions surrounding the great "Fertile Crescent" which starts in the valleys of the Tigris and Euphrates Rivers, sweeps around to the north to touch southern Turkey and Syria, then curves south to the shores of the Mediterranean and into Egypt. One radioactive-carbon date suggests that this development was well advanced by 4000 B.C.

Sheep, goats, pigs, cattle and some kind of horse-like animal were used by those living in the area. Their plants were wheat and barley. BRAIDWOOD notes that some sort of hybridization or mutation, particularly in domesticated plants, must have taken place before certain species could have been moved to other areas. However, they seem to have moved into the Danube Valley by 4000 B.C., and into western Europe by 2500 B.C.

In other words, man was learning to utilize his environment more efficiently; thus it could support more people than ever before. But numbers were still regulated by the food-producing quality of the land. Population grew in times of plenty and declined when food became scarce and when disease decimated large populations, as it did in Europe during the Dark Ages.

During the Bronze Age, man began to use copper and bronze and to build towns, cities and states. Kings, advanced religions, social classes, writing, and enduring monuments, such as the Nile pyramids, appeared during this period. The Iron Age brought iron metallurgy, the invention of the alphabet, the use of coined money, and the spread of commerce and navigation.

The early and great empires and cultures developed: those of Egypt, Rome and Greece; of King Asoka in India; of the Han dynasty in China; and, later, the empires of the Mayas and the Incas in the New World. The Hindu, Confucian, Buddhist, Jewish, Christian, Muslim and other great religions emerged.

The City – Period II

The great cities of ancient times rose in rich valleys adjacent to the Mediterranean, the Red Sea and the Persian Gulf, along the Indus and the Nile, and along the Yangtze in China. The first great urban civilization arose about 3500 B.C. in Mesopotamia, along the Tigris and Euphrates. Another grew up in Egypt before 3000 B.C. and still another in Crete. A fourth arose along the banks of the Indus in western India, but whether this grew directly out of Neolithic beginnings or was a transplant of the Sumerian culture of Mesopotamia is a matter of dispute. Urban civilizations developed in China at a later date, and still later in some areas of tropical Central America and in Peru.

The urban societies of Mesopotamia, China and Egypt maintained complex centralized control of soil and water resources in order to provide irrigation and to control floods. These "hydraulic" civilizations supported very dense populations with highly integrated social systems. The individual peasant was allowed a small land area which produced more food than his family needed. Such civilizations have persisted in Egypt, India, China and elsewhere to the present day, with little change in the economic basis of life but with periodic rises and declines.

The ancient Mediterranean, Asian and American urban civilizations appear to have been isolated flowerings of human culture which culminated in "golden ages" and then declined. The archeological record abundantly reveals their wave-like nature. For additional information, readers are referred to an earlier issue of *Population Bulletin*, "The World's Great Cities: Evolution or Devolution?" (September 1960).

The A.D. Era of Period II

The United Nations study previously mentioned states that, at the beginning of the Christian era, the world's population was likely to have been between 200 and 300 million people. Discussing the lack of historic demographic information, the Report states:

Various kinds of evidence indicate that man's numbers became adjusted to the food-producing capacity of the land in ancient times – increasing as it rose and declining as it fell. Unfortunately little of this evidence is of a census type, and most of the remainder does not provide a basis for estimating the number of inhabitants of an area. Large parts of the world's population were subject to some sort of census enumeration near the beginning of the Christian era, but the information available from these censuses has limited value. Roman censuses were taken for administrative purposes and were restricted to "citizens," an expanding category as citizenship rights were extended to outlying regions. Moreover only adult males were included in some of these censuses, while all household members except "children" were included in others. Chinese censuses at about this time provided reports on total population but interpretation of the results involves many difficulties. Elaborate records were kept by the ancient Incas, but their meaning is obscure.

J. C. RUSSELL, Professor of History at the University of New Mexico, who has contributed much to the demographic history of the West, has traced the population changes within the Roman Empire from the second century A.D. to the year A.D. 543, a period he characterizes generally as one of imperial decline:

... However, within the general picture there are great differences in the trends. Actually most of the decrease occurred in western Mediterranean lands: Italy, Gaul, Iberia, and North Africa, together with Greece and Egypt. In Syria the population seems to have held even while in Gaul and Britain something like recovery must have occurred at the end of the period. Eastern Asia Minor and the Slavic area probably increased markedly. The German and Scandinavian spheres apparently held even in spite of emigration. The information about the central, eastern, and northern parts of Europe is so vague and uncertain that there may have been a considerable increase in population. The general rise in temperature should certainly have reduced the semiglacial conditions of the northern countries and made them attractive for grain-growing groups.

In the second and third centuries A.D., Rome suffered two devastating epidemics which have not been identified but their virulence suggests bubonic plague. According to Dr. RUSSELL:

The period from A.D. 543 to 950 probably marks the lowest ebb of population in Europe since the early Roman Empire. It covers the first great attack of the plague, the worst epidemic to strike the area with which we are concerned. Following it came the Mohammedan invasions from the semi-nomadic areas of the lands surrounding the Mediterranean. From the east in the tenth century the Hungarians scourged most of Europe and what they missed was visited by the terrible raids of the Vikings from the north. Some measure of the weakness of the European population is indicated by the feeble defense put up against these invaders by the governments of Europe....

Endemic diseases such as malaria and tuberculosis were prevalent, and the latter was particularly fatal among young people. In fact, the combination of both diseases occurred quite frequently and was highly fatal. Dr. RUSSELL speculates that during the periods of population decline in early medieval Europe, much carefully tilled and drained acreage lapsed into breeding grounds for mosquitoes; and that a period of wet, warm weather about 800–900 A.D. greatly increased the incidence of malaria.

The span of life (extreme length of life) seems to have been around 100 years, as it is now. Those who could avoid infection were likely to live to considerable ages. According to JOHN DURAND, Assistant Director in Charge of Population, the United Nations Bureau of Social Affairs, the best basis for making mortality estimates of the Roman period is a study of tombstone

TABLE I

Area and Estimates of Population of the Roman Empire, A. D. 14

	Area (thousands of sq. mi.)	Population (thousands)	Persons per sq. mi.
Total Empire	1,289	54,000	41
European part	861	23,000	26
Asiatic part	257	19,500	77
African part	171	11,500	67

Source: 7

inscriptions for males dying between the ages of 15 and 42. This method corrects the exaggeration of years that humans are apt to indulge in, even on tombstones, and allows for the under-representation of children's deaths. On this basis, DURAND concludes that life expectancy at birth for the whole population of the Roman Empire was probably only about 25 or 30 years.

After the year 1000, it appears that population began to increase; and, between 1000 and 1348, that growth was phenomenal, particularly in northern Europe. The Empire of Charlemagne had already capitalized on the upward population movement, and stronger governments began to develop in Germany, Scandinavia and even in Russia. The Crusades spread Christianity throughout the Middle East and brought contact between the Muslim and Christian worlds.

Then in 1348, the bubonic plague, which seems to have first appeared in the sixth century in Egypt, suddenly erupted in Europe in a more virulent form, taking a frightful toll of lives. RUSSELL states that "the years 1348–1350 saw a very heavy loss of life, 20 to 25% in most European countries. The decline continued with later epidemics until the population of about 1400 was near 60% of the pre-plague figures...."

TABLE II

Approximate Population of the World and Its Subdivisions, 1000–1600 (in millions)

Year	World	Europe	Asiatic Russia	South West Asia	India	China Major*	Japan	South East Asia, Oceania	Africa	The Americas
1000	275	42	5	32	48	70	4	11	50	13
1100	306	48	6	33	50	79	6	12	55	17
1200	348	61	7	34	51	89	8	14	61	23
1300	384	73	8	33	50	99	11	15	67	28
1400	373	45	9	27	46	112	14	16	74	30
1500	446	69	11	29	54	125	16	19	82	41
1600	486	89	13	30	68	140	20	21	90	15

* China proper, plus Manchuria and Korea, Outer Mongolia, Sinkiang and Formosa.
Source: 1

Between 1500 and 1700, far-ranging social, economic and intellectual revolutions began which formed the basis for the modern world. The era of medieval authority was first challenged in northern Italy, at the time of the Renaissance. This was followed by the age of discovery, with voyages around Africa and to the New World. At the same time, the Reformation set the stage for the revival of intellectual development in northern Europe. For the first time since the Golden Age of Greece, the human intellect began to look at the world objectively. This led to the birth of the scientific method: new concepts of the nature of matter, energy and, ultimately, of life began to capture the minds of men. Out of this intellectual revolution came powerful new insights which were eventually to greatly change man's pattern of living and dying.

In Europe about the middle of the 17th century – after the end of the Thirty Years' War and the period of peace and stability which followed – agricultural methods improved, slowly at first and then rapidly. New crops were introduced and crops were rotated; manure and fertilizers were used more generally; and the soil was cultivated more extensively. Even though these more advanced methods increased food production, the margin of plenty continued to be precarious, especially for those who lived in cities. A comparable agricultural expansion seems to have occurred in China at about the same time.

Unfortunately, little is known about population growth and decline during this period for the vast continent of Asia, particularly for India and China. M. K. BENNETT, Director of the Food Research Institute, Stanford University, has recognized the need for a continent-by-continent or region-by-region survey. He estimates that world population in 1000 A.D. was somewhere around 275 million, or "probably less than half of the population of Europe in 1949; . . . that there has been one century, the fourteenth, [the century of the Black Death in Europe] in which world population did not increase at all, but declined. . . ."

The earlier "hydraulic" civilizations became subject to disorders which checked and, in some cases, reversed their population growth.

The Americas had an estimated population of 16 million at the time of their discovery by COLUMBUS. JULIAN STEWARD, Research Professor of Anthropology, University of Illinois, has estimated the population of the different regions of the American Hemisphere in 1492 as follows:

North America:	
North of Mexico	1,000,000
Mexico	4,500,000
West Indies	225,000
Central America	736,000
South America:	
Andean Area	6,131,000
Remainder	2,898,000
Total	15,490,000

PERIOD III – 1650–1962 A.D.

If man's existence on earth is viewed as a day, this period is less than a minute. But a fourth or more of all human beings ever born have lived during this brief span.

The period brought a sixfold increase in human numbers: from an estimated half-billion in 1650 to over three billion in 1962. There were approximately 23 billion births during this period – over half as many as in the preceding 76 centuries!

World population doubled between 1650 and 1850, growing beyond the one-billion mark. It doubled again, to reach two billion by 1930, in only 80 years. Since that time, the rate of growth has accelerated steadily. Now over 50 million more people are added each year. If the current rate remains unchanged, today's population will double again in less than 40 years.

A steadily falling death rate, especially during the last century, is mainly responsible for the very rapid acceleration in population growth. It is estimated that during 1650–1750, population was growing at about 0.3% a year; during 1750–1850, at about 0.5%; 1850–1950, at 0.8%. Currently, the rate is somewhere between 1.6 and 1.9%.

This period brings man through to the modern agricultural-industrial age with its tremendous scientific and technological discoveries which have greatly speeded up the rate of social change in the Western world and which have revolutionized agriculture, industry, communication, transportation, etc. These developments have made possible the support of the mammoth populations in numerous areas of the world. However, many of those technological advances are only beginning to touch the less developed areas where living levels for over half of the world's people are only a little, if any, above what they were during much of the earlier history of the race.

For the world as a whole, the mid-17th century is a bench mark in the pattern of population growth. Then, the upward surge in the numbers of people began. Just why the response to the early stirrings of the modern age was so rapid is not entirely clear, though many of the major factors which stimulated the increase in human numbers can be recognized. In Europe, the frightful famines and epidemics that marked the Dark Ages seem to have decreased, although hunger and disease were still endemic. The discovery of the New World opened the way for great transatlantic migrations to the rich, sparsely settled lands of the Americas. To some extent, this relieved the growing population pressure in Europe and provided a new source of food for the Old World. It also gave impetus to the tremendous growth of populations of European origin – at home and in European colonies – which amounted to a ninefold increase during the period.

The development of the scientific method and the application of this new knowledge to technology stimulated the Industrial and Vital Revolutions which so greatly changed man's way of life throughout the Western world. The industrial Revolution brought the transition from agrarian to industrial societies – a transition which is beginning only now for large areas of Africa, Asia and Latin America. The Vital Revolution

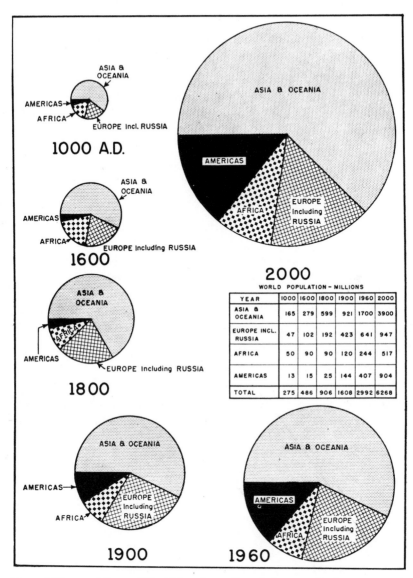

WORLD POPULATION - MILLIONS

YEAR	1000	1600	1800	1900	1960	2000
ASIA & OCEANIA	165	279	599	921	1700	3900
EUROPE INCL. RUSSIA	47	102	192	423	641	947
AFRICA	50	90	90	120	244	517
AMERICAS	13	15	25	144	407	904
TOTAL	275	486	906	1608	2992	6268

Fig. 2. A Thousand Years of World Population Growth. In 1000 A.D., Asia accounted for 60% of the world's population, Europe, including Russia, for about 17%, Africa, 18% and the Americas, 4%. By 1960, Asia's percentage had declined to somewhat under 60, that of Europe and the USSR had increased to 22% and the Americas, to 14%. Africa's portion declined to 8%. By 2000, Asia may comprise about 65% of the total, Europe and the USSR, 15%, the Americas, 15% and Africa, 8%. Russia includes Asiatic and European Russia.

brought the Western industrial nations through the demographic transition: from high birth and death rates to low birth and death rates.

More facts and learned estimates concerning world population are available for this period since census-taking began during the 17th century. The first censuses were conducted in 1655 by the French and British in their Canadian colonies. Iceland took a count in 1703, Sweden in 1748 and Denmark in 1769. The United States took its first national census in 1790. Great Britain took its first in 1801.

The first estimate of world population ever to be compiled was published in the 17th century by a Jesuit priest named RICCIOLI who estimated that one billion people then inhabited the earth: 100 million in Europe, 500 million in Asia, 100 million in Africa, 200 million in America and 100 million in

TABLE III

Estimates of World Population by Regions, 1650–1960

Source of estimates and date	World	Africa	Northern America[a]	Latin America[b]	Asia (excl. USSR)[c]	Europe and Asiatic USSR[c]	Oceania	Area of European Settlement[d]
WILLCOX's estimates:								
1650	470	100	1	7	257	103	2	113
1750	694	100	1	10	437	144	2	157
1800	919	100	6	23	595	193	2	224
1850	1,091	100	26	33	656	274	2	335
1900	1,571	141	81	63	857	423	6	573
CARR-SAUNDERS' estimates:								
1650	545	100	1	12	327	103	2	118
1750	728	95	1	11	475	144	2	158
1800	906	90	6	19	597	192	2	219
1850	1,171	95	26	33	741	274	2	335
1900	1,608	120	81	63	915	423	6	573
United Nations estimates:								
1920	1,810	140	117	91	966	487	9	704
1930	2,013	155	135	109	1,072	532	10	786
1940	2,246	172	146	131	1,212	573	11	861
1950	2,495	200	167	163	1,376	576	13	919
1960	2,972	244	200	207	1,665	641	16	1,064

[a] United States, Canada, Alaska, St. Pierre and Miquelon.
[b] Central and South America and Caribbean Islands.
[c] Estimates for Asia and Europe in WILLCOX's and CARR-SAUNDERS' series have been adjusted so as to include the population of the Asiatic USSR with that of Europe.
[d] Includes northern America, Latin America, Europe and the Asiatic USSR and Oceania.
Source: [7]

Oceania. It appears that RICCIOLI reported the conjectures of others rather than his own. Other contemporary estimates of the 17th century all range below RICCIOLI's and one as low as 320 million.

G. KING, a 17th-century English scholar, estimating population densities for the various continents, allocated 17 acres per head for Europe, 20 for Asia, 64 for Africa and 129 for America. This yielded a total of 700 million for the world, or 600 million, rejecting a hypothetical southern continent. If correct land areas as now known are substituted, the estimate would be 874 million. It should be noted that this estimate is two thirds higher than the estimate of approximately 500 million accepted by modern scholars.

Even though Asia's population continued to increase during the period, its proportion of world population declined from about 58% in 1650 to 53% in 1920 (excluding the Asiatic part of the USSR). Africa's proportion also declined, from 20% to 8%. But the proportion for Europe, including all of the USSR, rose from 20% to 27%. Since 1920, the proportion for Asia and Africa has again increased, while that for Europe has declined.

Today, the combined population of the Americas is about 400 million. Their proportion of world population increased from approximately 2% in 1650 to 14% at the present time. As previously mentioned, the indigenous American populations were heavily decimated by diseases brought in by Europeans and by wars with early colonizers. Much of the subsequent increase was due to immigration and to the proliferation of the immigrant groups. More recently, the descendants of the indigenous Americans have been increasing rapidly.

The Demographic Transition of Period III

Application of the scientific method to medical technology brought man the ability to defer death. In the Western industrial countries, this has changed his pattern of survival far more rapidly than any other major social development throughout his long history. Similarly, in the Western world, knowledge about the control of fertility is widespread. As the traditional pattern of high birth and death rates changed to one of low birth and death rates, man's reproductive process has become much more efficient.

In the heavily populated, less developed countries of Africa, Asia and Latin America, the application of scientific techniques to defer death is generally accepted and quite widely practiced; but the control of fertility has not begun to be practiced extensively enough to affect birth rates. As a result, rapidly falling death rates combined with traditionally high birth rates have touched off a surge in the rate of population growth.

Modern public health methods have cut death rates by one third or more in a single year in some countries. With the drastic decline in infant and child mortality, the proportion of the population under 15 years of age tends to increase. It is now over 40% in many of these countries, as compared with about 20% in some countries of western and northern Europe.

It is expected that the growth rate will increase even further in many areas of Africa, Asia and Latin America, as death rates continue to decline. This will surely happen unless effective measures can be devised which will

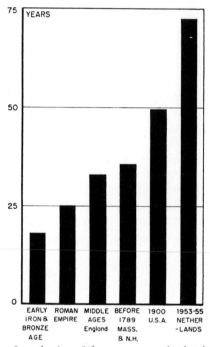

Fig. 3. Life Expectancy Over the Ages. Life expectancy at birth is believed to have been about 18 years in prehistoric times. It has quadrupled today in some of the Western industrialized countries.
(Source: *Length of Life: A Study of the Life Table* by LOUIS I. DUBLIN, ALFRED J. LOTKA and MORTIMER SPIEGELMAN, and 8A.)

speed up the demographic transition and the rate of social change. Simply stated, acceptable measures must be found to bring birth rates into balance with modern low death rates, thereby completing the demographic transition. Unless birth rates are reduced, population growth rates will continue upward until they are checked eventually by a rise in the death rate.

Discussing the present rapid rate of population growth, the latest United Nations *Demographic Yearbook* points out that approximately one half of the world's population lives in only four countries – China (mainland), India, the USSR and the USA – and that the reliability of world population estimates depends largely on the accuracy of the information available about the population of these countries:

Similarly the 1950–59 average rate of increase, estimated in the range of 1.5 to 2.0% per annum for the four largest populations and 1.6 to 1.9% per annum for the remainder of the world, can be placed, in view of possibly compensating errors, between 1.6 and 1.9% per annum for the world as a whole....

Actually in view of declining mortality, it is virtually certain that the rate of world population growth has now surpassed 1.5% per annum, and quite possible that it has attained 2.0%. Because of this decline of mortality, world population certainly increased in the year 1959 by at least 45 million, and possibly by as much as 55 million. Again it is evident that much of the uncertainty is caused by the lack of precise knowledge regarding the population of China (mainland). Large margins of error must also be allowed for in the estimated annual increases in India, in other parts of Asia, and in Africa.

TABLE IV

Estimated Population and Vital Rates for the World by Region, 1950–1975

Continent & Region	Midyear population (millions) 1959	Annual rate of increase (percent) 1950–1959	Vital Rates 1955–1959 Birth Rate	Vital Rates 1955–1959 Death Rate	Medium Projection to 1975 (millions)
WORLD TOTAL	2,907	1.7	36	19	3,830
AFRICA	237	1.9	46	27	303
Northern Africa	78	1.9	45	26	76*
Tropical & Southern Africa	159	1.9	47	28	226
AMERICA	398	2.1	34	14	543
Northern America	196	1.8	25	9	240
Middle America	65	2.7	45	18	99
South America	137	2.3	42	19	204
ASIA	1,622	1.8	42	23	2,210
South West Asia	74	2.5	46	21	116
South Central Asia	546	1.8	44	26	737
South East Asia	208	2.1	44	23	280
East Asia	794	1.8	39	21	1,075
EUROPE	423	0.8	19	10	476
Northern & Western Europe	141	0.7	18	11	154
Central Europe	137	0.8	19	10	156
Southern Europe	145	0.9	21	10	166
OCEANIA	16	2.4	25	9	21
UNION OF SOVIET SOCIALIST REPUBLICS	211	1.7	25	8	275

* The United Nations estimate for 1975 was surpassed by 1959; and it has issued no new projections for this area.
Source: 8A.B

The Chinese census of 1953 is very difficult to appraise and might introduce an error of as much as 90 million in the present world population!

What is Past is Prologue

Since man first appeared on earth, human arithmetic has moved from a relatively simple exercise in addition to a complicated one of geometric progression. It took all of the vast reaches of time to build today's population of slightly over three billion. But it will take only 40 more years for population to reach six billion, if the present growth rates remain unchanged.

It is noteworthy that the desire to control fertility has never had the emotional imperatives which brought the power over death. Only modest efforts have been made thus far to discover effective methods of fertility control which would be acceptable to the people of all cultures and religions. Less than modest efforts have been made to disseminate what knowledge is now available to all of the world's people who would benefit from that knowledge. Consequently, during the past decade of rapid death-rate decline in the less developed countries, there has been no measurable reduction in high birth rates; so population growth has increased.

Rapid population growth cannot be maintained indefinitely in any part of the world. If birth rates do not decline in overcrowded lands, death rates eventually will rise to check growth.

The gulf which exists today between the peoples of the world has widened: life is better than ever before for those who live in the Western industrial countries. But the majority of the world's people still live close to the subsistence level, in poverty and squalor reminiscent of the Middle Ages. If the demographic transition to a balance between low birth and death rates could be hastened in the less developed countries, this gulf might yet be bridged in time to avert a Malthusian disaster.

BIBLIOGRAPHY

1. BENNETT, M. K. *The World's Food.* New York: Harper and Brothers, 1954.
2. BRAIDWOOD, ROBERT J. "Near Eastern Prehistory." *Science.* 127 (3312), June 20, 1958.
3. CARR-SAUNDERS, A. M. *World Population, Past Growth and Present Trends.* Oxford: Clarendon Press, 1936.
4. DURAND, JOHN. "Mortality Estimates from Roman Tombstone Inscriptions." *American Journal of Sociology.* 45(4) January 1960.
5. RUSSELL, J. C. "Late Ancient and Medieval Population." *Transactions of the American Philosophical Society.* New Series 48 (part 3). June 1958.
6. STEWARD, JULIAN. "The Native Population of South America." *Bureau of American Ethnology Bulletin.* No. 143.
7. United Nations. Department of Social Affairs. Population Division.
   A. *The Determinants and Consequences of Population Trends.* New York, 1953.
8. United Nations. Department of Economic ánd Social Affairs. Statistical Office.
   A. *Demographic Yearbook, 1960.* New York, 1960.
   B. *The Future Growth of World Population.* New York, 1958.

C. *Population and Vital Statistics Reports* (Statistical Papers, Series A, Vol. XIII, No. 1). New York, 1961.

9. WILLCOX, WALTER F. (editor). "Population of the Earth," by WILLCOX in *International Migrations*, Vol. II, Part I. New York: National Bureau of Economic Research, Inc., 1931.

APPENDIX

The statistical and general demographic assumptions used to determine the number of people who have ever been born were provided the Population Reference Bureau by J. FLETCHER WELLEMEYER, an independent manpower consultant, Washington, D.C., in consultation with FRANK LORIMER, American University, Washington, D.C.

The estimate was made on the basis of three time periods:

		Number of years in period	Number of births per year at beginning of period	Number of births per year at end of period	Number of of births in period
I.	600,000–6000 B.C.	594,000	"1"	250,000	12 billion
II.	6000 B.C.–1650 A.D.	7,650	250,000	25,000,000	42 billion
III.	1650–1962 A.D.	312	25,000,000	110,000,000	23 billion
				Total	77 billion

To obtain the number of births at the beginning and end of these periods, certain assumptions were made regarding birth rates and the size of populations. It was assumed that at the beginning of the Neolithic era the population was five million and that the annual birth rate was 50 per thousand. The procedure assumes a smooth increase. The growth was undoubtedly irregular, but the estimates may fairly represent the net effect of the ups and downs.

By 1650, the annual number of births was estimated at 25 million, corresponding to a population of about 500 million. The 1962 world population of 3.05 billion, the number of births and birth rate of 36 per thousand are based on United Nations estimates.

The 600,000 years' duration of the Paleolithic era is based on the assumption that man-like types were then in existence but in very small numbers. Earlier dates have been given a few species by certain authorities, but some of these dates are questionable, and the earlier species may have been considerably less than man-like. The 600,000-year period seems a reasonable compromise between extreme possibilities.

Once the number of births at the dates indicated was determined, the total number of births for each period was calculated at a constant rate of increase for the period.

The estimated rates of increase differ sharply. For the long Paleolithic period, the average annual rate of increase was only 0.02 per thousand; during 6000 B.C. to 1650 A.D., it rose to 0.6; and during 1650–1962, it reached 4.35.

For the figures derived here, the following equation was used:

$$\Sigma\, B_t = \frac{B_o e^{rt}}{r}$$

B_o is the number of births per year at the beginning of the period; t is the number of years in the period; e is the base of natural logarithms; and r is the annual rate of increase during the period.

The value of r is obtained by solving for r the equation $\dfrac{B_t}{B_o} = e^{rt}$

where B_o is the number of births the first year of the period, and B_t is the number of births the final year of the period.

ANNABELLE DESMOND (Mrs. ROBERT COOK) is the distaff member of a team which has built the Population Reference Bureau into an increasingly effective educational force during the past 12 years. A science writer with a gift for putting complex scientific facts into simple, meaningful terms, she has edited a book on deafness and has co-authored articles for professional and popular magazines. She served as a health education specialist in a government nutrition program during the war. She is a member of several scientific organizations.

World Population Growth: An International Dilemma*

by

HAROLD F. DORN

During all but the most recent years of the centuries of his existence man must have lived, reproduced, and died as other animals do. His increase in number was governed by the three great regulators of the increase of all species of plants and animals – predators, disease, and starvation – or, in terms more applicable to human populations – war, pestilence, and famine. One of the most significant developments for the future of mankind during the first half of the 20th century has been his increasing ability to control pestilence and famine. Although he has not freed himself entirely from the force of these two regulators of population increase, he has gained sufficient control of them so that they no longer effectively govern his increase in number.

Simultaneously he has developed methods of increasing the effectiveness of war as a regulator of population increase, to the extent that he almost certainly could quickly wipe out a large proportion, if not all, of the human race. At the same time he has learned how to separate sexual gratification from reproduction by means of contraception and telegenesis (that is, reproduction by artificial insemination, particularly with spermatozoa preserved for relatively long periods of time), so that he can regulate population increase by voluntary control of fertility. Truly it can be said that man has the knowledge and the power to direct, at least in part, the course of his evolution.

This newly gained knowledge and power has not freed man from the inexorable effect of the biological laws that govern all living organisms. The evolutionary process has endowed most species with a reproductive potential that, unchecked, would overpopulate the entire globe within a few generations. It has been estimated that the tapeworm, *Taenia*, may lay 120,000 eggs per day; an adult cod can lay as many as 4 million eggs per year; a frog may produce 10,000 eggs per spawning. Human ovaries are throught to contain approximately 200,000 ova at puberty, while a single ejaculation of human semen may contain 200 million spermatozoa.

* Extracted from *Science* 26 January 1962, Volume 135, Number 3500, by permission.

This excessive reproductive potential is kept in check for species other than man by interspecies competition in the struggle for existence, by disease, and by limitation of the available food supply. The fact that man has learned how to control, to a large extent, the operation of these biological checks upon unrestrained increase in number has not freed him from the necessity of substituting for them less harsh but equally effective checks. The demonstration of his ability to do this cannot be long delayed.

IMPLICATIONS

The accelerating rate of increase in the growth of the population of the world has come about so unobtrusively that most persons are unaware of its implications. There is a small group who are so aroused by this indifference that, like modern PAUL REVERES, they attempt to awaken the public with cries of "the population bomb!" or "the population explosion!"

These persons are called alarmists by those who counter with the assertion that similar warnings, such as "standing room only" and "mankind at the crossroads," have been issued periodically since MALTHUS wrote his essay on population, about 200 years ago. Nevertheless, says this group, the level of living and the health of the average person has continued to improve, and there is no reason to believe that advances in technology will not be able to make possible a slowly rising level of living for an increasing world population for the indefinite future. Furthermore, the rate of population increase almost certainly will slow down as the standard of education and living rises and as urbanization increases.

A third group of persons has attempted to estimate the maximum population that could be supported by the world's physical resources provided existing technological knowledge is fully utilized. Many of these calculations have been based on estimates of the quantity of food that could be produced and a hypothetical average daily calorie consumption per person.

As might be expected, the range of the various estimates of the maximum world population that could be supported without a lowering of the present level of living is very wide. One of the lowest, 2.8 billion, made by PEARSON & HARPER in 1945 on the assumption of an Asiatic standard of consumption, already has been surpassed (1). Several others, ranging from 5 to 7 billion, almost certainly will be exceeded by the end of this century. Perhaps the most carefully prepared estimate as well as the largest – that of 50 billions, prepared by HARRISON BROWN – would be reached in about 150 years if the present rate of growth should continue (2).

I believe it is worth while to prepare estimates of the maximum population that can be supported and to revise these as new information becomes available, even though most of the estimates made in the past already have been, or soon will be, demonstrated to be incorrect (in most instances too small), since this constitutes a rational effort to comprehend the implications of the increase in population. At the same time it should be recognized that estimates of the world's carrying capacity made in this manner are rather unrealistic and are primarily useful only as very general guidelines.

In the first place, these calculations have assumed that the earth's resources and skills are a single reservoir available to all. In reality this is untrue. The U.S. government attempts to restrict production of certain agricultural crops by paying farmers not to grow them. Simultaneously, in Asia and Africa, large numbers of persons are inadequately fed and poorly clothed. Except in a very general sense there is no *world* population problem; there are population problems varying in nature and degree among the several nations of the world. No single solution is applicable to all.

Since the world is not a single political unity, the increases in production actually achieved during any period of time tend to be considerably less than those theoretically possible. Knowledge, technical skill, and capital are concentrated in areas with the highest level of living, whereas the most rapid increase in population is taking place in areas where such skills and capital are relatively scarce or practically nonexistent.

Just as the world is not a single unit from the point of view of needs and the availability of resources, skills and knowledge to meet these needs, so it also is not a single unit with respect to population increase. Due to political barriers that now exist throughout the entire world, overpopulation, however defined, will become a serious problem in specific countries long before it would be a world problem if there were no barriers to population redistribution. I shall return to this point later, after discussing briefly existing forecasts or projections of the total population of the world.

Most demographers believe that, under present conditions, the future population of areas such as countries or continents, or even of the entire world, cannot be predicted for more than a few decades with even a moderate degree of certainty. This represents a marked change from the view held by many only 30 years ago.

In 1930 a prominent demographer wrote, "The population of the United States ten, twenty, even fifty years hence, can be predicted with a greater degree of assurance than any other economic or social fact, provided the immigration laws are unchanged" (3). Nineteen years later, a well-known economist replied that "it is disheartening to have to assert that the best population forecasts deserve little credence even for 5 years ahead, and none at all for 20–50 years ahead." (4).

Although both of these statements represent rather extreme views, they do indicate the change that has taken place during the past two decades in the attitude toward the reliability of population forecasts. Some of the reasons for this have been discussed in detail elsewhere and will not be repeated here (5).

It will be sufficient to point out that knowledge of methods of voluntarily controlling fertility now is so widespread, especially among persons of European ancestry, that sharp changes in the spacing, as well as in the number, of children born during the reproductive period may occur in a relatively short period of time. Furthermore, the birth rate may increase as well as decrease.

FORECASTING POPULATION GROWTH

The two principal methods that have been used in recent years to make population forecasts are (i) the extrapolation of mathematical curves fitted to the past trend of population increase and (ii) the projection of the population by the "component" or "analytical" method, based on specific hypotheses concerning the future trend in fertility, mortality, and migration.

The most frequently used mathematical function has been the logistic curve which was originally suggested by VERHULST in 1838 but which remained unnoticed until it was rediscovered by PEARL & REED about 40 years ago (6). At first it was thought by some demographers that the logistic curve represented a rational law of population change. However, it has proved to be as unreliable as other methods of preparing population forecasts and is no longer regarded as having any unique value for estimating future population trends.

A recent illustration of the use of mathematical functions to project the future world population is the forecast prepared by VON FOERSTER, MORA & AMIOT (7). In view of the comments that subsequently were published in "Science", an extensive discussion of this article does not seem to be required. It will be sufficient to point out that this forecast probably will set a record for the entire class of forecasts prepared by the use of mathematical functions, for the short length of time required to demonstrate its unreliability.

The method of projecting or forecasting population growth most frequently used by demographers, whenever the necessary data are available, is the "component" or "analytical" method. Separate estimates are prepared of the future trend of fertility, mortality, and migration. From the total population as distributed by age and sex on a specified date, the future population that would result from the hypothetical combination of fertility, mortality, and migration is computed. Usually, several estimates of the future population are prepared in order to include what the authors believe to be the most likely range of values.

Such estimates generally are claimed by their authors to be not forecasts of the most probable future population but merely indications of the population that would result from the hypothetical assumptions concerning the future trend in fertility, mortality, and migration. However, the projections of fertility, mortality, and migration usually are chosen to include what the authors believe will be the range of likely possibilities. This objective is achieved by making "high," "medium," and "low" assumptions concerning the future trend in population growth. Following the practice of most of the authors of such estimates, I shall refer to these numbers as population projections.

The most authoritative projections of the population of the world are those made by the United Nations (8, 9). Even though a recent projection was published in 1958, it now seems likely that the population of the world will exceed the high projection before the year 2000. By the end of 1961 the world's population at least equaled the high projection for that date.

Although the United Nations' projections appear to be too conservative in that even the highest will be an underestimate of the population only 40 years from now, some of the numerical increases in population implied by these projections will create problems that may be beyond the ability of the nations involved to solve. For example, the estimated increase in the population of Asia from A.D. 1950 to 2000 will be roughly equal to the population of the entire world in 1958! The population of Latin America 40 years hence may very likely be four times that in 1950. The absolute increase in population in Latin America during the last half of the century may equal the total increase in the population of *Homo sapiens* during all the millennia from his origin until about 1650, when the first colonists were settling New England.

Increases in population of this magnitude stagger the imagination. Present trends indicate that they may be succeeded by even larger increases during comparable periods of time. The increase in the rate of growth of the world's population is still continuing. This rate is now estimated to be about 2% per year, sufficient to double the world's population every 35 years. It requires only very simple arithmetic to show that a continuation of this rate of growth for even 10 or 15 decades would result in an increase in population that would make the globe resemble an anthill.

But as was pointed out above, the world is not a single unit economically, politically, or demographically. Long before the population of the entire world reaches a size that could not be supported at current levels of living, the increase in population in specific nations and regions will give rise to problems that will affect the health and welfare of the rest of the world. The events of the past few years have graphically demonstrated the rapidity with which the political and economic problems of even a small and weak nation can directly affect the welfare of the largest and most powerful nations. Rather than speculate about the maximum population the world can support and the length of time before this number will be reached, it will be more instructive to examine the demographic changes that are taking place in different regions of the world and to comment briefly on their implications.

DECLINE IN MORTALITY

The major cause of the recent spurt in population increase is a world-wide decline in mortality. Although the birth rate increased in some countries – for example, the United States – during and after World War II, such increases have not been sufficiently widespread to account for more than a small part of the increase in the total population of the world. Moreover, the increase in population prior to World War II occurred in spite of a widespread decline in the birth rate among persons of European origin.

* *
*

The precipitous decline in mortality in Mexico and in the Moslem population of Algeria is illustrative of what has taken place during the past 15 years in Latin America, Africa, and Asia, where nearly three out of every four persons in the world now live. Throughout most of this area the birth rate has changed very little, remaining near a level of 40 per 1000 per year, as can be seen from *Fig.* 1, which shows the birth rate, death rate, and rate of natural increase for selected countries.

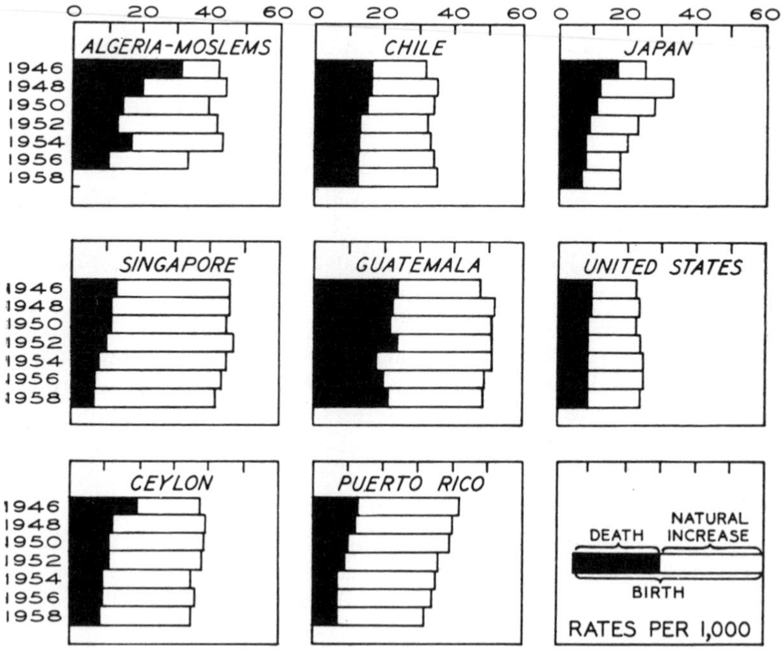

Fig. 1. Birth rate, death rate, and rate of natural increase per 1000 for selected countries for the period 1946–58.

Even in countries such as Puerto Rico and Japan where the birth rate has declined substantially, the rate of natural increase has changed very little, owing to the sharp decrease in mortality. A more typical situation is represented by Singapore, Ceylon, Guatemala, and Chile, where the crude rate of natural increase has risen. There has been a general tendency for death rates to decline universally and for high birth rates to remain high, with the result that those countries with the highest rates of increase are experiencing an acceleration in their rates of growth.

REGIONAL LEVELS

The absolute level of fertility and mortality and the effect of changes in them upon the increase of population in different regions of the world can be only approximately indicated. The United Nations estimates that only about 33% of the deaths and 42% of the births that occur in the world are registered (10). The percentage registered ranges from about 8 to 10% in tropical and southern Africa and Eastern Asia to 98 to 100% in North America and Europe. Nevertheless, the statistical staff of the United Nations, by a judicious combination of the available fragmentary data, has been able to prepare estimates of fertility and mortality for different regions of the world

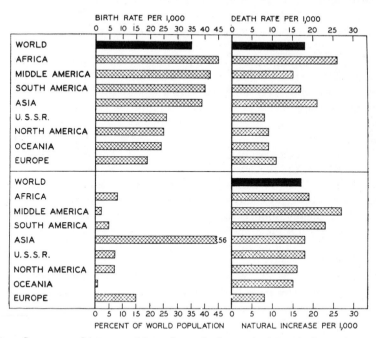

Fig. 2. Percentage of the 1958 world population, birth rate, death rate, and rate of natural increase, per 1000, for the period 1954–58 for various regions of the world.

that are generally accepted as a reasonably correct representation of the actual but unknown figures. The estimated birth rate, death rate, and crude rate of natural increase (the birth rate minus the death rate) for eight regions of the world for the period 1954-58 are shown in *Fig. 2*.

The birth rates of the countries of Africa, Asia, Middle America, and South America average nearly 40 per 1000 and probably are as high as they were 500 to 1000 years ago. In the rest of the world – Europe, North America, Oceania, and the Soviet Union – the birth rate is slightly more than half as high, or about 20 to 25 per 1000. The death rate for the former regions, although still definitely higher, is rapidly approaching that for people of European origin, with the result that the highest rates of natural increase are found in the regions with the highest birth rates. The most rapid rate of population growth at present is taking place in Middle and South America, where the population will double about every 26 years if the present rate continues.

These regional differences in fertility and mortality are intensifying the existing imbalance of population with land area and natural resources. No matter how this imbalance is measured, that it exists is readily apparent. Two rather crude measures are presented in *Figs. 2* and *3*, which show the percentage distribution of the world's population living in each region and the number of persons per square kilometer.

An important effect of the decline in mortality rates often is overlooked – namely, the increase in effective fertility. An estimated 97 out of every 100 newborn white females subject to the mortality rates prevailing in the United States during 1950 would survive to age 20, slightly past the beginning of the usual childbearing age, and 91 would survive to the end of the child-bearing period (*Fig. 4*). These estimates are more than 3 and 11 times, respectively, the corresponding estimated proportions for white females that survived to these ages about four centuries ago.

In contrast, about 70% of the newborn females in Guatemala would survive to age 20, and only half would live to the end of the childbearing period if subject to the death rates prevailing in that country in 1950. If the death rate in Guatemala should fall to the level of that in the United States in 1950 – a realistic possibility – the number of newborn females who would survive to the beginning of the childbearing period would increase by 36%; the number surviving to the end of the childbearing period would increase by 85%. A corresponding decrease in the birth rate would be required to prevent this increase in survivorship from resulting in a rapid acceleration in the existing rate of population growth, which already is excessive. In other words, this decrease in the death rate would require a decrease in the birth rate of more than 40% merely to maintain the status quo.

As can be seen from *Fig. 1*, the birth rate in countries with high fertility has shown little or no tendency to decrease in recent years. Japan is the exception. There, the birth rate dropped by 46% from 1948 to 1958 – an

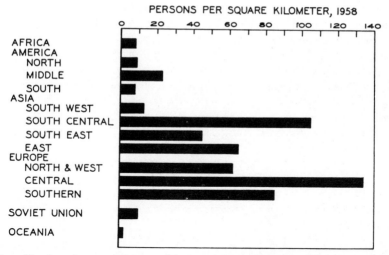

Fig. 3. Number of persons per square kilometer in various regions of the world in 1958.

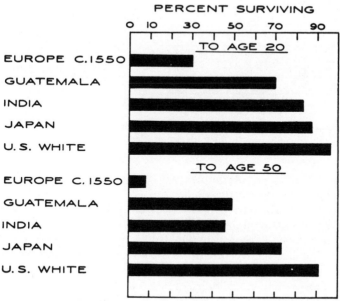

Fig. 4. Percentage of newborn females who would survive to the end of the reproductive period according to mortality rates in Europe around A.D. 1500 and in selected countries around 1950.

amount more than enough to counterbalance the decrease in the death rate, with the result that there was a decrease in the absolute number of births. As yet there is very little evidence that other countries with a correspondingly high birth rate are likely to duplicate this in the near future.

Another effect of a rapid rate of natural increase is demonstrated by *Fig. 5*. About 43% of the Moslem population of Algeria is under 15 years of age; the corresponding percentage in Sweden is 24, or slightly more than half this number. Percentages in the neighborhood of 40% are characteristic of the populations of the countries of Africa, Latin America, and Asia.

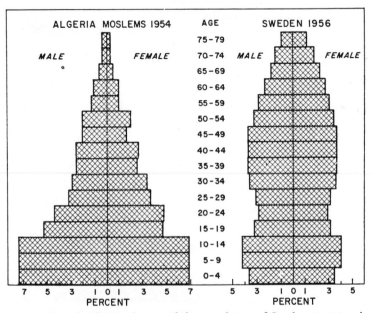

Fig. 5. Percentage distribution by age of the population of Sweden in 1956 and the Moslem population of Algeria in 1954.

This high proportion of young people constitutes a huge fertility potential for 30 years into the future that can be counterbalanced only by a sharp decline in the birth rate, gives rise to serious educational problems, and causes a heavy drain on the capital formation that is necessary to improve the level of living of the entire population. A graphic illustration of this may be found in the recently published 5-year plan for India for 1961–66, which estimates that it will be necessary to provide educational facilities and teachers for 20 million additional children during this 5-year period (11).

HISTORICAL PATTERN IN WESTERN EUROPE

Some persons, although agreeing that the current rate of increase of the majority of the world's population cannot continue indefinitely without giving rise to grave political, social, and economic problems, point out that a similar situation existed in northwestern and central Europe during the 18th and 19th centuries. Increasing industrialization and urbanization, coupled with a rising standard of living, led to a decline in the birth rate, with a consequent drop in the rate of increase of the population. Why should not the rest of the world follow this pattern?

There is small likelihood that the two-thirds of the world's population which has not yet passed through the demographic revolution from high fertility and mortality rates to low fertility and mortality rates can repeat the history of western European peoples prior to the development of serious political and economic problems.

A brief review of the circumstances that led to the virtual domination of the world at the end of the 19th century by persons of European origin will indicate some of the reasons for this opinion.

Just as THOMAS MALTHUS, at the end of the 18th century, could not foresee the effect upon the peoples of western Europe of the exploration of the last great frontier of this earth, so we today cannot clearly foresee the final effect of an unprecedented rapid increase of population within closed frontiers. What seems to be least uncertain in a future full of uncertainty is that the demographic history of the next 400 years will not be like that of the past 400 years.

WORLD PROBLEM

The results of human reproduction are no longer solely the concern of the two individuals involved, or of the larger family, or even of the nation of which they are citizens. A stage has been reached in the demographic development of the world when the rate of human reproduction in any part of the globe may directly or indirectly affect the health and welfare of the rest of the human race. It is in this sense that there is a world population problem.

One or two illustrations may make this point more clear. During the past decade, six out of every ten persons added to the population of the world live in Asia; another two out of every ten live in Latin America and Africa. It seems inevitable that the breaking up of the world domination by northwest Europeans and their descendants, which already is well advanced, will continue, and that the center of power and influence will shift toward the demographic center of the world.

The present distribution of population increase enhances the existing imbalance between the distribution of the world's population and the distribution of wealth, available and utilized resources, and the use of nonhuman energy. Probably for the first time in human history there is a universal aspiration for a rapid improvement in the standard of living and a growing impatience with conditions that appear to stand in the way of its attainment. Millions of persons in Asia, Africa, and Latin America now are aware of the standard of living enjoyed by Europeans and North Americans. They are demanding the opportunity to attain the same standard, and they resist the idea that they must be permanently content with less.

A continuation of the present high rate of human multiplication will act as a brake on the already painfully slow improvement in the level of living, thus increasing political unrest and possibly bringing about eventual changes in government. As recent events have graphically demonstrated, such political changes may greatly affect the welfare of even the wealthiest nations.

The capital and technological skills that many of the nations of Africa, Asia, and Latin America require to produce enough food for a rapidly growing population and simultaneously to perceptibly raise per capita income exceed their existing national resources and ability. An immediate supply of capital in the amounts required is available only from the wealthier nations. The principle of public support for social welfare plans is now widely accepted in national affairs. The desirability of extending this principle to the international level for the primary purpose of supporting the economic development of the less advanced nations has not yet been generally accepted by the wealthier and more advanced countries. Even if this principle should be accepted, it is not as yet clear how long the wealthier nations would be willing to support the uncontrolled breeding of the populations receiving this assistance. The general acceptance of a foreign-aid program of the extent required by the countries with a rapidly growing population will only postpone for a few decades the inevitable reckoning with the results of uncontrolled human multiplication.

The future may witness a dramatic increase in man's ability to control his environment, provided he rapidly develops cultural substitutes for those harsh but effective governors of his high reproductive potential – disease and famine – that he has so recently learned to control. Man has been able to modify or control many natural phenomena, but he has not yet discovered how to evade the consequences of biological laws. No species has ever been able to multiply without limit. There are two biological checks upon a rapid increase in number – a high mortality and a low fertility. Unlike other biological organisms, man can choose which of these checks shall be applied, but one of them must be. Whether man can use his scientific knowledge to guide his future evolution more wisely than the blind forces of nature, only the future can reveal. The answer will not be long postponed.

REFERENCES AND NOTES

1. F. A. PEARSON & F. A. HARPER, *The World's Hunger* (Cornell Univ. Press, Ithaca, N.Y., 1945).
2. H. BROWN, *The Challenge of Man's Future* (Viking, New York, 1954).
3. O. E. BAKER, "Population trends in relation to land utilization," *Proc. Int. Conf. Agr. Economists, 2nd Conf.* (1930), p. 284.
4. J. S. DAVIS, *J. Farm Economics* (Nov. 1949).
5. H. F. DORN, *J. Am. Statist. Ass.*, 45, 311 (1950).
6. R. PEARL & L. J. REED, *Proc. Nat. Acad. Sci.*, 6, 275 (1920).
7. H. VON FOERSTER, P. M. MORA & L. W. AMIOT, *Science* 132, 1291 (1960).
8. "The future growth of world population," *U.N. Publ. No. ST/SOA/Ser. A/28* (1958).
9. "The past and future growth of world population – a long-range view," *U.N. Population Bull. No. 1* (1951), pp. 1–12.
10. *Demographic Yearbook* (United Nations, New York, 1956), p. 14.
11. New York *Times* (5 Aug. 1961).

HAROLD F. DORN, Ph. D., has been a statistician in the United States Public Health Service since 1936. He has been Cutter Lecturer in Preventive Medicine at Harvard since 1959. Dr. DORN has served on numerous commissions on public health and population problems. He was Director of the Medical Statistics Division, Office of the Surgeon General of the U.S. Army 1943–46, and was awarded the Medal of Award for Superior Service by the U.S. Department of Health, Education, and Welfare in 1961. Dr. DORN was a Past-President of the Population Association of America.

The Editors regret that Dr. DORN suddenly died on May 9, 1963.

Economic, Social and Political Analysis

Address to the Economic and Social Council of the United Nations, New York, April 24, 1961

by

Eugene R. Black

I am making my annual report to you in a period when world tensions are particularly acute. Like millions of other people, I have been following events in this United Nations building with deep and anxious concern over the past 12 months. I am aware, of course – as all of us are – that the political difficulties with which the United Nations is struggling are reflections in many cases of economic problems; no lasting political solutions can be expected until much more is done to remedy the economic ills which afflict so many countries.

In these circumstances it is all the more important that the Economic and Social Council should continue to seek cooperation among nations to deal with the financial problems of our time. It is now acknowledged everywhere that much more assistance must be rendered to the less developed countries by those more fortunately placed. But the needs for financial assistance are of such great magnitude that it is vitally important to ensure that aid is used in such a way as to contribute the maximum to the economic growth of the recipient countries.

The World Bank is itself, of course, a great cooperative of nations. What has been going on in our affairs over the past year can be taken as a good sample of the whole picture – and the past year has been a very busy one for us. Our rate of lending in the last fiscal year was maintained close to $700 million for the third successive year. In the first nine months of this fiscal year new loans have totaled $380 million. That our volume of loans remains high despite the several new sources of finance which have become available indicates how large is the demand for development investment.

Geographically, the bulk of our lending continues to be in Asia, but Africa accounted for almost one-third of the Bank's lending in the last fiscal year. There has also been increased lending in Latin America, a development which reflects the degree to which some Latin American countries, despite reduced prices for their products, particularly coffee, have taken hold of their internal economic affairs and brought them to a state of order which provides a suitable basis for further economic growth. I think that the Council should take note of the increasing number of Latin American countries which have recently attained relative stability after several years of acute inflationary difficulties. Readjustment in such circumstances is not easy and calls for sacrifice and discipline on the part of the peoples concerned. It is my hope that this new outlook on the part of those responsible for financial affairs in the Latin American countries will be sustained. For our part we look forward to increasing activity in that region.

In reporting these increases of Bank lending in the less developed regions I must also report a balancing factor, a considerable decrease in our lending in Europe. In calendar 1960 we made only one loan in Europe, of $25 million. It is cause for great satisfaction that Western Europe is in a position to satisfy its own needs for capital.

But Western Europe has not only made a negative contribution to the Bank, in the sense of abstaining from drawing on our loan funds. It has also made positive contributions of great importance by providing increasing amounts of money for lending elsewhere, both through the Bank and in other ways. The Annual Report records that, in our last fiscal year, two-thirds of the Bank's borrowing was outside the United States and included issues of bonds or notes in Germany, Switzerland and the United Kingdom. This situation has continued to prevail and all our borrowing so far in this fiscal year has been outside the United States. In September last we sold a $100 million issue of bonds by private placement with 47 institutional investors in 29 countries outside the United States. And we have made two public issues of bonds on the Swiss market, borrowing a total of 160 million Swiss francs equivalent to about $37 million. In January of this year we made very satisfactory arrangements with the Deutsche Bundesbank, the Central Bank of West Germany, regarding the equivalent of $360 million of our notes held by the Bundesbank which were due to mature at intervals during 1961 and the ensuing two years. The effect of these new arrangements was to lengthen these maturities so that we shall not be called upon to redeem the earliest of them until 1964. Agreement by the Bundesbank to these transactions was very helpful to us and was one more example of the cordial cooperation which we continue to receive from the Bundesbank and from the West German Government in financing our operations. In fact, Germany has been the largest provider of funds for World Bank operations for the past three years – total outstanding Bank borrowing from Germany, public and private, is now equivalent to over $750 million.

So much for the financial aspects of the past year. But I often feel that the Bank's lending and borrowing are only the most noticeable part of the iceberg – the fraction which shows above the surface. A great deal of the

Bank's time is spent on a variety of other, less publicized, activities directed at trying to assist the economic growth of our member countries. Our engineers and financial experts are engaged in regular visits to our member countries, investigating on the spot not only the progress of existing projects but the proposals for new projects which are constantly coming in. In the course of their duties these men are often able to render important technical assistance, especially when, as so often happens, the type of project being embarked upon is novel and requires new kinds of expertise on the part of the member country. Others of our staff, often accompanied by consultants employed especially for the purpose, are engaged directly in technical assistance work, advising our less developed member countries on ways of coping with particular problems. Of particular interest in this connection are national transportation surveys which we have helped to organize in Argentina, Colombia, Peru and Spain. We have also continued to respond to requests from many countries for assistance in the establishment, reorganization and operation of industrial development banks.

And during the past year we have had three general economic survey missions out in the field – in Venezuela, Tanganyika and Uganda. Reports of two survey missions, which recommend the basis for long-term development programs, have recently appeared in book form, concerning Libya and Tanganyika. A third report, on Venezuela, will be published in May and the report on Uganda is now being written. I am glad to say that in all cases the governments have begun to act along the lines of the mission reports even before they were published to a wider audience. Demand for this kind of help continues. We have one mission in Spain now, another in Kuwait, and we are considering a mission to Kenya. In addition, within the next month or two, missions of slightly narrower scope will go to Chile and the Philippines to review their development programs.

Another important field of technical assistance is our work for the United Nations Special Fund. Mr. HOFFMAN had asked us to be Executing Agent for several of the projects undertaken by the Special Fund and we have handled a wide variety of surveys, including power and transportation in Argentina, a river valley development study in Nigeria and a mineral survey in Surinam. In all the Bank has been asked to act as Executing Agent for eight Special Fund projects in seven countries.

Then there is another type of effort in which we are engaged. We now call together at regular intervals a consortium of countries interested in the financing of the Indian Five-Year Plans. We have also organized a similar consortium to coordinate ways of assisting the Pakistan economic plan.

Our work in connection with the Indus Basin has now, I am happy to say, moved from negotiation to action. Last year I was able to be optimistic about the chances of an Indus Basin agreement and my optimism turned out to be well founded. The Indus Waters Treaty was signed last fall and also the Indus Basin Development Fund Agreement, whereby several countries generously joined to contribute almost the entire cost – about $1,000 million – of the massive works which are needed in Pakistan to carry out the settlement. The Bank is administrator of the Development Fund and no time has been lost in calling for international tenders for the large projects which are involved.

Turning to another subject, I have to report to you, as Chairman of the International Finance Corporation, that the investments made by the Corporation during the past year have continued at the level reached in the previous year; 14 new investments have been made, aggregating about $16 million. The Corporation has now made 37 investments totaling $42.2 million in 17 member countries. Of the projects in which IFC has invested during the year, eight are owned and managed by residents of the country where the project is located; five are joint enterprises of local and foreign ownership and management; and one is a subsidiary of a foreign firm.

Of considerable importance is the move to amend the Corporation's Charter to permit it to make investments in capital stock. Under its Charter at present, IFC is prohibited from investing in capital stock or shares, and the experiences of four and one-half years has now convinced the Directors and Management of IFC that this restriction is in practice a serious handicap both to the growth of IFC's operations and the mobilization of private capital for foreign investment. The proposed change is being submitted to IFC's Board of Governors for action.

In addition to these varied activities, the Bank has been very busy bringing into being the International Development Association. IDA already has over 45 signatories, with subscriptions totaling $900 million, and we have a lengthening list of likely IDA projects under investigation.

The range of these projects is wide, both in geography and type. They are located in Asia, the Middle East, Latin America and Africa, and they include water supply, irrigation works, road development, port facilities, rural electrification, telecommunications and industrial estates. Under its charter, IDA is to support projects which can contribute most to the development of the country concerned, whether or not they are directly productive. IDA will finance all the kinds of projects which the Bank finances and a broader range as well, including, I hope, a number in which other specialized agencies of the United Nations will have a direct interest. This wide variety of projects, many in countries at very early stages of development, may well make the task of processing IDA credits more difficult than processing Bank loans. Nevertheless, IDA will apply the same high standards in project preparation and execution as does the Bank. The fact that IDA's management and staff are the same as the Bank's will facilitate this.

IDA's charter does not prescribe terms of financing, other than to specify that they shall be flexible and shall bear less heavily on the balance of payments of borrowers than the terms of conventional loans. Although this does not necessarily establish a general pattern, we have decided for the first projects to provide IDA financing in the form of 50-year development credits, free of interest or commitment charge. These development credits will be repayable in foreign exchange, thus avoiding the accumulation of large quantities of local currencies. Amortization will begin after a ten-year period of grace, and the credits will carry a small service charge, designed to provide IDA with income to meet its administrative expenses. I was pleased to note that the United States Administration wishes to adopt similar terms for its bilateral development loans.

We believe that IDA's objectives can best be served by limiting the availability of IDA funds to countries which, for reasons beyond their control, are not able to finance a satisfactory rate of development with their own resources plus conventional financing. Thus IDA borrowers can be expected to include not only countries whose foreign exchange situation is such that they cannot borrow abroad at all on conventional terms, but also those whose foreign debt service burden over the short and medium term is already so high that they cannot prudently borrow, on conventional terms, all of the external capital which they require to carry out their priority programs. It is already clear that the needs of these potential borrowers for development credits of the type which IDA can provide are far greater than can be satisfied with IDA's present resources. I am hopeful that in due course the obvious need, and IDA's record of performance, will together justify a substantial increase in IDA's financing capacities. I would hope, too, that countries contemplating an expansion of their aid programs may see fit to channel a part of the additional funds through IDA. Such a pooling of resources, I am convinced, is by far the most effective and satisfactory means of coordinating development aid.

But we should be less than wise if we were to place all reliance on new institutions providing development finance on easier and easier terms. There is a limit to the funds that capital-exporting countries are willing to provide. There are also movements in the less developed countries themselves which vitiate all efforts to raise world living standards. One of the most massive of these obstacles is the tremendous rise in the populations of already crowded countries.

Three hundred years ago there were probably no more than 500 million people alive in the world, and the total was increasing only slowly. This stability was maintained by an uneasy balance between high birth rates and death rates. Many babies were born, but many also died. Living conditions were such that many of the remaining children failed to survive beyond the age of thirty.

In Europe, the picture began to change in the late eighteenth century. Populations began to grow, sometimes very fast. Elsewhere the balance of new lives against deaths has been upset largely in our own lifetime. The pattern has been a steep fall in death rates, with birth rates little changed. But the circumstances have been somewhat different from the earlier European experience. The population revolution has often been achieved very cheaply. In Ceylon, to take the best-known example, the expenditure of $2 a head on a public health campaign with the prime purpose of eradicating malaria reduced the death rate by three-quarters over a single decade. Similar stories can already be told of public health programs undertaken in other countries, and there will undoubtedly be more in the future.

Of course we welcome this trend, whatever the problems it may set for us. We all want to reduce the suffering and waste involved in premature death or disabling disease, and we can expect death rates to go on falling in the developing countries. Medical science continues to discover increasingly effective ways of promoting public health, and since governments can usually act on behalf of the community in putting these new techniques to work, we may expect them to be applied as soon as the money can be found to pay the accompanying bill. People will live longer in the future.

But if only 20 people – or even fewer – in every thousand are hence-forth to die each year, then a birth rate of 40 per thousand, which formerly just kept the population steady, will bring an explosive growth in numbers. And there is little reason to suppose that birth rates will soon decline to match the fall in death rates. It is much simpler to attack disease than it is to alter the reproductive pattern of a society. Medicine has yet to make available a cheap and easy method of regulating births. And not everyone wants fewer children.

*   *
*

What view are we to take of all this?

I am not convinced that population growth will eventually outrun the development of the world's resources. It is true that at present rates of consumptions we will use up the known reserves of several important fuels and minerals within a few decades. Heavy demands will certainly be made on our agricultural resources, and there may be acute difficulty in organizing the movement of food and other necessities about the world on the scale required to meet the needs of a population twice its present size. But I am inclined to think that those prophets who forecast the exhaustion of the earth's resources, underestimate the ingenuity of man and the potentialities of science. And I am not too disturbed about the long-run problems of feeding the extra persons we expect, although I find myself a little out of sympathy with some of our professional agricultural optimists – it seems to me Utopian to expect that every country will be cultivated as efficiently as Denmark, and that thereby, the world could easily feed twice its present population.

But all this does not mean that we ought to welcome population growth on the scale that we see it today.

Some people argue that a big population implies a good market for the businessman's product: he can use mass production techniques and charge low prices. They insist, too, that with a growing population, the businessman constantly finds demand exceeding his estimates. Optimism and production run high; new products win ready acceptance, while obsolete industries die painlessly; the incentive to invest is strong; and social mobility and change are encouraged. The burden of social costs is spread widely. By contrast, they suggest, a declining or even stationary population brings pessimism and economic stagnation; there is insufficient reward for private enterprise, and the state is thereby forced to intervene increasingly in fields better left to the private citizen.

This body of theory may conceivably be true in the circumstances of a rich country with resources to spare. But it is wildly irrelevant to the problems of most developing countries today.

It is, of course, a fact that some of the poorer countries do not have domestic markets big enough to support mass production industries. But it is clearly ridiculous to suggest that inadequate population is holding back the development of, say, India, which packs more than twice the population of the United States into less than half the space. Where most people go barefoot for lack of shoes, industry is not failing to grow because its products are not wanted. Where the agricultural laborer can find work to occupy him for only half the year, no further pressure is needed to make him wish for a different occupation. Where two-thirds of every dollar of income must be spent on food, where manufacturing industry is almost nonexistent, one need not worry that excessive saving will lead to underemployment of resources. The lash of further poverty is not required to drive these people to action. The developing countries need many things – not only capital, but the skills and health to make good use of it. By no means do all of them need population growth.

* *
*

But need it or not, they have it. They should ask themselves if they can afford it. In Asia, in the Middle East, in Latin America, in Africa, the population of most countries is growing at the rate of 2% annually – and sometimes 3½% or more. In most of Latin America and Africa there is fortunately room for the extra people. In the long run, although not now, there should also be adequate resources available to feed, clothe and house them. But in many parts of Asia and the Middle East, resources are few, and there is not nearly enough room. Agricultural land which once sufficed to support a stationary and much smaller population has already been divided and subdivided beyond the limits of effective cultivation. Cities are crowded to bursting, and are still getting bigger.

Population growth on this scale would be a serious challenge to a country with adequate living standards. Where incomes are very low, and economic development is a desperate need, such growth can be a crippling handicap.

The speed at which a country develops depends largely upon its ability to direct its growing resources to investment rather than to consumption, to uses which will raise tomorrow's output rather than satisfy today's demands. A poor society finds it difficult to save at all, and will be doing well if it can set aside 10% of its income. At this rate, if its population is growing, it will barely be investing enough to stay where it is. Yet the likelihood must be that it will invest not more than 10%, but less: a growing population with a high proportion of dependent children will find it increasingly difficult to spare any of its income from consumption.

Unless foreign aid can be increased, a country in this position is faced with a stark alternative. It must reduce its savings, or lower its living standards – although both are already inadequate.

The industrialized countries have shown their willingness to help. Common humanity and self-interest alike impel them to do so. All the evidence points to a greater flow of aid in the coming years. But I find myself increasingly doubtful whether domestic savings and foreign aid together will be sufficient to allow real progress, if present rates of population growth continue for long.

Figures are hard to come by in this field. But it may be possible to indicate some orders of magnitude.

Some calculations have been made about the cost of providing houses in India during the next generation, if the population continues to grow at its present rate of about 2% a year. If you disregard the cost of rural housing, on the somewhat optimistic assumption that it can be carried out entirely with local materials and labor, then you still have to pay for the homes of nearly 200 million extra people who, it is expected, will be living in India's cities 25 years hence. Making full allowance for the fact that many of the extra persons will be children needing not new houses, but simply more space in existing households, a sober estimate of the cost suggests that in the 30 years between 1956 and 1986 a total investment in housing of the order of 118 billion rupees, or roughly $25 billion, will be needed. If you find a figure like that difficult to grasp, I may say that it is well over four times the total lent by the World Bank in all countries since it started business 15 years ago. Put another way, it is more than 30 times the initial resources of the International Development Association – and those resources are supposed to cover IDA's first five years of operations.

My cost estimate takes no account of the need to improve existing housing in such cities as Calcutta. It leaves out the cost of roads, sewage systems, water supplies and other services. Yet the problems of urban growth form only a small part of the challenge presented when economic development is attempted in the context of a vast expansion in population·

In the social field, many more new hospitals and clinics will be needed, simply to maintain present standards – standards which by common consent are sadly inadequate. Far more must be spent on education. Here look again at India, not because its problems are unusual, but because they are well documented. In 1956, about 31 million Indian children were getting an education – less than 40% of those of school age. It is mathematically certain that if the population grows as expected, a three or fourfold increase in educational investment will be needed if all children are to be receiving an education by 1976. When you come to productive investment, the story is similar. Enormous investments will be needed. But population growth does not only tend to reduce the flow of investment funds. It also means that the capital invested in industry must be spread increasingly thinly over the labor force: each pair of hands is backed by fewer dollars of capital. Productivity suffers, and the gap in living standards between the developing and the industrialized countries widens, instead of narrowing.

I must be blunt. Population growth threatens to nullify all our efforts to raise living standards in many of the poorer countries. We are coming to a situation in which the optimist will be the man who thinks that present living standards can be maintained. The pessimist will not look even for that. Unless population growth can be restrained, we may have to abandon for this generation our hopes of economic progress in the crowded lands of Asia and the Middle East. This is not a field in which international agencies can do much. But there is scope for governments to act: it is time that they gave earnest attention to this threat to their aspirations.

* *
*

Population growth does not alter the rules for successful economic development. On the contrary, it reinforces their strength by increasing the penalties for breaking them. In relation to the need, capital is short, and must be stretched as far as it can possibly go. In the developing countries, therefore, the first question to be asked of any economic policy must be: "Is this the road to maximum economic growth?", and if the answer is "No" we must look very closely at any doctrines which are put forward to excuse this sacrifice of economic advancement.

For the providers of economic aid, this situation implies a duty not only to see that the money is properly and efficiently applied, but also to guard against the temptation to use development assistance to achieve their own commercial or short-term political objectives, rather than to serve the priority needs of the recipient countries. For the developing countries themselves, it implies that they must realize that they least of all can afford to accept low returns on their investments. They cannot afford to waste scarce resources by putting prestige ahead of real need, by ignoring hard economic calculations, by refusing to accept productive capital while they debate for years the respective roles of public and private enterprise.

At best, and even if real sacrifices are made by the industrialized nations to increase the flow of aid, there is grave danger that, in the face of existing rates of population growth, the resources available for economic development will fall short of the needs of the developing countries. We bear a heavy responsibility toward succeeding generations to make the best use of all our resources.

EUGENE ROBERT BLACK, LL.D., was President of the International Bank for Reconstruction and Development (World Bank) from 1949 through 1962, and is now Special Financial Consultant to the Secretary General of the United Nations, and a member of General CLAY's Presidential Committee – The Committee to Strengthen the Security of the Free World. Mr. BLACK is Chairman of the Board of Trustees of the Brookings Institution. Mr. BLACK's Board memberships include The Chase Manhattan Bank, American Express Company, Olin Mathieson Chemical Corporation, Electric Bond and Share Company and The New York Times.

The Economics of Population Growth*

by

JOSEPH J. SPENGLER

> "It is never the question whether a country will produce
> any more but whether it may be made to produce a suf-
> ficiency to keep pace with a nearly unchecked increase of
> people."
> T. R. MALTHUS, in *Essay on the Principle of Population*, Bk. 3,
> chap. 14.

This chapter has to do both with the economic adjustments that a population makes when it is growing and with the manner in which a population's reproductive behavior may respond to economic changes. It is
made up of five parts which relate to three somewhat distinct problems.
The first two parts deal with what may be called the supply aspect of population growth; in the first we inquire into the immediate disadvantages of
population growth as such, and in the second we look at the economic
advantages and disadvantages which are consequent upon a country's
population being larger rather than smaller. The second problem is treated
in Part III which deals with what may be called the demand for population,
or the manner in which fertility changes as a result of economic changes
which bring about modifications in income, price-structure, tastes, etc.
Parts IV and V deal with the economic policy implications of what has been
set down in the earlier parts and with conflicts between individual and
social interests in respect of marriage and family size that have emerged or
may emerge in both developed and underdeveloped countries.

I. POPULATION GROWTH

Population growth is normally and primarily the result of an excess of
births over deaths, though the rate of increase resulting may be augmented

* This paper was written while I was the holder of a John Simon Guggenheim Memorial
Fellowship.

through net immigration or diminished through net emigration. Population growth entails the conversion of substances and services into the origination, development, repair, replacement, and increase of the inhabitants of a given area or country. It entails the transformation of a given population, together with its replaceable and irreplaceable environment, into a successor population and environment; and this transformation involves the dissipation of that part of the environment which is not susceptible of replacement or increase.[1] Population growth thus entails a number of costs, among them an unfavorable age composition, capital outlays, and possibly unemployment.

Population growth may take place either under steady-state conditions or under conditions that give rise to fluctuations in the rate of growth and the age composition of a population. In reality the former mode of growth is merely a theoretical possibility, though it has been approximated at times; for many of the conditions which can affect mortality or fertility change from time to time. Even so, the analysis of potential economic effects of population growth is simplified when one supposes this growth to be taking place under steady-state conditions, that is, under conditions associated with a stable population. I shall, therfore, first postulate that growth is taking place under these conditions and then allow for modification of these conditions.

(1) *Steady-state Growth*

If age-specific mortality and fertility, together with the sex-ratio at birth, stay put long enough and there is no migration, a population will finally assume a stable form and the fraction of this population in each age-group will become constant. Moreover, the rate of natural increase of this population will be constant, be the population growing, declining, or stationary in number; what this constant rate is depends, of course, upon the underlying mortality and fertility rates. A stable population may, therefore, include a relative small or a relatively large number of persons of productive age. The data in Tables I and II illustrate how age composition and other characteristics of a stable population vary as fertility (as reflected in the gross reproduction rate) and mortality (as reflected in the expectation of life at birth) vary. The implications of these variations will be discussed here and there in what follows.[2]

---

1. On man's environment-transforming behavior see W. L. THOMAS, ed., *International Symposium on Man's Role in Changing the Face of the Earth*, University of Chicago Press, Chicago, 1956, *passim*. Virtually all aspects of this behavior are dealt with.
2. On stable populations, aging, etc., see United Nations, *The Aging of Populations and its Economic and Social Implication*, Population Studies, No. 26, United Nations, New York, 1956.

(a) Age Composition

Changes in a population's age composition may reflect changes in either its fertility, its mortality, or both. When mortality remains constant, a decrease in fertility is accompanied by a decrease in the relative number of persons under 15 years of age and by increases both in the fraction of the population of productive age (represented in our tables by those aged 15–59) and in the relative number aged 60 or more years. An increase in fertility produces an opposite set of effects. When fertility remains constant, a decrease in mortality is accompanied by a decrease in the relative number aged 15–59 and by increases in both the relative number under 15 years of age and that of persons aged 60 or more years. An increase in mortality produces an opposite set of effects.

For purposes of the present discussion we shall consider only more probable tendencies, namely, falling mortality in nearly all countries, falling fertility in high-fertility countries, and rising or constant fertility in low-fertility countries. Life expectancy by country usually fell within the range 30–35 years in the late eighteenth century and within the range 30–50 years a century later. It now lies and is likely to continue to lie largely within the range 50–75, at least until late in this century, though in important parts of the world (especially in Asia and Africa) it still remains far below 50. The prospective tendency, therefore, will be for mortality to continue to fall at least until the limits of life expectancy have been closely approached or economic adversity has counterbalanced forces making for death control. Turning to fertility, we may assume that if fertility is high, it will eventually begin to decline, and that if it is low, either it may remain so or it may rise somewhat only subsequently to decline.

TABLE I.

High-Mortality Stable Population

G.R.R.	E = 20					E = 30					E = 40				
	P.	A.	B.R.	D.R.	N.I.	P.	A.	B.R.	D.R.	N.I.	P.	A.	B.R.	D.R.	N.I.
4.0	52.4	2.4	63.8	53.0	10.8	49.2	2.6	59.8	35.3	24.5	47.3	2.7	57.3	24.1	33.2
3.0	57.6	3.9	50.5	50.2	0.3	54.5	4.1	47.7	33.7	14.0	52.5	4.4	46.0	23.3	22.7
2.5	60.7	5.2	42.8	49.1	— 6.3	57.6	5.5	40.6	33.2	7.4	55.6	5.9	39.3	23.2	16.1
2.0	64.0	7.1	34.2	48.6	—14.4	60.9	7.7	32.7	33.6	— 0.9	58.8	8.3	31.7	23.7	8.0
1.5	66.9	10.5	24.8	49.7	—24.9	63.8	11.5	23.8	35.0	—11.2	61.6	12.5	23.1	25.6	— 2.5
1.0	68.3	16.9	14.6	54.4	—39.8	65.0	18.7	14.0	39.9	—25.9	62.6	20.4	13.6	30.9	—17.3

Source: p. 24 of study cited in footnote 2.
Abbreviations: G.R.R. – Gross Reproduction Rate; E – Expectation of life at birth; P – Percentage of Stable population aged 15–59; A. – Percentage of stable population aged 60 and over; B.R. – Births per 1,000 inhabitants; D.R. – Deaths per 1,000 inhabitants; N.I. – Excess of births over deaths per 1,000 inhabitants.

A glance at the columns under the heading P in Tables I and II indicates that the fraction of the population aged 15–59 is higher in stable populations with low fertility than in those with high fertility. For example, in populations with a G.R.R. of 1.5 this fraction is about 17–19% higher than in populations with a G.R.R. of 3, which corresponds fairly closely to the fertility patterns found in much of the underdeveloped, low-income world. This comparison indicates that reducing gross reproduction from around 3 to around 1.5 (which corresponds to a birth rate in the low 20's) serves to increase by about one-sixth the fraction of the population of reproductive age. It suggests also, as does a glance down the columns headed P and N.I., that when the rate of natural increase is relatively low, the fraction of the population aged 15–59 is much larger than when the rate of natural increase is high. In short, we find associated with low fertility and low rates of natural increase a significantly larger relative number of persons of productive age and a relatively smaller number of persons of non-productive or dependent age.

TABLE II.
Low-Mortality Stable Population

G.R.R.	E = 50					E = 60.4					E = 70.2				
	P.	A.	B.R.	D.R.	N.I.	P.	A.	B.R.	D.R.	N.I.	P.	A.	B.R.	D.R.	N.I.
4.0	45.8	2.7	55.7	16.2	39.5	44.4	2.7	54.1	9.4	44.7	43.3	2.6	52.7	4.1	48.6
3.0	50.9	4.5	44.9	15.8	29.1	49.6	4.4	43.8	9.6	34.2	48.4	4.3	42.9	4.8	38.1
2.5	53.9	6.1	38.4	16.0	22.4	52.6	6.0	37.7	10.1	27.6	51.4	5.9	37.0	5.5	31.5
2.0	57.2	8.6	31.1	16.8	14.3	55.8	8.6	30.6	11.1	19.5	54.7	8.5	30.1	6.8	23.3
1.5	60.0	13.0	22.7	18.8	3.9	58.7	13.1	22.5	13.5	9.0	57.7	13.0	22.3	9.4	12.9
1.0	60.7	21.5	13.4	24.3	−10.9	59.4	21.9	13.3	19.0	−5.7	58.6	21.9	13.3	15.1	−1.8

Source and Abbrevations: Same as in Table I.

What is the economic significance of this association? The answer turns on the use that is made of a population's potential labor force. If, of two populations, one-sixth more of the one than of the other is of working age, then potential productivity per capita in the former is one-sixth greater than in the latter under conditions otherwise similar, and per capita output and income can be one-sixth greater. Furthermore, it will be easier to provide education in the one population than in the other, for in it there will be only about half as many children per 100 adults as in the other population (though this advantage will be partly offset by the relatively greater number of older dependents in the low-fertility population). It does not follow, however, that because there are more persons of working age in one population than in the other, that all will be employed, and for the same number of hours per week and per year. How many persons enroll in the labor force, together with the average length of the work-week and the work-year, depends upon a variety of circumstances, among them the demand for leisure, the rate of capital formation, the degree of industrialization, the wage structure, and so on; it depends only in part upon the age structure. In consequence, only a portion of the potential advantage associated with a more favorable age composition is utilized in the production of goods and services. Even so, around 1950 one found about 5–6% more males and somewhat more females economically active in low-fertility than in high-fertility countries. The advantage enjoyed by low-fertility countries is somewhat greater even than these figures suggest, for in these countries there is less pressure upon the children to enter the labor force at an early age and more pressure upon them to acquire an education compatible with the requirements of a modern economy, with the result that the present value of their life-time earnings will be greater.

Two conclusions and a corollary follow from what has been said. First, when a population's gross reproduction rate is relatively low instead of relatively high and its age composition consequently is favorable, a relatively large fraction of its members can engage in economically productive activity and a relatively large fraction of its youth can be provided with a technically suitable education. Second, even when a country's population is too small to permit it to exploit its economic potential fully, it will find it economically advantageous if its rate of natural increase remains low enough to assure a favorable age composition. Corollary to these conclusions is the inference developed below, that savings per capita tend to be lower in consequence of an unfavorable age composition.

(b) Capital Absorption

When a population is growing, increments in its number must be provided with public, industrial, and consumer's capital as well as with the educational and other services involved in the reproduction of a child and its conversion into a productive adult. How much capital is required for this purpose depends largely upon a country's economic situation. A rough, rule-of-thumb approach enables us to estimate how much capital must be formed to offset a rate of population growth of one or more per cent per year. Suppose that a country's wealth amounts to 3 or 4 times its national income and that a population is concerned only to maintain its wealth per capita, or wealth-population ratio, unchanged. Then, if a country's population is growing 1% per year, it needs to save 3–4% of its income, convert these savings into wealth, and thereby increase its wealth 1%. If this country's population were growing 2 or 3% per year, the required saving rate would have to be increased correspondingly; it would lie between 6 and 12%. Under the circumstances supposed per capita income would tend to rise somewhat even though wealth per head (as conventionally measured) remained unchanged, since such improvements in technology as were embodied in the labor force and its capital equipment would tend to increase output per worker. The measure proposed does not directly take into account the effects of differences in a country's age composition, but these, if they exist, will be reflected in a country's wealth-population ratio; for wealth per capita tends to be somewhat lower, under otherwise roughly similar conditions, in a country with high fertility and a low average age than in one with low fertility and a high average age.

A more specific approach to the cost of providing for population growth in the United States is employed by J. W. KENDRICK. He multiplies "the net population increment of each year by the average per capita consumption and reproducible stock of the previous year." His estimates suggest that provision for the growth of population in 1889–1953 absorbed goods and services at a rate of around 3.1–3.2% of real gross national product per 1% per year of population growth; this provision (amounting to somewhat less than 4% of national income) often appreciably exceeded that made for increase in capital per head.[3] Moreover, the impact of this capital-absorption was often reflected in the composition of the additions made to the stock of capital in the United States. For, since the volume of savings was too small to finance all capital requirements, and since upsurges in population growth made for upsurges in investment in population-sensitive capital (e.g., residential, construction, and equipment capital), these upsurges were accompanied by downswings in investment in various other forms of capital.[4]

The absorption of capital by population growth operates in various ways to reduce the rate at which output and income per capita can be made to advance. It slows down the rate of increase in capital per head and it may cause a relatively large fraction of the capital formed to be invested in activities (e.g., construction, housing) in which the capital-output ratio is relatively high and the marginal productivity of capital may be relatively low. Suppose a population is growing 1% instead of 0% per year. The capital used to equip this increment of population might otherwise have been used to increase capital per head by 1%, with the result that output per worker might have been something like 0.2 to 0.5% higher than it otherwise would have been. The role which inputs absorbed by population growth could play in the augmentation of per capita income may be even greater, for some of these inputs could be devoted to the increase of education per capita and some could implement the scientific findings that make income-increasing technical progress possible.

It may be noted at this point that high fertility and a high rate of population growth diminish the per capita supply of savings at the same time

3. J. W. KENDRICK, *Productivity Trends in the United States*, Princeton UniversityPress,Princeton 1961, pp. 99–101.
4. See S. KUZNETS, *Capital in the American Economy*, Princeton, 1961, Princeton University Press, pp. 327–41.

that they augment the demand for savings. This effect may be illustrated in two ways. First, individual savings per capita are reduced inasmuch as these include family savings and large families save less than small families receiving similar incomes; the pressure to consume is greater in large families and its adult members tend to look upon investment in children as a source of security and hence as a substitute for investment in non-human capital. There does not exist an offset to this effect in the form of a positive correlation between family size and family income, or in the form of a sufficiently marked increase of entrepreneurial and governmental savings. Furthermore, the age composition of a population is somewhat more favorable to saving per capita when fertility is relatively low. It has been estimated that, because of changes in the age structure and in the family-size structure of the American population between 1900 and 1950, the ratio of individual savings to national income should have virtually trebled. This ratio changed very little, however, the impact of demographic changes having been offset by various changes making for decline in the propensity to work and save.[5] Second, one may allow for the loss in potential saving capacity caused by a reduction in per capita output associated with changes in age compositon occasioned by a shift from low to high fertility. Suppose this reduction amounts to one-tenth in terms of national income and that the marginal propensity to save is 0.4; we may then infer that savings have been reduced by an amount approximating 4% of national income.

It may also be noted parenthetically that variation in the rate of population growth affects the volume of saving because saving varies with age. Typically an individual dissaves in his early years and after he retires and saves in most of his productive years (say 25–65); moreover, after he retires he may use up all the savings which he accumulated during his productive life-time. If everyone saved only for old age, and if through insurance arrangements a community could so plan that per capita dissaving in old age would consume per capita accumulated earlier, we should have three possibilities. If a population were stationary, savings and dissaving would balance, and if it were declining, dissavings would exceed savings. If, however, a population were growing and additions to the labor force exceeded withdrawals, the savings of individuals in the saving stage of life would exceed the dissavings of older persons no longer saving, with the result that the aggregate volume of savings as well as the stock of capital would be increasing even though each individual had so ordered his life as to permit his dissavings to wipe out his savings. In reality, of course, what is said pertains only to a portion of a population, since many individuals plan to

5. See W. EIZENGA, *Demographic Factors and Savings*, North Holland Publishing Co., Amsterdam, 1961, esp. chap. 8. On age composition, family size, and savings in the United States see also R. W. GOLDSMITH, D. S. BRADY & H. MENDERSHAUSEN, *A Study of Saving in the United States*, III, Princeton University Press, Princeton, 1956, pp. 193–223, and MILTON FRIEDMAN, *A Theory of the Consumption Function*, Princeton University press, Princeton, 1957, pp. 121–23.

save more than they dissave.[6] Furthermore, cumulating savings of the sort just described as associated with population growth are not sufficient in volume to counterbalance the tendency of savings per capita to be negatively associated with fertility and natural increase.

(c) Labor-Supply-Demand Relations

What may loosely be called labor-supply-demand relations tend to be affected by the level of fertility and the rate of population growth. This effect is associated with variation in the ratio of persons of dependent age to those of productive age. We may, for example, use as indicator of this variation changes in the ratio of persons under 15 and over 59 to those aged 15–59. Let us turn to the P-columns in Tables I and II. Given a G.R.R. of 3 and a life expectancy of 50, we find in a stable population 50.9% aged 15–59 and hence 49.1 aged under 15 and over 59, or a ratio of 0.96, together with a rate of natural increase of 2.91%. By contrast, in a stable population based on a G.R.R. of 1.5 or less and a life expectancy of 70.2 years, we find corresponding ratios of 0.73 or somewhat less and a rate of natural increase of 1.29% or less. These data indicate that with high fertility there is associated a high dependency ratio and there will be associated a relatively high rate of natural increase unless mortality remains very high. It will be indicated that both the propensity to consume and that to invest may be positively associated with high fertility and a high rate of natural increase. It will also be indicated that the nature of this association, together with its impact on employment, is conditioned by a country's stage of economic development.

For convenience of discussion, let

$$T = C + I + G + U$$

where T stands for the total amount of income (in the sense of Net National Product) that would be produced, given full employment (say 97% of the labor force); where C, I, and G, respectively, represent consumption, private investment, and governmental expenditure on goods and services; and where U stands for the additional net income that would be produced if unemployed and partially unemployed labor were productively employed at normal work-week rates. If Y represents realized net national product, $U = T - Y$; and $U = 0$ when $T = Y$. Unemployment may exist and hence U may be positive for a variety of reasons, of which only two are of particular concern here: (a) the rate of planned investment (and related expenditure) associated with full employment and $T = Y$ is inadequate to offset the rate of planned saving associated with $T = Y$ and $U = 0$. (b) the stock of capital requisite for the employment of labor is too small to permit setting the whole of the labor force to work. Unemployment associated with condition (a) is more likely to be pronounced in a developed country than in an underdeveloped country; it would not arise, of course, given

6. E.g., see SIMON KUZNETS' analysis of this problem in M. ABRAMOVITZ, ed., *Capital Formation and Economic Growth*, Princeton University Press, Princeton, 1955, pp. 100–103.

appropriate combinations of price flexibility and monetary policy. Un-employment associated with condition (b) is far more typical of under-developed countries than of those which are quite advanced; for it is in high-fertility, underdeveloped countries that the average rate of saving often is too low to supply as much capital as full employment (i.e., $U = 0$) requires.

When condition (a) emerges, aggregate expenditure is inadequate to absorb the volume of output corresponding to T, with the result that Y falls short of T and U is positive. Under otherwise similar circumstances, how-ever, condition (a) is less likely to emerge when fertility and the rate of population growth are relatively high. Then income per capita will be relatively low because the number of persons of working age is relatively low. Moreover, the pressure to spend and hence the propensity to consume will be relatively high because the dependency ratio is relatively high and because growth of population, together with family formation, makes for increase in expenditure by households and governments upon current needs and, along with business enterprise, upon investments designed to increase the flow of goods and services in the future. The initial expendi-ture-increasing effects noted will be augmented several times, through successive impacts of secondary or derivative expenditure in keeping with the multiplier-process. An accelerator effect may also be present. Antici-pated increase in prospective expenditure gives rise to increase both in investment induced by such prospect and in investment (i.e., so-called autonomous investment) which is less intimately connected with such prospect; and this rise may in turn cause aggregate investment to rise even more rapidly than anticipated consumption and related expenditures. A limit is set to the cumulative impact of these direct and indirect effects, of course, by the current capacity of the economy which normally exceeds T only slightly.

What has been said may be stated even more tersely in respect of de-veloped countries. Let E represent the rate of aggregate expenditure, or the sum of the expenditures per year (or other period) included under the heads of C, I, and G, when all primary and secondary multiplier and ac-celerator effects are taken into account. Let E' represent the value of E in a country with relatively low fertility and natural increase and E'' the value of E in a country quite similar in all respects other than fertility and natural increase which are relatively high. Under these conditions the ratio E'' to T would be higher than the ratio of E' to T and hence U would be smaller in the high-fertility country. Should the rate of population growth and hence expenditure be sufficiently high, E'' would be pressed to the point where Y would approximate T and inflation would tend to develop.

It does not follow from the preceding paragraph that high fertility and natural increase are advantageous even when capital is being formed at a rate high enough to permit continuous full employment. First, output and income per capita almost certainly will increase less rapidly in a high- than in a low-fertility country; age composition is less favorable in the former country, and its capital per head increases less rapidly. Second, even though it be true that the ratio of E to T is higher in a high- than in a low-fertility advanced country, it is possible to manipulate G and perhaps also C and I and thereby eliminate U in a low-fertility country. It is possible also, at least in advanced countries, to manipulate G and perhaps C and I and thereby prevent the inflation that can result if increase in population is allowed to press E close to and beyond the point where T and Y coincide.

In typical underdeveloped countries the impact of high fertility and population growth is different than in advanced countries with fairly high fertility and population growth. Above all, population would tend to accentuate rather than to reduce unemployment. Such countries are characterized by a low ratio of capital to population and by rates of saving that often are insufficient to balance population growth. In such countries, therefore, one encounters considerable unemployment which is associated with sheer dearth of capital; there is not enough capital, even of quite primitive sorts, to equip all the population, even at very low capital-worker ratios.

(2) *Fluctuating Population Growth*

When a population is growing under steady-state conditions, the rate of growth of such population remains constant as does that of each áge group included therein. This rate may be positive, zero, or negative, but whatever it is, the age and sex composition of the population remains unchanged; changes in age composition do not therefore accentuate other of the unfavorable conditions that sometimes accompany population growth. Moreover, because the composition and rate of growth of the population stay put, the economy can become adjusted to these unchanging conditions. It can even become optimally adjusted thereto; for it may become feasible in time to accomodate consumption, saving, investment, and aggregate expenditure, together with the composition of demand, to whatever rate of growth and age composition have emerged, and in such manner as to minimize unemployment and perhaps even to alleviate emerging capital shortages. The capacity to make such accomodation is much more powerful, however, in a low-fertility, advanced economy than in a high-fertility, underdeveloped society; for in the former it is essential only to maintain aggregate expenditure whereas in the latter it is necessary greatly to elevate investment in capital equipment and the education and improvement of the young.

Population seldom grows under steady-state conditions. Prior to the nineteenth century fertility and, in greater measure, mortality and the rate of growth fluctuated, though seldom enough to modify the age composition of large population aggregates appreciably. Today in advanced countries fertility may fluctuate considerably and mortality may decline, (though hardly enough to modify age composition appreciably). In under-developed countries mortality is likely to decline appreciably and fertility may eventually decline as it has in Japan. Departures from steady-state growth conditions are much more likely, however, to intensify problems in advanced countries than in underdeveloped countries. For in advanced countries these departures usually result in a worsening of age composition whereas in underdeveloped countries they usually result in an improvement in age composition.

(a) Age Composition

When, after a population has been growing under steady-state conditions, fertility and/or mortality begins to change, age composition changes. Possible patterns of change have already been described. We may, however, turn to American experience for purposes of illustration. So late as 1850, even though fertility had been declining for half a century, the age compo-sition of the American population remained that of a present-day backward country, but after 1860 the rate of growth began to fall appreciably. Between

TABLE III.

Population of the United States, by Age, 1940–1970

Age Group	Population					
	1940		1960		1970	
	Absolute (in thousands)	Relative	Absolute (in thousands)	Relative	Absolute (in thousands)	Relative
0–14	32,972	100	56,081	170	67,750	206
15–19	12,334	100	13,466	109	18,910	153
20–64	77,344	100	94,498	122	107,525	139
65 & over	9,019	100	16,645	184	20,035	221
Total	131,669	100	180,670	137	214,220	163
$\dfrac{15\text{–}19}{65\text{–}69}$	3.24	100	2.14	0.66	2.71	0.83

1870 and 1930 the fraction of the American native white population under 20 years of age fell from about 56% to about 43% of the total while the fraction aged 20–64 years rose from about 41 to about 52%. After the 1930's, as the data in Table III indicate, earlier trends were somewhat reversed, under the impact of a sustained upsurge in natality. The population of dependent age, both under 15 and over 64 years old, increased more than 3 times as fast as the population of working age between 1940 and 1960, and it will increase about 1.5 times as fast in the 1960's. In subsequent decades, however, should fertility and mortality change very little, the rates of increase of the several age groups will converge and the population's age composition will become relatively stable. Moreover, this age composition will be more favorable to productivity than was that of 1960, though less favorable than was that of 1940.

(b) Capital Absorption

The capital requirements associated with a given rate of natural increase are somewhat less when, as in the 1940's and 1950's, the growth of population is concentrated among the young and the old who have less need of equipment and other forms of capital than do those of working age. This qualification may be disregarded, however, in that it is really a source of disadvantage; for it is the equipping of persons of working age with productive capital that augments output per worker and per capita. Even when a population is in transition from one level of fertility to another, say from lower to higher fertility, one may still form a rough estimate of the capital required by supposing, as we did earlier, that a saving rate of 3–4% of national income is required to offset a rate of population growth of 1%. The physical forms assumed by the capital will be relatively more oriented to the wants of the young in such a transitional population than in a stable one.

(c) Labor-Supply-Demand Relations

A rise in fertility may serve for a time to increase the demand for labor more than its supply, since it is the relative number of young dependents that is augmented at first. The data presented in Table III lend support to this inference, given that changes in newly entering, retiring, and employed workers are roughly indicated by those aged 15–19, 65–69, and 20–64, respectively. If we indicate changes in the ratio of labor-force entrants to departures by changes in the ratio of persons aged 15–19 to those aged 65–69 years, we find this ratio declining between 1940 and 1960 and then rising after 1960 as those born in the 1940's and 1950's began to age into the labor force. Similarly, we find the ratio of new labor-force entrants (i.e., those aged 15–19) to its supposedly regular membership (i.e., those aged 20–64) falling from about 0.16 in 1940 to about 0.14 in 1960; thereafter it will rise to about 0.176 in 1970. A fall in fertility between 1940 and 1960 would have produced a somewhat opposite set of effects.

A rise in fertility and the rate of population growth also exercises influence on the demand for goods and labor through the medium of the accelerator principle; it steps up the *rate* at which *additions* must be made to the nation's stock of durable equipment whilst leaving temporarily unchanged the rate at which components of this stock must be replaced. A fall in fertility and the rate of population growth produces a decline in the rate of *additions* though not in that of replacements unless the population decreases sufficiently. When the rate of population growth fluctuates, economic fluctuations of a more diverse and irregular character are occasioned; they are occasioned immediately by the irregular manner in which *additions* to the nation's stock of durable goods and capital, together with equipment oriented to the production of these products, respond to variations in the rate of population growth. These fluctuations in turn may set up secondary fluctuations via the medium of the multiplier process. What takes place in any concrete instance, of course, depends upon the pattern of population fluctuation, upon the technological ties connecting industries, and upon the extent to which inputs are mobile and compensatory actions and activities are available. It is easier, however, under any given set of conditions, to adjust an economy to accelerator effects when the rate of population growth, be it positive or negative, is constant than when it fluctuates.[7]

II. POPULATION-RESOURCES RATIO

In this part we are concerned with the significance of variation in the size of a country's population, its territorial extent and resource-equipment being given. We are concerned, that is, with what many nineteenth-century writers considered to be the fundamental population problem. Our concern thus differs from that treated in Part I where attention was given to growth patterns as such. It differs also from a somewhat related though essentially different concern suggested in part by the question, How large need a country be to permit it to make optimum use of land and other resources? Our concern here is suggested by the question, How large need the population of a given country be to permit it to make optimum use of its land and resources? This question is touched upon in section (b) below where the policy implications of section (a) are discussed. In section (a) emphasis is solely upon how economic indicators may vary with variation in the size of a country's population.

(1) *Variation in the Population-Resources Ratio and the Behavior of Economic Indicators*

How an economic indicator responds to variation in the ratio of a country's population to its resources depends upon the indicator and the natural resource in question. For example, when a population is larger rather than smaller, the imputed product and hence the rent of urban and perhaps also of rural land tends to be higher. Similarly, when a population is larger rather than smaller, the marginal cost of extracting some raw materials may be higher. In either instance a population must be sufficiently large before such upward trends in rents or costs tend to emerge. Until then variation in population size will have little noticeable effect upon rents and

7. See J. J. SPENGLER & OTIS DUDLEY DUNCAN, eds., *Population Theory and Policy*, Free Press, Glencoe (Illinois) 1956, pp. 245-48.

costs; and even after such effect has begun to be present, it may again be countervailed by technical progress, the discovery of effective substitutes, etc. For purposes of the present discussion no further attention will be given to such particular indicators as rents, specific marginal costs, etc. Instead attention will be focused upon the behavior of output per capita as reflected in (say) the movement of Net National Product per head and upon the response (if any) of this behavior to variation in the size of a country's population.

When a population is larger rather than smaller, two sorts of effects may be experienced. (i) There is opportunity for division of labor and specialization to be carried further and for larger and more economical types of firms to be established. There is also the possibility that, if creative minds increase as fast as population, they will generate technological progress under conditions of increasing return.[8] It may also prove easier to keep the economy quite competitive and hence to place entrepreneurs under continuous pressure to introduce cost-reducing methods as well as to force price-makers to keep prices flexible. (ii) There may be need, particularly if a country is well settled and its mineral and other resources have become sufficiently exploited, to make quite intensive use of a country's land and resource equipment, with the result that, in the absence of improvements in technology, there is a rise in the composite input per unit of output of landed products, raw materials, certain types of transport services, etc. What happens in a given country will be conditioned by the extent to which trade with other countries permits it to alleviate shortages and prevent rising costs through imports purchased with exports in which it enjoys a persisting comparative advantage.

There are limits to the extent to which it is possible to carry division of labor, or to avert or counterbalance the tendency of raw material costs to rise. When, with a given technology and external relations, the population of a country has reached some size – call it O –, it will have exhausted the advantages it can derive from increasing division of labor; while further population growth may not at once diminish these advantages, it will no longer intensify them. Changes in technology may change the population size with which a maximum of these advantages is associated, though it need not always affect this size; while such changes increased that size in the nineteenth century, they may no longer do so in the present century. Turning to the matter of the costs of raw materials, we find that some have been reduced and some have been prevented from rising, by technological improvements and new discoveries; and we note that the consumption of some (e.g., agricultural products) has not kept pace with the growth of national income. Yet there are limits; the supply of suitably situated space

8. SIMON KUZNETS, "Population Change and Aggregate Output" in A. J. COALE, ed., *Demographic and Economic Change in Developed Countries*, University of Princeton Press, Princeton, 1960, pp. 324–330.

and of exploitable raw materials is fixed by country and region, with the result that less and less of these fixed-supply items can be made continuously available per capita as population is enlarged.

In view of what has been said many countries are describable as overpopulated; that is, had they fewer people the average person would be better off. Such overpopulation is not, however, the main immediate cause of the lowness of average income encountered in much of the world at present. At present incomes are so very low in these parts because technological levels are so low; incomes would be much higher if the populations of these countries were better educated and could and would make use of modern technology adapted to their circumstances. Yet, even were this done, the high overall density of population encountered in some of these countries would set limits to the augmentability of average income, as has already been demonstrated in relatively advanced economies in which overall density of population is very high. Moreover, as was shown in Part I, it is very difficult if not almost impossible to modernize a densely populated underdeveloped economy, so long as population growth continues to absorb a great deal of its saving and to limit its capacity to supply education to the young.

(2) Population Optima

The concept, "optimum population", is employed to signify that under given conditions in a country there is a population size that is preferable to any other larger or smaller size. What this size is depends upon the conditions that supposedly are given and upon what it is that a population wants. For purposes of the present discussion it will be supposed that what a population seeks to maximize is per capita income over the relatively long run, or the present value of future per capita income, or some other such indicator of economic "welfare". Such population may be designated an income-optimum population. If a population had some other indicator of welfare than income, say one in which populousness itself was assigned appreciable weight, we should have a different sort of optimum population and one larger than an income-optimum population. In general, therefore, what constitutes a population of optimum size for a country depends upon what kind of welfare its people want and how this kind of welfare varies with size of population.

It was suggested under (a) that up to a point a larger population made for higher average output than did a smaller population in a given country under given conditions. This increase in average output comes about principally because, up to a point, greater division of labor, together with greater external economies generally, is realized. It was also suggested that, because various of the natural resources and land available for exploitation are limited in amount, growth of population would finally be attended by relative declines in output per composite unit of input in activities based upon resources limited in availability. A point is reached therefore when increase in external economies no longer suffices more than to offset adverse influences attendant upon increase in size of population. It is the population size roughly associated with this point that is describable as the income-optimum. A population of greater size is not advantageous on income grounds though it may be advantageous on grounds other than income. This optimum point may or may not be stationary; it may or may not shift with changes in conditions. It shifted in the nineteenth century as changing conditions made larger populations advantageous in advanced countries. There is little basis today, however, for supposing that further increases in the income-optimum size are indicated for many countries with technologically advanced economies. At the same time it is evident that parts of Africa, South America, and Australia require larger populations than they now have for the optimum exploitation of their resources under modern conditions.

In what has been said account was not taken of whether the economy was open or closed. What constitutes optimum size population for a given country may, however, be made larger or smaller by the establishment of external trading relations; it depends partly on the nature of a people's wants and how their ability to satisfy these wants is affected by trade. Here it will be noted only that what constitutes a country's income-optimum population is increased by measures which render a part of population unproductive as does, for example, the engagement of a considerable part of the labor force in military activity. In such a population realized per capita output will be lower than it would have been, had part of the population not been unproductively engaged. Thus, if the United States must support large troop installations abroad, together with extensive foreign aid, it derives no income from these activities and it requires a larger labor force than it would otherwise need, in order to support these activities and keep domestic average consumption as high as possible.

III. ECONOMIC CHANGE AND THE BEHAVIOR OF FERTILITY

Economic change is likely to be accompanied by changes in both fertility and the rate of population growth, particularly if contraceptive information is widespread; it affects patterns of consumption and the capacity of a country to support population at given levels of living. Economic change also affects mortality; for with such change we usually find associated specific changes in environment and living conditions that make for improvement in therapy and for reduction in the sources and the carriers of disease. My discussion here, however, will be confined to the incidence of economic change upon fertility; it is taken for granted that mortality falls as economic conditions improve, until life expectancy is in the 70's.

Economic change affects fertility through its impact upon income, the price structure, and the cost and utility of children. An increase in average income, if unattended by other changes, would normally bring about an increase in fertility in the population of reproductive age. Such increase in income is usually accompanied, however, by a more or less corresponding increase in the 'quality' of the children reproduced and reared, since outlay upon children is much influenced by the income and other characteristics of the family into which a child is born. Furthermore, an increase in a family's income may so modify its expenditure pattern as to increase various of its expenditures as much as income has risen and even more. In general, then, while increase in average family income may make for increase in fertility, it does not always do so; and when it does, the effect may prove temporary, and eventually be reversed if the overall family expenditure pattern is adjusted sufficiently upward.

Changes in price structure may also affect fertility. In general, if the prices of goods and services that enter largely into the cost of reproducing and rearing children fall relatively to other prices, fertility will tend to be stimulated since the relative money cost of children will be reduced. If, however, the prices of goods and services that may be said to compete with children fall relatively, fertility will tend to be diminished; the cost of children will be relatively high while that of competing goods and services will be relatively low and hence relatively attractive. This is what has happened during much of the past 150 years. The prices of so-called conveniences and luxuries have fallen so much in relation to income and other prices that they have often absorbed outlays that might otherwise have been made upon children.

It has been implied that children possess utility and occasion costs and that when the cost of children of given quality rises fertility tends to fall and conversely. Similarly, if the utility derivable from children diminishes, fertility will tend to fall. In the past among the forms of utility derived from children were the income they could produce when young and the security they might supply their parents in old age. Today child labor is common only in underdeveloped countries; it has almost been legislated out of existence in many developed countries. In advanced countries, moreover, security in old age is now provided through collective private, or through governmental arrangements. It is probable, therefore, that the decline experienced in these forms of utility formerly derived from children has made for a decline in fertility. In many instances, of course, this decline has been offset by increase in other forms of utility derived from children, but on balance it is probably true that as the number of children per family increases their marginal utility to their parents diminishes much more rapidly than it did in the past.

Fertility may also change because of changes in tastes that are not immediately connected with economic change. It is probable, however, that most changes in tastes are associated with economic and technological change and that what at times appear to be changes in tastes are merely the actualization of latent tastes or demands already potentially present in a society. Fertility cannot respond readily to economic change or to changes in tastes unless either knowledge of contraception is widespread, or substitute methods of fertility control (e.g., abortion in Japan; deferment of marriage in pre-1800 Western Europe) are readily available.

IV. IMPLICATIONS FOR UNDERDEVELOPED COUNTRIES

In view of what has been said it is virtually impossible for economic development to get under way and persist in low-income, backward countries unless fertility is greatly reduced. In most of these countries the rate of natural increase falls within or close to a range of 2–3% per year; it is thus 2–3 times as high as was the rate of increase in Western Europe in the early nineteenth century at the time development was getting underway. The rate of natural increase is so high in underdeveloped countries because, unlike pre-1900 Western Europe, these countries have introduced death control but not birth control from advanced countries and so have disrupted their former ecological balance. Moreover, in many present-day underdeveloped countries, population is more dense than it was in much of Europe around 1800, and there is less wealth per capita and less real income to supply consumption and savings. It is essential, therefore, to bring fertility down rapidly; and this objective can be furthered not only by actively disseminating contraceptive controls but also by directing investment into activities which increase per capita income both by augmenting national income and by depressing fertility. Many underdeveloped countries are in a Malthusian trap and can be extricated only by forceful means.[9]

The extent of the gain to be realized through fertility reduction is suggested by a study of India's prospects by A. J. COALE & E. M. HOOVER.[10] They estimated that if India's fertility were cut in half between 1956 and 1986, during which interval life expectancy will rise from about 32 to about 52 years, then by 1986 income per consumer would be increasing about four times as fast as it would have increased had fertility not declined at all: and even total output would rise faster. Furthermore, India's population, though still increasing 0.9% per year, would be approaching a stationary state whereas, if fertility had remained at the 1956 level, numbers would be increasing 2.6% per year and thereby making escape from the Malthusian trap even more difficult than it was in 1956. Analogous results were yielded

9. HARVEY LEIBENSTEIN, *Economic Backwardness and Economic Growth*, John Unley and Sons, Inc., New York, 1957, chaps. 3, 8, 10.
10. A. J. COALE & E. M. HOOVER, *Population Growth and Economic Development in Low-Income Countries*, Princeton University Press, Princeton. 1958, Part Five.

by a similar inquiry in Mexico where, though the economy remained underdeveloped and income was much higher than in India, population was growing much faster than in India. One can also show, as was suggested in Part I, that countries whose populations still remain below optimum size (e.g., Brazil) can progress much more rapidly if they grow (say) one per cent per year instead of two or three.

V. INDIVIDUAL VERSUS SOCIAL INTEREST

Because of the disadvantages that may accompany population growth, two sorts of conflicts arise between individual and social interest. There is conflict between the desire of individuals for relatively large families and the desire of the population at large that current and prospective average income levels rise as rapidly as possible. There is conflict also between those who stand to benefit from population growth and those who are adversely affected by such growth in the longer run if not also at present.

We may turn to the United States for an example of the first type of conflict. Today American parents appear to prefer 2–4 children, as a rule. Furthermore, the frequency of childlessness among married couples has been greatly reduced, and a much larger percentage of women marry and marry early than was formerly the case. These changes, as A. J. COALE has suggested, probably conduce to increase in welfare at the family or individual level, given that spinsterhood and childlessness are deemed undesirable and that a two- or three-child family is considered more conducive to the welfare of children than is (say) a one-child family. Yet, under present conditions a three-child family system increases the American population about 1.3% per year, and this rate can easily go to 1.5% if the average number of children per family rises somewhat above three. An annual rate of increase of 1.5% doubles a population every 47 years; in a mere 200 years it would elevate the overall density of the American population to about 1200 persons per square mile, a level of density that is about double that presently found in Massachusetts and New Jersey. If this rate of increase continued there would soon be little room for any sort of activity. Compound growth rates are inexorable; as COALE has remarked, "At current growth rates, the population of the United States would outweigh the earth in 2500 years."[11]

It was suggested earlier that when a country's population approximates optimum size, further increase in number is not advantageous unless technological and other changes operate to increase that optimum size. For convenience of discourse we shall couch our discussion in terms of an income-optimum. It may be said, therefore, that even should this income-optimum undergo some increase in size, there is a limit to the size that such an optimum might assume. The time must come when, if

11. *Ibid.*, pp. 330–31.

maximization of per capita income (or, for that matter, of almost any other sort of index) be the objective, further increase in population is disadvantageous. Yet, as will be shown, a conflict with shorter run objectives may therewith be precipitated.

While it is generally admitted that population growth in most underdeveloped countries is a source of disadvantage, or can easily become one, it sometimes is contended that population growth is a source of advantage in an advanced economy, at least until it has become quite densely populated. Mention has already been made of the increase in division of labor and the availability of external economies that may accompany population growth as well as of the supposed tendency of such growth to generate an even high r rate of growth of technical progress. It is also asserted that interoccupational and interregional mobility of labor will then be greater, with the result that a more economic distribution of the labor force among industries and occupations is easily realised. It is also supposed that when a relatively large fraction of a population is relatively young, it will be more disposed to adjust its tastes to technological progress and related changes in the composition of final output. It is also inferred that the rate of saving will not be appreciably depressed by population growth, in part because with population growing investors are optimistic about the future and disposed to encourage saving and to employ whatever savings are forthcoming; and it is added that if savings do become more scarce, innovation and invention will take a more capital-saving turn. Finally it is indicated that shortages of produce and raw materials can easily be overcome through input-saving technological progress and through the substitution of more abundant materials and grades of material for those that are relatively scarce. In sum, it is contended that population growth per se makes for increase in output per capita, or, if this is no longer the case, it is contended that productive full employment is hardly attainable in the absence of population growth.

A conflict thus emerges between the view that beyond a certain point further population growth is no longer advantageous and the view that population growth as such continues to be advantageous until an economy is quite crowded. Regarding the various forms of external economies that supposedly accompany population growth, it may be said that these tend to come into being when international trade is quite free, or when a country is territorially large enough to realize internally most of the economies associated with unimpeded international trade. It is fairly easy to keep a labor force appropriately distributed among occupations, since a high rate of interoccupational mobility is easily achieved, especially among younger workers, and since death and retirement can serve to reduce rapidly the number of workers attached to declining occupations. Tastes appear to be flexible enough, even among middle-aged and older persons in advanced societies; the assistance of youth is hardly needed. It is doubtful, on grounds remarked earlier, that population growth per se will operate to elevate the rate of saving or to render invention more capital-saving. The argument that population growth becomes economically disadvantageous when a population achieves some given optimum size seems much more persuasive than the argument that notable advantages continue to be associated with population growth as such even after the population optimum has been exceeded. This, however, is an argument that will be resolved by the habits and aspirations of a population and by the extent to which the state intervenes for good or ill to alter the rate of population growth.

Caution is indicated because population growth is asymmetrical. A population increases in number but does not decrease. When numbers become too large, rectificatory action is not possible as it would be if (say) the cattle population of a country had become too large (as in India). It is the part of politico-economic wisdom, therefore, not to encourage population growth. For the propensity of numbers appears to be to grow, even in the absence of the many stimuli to population growth provided by short-sighted or "welfare"-oriented governments of the sort that have become common in the West. It is highly probable, in fact almost inevitable, that whatever be the kind of welfare indicator any given population is interested in maximizing, this population will grow in number far beyond the point at which this welfare indicator is at a maximum.

JOSEPH JOHN SPENGLER, Ph. D., has been Professor of Economics at Duke University since 1937. He has taught at the University of Arizona, the University of North Carolina, the University of Chicago, Kyoto University, the University of Malaya and the University of Pittsburgh. Professor SPENGLER has served as consultant to the National Resources Planning Board, and to the Department of Agriculture. He is a Past-President of the Southern Economics Association of America and the Population Association of America and has been a Director of the Social Science Research Council. His published works relating to population problems include France Faces Depopulation (1938); French Predecessors of Malthus (1942); (as co-author and co-editor) Population Theory and Policy (1956); Demographic Analysis (1956) and Natural Resources and Economic Growth (1961).

Problems of Fertility Control in Under-developed Areas*

by

J. MAYONE STYCOS **

Because the size, distribution and rate of increase of population are closely related to questions of national power and economic development, population has long been a topic of interest for most nations. The science of demography, moreover, has a long and distinguished history within the social sciences. It is all the more surprising, then, that until the past few years scientific research on motivational aspects of demographic problems has been virtually nonexistent. In a science dealing with three of the most basic human events and processes – birth, death, and migration – psychological, social, and cultural factors have been all but ignored as objects of scientific inquiry. It is probably fair to say, even now, that we know more about what people expect, want, and do with respect to planting wheat or purchasing TV sets than with respect to having babies.

Part of the explanation lies in the fact that demographers have tended to ignore or minimize certain types of data. The field has recruited many of its personnel from economics, actuarial science, and statistics, disciplines highly suspicious of "soft" data collected in the area of attitudes and opinions; and has relied almost exclusively on the "hard" data provided by national censuses and vital statistics. Since these data are not collected primarily for social scientists, and since they are subject to a number of inadequacies, an important aspect of the role of demographer is ingenuity at upgrading data (often from poor to fair) by conceptual and statistical manipulation. In a sense demographers have been seduced by the enormous volume of free data provided them by national governments, and have been lulled into asking limited questions of these data, rather than raising new questions which can only be answered by collecting other types of information. Demographers tend to be disdainful, on the one hand, of the social scientist who collects superb original data on his Sociology 101

* Reprinted from "Marriage and Family Living," February 1963, by kind permission of the editor.
** Director, International Population Program, Cornell University.

students, and on the other, of the grand theorist who requires little empirical data for reaching conclusions.[1]

With respect to fertility research there have been special obstacles. Demographers are part of a general culture which has regarded the sexual sphere as an intensely private and personal affair. As most social scientists, demographers have not only been members of the middle class, the major bastion of restrictive sexual norms, but in their very role of social scientists, have perhaps been overly sensitive to taboos in the sexual sphere. Inquiry into sexual matters has, until recently, been largely within the confines of the psychiatrist's couch, and it is of interest that it took a zoologist (KINSEY) to crack the myth that *normal* people will not talk about their sexual behavior to a social investigator.

Fortunately, for the field as a whole, if not for population experts in particular, practical exigencies have forced demographers to stick their necks out in a way rarely demanded of social scientists.[2] They have been repeatedly asked to *predict* future population, and, more recently, are being asked what to do about it. On both counts the field has been found deficient and this discovery has in large measure been responsible for a rather sudden spate of motivational studies in a wide variety of countries.

As is usually the case in the early stages of research, the studies have been generally marked by an absence of theoretical sophistication, and by a failure to build in comparability with investigations of a similar nature done elsewhere. Nevertheless, they have provided an invaluable baseline of information from which a number of crude hypotheses is emerging. It is not the objective of this paper to summarize or evaluate these studies in any systematic fashion. Rather, these studies will be drawn upon, along with the personal experience of the writer, to outline some of the real and mythical obstacles in the way of planned programs of fertility control.

At the most general level, the explanation for a durable demographic gap (a discrepancy between low death rates and high birth rates) goes something like this. Until recently, most under-developed areas had very high death rates, perhaps forty or more per thousand population. In order to survive, such societies *had* to have comparably high birth rates. Any

---

1. The very insularity of the demographer has in some ways produced salutary results not unlike those produced among artists working in a highly limited medium. In addition to milking with great imagination every drop of significance out of unimaginative data, demographers have been impelled to make various sorts of assumptions about human attitudes and behavior which, although often unrealistic, have allowed the development of very elegant and useful mathematical models.

2. Prediction is usually less hazardous in other branches of the social sciences. The predictions are often not quantified, as is necessarily the case in demography; or there is little danger that adequate data will be collected to test the accuracy of the prediction. The extensiveness, pervasiveness, and regularity of crude population data foster both caution and constant re-examination of assumptions on the part of demographers, no small advantages in the social sciences.

cultures which did not develop mechanisms for maintaining high fertility in the face of high mortality have disappeared. Consequently, customs such as early marriage emerged and survived along with various beliefs and values emphasizing the desirability of maximum fertility. The introduction of fertility control techniques into such societies runs counter, therefore, to some of the most basic customs and values, and can be expected to meet with considerable resistance or indifference.

At the same time, good health and long life are almost universal values, so that modern technology for saving lives is readily accepted. Moreover, unlike birth control, many public health measures do not require individual commitment, but can be carried out by draining swamps, improving sewage disposal, purifying the water supply, etc. Consequently, death rates can be expected to decline rapidly wherever the technological means are made available.

This general explanation is quite plausible and may even be valid. However, the well-known fact that fertility can be expected to decline very slowly by "natural" means would seem to argue the necessity for public programs to speed up the process. Why have so few governments in areas of high growth rates introduced such programs? Obviously, democratic governments are reluctant to introduce policies they believe contrary to the values of the majority of the people; but this would not be so serious a consideration for totalitarian societies, or for democracies where opposition parties are weak. In order to understand the typical reluctance of governments, it would be useful to discuss in some detail the attitudes of the elite and of the masses toward population growth and fertility control.

ELITE ATTITUDES

We can discuss reasons for the reluctance of governments to introduce family planning programs under three major headings: (1) ideas about population and population control closely related to nationalism; (2) naive faith in the "demographic miracle"; (3) erroneous theories about the causes of high fertility.

Nationalism

Throughout the world, under-developed societies are experiencing waves of nationalism. Perhaps an essential condition of significant economic development, it is actively fostered by national leaders. Several common ingredients of nationalism present obstacles to programs of fertility control.

Pride in Numbers. A large population, while not guaranteeing international power, is probably a necessary condition of power. Giant armies and industries both require large population bases, and the total national product of a nation is greatly influenced by the sheer weight of numbers. Chinese leaders have even suggested maximizing their population size to guarantee survival in strength following an atomic decimation. Mixed with such more or less rational beliefs are more sentimental notions. Leaders of the new nation, Nuvela, become passionately convinced that there is something valuable in being a Nuvelian. More of a good thing – more Nuvelians for the world – emerges as a goal or at least as a vague feeling obstructing policies for reduction of numbers. Low birth rates may even be viewed as a sign of the decadence of nations surfeited with "civilization" and approaching cultural senescence. Views similar to these have been current among leaders in nations as disparate as Mexico and the Soviet Union.

Anti-colonialism. An almost invariable aspect of nationalism is the channelling of aggressions toward a common scapegoat, usually the foreign country which has historically exercised the greatest degree of political or economic control. Any lever for pinning responsibility on this country for a host of local ills will receive maximum exploitation. If the suggestion of a population control program can be in any way linked to the "imperialist" nation, an unusually powerful and effective anti-colonialist charge can be advanced – that the colonial power wishes to "do away with" Nuvelians or at least inhibit their growth, a subtle and insidious form of genocide.

Faith in Economic Policies. The new government also wishes to show that its past backwardness was due to the economic and political policies of the imperialist nation. Freed of such tyrannical shackles, its new program of economic and social reform can provide adequately for its present and future population. Admission of a population problem may sound like an admission of programmatic defeat. Marxist ideology, and to a large extent Roman Catholic ideology, regard "population problems" as smokescreens concealing inadequacies of the economic and social system; but the argument has great appeal (as well as a certain amount of truth) in areas where neither Marxism nor Catholicism reigns.

Where democratic forms of government are emerging, the party in power is wary of population programs, since many of these same arguments used against the colonial powers can be used against it by the opposition party. Within the West Indies, cleavages of color (black versus white), ethnicity (East Indian versus colored West Indian), and class (rich versus poor) have variously been used by politicians when family planning programs have been publicly discussed. In addition to charges of genocide, admission of a population problem by the majority party has been used as evidence of the inadequacy of the party's reform policies. In China, a major governmental program of family limitation was short-lived, partly because orthodox groups regarded it as an admission of weakness of the nation's economic policies. In other communist countries, birth control programs are carefully labeled as maternal health programs.

Population Pressure as an Instrument of Nationalism. Population growth is typically viewed as a phenomenon which is not influenced but which influences other things. In its most extreme form it has been used as a rationale for territorial expansion, as in the case of Japan, Italy, and Germany prior to World War II. Currently, under-developed nations use population growth to justify the necessity for new markets, the need for more foreign aid, etc., and to stir up national enthusiasm for expensive programs of education, social and medical services, and industrialization. Programs for more houses, jobs, land, schools, and hospitals are intrinsically more appealing than programs for less babies. The former programs become even more appealing if it can be shown that there are more babies every day who need and deserve such services.

The Demographic Miracle

It is common knowledge that western countries once had high fertility and that following their industrial revolution fertility declined to "modern" levels. Faced with high birth rates and high rates of population growth, many leaders of under-developed areas place their trust in the magic of economic development. If we invest in schools, factories and cities, they argue, the population problem will take care of itself. The argument is subject to at least two important limitations.

First, demographers do not know exactly why or how fertility rates have declined. In the absence of such knowledge there is no guarantee that what happened in one set of societies in the past will happen to a quite different set in the future. Indeed, under certain conditions, improved economic circumstances and the breakdown of traditional patterns can cause increases in fertility. For example, such changes might bring about greater marital stability to non-legal unions which now have decidedly lower fertility than more stable legal unions; or, as in India, the breakdown on taboos on the remarriage of widows could lengthen the average reproductive period. A growing body of evidence indicates that fertility did in fact increase among western nations in the early periods of industrialization, as a result of such changes as increased and earlier marriage and reduced maternal mortality.

Second, mortality in the western nations declined much more rapidly than fertility, and closure of the ensuing "demographic gap" took some nations up to two-hundred years. It was during the industrial revolution that Europe's great population increases occurred. Because of modern medical technology, mortality among contemporary under-developed nations is declining far more rapidly than has ever been the case in the past, with little indication that fertility will show a similarly accelerated decline.[3] Even assuming that the decline will occur *eventually*, how long can a society

3. Japan seems to be an exception but the case may be unusual for a number of reasons including the abortion program, the long period of industrialization, and traditional attitudes favoring family limitation.

afford to wait when annual rates of increase are such that the population will double in thirty or forty years?

Another comfortable belief about the population problem stems from the theories of JOSUE DE CASTRO. In *the Geography of Hunger*, DE CASTRO popularized the notion that protein deficiency accounts for the high fertility of the lower classes. Despite the disrepute with which this theory is regarded by demographers, it has captured the imagination of many of the educated elite in a number of countries. It has the familiar twin advantage of simplicity and of avoidance of the real problem. With economic development, the population will eat better and therefore bear fewer children. No direct attack on the problem is necessary.

Elite Theories about Lower Class Fertility

Upper class explanations for the high fertility of lower class groups are similar in most societies with which the writer is acquainted. It is argued that the lower classes want many children or it is argued that they do not care how many they have. Religious values are also viewed as major obstacles to fertility control. In addition, the lower classes have certain needs such as an unusually high drive for sexual relations which are uninhibited by a sense of morality or social responsibility. In the face of such values and biological drives, birth control programs are doomed to failure, and might even increase the immorality of these classes. In any event, the problem should be attacked more directly by teaching "self-control," reducing sexual frequency by state-provided avenues for sublimation, and the reduction of illegitimacy by legal, religious, and social pressures.

The Desire for Large Families. Because the typical couple in underdeveloped areas in fact produces a large family, it is tempting to conclude that this is the desired state of affairs. The available evidence, while not entirely satisfactory, would suggest the contrary. When asked to name the ideal number of children, or when asked whether or not they want more children, lower class women in societies as different as Peru, Lebanon, Puerto Rico, Jamaica and India do not regard the question as meaningless, and do not favor very large families. Three or four children is generally seen as the ideal number, and most women who have four children do not want any more.

Religious Values. The major religions of the East do not contain explicit ideologies with respect to fertility control. While there are certain aspects of the philosophy of such faiths which encourage the having of large families, respondents in surveys rarely cite religious objections to family planning; and it is generally agreed that religious ideology is not a major factor in resistance to population control for non-Christian religious groups.

While the Catholic religion strongly and explicitly condemns most forms of birth control, and while the Church as an organization can be highly influential in the determination of international, national and local policies with respect to population control, the weight of the evidence suggests that its impact on attitudes and behavior of individual couples is small. Studies comparing Catholic and non-Catholic beliefs and behavior with respect to family planning have been conducted in countries where Catholics are in the majority (Puerto Rico), minority (Jamaica), or evenly-balanced (Lebanon). In none of these areas is there any significant difference in attitudes or behavior with respect to family planning.[4] Such results almost invariably astonish national leaders, who tend to assume that the teachings of the Church are followed by its members.

Sex Relations and Fertility. Just as it is tempting to deduce attitudes from behavior, so it is tempting to deduce a high frequency of sex relations from high fertility, since sex relations are a necessary antecedent to fertility. The temptation is made all the more attractive by the generally condescending and patronizing attitudes of the upper classes toward the lower classes. The latter are variously viewed as 'children,' as primitive or animal-like, or as amoral or immoral. Thus, biological urges are stronger and inhibitions are weaker than among the upper classes. Finally, lacking electric lights and civilized means of diversion, the lower classes retire early. The entire complex is expressed in a saying, "Procreation is the poor man's recreation."

Again, the available evidence, while unfortunately limited, points in the opposite direction. First, there is no assurance that high sexual frequency increases fertility: indeed, there is a current plausible hypothesis suggesting that it inhibits it because of lower sperm counts per act of coitus. Second, there is no reason to believe that lower class sexual frequency is higher than that of the upper class and, because of malnutrition and fatigue, it may well be lower. In limited studies in the United States, Lebanon and India, lower educational groups have not been found to have higher sexual frequencies than better educated groups. Third, the notion that night baseball will substitute for sex seems somewhat naive. Lest the reader think we are building straw men, let us recall the advice of the ex-Governor General of Ceylon:

---

4. Recent studies in the United States show that the completed family size of Catholics is about the same as that of non-Catholics, but that Church-approved methods (rhythm and delayed marriage) are more characteristic of Catholics, especially the better educated ones. It may be that as Catholics become more sophisticated and better educated, they become more accessible to Church teaching. In Latin America where educational levels have been low and the number of priests few, relative to population, it is probable that Church influence will increase with economic development. There are already signs of religious revivalism in a number of countries, an additional argument against the assumption that education and economic progress will automatically bring fertility declines.

"He who goes to bed early to save candles begets twins," said Viscount Soulbury...
Ceylon's former Governor General quoted this ancient Chinese proverb to illustrate
what he considers the cause for the alarming increase in Ceylon's population. He said
he had advised Ceylon's Prime Minister to introduce electric lighting to the villages to
counter the population rise.... "There has been a lot of glib talk about family planning,"
said the Viscount, "but that was not very easy – electric lights are the solution." [5]

Such notions are not limited to Europeans. In an opening speech to
an international Planned Parenthood Conference, Prime Minister NEHRU
announced, "I was told only today about the possible consequences
of, let us say, electricity going to a rural area..... the period for which
they can work or amuse themselves or do other things is enormously
lengthened and thereby, indirectly perhaps, it effects even this family
planning business." [6] A vice-president of India has publicly commented
that "Sex is the only indoor sport open to us, and large families are
produced. It is the poor people that produce large families and not
the rich ones." [7] In recommending the rhythm method for India's masses,
another high-ranking Indian official pointed to its salutary effects on "self-
indulgence:" "The task is essentially that of educating the individual in a
manner which will enable him to sublimate his sexual urge into channels
of activity which are productive of gain to the community... instead of
yielding without even a thought of self-restraint to the desire for self-
indulgence." [8]

Illegitimacy and Promiscuity. A frequent phrase heard in the West Indies is
"irresponsible paternity," referring to the common pattern of having
children out of wedlock. The fact that a large proportion of children are
born illegitimate in the West Indies leads the middle classes to make a causal
connection with high fertility rates. Religious leaders and social reformers
appear to view males as casting their seeds indiscriminately throughout the
female population. The young are therefore exhorted to marry as a curb
to irresponsible paternity and high fertility. In point of fact, most illegitimate births are the produce of common-law or consensual unions rather
than of promiscuity. Moreover, if the young entered legal unions as recommended, there is good reason to believe that their fertility would show
marked increases, since they would be changing from transitory relationships to more permanent ones. In short, the relation between legitimacy
and fertility in the West Indies, and perhaps in many regions of the world,
is the opposite of what is usually assumed.

5. *News of Population and Birth Control*, London, February, 1955.
6. The Sixth International Conference on Planned Parenthood, London: International
Planned Parenthood Federation, 1959, p. 10.
7. S. RADHAKRISHNAN, Third International Conference on Planned Parenthood, Bombay: Family Planning Association of India, 1952, p. 12.
8. K. C. K. E. RAJA, "Family Planning in Public Health Programs," Third International
Conference on Planned Parenthood, ibid., p. 64.

PROGRAMS OF FERTILITY CONTROL

If middle-class notions have deflected attentions from the real problems and
solutions, they have also profoundly affected the programs of fertility
control where these have occurred in under-developed areas. This is the
case because private programs are largely controlled by urban middle class
women, and because the basic philosophy and methods of such programs have been borrowed from American and British experience. The latter programs
were formed by crusading middle class women battling simultaneously
against the shackles of puritanism and the tyranny of men. What have been
the implications of this historical background and how appropriate are
western patterns for non-western countries?

The Dominance of Feminism

As most voluntary organizations, planned parenthood groups have been
led by women. Unlike most voluntary organizations, however, they
adopted explicit and implicit female policies because they were part of the
whole movement to emancipate the women. Specifically, they were
aimed at freeing the woman from the pain and drudgery of child bearing
and child rearing as well as from the consequences of male sexual exploitation. It is no surprise, therefore, that a major intent of the movement,
perhaps only partly conscious, has been to wrest control of fertility from
males and give it to females. We say "wrest control" since there is overwhelming evidence that insofar as western fertility declines are due to
contraceptive techniques, these techniques have been predominately male
methods. In their almost exclusive concern with female methods and
female audiences, planned parenthood groups have been swimming upstream.

In under-developed areas, the emphasis may be even more misplaced,
since male dominance in general and specifically in the sexual sphere is
much more marked than in the modern western societies. In justification
of its position, planned parenthood advocates repeat their plaints about the
irresponsibility of males, and the lack of male motivation for controlling
fertility. However, in western nations of low or moderate fertility the
evidence is against this hypothesis; and in under-developed nations, while
the evidence is scanty, male sentiments favoring small families do not seem
markedly different from female and, in certain aspects, may be stronger.
Interestingly enough, a major reason for the scantiness of the evidence is
that the typical survey concentrates on females and never elicits the
opinions of the male.

The Clinical Approach

Partly because of the medical orientation of MARGARET SANGER, and primarily because of the legal difficulties under which the movement in this country has labored, a very strong medical bias dominates the Planned Parenthood movement in the United States. Among other things, this has meant a concern with "maximum protection" methods and concentration on the individual case rather than a mass approach utilizing less effective but simpler techniques. It has meant the clinical system which waits for patients to come to it, and it has meant examination rooms, case histories and white coats. It has also meant a highly conservative attitude toward abortion, sterilization, publicity and non-medical personnel.

While a good case can be made for the tactical necessity for medical sponsorship in puritanical nations, no such necessity exists in most under-developed areas, a fact which makes examination of the efficacy of the clinical system quite relevant.

An important limitation of birth control clinics is that they are not used. In England, according to a recent national sample, only 6% of those who have used birth control have ever received family planning advice from a clinic.[9] In Japan, where over 800 health centers include family planning, an experienced observer estimates that: "Of the families utilizing birth control in Japan, not more than 10% have received instruction or material from government services."[10] In Puerto Rico, despite the existence of an extensive network of birth control clinics for two decades, less than one in ten families has ever obtained birth control materials from a clinic. In less developed areas, wherever clinics exist they show pitifully small case-loads.

The explanations of clinical services probably lie on several levels only some of which have to do with the clinics *per se*. For the time being let us enumerate three.

(1) The methods typically offered by the clinics are not those most popular with most people. Neither male methods nor abortion are ordinarily offered in private or public clinics.

(2) The clinical atmosphere discourages many women and all but the most stout-hearted of men. On the one hand, it is too public in the sense that to be seen there may be embarrasing. On the other hand, the intimate private examination and case-histories rituals frighten and embarrass many women in cultures where female modesty is an important value.

(3) Being under-publicized, clinics are not known about by large groups of the population. The very people who most need their services are least likely to know about them. Moreover, the clinics' emphasis on child

9. R. M. PIERCE & G. ROUNTREE, "Birth Control in Britain, Part II," *Population Studies*, XV, No. 2.
10. M. C. BALFOUR, "Family Planning in Asia," *Population Studies*, XV, No. 2.

spacing and on the advantages to health of family limitation are not the most effective appeals in under-developed areas at this time. Among lower class and peasant populations, the having of children is the most natural thing in the world. Women do not become concerned until they have four or five children and then want to *stop* having children for reasons that have less to do with health than with economics.

The Chimerical Contraceptive

Hardly a planned parenthood conference goes by without at least one speaker accounting for the failure of birth control programs in the following terms: "Because of crowded living conditions and the absence of privacy, and due to the lack of running water and sanitary facilities, a cheap, simple contraceptive must be developed appropriate for use under such conditions." In the light of the number of bodily and household functions which are daily performed without running water in lower class houses, we feel that the concern over this matter is somewhat excessive. Further, one can only conclude that the same lower class ingenuity which manages such "prodigious" sexual frequencies in the face of such strong needs for privacy could also deal with the "problem" of privacy for birth control. Curiously, while the middle class ascribes sexual attitudes and behavior to the lower class different from its own, it projects its own attitudes with respect to needs for privacy and sanitary facilities. This is not to say that simpler contraceptives are not desirable; it is merely to point out that inadequacies in organization, educational techniques, and basic approach should not be concealed by fanciful explanations for programmatic failure.

A cheap, safe, and relatively simple contraceptive will soon be generally available in the form of an oral pill. It will prove more popular than any other female method, but whether it will solve by itself the kind of problems outlined below is questionable. As well phrased by one writer, ".... the governments of underdeveloped areas that have launched such programs seem to have fallen into the 'technological fallacy' which has long marked Western thinging in this area. They have adopted, in other words, a kind of blind faith in the gadgetry of contraception....." [11]

SOME REAL PROBLEMS

We have discounted a number of popular explanations for the failure of birth control programs. Are there no real problems? There are, and they are at least as numerous as the fallacious ones. Let us summarize a few.

11. LEO F. SCHNORE, "Social Problems in the Underdeveloped Areas: An Ecological View," *Social Problems*, VIII (Winter 1961), p. *187.*

Ignorance

Wherever studies have probed lower class knowledge of sexual physiology, including the United States, the degree of ignorance has been startling. Maintained by strong taboos on discussion of sexual matters in many countries, this basic ignorance extends to the area of modern contraceptive techniques. While it is generally known that *something* can be done, only vague notions exist about *what*. "Birth control" or "family planning" is often confused with abortion, with the permanent stopping of child bearing, or with something done by prostitutes to avoid pregnancy or by men to avoid venereal disease. In the light of such ignorance and misinformation it is little wonder that people stay away from clinics, the functions of which must seem mysterious and faintly nefarious.

Indifference

In the absence of information about contraceptive means, commitment to small family goals should not be expected to be strong. While we have seen that the average woman wants only three or four children, in studies conducted by the writer high proportions of these same women say they have never *thought of the matter before*. In the absence of information on means, questions on ideal size must be interpreted carefully. Most of these women would probably reply positively if asked whether they would like to own Cadillacs – but lacking the remotest chance of doing so, they have never seriously considered the matter before. Desiring three children may be in the same category for women ignorant of anything but sexual abstention as a contraceptive technique.

Ambivalence

While women or men may express sentiments generally favorable to small families, it is not difficult to get them to admit favorable sentiments toward large families as well. Because of the fear of high infant mortality, the need for support in old age, and the emotional satisfaction of children, parents can simultaneously favor small and large familes. Moreover, in the absence of knowledge for achieving small families, large ones are achieved and are *post hoc* likely to be rationalized as a good thing, especially in public situations.

Late Motivation

Analysis of the data from almost any birth control clinic in the world will show that the average woman seeks family planning assistance only after she has had several children. Sample surveys also disclose that women become seriously interested in birth control only after several births and then want to *stop* having children. However, contraceptive activity at this late date tends to be relatively inefficient because of lack of experience and because sexual patterns have become fairly routinized and difficult to change. Thus, even if birth control is introduced at this point, its impact on fertility is relatively minor.

SOLUTIONS

The initial and perhaps major hurdle of programs for fertility control in under-developed areas is the elite ruling classes. These groups must be informed about the gravity of the population problem, disabused of comfortable beliefs about the problem taking care of itself, and educated concerning the values, attitudes and behavior of the lower classes in the population. The programs themselves should be government sponsored rather than private for several reasons. Private programs cannot marshall the economic and human resources necessary to make a major impact on the birth rate. Moreover, the prestige of government backing is highly important in an area which is characterized by ambivalent attitudes. Finally, and perhaps most important, such programs should be taken out of the hands of do-gooding amateurs and put in the hands of professionals. While medical aspects and personnel may be included in such a program, basic policies and administration should be turned over to non-medical professionals – social scientists, community development experts and communications media specialists.[12] What might the broad outlines of such a program be?

(1) It would give at least as much attention to males as to females, and, possibly more attention. Given the fact of male dominance and the fact that fertility declines have historically been accomplished by means of male contraceptive techniques in many countries, males cannot be ignored. Moreover, because of their generally higher literacy, prestige, sophistication, and range of social relationships, they would not only be accessible to more new ideas but more effective disseminators of these ideas.

(2) Far more resources, and probably the bulk of them, should be put into non-clinical systems of education and contraceptive distribution. Normal retail channels should be maximized by education and subsidization of key shopkeepers, druggists, healers, midwives, barbers, etc. Most of these would be dealing with men in the normal atmosphere of economic transaction rather than the strange world of the clinic. Insofar as possible, local organizations should be formed, with volunteer and paid workers serving as agents for distribution of materials and ideas. Extension workers, home

12. In some countries there is a growing tendency to rely on demographers for shaping such programs. While a gesture in the right direction, this is basically an error. The traditionally trained demographer has little more to offer in this field than has an actuary to programmatic solutions of problems of mortality and morbidity.

economists, and community development and public health personnel should receive special educational programs.

(3) The mass media, especially the printed word, should be given much more emphasis than is usual in such programs. Experimental programs in Puerto Rico and Jamaica have shown pamphlets to be as effective as personal visits or group meetings in getting people to adopt birth control. In Japan, according to recent studies, half of the women knowledgeable about birth control learned of it through magazines, nearly 20% through newspapers, and nearly 10% through books.[13] Even in nations of high illiteracy, written materials can be utilized with much greater effectiveness than is usually supposed.

(4) Every effort should be made to reach young couples with the object of initiating contraceptive practice at an early date for child-spacing purposes. Relatively simple techniques such as coitus interruptus should be encouraged, with no great expectations of high individual effectiveness. This will have the advantages of effecting a significant reduction in fertility on a mass basis and of preparing couples for more efficient but difficult contraceptive techniques after they have as many children as they desire.

(5) Particularly with younger couples, the reputedly deleterious effects to health of rapid child bearing should be ignored or minimized, and social and economic disadvantages of excessive child bearing stressed.

(6) For women and men who have had all the children they desire, sterilization facilities should be provided. Female sterilization in Puerto Rico has enjoyed enormous popularity and in India and Puerto Rico male sterilizations, especially where subsidized, are gaining rapidly. Legalized abortion programs similar to the Japanese should receive careful consideration. Programs such as these which are often viewed as immoral or at least "drastic" in western eyes, do not appear so to many other populations where they tend to be considered safer, more efficient and less troublesome than contraception. At the very least, such programs could be viewed as interim measures until efficient contraceptive practice becomes widespread.[14]

CONCLUSIONS

As demonstrated by several of the articles in this volume, the population program in many under-developed areas is serious and can be expected to grow worse. Slowing the rate of population increase is no substitute for economic development, but can make possible, assist, or accelerate that development. Programs of fertility control are entirely feasible but face major obstacles in elite attitudes and beliefs about population dynamics

13. *Family Planning in Japan* (Tokyo: Asia Family Planning Association, 1961).
14. The Japanese have been made to feel defensive and apologetic about their abortion program, which is probably the only case in the world to date of a successful mass program of fertility control.

and lower class culture; as well as in the dominance of ideas about family planning programs imported from the United States and England. There are also problems associated with informing and motivating the mass of the population, but, in the writer's opinion, these are less serious than of informing, motivating and activating ruling groups into creating careful and intelligent programs. Given the seriousness of the consequences of continued population growth in under-developed areas, optimism about the possibilities of fertility control programs is a necessity – and *cautious* optimism is justified.

J. MAYONE STYCOS, Ph. D., is Professor of Sociology and Director of the International Population Program at Cornell University. He has conducted studies of fertility and family planning in Caribbean and South American countries. The findings of these investigations have been reported in several books: "Family and Fertility in Puerto Rico" (Columbia University Press, 1955), "The Family and Population Control" (University of North Carolina Press, 1959), "Human Fertility and Fertility Control in Jamaica" (Ithaca: Cornell University Press, 1963). Dr. STYCOS recently edited a special issue of the Journal of *Marriage and Family Living* entitled "Family Planning in Modernizing Societies" (February, 1963).

Demographic Dimensions of World Politics*

by

Philip M. Hauser

Politics in general, as well as world politics, is a branch of engineering – social engineering – not of science. Yet the consideration of the demographic aspects of world politics is not an inappropriate subject to be treated in this book. It is the purpose of this chapter to point to ways in which the findings of the science of demography illuminate various aspects of the world political scene.

There are various ways in which this subject can be developed, but I have arbitrarily chosen to discuss population factors in relation to politics, broadly conceived, on the global and on the international levels, respectively. By "global" problems I mean those that concern the earth as a whole; by "international" problems I mean those that arise among the various political subdivisions of the globe.

GLOBAL CONSIDERATIONS

There is no world government charged with the task of achieving world order and performing other civil governmental functions for the earth as a whole. This, however, does not mean that there are no political problems of a global, as distinguished from an international, character. Some such global problems are in fact dealt with by the United Nations and its specialized agencies, which are, of course, organizations of individual sovereign nations rather than organs of world government. Examples of global problems – problems which transcend and cannot be contained within national boundaries – include health, weather, fallout, and the newly emergent problems of outer space. It is easy to demonstrate that the contemporary rate of world population growth also constitutes a global problem – one which would be of great concern to a world government if we had one, and one which is of increasing concern to various organs of the United Nations and the specialized agencies.

* Reprinted from *Science* by permission.

Although the first complete census of mankind has yet to be taken, it is possible to reconstruct, with reasonable accuracy, the history of world population growth. This history may be encapsulated in the following estimates of the population of the earth: at the end of the Neolithic period in Europe (8000 to 7000 B.C.) (I), perhaps 10 million; at the beginning of the Christian era, 200 to 300 million; at the beginning of the modern era (1650), 500 million; in 1950, 2.5 billion.

These four numbers constitute a measurement of one of the most dramatic aspects of man's existence on the globe, and they explain the purple language of the demographer in describing the changes in rates of population growth during the modern era as a "demographic revolution" or "population explosion" (2).

TABLE I.

Population, income, and energy consumed per capita, by continent, about 1950. Source of data: United Nations, except where otherwise indicated.

Area	Total population		Aggregate income		Per capita income ($)	Energy consumed per capita (kw-hr)**
	No. (millions)	(%)	Dollars* (billions)	(%)		
World	2497	100.0	556	100.0	223	1676
Africa	199	8.0	15	2.7	75	686
Northern America***	219	8.8	241	43.3	1100	10,074
South America	112	4.5	19	3.4	170	741
Asia	1380	55.3	69	12.4	50	286
Europe (exclusive of U.S.S.R.)	393	15.7	149	26.8	380	3117
U.S.S.R.	181	7.2	56	10.1	310	1873
Oceania	13	0.5	7	1.3	560	3543

* See (8, 9).   ** See (33).   *** Central America included.

The demographer's concern is not based only on considerations of the past. It is even more justified by postwar developments in population growth.

Since the end of World War II the rate of population increase has continued to accelerate and has reached a level of about 1.7% per year. There is justification, indeed, for pointing to a new population explosion in the wake of World War II of a greater magnitude than that previously observed. At the rate of world population increase for the period 1800–1850, for example, the present population would double in 135 years; at the 1900–1950 rate, in 67 years; and at the postwar rate, in only 42 years.

Projection of the post-World War II rate of increase gives a population of one person per square foot of the land surface of the earth in less than 800 years. It gives a population of 50 billions (the highest estimate of the population-carrying capacity of the globe ever calculated by a responsible scholar) in less than 200 years! This estimate, by geochemist HARRISON BROWN (3), is based on the assumptions that developments in the capturing of solar or nuclear energy will produce energy at a cost so low that it would be feasible to obtain all the "things" we need from rock, sea, and air, and that mankind would be content to subsist largely on food products from "algae farms and yeast factories!"

Moreover, the United Nations estimates of future world population indicate even further acceleration in the rate of world population growth during the remainder of this century. Between 1950 and 1975 the average annual percentage of increase, according to the United Nations "medium" assumptions, may be 2.1%, and between 1975 and 2000, almost 2.6% (4). Such rates of increase would double the population about every 33 and 27 years, respectively.

It is considerations of this type that would make it necessary for a world government to exercise forethought and planning, which constitute rational decision making, in facing the future. This, of course, is the purpose of the projections. The figures do not show what the future population of the world will be – for the world could not support such populations. They do demonstrate that man, as a culture-building animal, has created an environment in which the rhythm of his own reproduction has been modified in such a manner as to point to crisis possibilities.

CRISIS POSSIBILITIES

The crisis possibilities are of several forms, each posing major world political problems. The first, we may note, is the ultimate crisis, which would result from the fact that the globe is finite (5) and that living space would be exhausted. Unless one is prepared to argue that future technological developments will enable man to colonize other globes (6), it is clear that present rates of population increase must come to a halt by reason of lack of space. No facts or hopes as to man's ability to increase his food production and to increase other types of goods and services can indefinitely increase man's *Lebensraum* (or could do so even if we accept the absurd assumption that man, at terrific cost, could burrow into the earth, live in man-made layers above it, or live on the seas).

In the short run, let us say to 1975 or to 2000, world population will be confined to much more manageable numbers. The United Nations projects, on the basis of its medium assumptions, a world population of about 3.8 billion by 1975 and 6.3 billion by 2000 (1, p. 23).

In the short run there is no problem of exhausting the space on the globe, nor is there reason to fear serious decreases in world per capita food supply, as is evidenced by projections of The Food and Agricultural Organization, and others concerning foodstuffs (7). But there is great reason to be pessimistic about the possibility of greatly increasing the average world level of living during the remainder of this century.

In 1950, world per capita income was estimated at $223 (8, 9). In North America, per capita income was $1100. Had each person on the globe enjoyed the North American level of living in 1950, as measured by per capita income, the aggregate world product in 1950 would have supported only 500 million persons, as contrasted with the actual world population of 2.5 billion. For average world income to have matched income in North America, aggregate income would have had to be increased about fivefold. To bring world per capita income by 1975 to the level enjoyed in North America in 1950 would require about a 7.5-fold increase of the 1950 level in 25 years. To do the same by 2000 would require a 12-fold increase in the 1950 world income within 50 years.

Even if the more modest income level of Europe ($380 per capita in 1950) were set as the target, great increases in productivity would be necessary, because of prospective rates of population increase, to raise average world income to the required level by 1975 or 2000. To achieve this goal by 1975, world income would have to be increased 2.5-fold over the 1950 level, and to achieve it by 2000, the required increase would be greater than fourfold. A decline in the rate of world population growth to that of the period 1800 to 1850 – namely, to 0.5% – would decrease by three-fourths and four-fifths, respectively, the projected world-income requirements for attaining this goal by 1975 or 2000.

These considerations not only show the enormous difficulty of materially increasing the world level of living on the basis of present rates of population increase but indicate, also, the weakness of the argument that a solution to the population problem is to be found in more equitable distribution of the world's food supply or of goods and services in general (10). The equitable distribution of world income in 1950 would, to be sure, have raised the per capita income of Latin America by 31%; of Africa, almost threefold, and of Asia, four- to fivefold, but it would still have produced a per capita income per annum of $223, only one-fifth that in North America and only three-fifths that in Europe (exclusive of the U.S.S.R.). The miserably low level of living of most of the world's population is attributable not so much to maldistribution as to low aggregate product, the result of the low productivity of most of the world's peoples.

These political problems of a global character may perhaps be better understood through consideration of their international aspects, special attention being given to the plight of the two-thirds of the world's population resident in the underdeveloped areas of the world, in Asia, Africa, and Latin America.

INTERNATIONAL CONSIDERATIONS

The short-run implications of present rates of world population growth are manifest in specific forms and in varying degrees of intensity among the various regional and national subdivisions of the globe. The distribution of the world's population and of the world's utilized resources, manifest in differentials in levels of living, is the result, of course, of millenia of human history. The demographic dimensions of international politics may best be comprehended against the background of differences among peoples in levels of living and the significance of these differences at this juncture in world history (8, 11, 12) (Table I).

To note the extremes, North America in 1950, with about 16% of the earth's land surface, contained less than 9% of the world's population but about 43% of the world's income. Asia, in contrast, with about the same proportion of the world's land surface (18%), had 55% of the world's population but only 12% of the world's income. Per capita income in Asia was at a level of about $50 per year as contrasted with a level of $1100 in North America. Despite the fact that such comparisons are subject to considerable error (13), there is no doubt that a tremendous difference in per capita income existed, of a magnitude perhaps as great as 20 to 1.

The major factor underlying this difference is indicated by the contrast in the difference in nonhuman energy consumed in North America and Asia, respectively – over 10,000 kilowatt-hours per capita per year for the former in contrast to less than 300 for the latter. The availability of nonhuman energy for the production of goods and services is perhaps the best single measurement available of differences in capital investment, know-how, and technology which account for the great differences in productivity and, consequently, in the size of the aggregate product available for distribution.

The other relatively underdeveloped continents of the world also had relatively low shares of world income as compared with their proportions of world population. Africa, with a per capita income of about $75 per year, and South America, with $170, were also well below not only the level for North America but also the levels for Europe (exclusive of the U.S.S.R.), the U.S.S.R. and Oceania. There is a high correlation among these areas between per capita income and amount of non-human energy consumed (Table I).

These differences in levels of living, as it turns out, are in general inversely related to present and prospective rates of population increase. The populations of the relatively underdeveloped continents of the world are increasing at a more rapid rate than those of the economically advanced continents (4, 14). Between 1950 and 1975, to use the medium projections of the United Nations, while the population of Northern America is increasing at an average annual rate of 1.7% and that of Europe, at 1.2%, that of Asia will be growing at an average annual rate of 2.4%, that of Africa at 2.1%, and that of Latin America at 3.4%. Between 1975 and 2000, while the rate of increase for Northern America will average 1.2% per year and that for Europe, 1.0%, the rate for Asia will be 3.0%, that for Africa 2.8%, and that for Latin America 3.8%, a rate at which the population would double about every 18 years.

As I have indicated above, rapid increase in world population imposes a severe burden on efforts to raise levels of living. It is easy to demonstrate that the burden would become an impossible one for the economically underdeveloped areas should their rates of population increase follow the trends indicated in the United Nations projections.

TABLE II.

Summary of projections of urban population for the world and for Asia, 1975 (18).

Cities (category)	Population (millions)			Estimate of increase in population 1950–1975 (millions)		Estimate of increase in population 1950–1975 (%)		Proportion of total population in cities	
	Projection for 1975		1950					Projection	
	Upper	Lower		Upper	Lower	Upper	Lower	1975*	1950
The World									
100,000 and over	745	488	314	431	174	138	55	19	13
20,000 and over	1155	779	502	653	277	130	55	30	21
Asia									
100,000 and over	340	176	106	234	70	222	66	15	8
20,000 and over	544	283	170	374	113	220	66	25	13

* Figures are based on the "upper" projection, which assumes urbanization of an increasing proportion of the population.

For example, Asia, merely to maintain her present low level of living, must increase her aggregate product by 60% between 1950 and 1975, and by an additional 75% between 1975 and 2000. To raise her per capita income to the European level for 1950 while continuing to experience her rapid population growth, Asia would have to increase her 1950 aggregate income 12-fold by 1975 and 21-fold by 2000. Africa, to do the same, must increase her aggregate income eight-fold by 1975 and 13-fold by 2000, and Latin America would have to increase her aggregate income fourfold by 1975 and eightfold by 2000 (15).

To achieve a per capita income equal to that of Northern America in 1950 while experiencing the projected population growth, Asia would have to increase her aggregate income 35-fold by 1975 and 62-fold by 2000. Africa, to achieve a similar goal, would require 22-fold and 38-fold increases, respectively, in aggregate income, and Latin America, 12-fold and 23-fold increases.

These considerations provide additional justification for the use by the demographer of the phrase *population explosion*; and they certainly indicate the hopeless task which confronts the underdeveloped areas in their efforts to achieve higher levels of living while experiencing rapid population growth. The control of rates of population growth would unquestionably decrease the magnitude of the task of achieving higher levels of living in the underdeveloped areas, especially in those with populations that are large relative to resources (16).

Increasingly large proportions of the population in the underdeveloped areas of the world are becoming concentrated in urban places. The continued acceleration in the rate of world urbanization during the first half of this century was mainly attributable to urbanization in the underdeveloped areas, which proceeded at a pace considerably above that in the developed areas (17). I have had occasion to make projections of the urban population of the world and of Asia to 1975; these are presented in Table II as illustrative of what is in prospect in the underdeveloped areas of the globe (18). For the rate of urbanization in Latin America and Africa is, also, accelerating.

The projections for Asia indicate that in the 25 years between 1950 and 1975, in cities either of 100,000 and over or of 20.000 and over, urban population will increase by at least two-thirds and may perhaps triple. The lower projection is based on the assumption that the proportion of urban population in Asia will be the same in 1975 as it was in 1950. Under this assumption the projected increase would result from total population growth alone. But if it is assumed that the rate of urbanization in Asia will increase as it did between 1900 and 1950 while the total population continues to grow at the rate projected by the United Nations, then tripling of Asia's urban population is indicated.

Thus, while the nations of Asia are attempting to improve their miserable urban living conditions, their urban populations will continue to increase explosively – perhaps to triple within a period of less than one generation.

In the economically more advanced nations of the world, urbanization is both an antecedent and a consequent of technological advance and of a high level of living – a symbol of man's mastery over nature. In the underdeveloped nations, however, urbanization represents instead the transfer of rural poverty from an over-populated and unsettled countryside to a mass urban setting. In the economically underdeveloped areas of the world, urbanization is outpacing economic development and the city is more a symbol of mass misery and political instability than of man's conquest of nature (17, 19).

The prospect for individual nations, while variable, is in general the same – one of explosive growth. Between 1955 and 1975, according to the United

Nations medium projections, the population of China will increase by 294 million persons and that of India, by 177 million (4, 20). That of Pakistan will increase by 45 million persons, and that of Indonesia, by 40 million, in these 20 years. To confine our attention to the Far East for the moment, smaller countries with the most explosive increases include South Korea, Taiwan, and Ceylon. Each of these nations is faced with a task of tremendous proportions merely to maintain her present level of living, let alone to greatly increase it while continuing to grow at the projected rates.

POLITICAL INSTABILITY

What will happen if the underdeveloped areas in Asia are frustrated in their efforts to attain a higher standard of living?

WARREN S. THOMPSON devotes his latest book to providing an answer to this question (21). The larger of these nations are not apt to remain hungry and frustrated without noting the relatively sparsely settled areas in their vicinities – the nations in the South-East Asian peninsula: Burma, Thailand, and the newly formed free countries of Indochina, Laos, Cambodia, and Vietnam. (Vietminh, that is North Vietnam, is already engulfed by Communist China.) Even parts of thinly settled Africa may be subject to the aggressive action of the larger and hungrier nations as feelings of population pressure mount. Moreover, Communist China, the largest nation in the world by far, faced with the greatest absolute population increases to add to her already heavy burdens in striving for economic development, may not confine her attention only to the smaller nations within her reach. Her present actions relative to her boundaries with India and possible tensions over her boundaries with the U.S.S.R. contain explosive possibilities.

It is THOMPSON's conclusion that the larger nations in the Far East, including Japan, India, and Pakistan as well as China, may resort to force to achieve access to additional resources under sufficient population pressure. The smaller countries may not be able to resort to force but are almost certain to require outside aid to prevent chaos. Furthermore, Indonesia and the Philippines, under mounting population pressures, are likely to continue to experience growing internal political instability.

Population pressure as a factor in political instability is not confined to the Far East. Populations of the Middle East and North Africa – the Muslim area (exclusive of Pakistan) – may increase from 119 million in 1955 to 192 million by 1975, an increase of 73 million or 61% in 20 years (4). As IRENE TAEUBER has noted, this is an area "where internal instabilities and conflicts of religious and ethnic groups create recurrent crises for the region and world." TAEUBER observes that the immediate political instabilities in this area are attributable more to "diversities among the peoples and the nations than to population pressure or population growth" (22). But she points to the importance, in the decades that lie ahead, of economic advances to lessen tension in this region and to the barrier that rapid population growth may contribute to that development.

Latin America, although in large part still a sparsely settled area of the world, is already experiencing problems associated with rapid population growth which give promise of worsening. For Latin America, as has been reported above, is faced with a population increase of 86% between 1950 and 1975 and of 95%, almost a doubling, between 1975 and 2000 (4, 23). Especially difficult in Latin America are the problems posed by accelerating rates of urbanization. Recent measurements of rate of urban growth in Latin America indicated that of 15 countries for which data were available, urban population in one, Venezuela, was increasing at 7% per year, a rate which produces a doubling about every 10 years; seven had growth rates which would double their population in less than 18 years; and only two (Chile and Bolivia) had rates of urban growth of less than 1% per year (19, 24). Growth rates (total and urban) of the magnitude which Latin America is experiencing are likely to add appreciably to the difficulty of raising living levels and are likely to worsen already existent political instabilities that threaten internal order and may affect world peace.

Finally, a fourth region of political instability to which the population factor is a contributing element, and one where it will be increasingly manifest, is sub-Saharan Africa (22, 25). Middle Africa is sparsely settled, but increasing knowledge about the area indicates high birth rates, decreasing death rates, and explosive growth. The United Nations projections indicate a population increase from 154 million in 1955 to about 202 million in 1975, or an increase of 31%. The familiar syndrome of underdeveloped areas – malnutrition, disease, and urban and rural squalor on the one hand and aspirations for independence and economic development on the other – are now emergent in this most primitive continent of the globe. And here, as in the other underdeveloped areas, rapid population growth is likely to intensify political unrest.

In southern Africa another type of population problem is also a major element in a political problem that has grave implications for world order as well as for the stability of the Republic of South Africa. This is the problem arising from the conflict between the indigenous people and European settlers manifest in apartheid. Rapid and differential rates of growth of native and European populations are likely to intensify rather than to allay conflict in southern Africa.

The tensions and political instabilities generated by explosive population growth in the economically underdeveloped nations have a special significance in the contemporary world, characterized by the bipolar conflict between the Western and Communist blocs and the efforts on the part of each to win the allegiance of the uncommitted nations of the world. This conflict has several demographic dimensions of importance.

THE WESTERN AND COMMUNIST BLOCS

The first of these dimensions is evident in the way in which population is distributed among the three political blocs into which the world is divided. For in 1955 each of these political groups – the Western nations, the Communist nations, and the uncommitted nations – had approximately the same population. The Western and the Communist blocs, respectively, each have much to gain in the struggle to win the allegiance of the uncommitted third of the world's people. This titanic competition is focused primarily on South and Southeast Asia at the present time, because the bulk of the world's politically uncommitted population is located there.

In this war for men's minds, the competition between Western-world and Communist ideologies, each of the contestants has powerful weapons. Apart from military power which I will leave out on the assumption that a nuclear stalemate exists, the key weapons of the Communists, as is daily attested to by their propaganda, are the exploitation of the wide gap between the levels of living of the "have" and "have-not" nations and the attribution of blame for the misery of the "have not" nations on the imperialistic and colonial practices of the "have" powers. Needless to say, the fire of this propaganda is effectively fed by the frustration of the underdeveloped areas in their efforts to advance their levels of living, or in their efforts to win independence from imperial powers, where this is not yet accomplished.

The Communist bloc, with relatively little, but with increasing, surplus product, is attempting more and more to help the uncommitted nations in economic development. The U.S.S.R. may perhaps be departing from its postwar cold-war policy of trying to persuade uncommitted nations to accept its ideology by means either of internal coups or direct external aggression.

The chief weapon of the western nations, apart from the example of their free way of life is, undoubtedly, the provision of assistance to the underdeveloped nations to help them achieve their economic goals.

Thus, the success of failure of underdeveloped areas to raise their levels of living has the most profound world political implications. The most important immediate international political question is the question of whether the Western-world approach or the Communist approach is the more effective one for achieving economic development.

It is to be emphasized that this is not a rhetorical or hypothetical question. It is being answered by the course of events, the definitive test of achievement. It is being answered by what may be regarded as the most important experiments of all time – experiments under way in each of the three blocs of nations. A great race is on among the economically underprivileged nations to attain higher living levels – some by relatively free, and some by totalitarian and Communist, methods. The contests involve nations within each of which both economically advanced and underdeveloped areas are to be found (26).

The greatest single race under way is undoubtedly the race between the leaders of the Western and Communist blocs, respectively – that is, the United States and the U.S.S.R. The U.S.S.R. has certainly served notice that, by its methods, it hopes to surpass the level of living attained by the United States, and in the not too distant future. Overshadowed only by the direct contest between the United States and the U.S.S.R. is the race between India and Communist China (27), a race of special and direct immediate interest to the underdeveloped areas. For these mammoth nations, the two largest in the world, are bending every effort to achieve higher living standards – one through the Communist approach and the other by democratic methods. The outcome of this race will be of great interest not only to the underdeveloped nations in the uncommitted bloc but also to those in the Western bloc – the underdeveloped nations in Latin America as well as those committed to the Western bloc in Asia and in Africa.

The international political situation, then, as described above, gives a special significance to explosive population growth. For present and future rates of population growth may, indeed, prevent underdeveloped nations from raising their levels of living. SIMON KUZNETS' examination of the evidence indicates that the gap between "have" and "have-not" nations is increasing rather than decreasing (12). To the extent that underdeveloped nations are frustrated in their efforts to advance their living standards, they will, it may be presumed, be more open to the blandishments of the Communist bloc. Furthermore, if the underdeveloped Communist nations demonstrate that they can achieve more rapid economic progress than the underdeveloped Western nations, the free way of life may well be doomed. Success or failure in this fateful contest may well hinge on the ability of the nations involved to decrease their rates of population growth (28).

THE ALTERNATIVES

The "why" of the population increase, in an immediate sense, is readily identifiable. It is to be found in the great increase in "natural increase" – in the gap between fertility and mortality (1). Quite apart from the precise timing of changes in the relations between mortality and fertility, it is clear that explosive growth can be dampened only by decreasing natural increase. This is true for the world as a whole in the ultimate sense, with differences in timing for different parts of the world. For suggested solutions to the problems of present and prospective rates of population growth in the various subdivisions of the world through migration, foreign trade, redistribution of wealth, and similar means hold forth little promise, if any, even in the short run (21, chap. 18).

There are only three ways to decrease natural increase: (i) by increasing death rate; (ii) by decreasing the birth rate; and (iii) by some combination of the two.

Although it is true that decreased death rates were largely responsible for the population explosion in the past and are foreseen to be a large factor in the future, the adoption of a policy to increase mortality, or to diminish efforts to increase longevity, is unthinkable. Unless one is prepared to debate this, two of the three ways of decreasing natural increase are ruled out. For two of them involve an increase in death rates.

If longevity gains are to be retained, then, the only way to reduce explosive population growth is to decrease the birth rate. That is, the "death control" mankind has achieved can be retained only if it is accompanied by birth control. This proposition, even though it flows directly from the demographic facts of life, in view of prevalent value systems provokes heated debate of the type manifest in the press. Birth control has recently, indeed, made the front pages of the world press.

What is important about the value controversy under way is that it definitely affects global and international policy and action on matters of population and, therefore, on the crucial political problems involved. The most significant thing about all the available methods of birth control – a fact mainly obscured in the present public controversy – is that they are by no means adequate to the task of slowing down explosive world population increase, especially that in the underdeveloped areas. The great mass of mankind in the economically less advanced nations which are faced with accelerating rates of growth fail to limit their birth rates not because of the factors at issue in the controversy we are witnessing but because they do not have the desire, the know-how, or the means to do so. The desire to control fertility, arising from recognition of the problem, is, however, increasing. Japan is already well down the road to controlling its birth rate. although by methods which are not enthusiastically endorsed either by the Japanese themselves or by other peoples. China, India, Pakistan, and Egypt (29) have population limitation programs under way or under serious consideration, and other underdeveloped areas are showing increasing interest in this problem (30). The changes in value systems which will create mass motivation to adopt methods of family limitation are not easily brought about (31), but they are at least under way.

Birth control methods in use in the economically more advanced nations are not, in the main, well adapted for use in the underdeveloped areas. But the results of increased research and experimentation with oral contraceptives are encouraging (32), and there may soon be a breakthrough on obtaining adequate means for the task of limiting population growth in the underdeveloped areas.

CONCLUSION

The demographer and the increasing number of his allies, in directing attention to the implications of world population growth, are in fact pointing to major global and international political problems – problems that cannot be ignored. Needless to say, the solution to the problems is not to be found in appeals to the traditions of the past, sacred or secular. The solution is to be found in the policies and actions which man himself, as a rational animal, must work out and implement. The mind of man, which has conceived remarkable methods for increasing life expectancy, is probably ingenious enough to devise methods by which the population explosion can be controlled within the framework of man's diverse value systems.

REFERENCES AND NOTES

1. *Determinants and Consequences of Population Trends* (United Nations, New York, 1953), chap. 2.
2. See the objection to this phrase in "Statement by Roman Catholic bishops of U.S. on birth control," New York *Times* (26 Nov. 1959).
3. H. BROWN, *The Challenge of Man's Future* (Viking, New York, 1954).
4. *The Future Growth of World Population* (United Nations, New York, 1958).
5. This fact was ignored by Roman Catholic bishops [see New York *Times* (26 Nov. 1959)] and by the Pope [see "Pope denounces birth limitation," New York *Times* (15 Dec. 1959)].
6. The impracticability of colonizing other planets is considered by G. HARDIN [*J. Heredity* 50, 2 (1959)].
7. W. H. LEONARD, *Sci. Monthly* 85, 113 (1957).
8. "National and Per Capita Income of 70 Countries in 1949," *U.N. Statist. Papers, Ser. E, No. 1* (United Nations, New York, 1950).
9. The calculations were made by using United Nations per capita income figures for each continent applied to revised United Nations estimates of 1950 population of continents to obtain revised aggregate income by continent and for the world, as shown in Table I. A new world per capita figure of $223 was obtained, ás compared with the published figure of $230.
10. For the Communist position see F. LORIMER, "Population policies and politics in the Communist world," in *Population and World Politics*, P. M. HAUSER, Ed. (Free Press. Glencoe, Ill., 1958); for the Catholic position see "Pope denounces birth limitation," New York *Times* (15 Dec. 1959); for the Socialist position, see J. D. BERNAL, "Population growth is no threat for a free society," *Natl. Guardian* (7 Dec. 1959) (extract from J. D. BERNAL, *Science in History*).
11. W. S. WOYTINSKY & E. S. WOYTINSKY. *World Population and Production* (Twentieth Century Fund, New York, 1953).
12. S. KUZNETS, "Regional economic trends and levels of living," in *Population and World Politics*, P. M. HAUSER, Ed. (Free Press, Glencoe, Ill., 1958).
13. *Report on International Definition and Measurement of Standards and Levels of Living* (United Nations, New York, 1954).
14. Note the different definitions of area in Tables I and II. In Table II, which gives population projections to 1975 and 2000, "Northern America" includes only North America north of the Rio Grande; "Latin America" includes South America, Central America

and North America south of the Rio Grande. For the rough comparisons made, no adjustment of the data was necessary.

15. Calculations were based on revised data, as explained in (9). For Latin America the calculations were based on a comparison of estimated aggregate income for "Latin America" in 1950, per capita income for "South America" being used.

16. The "population problem" differs for areas with different ratios of population to resources; for example, see Political and Economic Planning, *World Population and Resources* (Essential Books, Fairlawn, N.J., 1955).

17. P. M. HAUSER, "World and urbanization in relation to economic development and social change," in *Urbanization in Asia and Far East* (UNESCO, Calcutta, 1957), p. 57, based on work of K. DAVIS and H. HERTZ.

18. —, "Implications of population trends for regional and urban planning in Asia," UNESCO Working Paper No. 2, U.N. Seminar on Regional Planning, Tokyo, Japan (1958).

19. —, Ed., "Urbanization in Latin America" (UNESCO, New York, in press).

20. "The Population of South Asia (Including Ceylon and China: Taiwan) 1950–1980," *U.N. Rept. No. 3 on Future Population Estimates by Sex and Age* (United Nations, New York, 1958).

21. W. S. THOMPSON, *Population and Progress in the Far East* (Univ. of Chicago Press, Chicago, 1959).

22. I. B. TAEUBER, "Population and political instabilities in underdeveloped areas," in *Population and World Politics*, P. M. HAUSER, Ed. (Free Press, Glencoe, Ill., 1958).

23. "The Population of Central America (Including Mexico), 1950–1980," *U.N. Rept. No. 1 on Future Population Estimates by Sex and Age* (United Nations, New York, 1954); "The Population of South America, 1950–1980," *U.N. Rept. No. 2 on Future Population Estimates by Sex and Age* (United Nations, New York, 1955).

24. "Demographic aspects of urbanization in Latin America," UNESCO Seminar on Urbanization Problems in Latin America, Santiago, Chile (1959).

25. *Social Implications of Industrialization in Africa South of the Sahara* (UNESCO, London, 1956).

26. K. DAVIS, "Population and power in the free world," in *Population and World Politics*, P. M. HAUSER, Ed. (Free Press, Glencoe, Ill., 1958).

27. W. LIPPMANN, "China is No. 1 problem," Chicago *Sun-Times* (14 Dec. 1959); "To live India must change its way of life. ...," Chicago *Sun Times* (15 Dec. 1959).

28. Nor is population a factor in political instability only in the underdeveloped areas. There are many other demographic dimensions of world politics which cannot be treated here because of limitations of space. The authors of a recent symposium volume which it was my privilege to edit include further considerations of population as a factor in world politics. Especially pertinent are the articles by KINGSLEY DAVIS, FRANK LORIMER, IRENE TAEUBER, and QUINCY WRIGHT, from which I have drawn material for this discussion.

29. "Japan's population miracle," *Population Bull.* 15, No. 7 (1959); "The race between people and resources – in the ECAFE region," pt. 1, *Population Bull.* 15, No. 5, 89 (1959).

30. *Asia and the Far East, Seminar on Population* (United Nations, New York, 1957).

31. E. W. NOTESTEIN, "Knowledge, action, people," *University – A Princeton magazine*, No. 2 (1959); P. STREIT and P. STREIT, "New light on India's worry," New York *Times Magazine* (13 Mar. 1960).

32. See, for example, G. PINCUS et al., *Science* 130, 81 (1959); —, "Field Trials with Norethynodrel as an Oral Contraceptive" (Worcester Foundation for Experimental Biology, Shrewsbury, Mass., in preparation).

33. Data are based on the following: J. J. SPENGLER, *Proc. Am. Phil. Soc.* 95, 53 (1951); original data (for 1937) from "Energy Resources of the World," *U.S. Dept. State Publ.* (Government Printing Office, Washington, D.C., 1949), p. 102ff.

PHILIP MORRIS HAUSER, Ph. D., is Professor and Chairman of the Department of Sociology, University of Chicago. Professor HAUSER served as Deputy Director of the Bureau of the Census in which he worked from 1938 to 1947, and was Acting Director of the Census for 1950. He was the United States Representative to the Population Commission of the United Nations from 1946 to 1951. Professor HAUSER has acted as consultant and participant on numerous commissions, and has served as advisor to the Governments of Burma and of Thailand. He was President of the American Statistical Association in 1962. Professor HAUSER is author or editor, among other works, of Population and World Politics (1958); Urbanization in Asia and the Far East (1958); The Study of Population: An Inventory and Appraisal (1959); and Population Perspectives (1960).

Regional Statements

Asian Populations: The Critical Decades*

by

Irene B. Taeuber

In the middle of the 17th century there were some 250 million people in that portion of the Asian Continent that lies below the present boundary of the U.S.S.R. In the two centuries from 1650 to 1850 Asia's population more than doubled. Growth was increasing in regularity and in pace, whether associated directly with colonial rule or indirectly with the crops, the economic techniques, and the social codes that came along with European expansion. In the 80 years of classic colonial rule, roughly from 1850 to 1930, population grew from 650 million to 1 billion. Then in the three decades of the Japanese drive for a continent of Asia for the Asians, the Pacific war, the nationalist struggles, and the revolutions that made half of Asia Communist, population increased a further 500 million to reach 1.5 billion in 1960.

Thus Asia begins it modernization, not with the 250 million people of 1650, or the 650 million people of 1850, but the 1.5 billion people of today. The tragedy of the period of European expansion for Asian countries inheres in this simple demographic fact. Populations multiplied again and again; once empty lands were filled, and once occupied lands were occupied even more densely. But economies remained primarily subsistence agricultural, people remained illiterate, and living and values alike remained traditional. Birth rates remained at the high levels appropriate to ancestral-oriented cultures where the succession of sons was essential and life was precarious. Social, economic, and demographic transformations that might have come slowly over centuries must come swiftly over decades if the good and the reasonably long lives that are the aspirations of Asian peoples become realities.

Asian populations total about 1½ billion people today.

What is the expectation for the future?

There is no precise answer to this question for individual countries, certainly not for the continent. Birth rates have not been reduced, nor can

* Presented to the Committee on the Judiciary, House of Representatives, the United States of America, September 13, 1962.

they be reduced quickly without major changes in the institutions of the peasant societies. If economic development and public health activities can be sustained so that there is food, shelter, and health protection for the increasing people, death rates will continue to decline. If family life remains traditional, illiteracy yields only slowly to advancing education, and the contraceptives appropriate to Asian peasant societies remain ideals rather than scientific achievements, birth rates may decline slowly in the cities and the modernizing areas. Declines in national birth rates will be slow indeed, though, unless rates decline swiftly and sharply in the rural areas.

Given declining death rates and unchanging birth rates, the $1\frac{1}{2}$ billion people in the Asia of 1960 will increase to more than 2 billion in 1975.[1] Then given continuities in the decline of death rates and lethargic stabilities in birth rates, numbers will exceed 4 billion by the end of the century. If this should occur, the net addition to the population of Asia below the Soviet boundary in the half century from 1950 to the year 2,000 would be larger than the population of the entire earth including Asia, in 1950.

The growth back of 1962 has occurred, but future numbers are conjectures. Moreover, the interpretation of the numbers that may exist in future decades is difficult. Their social, economic, and political significance depends on many developments – in economic growth, in social change, in educational achievements. And on these associated developments depend also the future of family life and aspirations and hence the future of the birth rate.

Analysis of the population growth and the population problems of the future is complex. We who failed to predict the growth of recent decades can hardly assert competence to predict the growth of future decades. Nor do theories and ideologies help particularly. Malthusianism proclaims imminent catastrophe while Marxism-Leninism asserts the value of the increasing hands and denies the problems of the increasing mouths. The relevance of either to analysis, policy formulation, or assessment of the future is limited. Malthusianism derived from dire expectations of the futures of European peoples, in Europe or elsewhere. Marxism-Leninism persists as theory while the U.S.S.R. undergoes a demographic transition quite similar to that in capitalist countries. The experiences of the Peoples Republic of China demonstrate that the population problems of Asian lands can neither be ignored with safety nor safely solved through defining hands as assets in great leaps and commune reconstructions.

A series of probing questions must be asked if the population growth of Asian countries is approached with a focus toward problems of resolution.

1. These overall figures of the past, present, and projected future populations are broad approximations made on a world basis by the United Nations and published in 1958. See: United Nations. "The Future Growth of World Population," Population Studies, No. 28. ST/SOA/Series A/28. New York, 1958. Prepared by the Population Branch of the Bureau of Social Affairs of the Department of Economic and Social Affairs.

There will be resolution, and it will involve economic, social, and political transformations, but the direction of movement may involve advance or retrogression. The demographic process may include declining birth rates, increasing death rates, or some combination of the two.

The first question is a series of questions. What happened to quicken growth rates? Why were governmental planners in countries and in international organizations so oblivious to the problems of growth? Why were there no plans for population development along with those for agricultural and industrial development, labor, education, and health?

The second question is a simple one. What are the dimensions of the problems of growth in the individual countries?

The third question is again a series, this time involving the future. What are the processes of resolution, and what are countries now doing or planning to do to secure that balance of low birth and death rates that reduces growth to manageable proportions? What is the role of migration, in this resolution, whether international or internal, whether planned or unplanned? What is the role of migration if population-resources relations remain acute and there is relative failure to move forward in peaceful internal solutions to economic-demographic difficulties?

SCIENCE, TECHNOLOGY, AND IMBALANCE IN GROWTH

Prior to the medical and public health breakthroughs that yielded the miracle-working chemicals and the antibiotics, death rates were tied inexorably to ways and means of living. It was natural, therefore, that the early planning of national governments and international organizations involved economic development and public health but not education concerning social change and family planning. It was argued that increases in per capita food production and income would surpass rates of population growth. Since it was also argued that birth rates would decline slowly in response to economic advance and rising expectations, no major problems of growth were anticipated, either in the long or the short run.

The postwar developments differed from those anticipated in the mid-forties. The major force of change was neither economic nor ideological but scientific and technological. In late 1946 and early 1947 the public health services of Ceylon had the houses of the island sprayed with DDT. The death rate was cut 40% within a single year. The miracles of modern public health were realities. In the short run, the ties that bound death rates to levels of living and ways of living were snapped. Death rates dropped, the rate of population growth moved upward. There were no economic developments to provide additional employment for the increasing labor force. There were no social changes in village life to stimulate declining family size.

Ceylon was the omen for the Asian future. Death rates declined rapidly

in country after country as national governments and international organizations cooperated in public health programs. Rates of population growth
moved upward as increasing numbers of countries and increasing proportions of people maintained the birth rates of ancient times alongside
the death rates of new times. The successive estimates of future populations
that were made by the United Nations Secretariat soon became antiquated,
for the high projections of one series were too low for the populations that
existed within a few years. The censuses of 1960 and 1961 indicate that India,
Pakistan, the Philippines, and other countries underestimated the rates at
which their populations were growing.[2]

The advances of science and technology in the public health field made
theories of automatic transitions to low birth rates as antiquated as those of
traditional Malthusianism. If a country is reasonably successful in its health
and agricultural programs, its rates of population growth should be, or
should soon become, 3, 3½, or even 4% a year. Computations of future
populations based on rates of growth such as these yield numbers difficult
to comprehend, whether the areas are coral atolls or continental countries.
Yet, given continuing progress in national and international activities to
provide freedom from hunger and disease, these are the rates of growth
that must be assumed for the future subject to three essential reservations:

1. That there is continuity in public order and public health activities.
2. That food produced or available is sufficient for the maintenance of the
   increasing populations.
3. That there are no increases in the control of fertility.

In simplest terms, the increasing rate of population growth reflects a
lack of balance in scientific and technological developments. Scientific
advances have freed death rates temporarily from the age-old ties with
nutritional deficiencies and environmental hazards. There have been no
comparable scientific advances to free birth rates from their intimate links
with traditional social structures, sex roles, and value systems. Is the villain
then science, the solution simply more science? The seemingly obvious
conclusion is enticing, but it is insufficient either as explanation or as sole
policy directive.

Today's rates of growth, as those of earlier centuries, are products of
reduced death rates. Most men view the prolongation of life with favor,
and they have always viewed it thus. A solution to the problems of population growth through increasing death rates is rejected. But if death rates
are to decline to ever lower levels in a finite world, birth rates must also
decline. There is no alternative. But declining birth rates mean controlled
fertility, and there is neither a universal good called the small family nor a

2. See "Population and Food," ch. IV, p. 119, in: United Nations. Economic Commission
for Asia and the Far East. "Economic Survey of Asia and the Far East 1961" Bangkok,
Thailand, 1962, viii, 215 pp. United Nations publication, sales No. 62, II. F 1.

universal ethic that interprets parental responsibilities as including limitation of offspring.

Thus there is approval of science, technology, and action programs that contribute to the health and longevity of people, and that provide increasing material goods. There is ambivalence to research and action programs in the field of human fertility. And this is true despite the increasing realization that the long and abundant physical life which is the goal of development activities can be preserved only if birth rates also decline.

A summary statement may be in order. The force that led to increasing rates of population growth was declining mortality. The demographic crisis is created by the failure of birth rates to decline along with death rates. Within a period of time whose duration no man can now foresee, the decline of birth rates becomes the only alternative to the increase of death rates.

The demographic, political, and other complexities of the Asian population situation can be reduced to one simple question: Will growth be reduced through the humane processes of declining birth rates or the ruthless processes of increasing death rates?

THE DIMENSIONS OF THE PROBLEMS

Two summary tables may serve as prelude to later discussion. In table I, the population of Asia east of Iran and south of the U.S.S.R. is compared with that in other regions. In table II, past and possible future growth are sketched for the Asian region.

Asia, as defined to exclude the southwestern region and the northern half of the geographic continent, includes extraordinary concentrations of people. More than half the earth's total population live on this one-sixth of earth's land surface.

The area of the south-central and eastern Asian region is comparable in size to that of the U.S.S.R., Northern America, or Latin America. The population is many times greater than that in any one of these other regions. The Soviet Union is relatively empty; so, too, is Northern America. These are advanced industrial areas, with educated and predominantly urban populations, with scientific and technological components that push knowledge ever forward and continually transform earth's environment and extend its horizons. In Latin America there is poverty, malnutrition, and illiteracy, and there are rates of population growth generally more rapid than those in Asia. But resources are immense, while people are sparse in relation to land and other resources. The problems of development are those of organization and management, not the niggardliness of nature or the huge population increases of past periods. The world's population problems, as its people, are concentrated in Asia.

The population growth that was described previously for continental

TABLE I.

World population in major regions, 1957

Region	Land area (in thousands of square kilometers)	Population, 1957 (in millions)	Percent of world total	
			Land area	Population
Total	135,335	2,795	100.0	100.0
Asia and the Far East [1]	21,178	1,483	15.6	53.0
Soviet Union	22,403	205	16.6	7.3
Northern America [2]	21,483	189	15.9	6.8
Latin America [3]	20,501	192	15.1	6.9
Rest of the world [4]	49,770	726	36.8	26.0

[1] Asia south of the Soviet Union and east of Iran, without New Guinea.
[2] Canada, Greenland, and the United States.
[3] America south of the United States.
[4] Africa, southwest Asia, Europe west of the Soviet Union, Oceania, and New Guinea.
Source: United Nations. Department of Economic and Social Affairs. "The Population of Asia and the Far East, 1950–80." Future Population Estimates by Sex and Age, Rept. IV, Population Studies No. 31. ST/SOA/Series A/31. New York, 1959. Table 1. From: "Demographic Yearbook, 1958," table 2.

Asia below the boundaries of the Soviet Union is given for the subregion the United Nations designates incongruously as "Asia and the Far East" in table II. A glance at this table corroborates the fact of acceleration in the rates of population increase among Asian populations and adds the further fact that growth is prevalent throughout the region. It also indicated that there were substantial differences in rates of growth among the subregions from 1920 to 1950 and suggests the possibility of similar differences from 1950 to 1980.

The depth of the Asian population problems is apparent, some of the dimensions measurable, if attention is turned to individual countries. We have selected five whose fates are highly significant for Asia and the world: India, Pakistan, Indonesia, Communist China, and Japan. The first four are underdeveloped, but the last is urban and industrial, with an educated citizenry, a rate of economic growth among the highest in the world, and a birth rate far below that of the United States.

The time span is limited to the near future, roughly the 15 years from 1960 to 1975. The nature of uncertainty is altered thereby, for all persons who will be aged 13 or above in the year 1975 are already born. If the basic data on population size and age structure in 1960 were correct, actual populations aged 13 and above in 1975 could be altered from those projected only by death rates different from those assumed in the projections. Populations already born cannot have their numbers altered by changes in birth rates.

TABLE II.

Population trends in Asia and the Far East, 1920–50

Year	Total	[Populations in millions] Regions [1]			
		Central-south	Southeast	Continental east	Maritime east
Estimated:					
1920	991	326	110	478	77
1930	1,074	362	128	496	88
1940	1,181	410	155	515	101
1950	1,317	466	172	599	120
Projected: [2]					
1960	1,572	555	210	670	137
1970	1,906	681	268	799	158
1980	2,268	833	348	906	181
Increase, amount					
1920 to 1950	326	140	62	81	43
1950 to 1980	696	278	138	236	44
Increase, percent:					
1920 to 1950	33	43	56	17	56
1950 to 1980	72	79	103	62	51

[1] The United Nations region designated as Asia and the Far East excludes southwest Asia and the Asian portion of the U.S.S.R. The regional groupings are as follows: Central-south Asia–Afghanistan, Bhutan, Ceylon, India, the Maldive Islands, Nepal, Portuguese India, and Pakistan; southeast Asia–Cambodia, Burma, Indonesia, Laos, Malaya, the Philippines, Timor, Singapore, Thailand, and Vietnam; continental east Asia–Peoples Republic of China, Hong Kong, Macau, and the Mongolian Peoples Republic; maritime east Asia–Taiwan, Japan, Korea, and the Ryukyu Islands. Vietnam and Korea are the undivided countries.
[2] The projected populations for the individual countries, and hence for the regions and the ECAFE area as a whole, are those regarded as most reasonable by the analysts of the United Nations.
Source of data: United Nations. Department of Economic and Social Affairs. "The Population of Asia and the Far East, 1950–1980." Future Population Estimates by Sex and Age, Rept. IV, Population Studies No. 31. ST/SAO/Series A/31. New York, 1959. Tables 4 and 6.

The conjectural "if" as to the accuracy of present knowledge is an immense one, for the largest of the populations of Asia is that of the Peoples Republic of China. A registration and investigation of the population in late 1953 and early 1954 yielded a population of 582 million for the mainland area. If the birth rate was 41.6 at this time and the death rate 20.4, and if the death rate declined in the general Asian pattern while the birth rate remained unchanged, population increased from 582 million in 1953 to 733 million in 1963. If the population had been 733 million in 1963 and the trends had continued for the 15 years from 1963 to 1978, the population would have exceeded 1 billion by 1978.

The construct for mainland China is an artifact already divorced from the realities of life in Communist China, though the extent of the departure is not measurable for a country where demographic ignorance or secretiveness on the part of the government creates and perpetuates levels of ignorance unparalleled in the modern world. Estimates and projections for Communist China are included, however, for the analysis of Asian populations cannot exclude the Chinese. Discussion may be highly conjectural, but discussion there must be. The projections for the underdeveloped countries other than China are also constructs whose relations to realities in the coming years may be impaired or shattered by the sudden mortality of cataclysm or the slowly increasing death rates that could accompany economic and political failures. This is neither a prediction nor an anticipation of tragic deterioriation in conditions of living. It is, rather, an affirmation of the awful vulnerability of most Asian populations, whether in India, Pakistan, Indonesia, mainland China, or elsewhere.

The projections of future populations for India, Pakistan, and Indonesia are similar to those for mainland China. All involve assumptions of unchanging fertility and declining mortality. These assumptions permit significant analysis of the problems of the near future. It is unlikely that there will be major declines in birth rates in the period of little more than a decade that separates late 1962 from 1975. If there is economic development and continuing public health expansion, death rates will decline. Thus the projected populations are those likely to exist unless there are failures in the plans of the countries, the international organizations, and the United States.

The problems of population growth are unavoidable components in ongoing economic and social developments. They are indicators of progress, not of failures.

Total populations

The total populations, the amounts of the increases, and the percentages of those increases are given in table III. The figures are staggering in their magnitudes. India must provide for an increase of 177 million within the next 15 years. Pakistan's increase will be 50 million.

East Pakistan's population was estimated at 53 million in 1961; in 1976, under the assumed conditions, it will be 84 million. More than 30 million people will be added in 15 years in a region without cities, industrial development, or substantial known resources for industrialization. If this growth occurs, the people of East Pakistan will be settled 600 to the square kilometre. Quoting conclusions from the United Nations: "The problems of economic development posed by East Pakistan's rapidly growing population are of a kind and dimension hardly encountered in any other part of the world at this time."[3]

Indonesia's projections are largely constructs built on reasoned assumptions.[4] Here, too, present living is difficult. People are vulnerable to interruptions in food supply, whether episodically through crop failures or continuously through economic deterioration. However, if mortality should decline to relatively low levels, population would increase from 93 million in 1961 to 137 million in 1975.

TABLE III.

Populations in selected Asian countries, 1960 and 1975.

Country	Population (in thousands)		Increase	
	1960–65	1975–78	Amount (in thousands)	Percent
India [1]	423,600	600,600	177,000	41.8
Pakistan [1]	95,387	145,630	50,243	52.7
Indonesia [1]	93,344	137,376	44,032	47.2
Mainland China [1]	732,900	1,112,700	379,800	51.8
Japan	93,371	102,729	9,358	10.0

[1] India, 1961–76; Pakistan, 1961–76; Indonesia, 1960–75; Mainland China, 1963–78.
Sources of data: United Nations. "The Population of Asia and the Far East, 1950–80." India, high fertility projection, table VIII; Pakistan, low mortality projection, table XVII; mainland China, high fertility projection, table II; Japan, medium projection, table XI. United Nations. "The Population of southeast Asia (Including Ceylon and China: Taiwan), 1950–80." Indonesia, low mortality projection, table III, pp. 138–139.

The island of Java is the world's classic illustration of population growth. Lord RAFFLES estimated the population as 4.5 million in 1815. Even then there was concern over the pressures of people on limited land. In 1960 there were more than 60 million people on the island of Java. If growth continues as projected, the population of this small island will exceed 100 million by 1975. Whether the Javan economy can absorb an additional 44 million people within the next 15 years is indeed debatable. The possibilities for population transfers from crowded Java to relatively empty Sumatra will be noted later.

In relative terms, the populations of these Asian giants were increasing in similar fashion in the past and, given continuities in development, they will do so in the future. Projected growth in the next 15 years ranges from a low of 42% in India to a high of 53% in Pakistan. The hypothetical progression of mainland China to its population of more than a billion in 1978

3. "The Population of Asia and the Far East, 1950–1980," p. 14.
4. The validity of the construct is attested by the results of the Indonesian census of 1961. The population at that time was 95.2 million.

implies rates of growth comparable to those assumed for the other underdeveloped countries.

That there are resolutions to growth and the problems of growth
is apparent in the figure for Japan – an anticipated growth of only 10%
in the 15 years from 1960 to 1975.

The productive ages

Is it correct to assume that rates of population growth of 40 to 50% within a
15-year period constitute major population problems in these great Asian
countries? The answer is unequivocal and it is affirmative. In Table IV,
populations in the productive ages from 15 to 59 are given for the years 1960
and 1975, together with increases and rates of increase in numbers in this
15-year period.

TABLE IV.

Populations in the productive ages, 1960 and 1975.

Country	Population aged 15 to 59 (in thousands)		Increase	
	1960–1963	1975–1978	Amount (in thousands)	Percent
India	233,300	316,600	83,300	35.7
Pakistan	50,137	74,036	23,899	47.7
Indonesia	51,521	72,289	20,768	40.3
Mainland China	376,800	551,300	174,500	46.3
Japan	57,529	70,206	12,677	22.0

For notes and source references, see table III.

The span of years from age 15 through age 59 is a long one. The activities
of men in these years are defined as labor, whatever the culture and whether
that labor involves working in the rice fields of the monsoon lands, in the
iron and steel works that are appearing in the new Asia, or in the service and
distribution sectors of the traditional societies. The activities of women are
more diverse, for these are the years that include marriage, homemaking,
childbearing, and childrearing, and some form of participation in economic activities. Overall, though, men and women in the central 45 years
of the life-span maintain themselves and persons in the younger and the
older ages. This is the economic responsibility. They produce the younger
generation for which they provide – thus fulfilling an essential demographic
responsibility. And then they provide for the aging and the aged – thus fulfilling the familial responsibilities that are as essential in modern as in
ancient societies.

If time and space were available, trends in the adult population would be considered for finer age groups and separately for men and women. In broad generality, though, the potentialities, the requirements, and the problems of development were apparent in the crude figures of table IV.[5]

The difficulties of an economic development sufficient to provide more adequate employment and income for the existing labor force are compounded immensely if that labor force increases in numbers some 35 to 50% in a decade and a half. This relation of the increasing labor force to modernization is so critical that it merits statement in another form. If there were no economic expansion, there would be two to three claimants for each economic position vacated by death or retirement. For the years from 1965 to 1970, the ratio of additions to departures from labor force ages is 229 for India, 285 for Pakistan, 262 for mainland China, and 283 for Indonesia. This is a rough index of the dynamism required in the economies.

Women and families

It is gross and perhaps unpardonable simplicity to move directly from population figures to the economic relations and the institutional structures of nations. The population facts place boundaries and impose directions of movement, however, and so they may be used as indicative of the extent of the dynamics required for continuing adjustment in the future.

In the years from 1960 to 1975, girls in their 'teens will increase by 50% or more in the underdeveloped Asian countries. If marriage ages and marriage frequencies remain unchanged, new families formed in 1975 will be half again as numerous as those formed in 1960. Given equal rates of childbearing, annual numbers of births in the late seventies will be $1\frac{1}{2}$ times as great as annual numbers in the early sixties. It should be noted that this does not imply a rise in fertility; it is an increase in numbers of births due to the fact that more women are marrying and having children at the same rates.

Constancy in birth rates combined with declining death rates and increasing numbers of women in the childbearing ages would produce the following numbers of children below age 5 in the specific countries, numbers being in thousands:

Country	1960–63	1975–78
India	68,300	98,500
Pakistan	16,651	25,597
Indonesia	15,441	21,773
Mainland China	122,100	193,100
Japan	7,357	7,326

5. In approximation, half the adult population consists of men, half of women, and the rates of change for the two groups are similar. This is crude, but the projected popu-

It may be noted that the projected numbers of young children increase at more rapid rates than the projected numbers of adults in the productive ages. The reason is a simple one; young women in the major ages of child-bearing will be increasing more rapidly than the older women, for the reductions in mortality to which they have been subjected will have been greater. And numbers of young children will have had their numbers increased in even higher proportions by the assumed declines in mortality. This characteristic pattern of mortality change compounds the increase in the numbers and the proportions of children and thus increases the relative burdens of dependent on productive age groups.

The dependent ages

In populations with high birth rates, there are high proportions of youth, small proportions of the aged. The ratios of total dependent to total pro-ductive age groups are high. And, given constant fertility and declining mortality, these dependency ratios increase. The picture of table V needs no elaboration beyond the figures themselves. Advancing consumption levels, personal development, opportunities for children, savings – all these are difficult when family maintenance requirements are so great.

TABLE V.

Dependent and productive age groups, 1960 and 1975

Country	Dependent ages		Productive ages		Dependent ages per 1,000 in productive ages	
	1960–63	1975–78	1960–63	1975–78	1960–63	1975–78
India	190,300	284,000	233,300	316,600	816	897
Pakistan	45,250	71,594	50,137	74,036	903	967
Indonesia	41,823	65,087	51,521	72,289	812	900
Mainland China	356,100	561,400	376,800	551,300	945	1,018
Japan	35,842	32,525	57,529	70,206	623	463

For notes and source references, see table III.

Education and the oncoming generation

Increasing numbers of men and women in the central ages, increasing numbers of families and households, growing burdens of youth and aged – these are the processes of past, present, and future. Numbers of children in elementary school ages are also increasing (table VI). There are a hundred

lations will also be more or less crude approximations to the true populations of the future.

million children aged 5 to 14 in India now; there will be 150 million in 15 years. Pakistan's 24 million children will increase to almost 40 million, the Indonesia's 21 million to 35 million. Given the achievement of the projected numbers, China's 180 million would increase to almost 300 million. The increase in children in school ages in India, Pakistan, Indonesia, and mainland China would amount to 187 million in the 15 years from 1960 to 1975.

Schools, teachers, and maintenance should be provided for the 300 million children now aged 5 to 14 – and then further schools, teachers, and maintenance should be provided for an additional number close to 200 million. While this drive for general elementary education is proceeding, higher schools, colleges, technical institutions, and universities are needed for the intermediate, technical, managerial and scientific personnel so essential to the future development of economies, societies, and political institutions.

TABLE VI.

Children in elementary school ages, 1960 and 1975.

Country	Number (age 5 to 14) (in thousands)		Increase	
	1960–63	1975–78	Amount (in thousands)	Percent
India [1]	100,100	150,300	50,200	50.1
Pakistan [1]	24,323	38,752	14,429	59.3
Indonesia [1]	21,363	34,666	13,303	62.3
Mainland China [1]	182,800	292,700	109,900	60.1
Japan	20,242	13,300	—6,942	—34.3

For notes and source references, see table III.

In 1975, children now below age 5 will be aged 15 to 19. The numbers of youth in the late teens and the increases in their numbers are given in table VII. If someway the breakthrough could be achieved and the young men and women who will be aged 15 to 19, 15 years from now could spend the major portion of these years in educational activities, if not in the types of school systems accepted as normal in developed countries, modernization could be accepted as a probability for the future. If the youth of 1975 are not educated, the workers and the parents of the following decades will not be educated, and the struggle against the manifold problems of ill-trained human resources will continue.

The advance of education is perhaps the single most critical factor beyond economic viability itself. The self-perpetuating mechanisms of traditional societies are nowhere more apparent and more serious than here, for the large families, the severe burdens on families and communities and the deterrents to economic growth are part of a complex of forces that preserve the traditionalism and the illiteracy – as these in turn perpetuate the early marriages, the abundant childbearing, and the high rates of population growth.

TABLE VII.

Youth aged 15 to 19, 1960 and 1975.

Country	Numbers (in thousands)		Increase	
	1960–63	1975–78	Amount (in thousands)	Percent
India [1]	41,500	60,000	18,500	44.6
Pakistan [1]	9,517	15,035	5,518	58.0
Indonesia [1]	8,416	14,275	5,859	69.6
Mainland China [1]	62,000	113,500	51,500	83.1
Japan	9,552	7,251	—2,301	—24.1

For notes and source references, see table III.

RESOLUTION: PROBLEMS AND PROCESSES

The outline of the problems of population and the growth of population yields a somber picture. So also does any projection of growth in a single component into the future. So also did estimates of the European population future in the late 18th and early 19th centuries and the estimates of the Japanese population future in the late 19th and early 20th centuries. Projection to catastrophe is simple. It might even be valid if science and technology remained constant, if people did not strive creatively to improve their own destinies and those of their children, and if governments did not develop their policies in some relationship to the realities of their problems.

Given the magnitude of the problems and the uncertainties concerning their resolutions, summary and conjecture in outline form seem the most feasible procedure.

1. The population growth now occurring is a measure of the greatest humanitarian achievement of all times. The maladjustment is not the advance of science that permitted the saving of life but the failures of a scientific development that would yield comparable reductions in birth rates.

2. The problems of population growth and the urgency involved in the reduction of birth rates are major concerns among many Asian governments. There are Government policies in India and Pakistan; there have been and there may again be policies in Communist China. The great questions concern means and motivations, not the goals of governments.

3. The rapid increases in persons in the productive ages, in families, and in youth in school ages will continue for the next 15 years, whatever the course of birth rates. The numbers of those already born can be altered by shifting death rates, not by shifting birth rates.

4. Any assumptions of or arguments concerning the priorities in economic development, social change, and population control are artifacts. All are essential to the achievement of modernization in the individual countries, as in the region as a whole. Success is not possible in any one without roughly parallel success in the others.

5. Urbanization, the expansion of the cultivated acreage, and the more intensive and more productive use of land already cultivated are essential to the modernization of economies and populations. Given the size of the populations, the high rates of growth, the paucity of prime lands now unused, and the density of settlement on existing lands, modernization is not likely to follow as byproduct of urban growth. The increase in the productivity of agriculture, the induction of social change in the villages, and the reduction of birth rates among rural people must be approached as urgent problems of modernization in the contemporary Asian setting.

6. There are possibilities for expansion in some Asian countries, particularly in southeast Asia. The availability of unused areas should ease the transition to modernization if the new resources are developed along with the transformation of the economies. If such areas are occupied in traditional ways, the only contribution of the occupation is an increase in the numbers of people and the extension of the areas of poverty.

7. Given the achieved size of the base populations and the rapidity of the growth, planned transfers of population are not feasible as solutions to problems of population pressure and population growth. The Governments of the Netherlands and Indonesia alike emphasized assisted movements from crowded Java to relatively empty Sumatra. The concept is illusory, for prohibitive investments of capital would be required to transport and resettle Java's increase. The illustrative computations in table VIII indicate the demographic consequences of the transfer of 20,000 households a year during each of the 30 years from 1950 to 1980. This activity would reduce the population projected for Java in 1980 from 92 million to 87 million. 12% of the population increase of Java would have been transferred to Sumatra, but 88% would remain in Java.

8. International migrations can be neither solutions nor major palliatives to the problems of population growth and economic development in Asian countries. The Asian future differs from the European past in four critical aspects:

(a) There are no empty hemispheres awaiting development by the modernizing Asians.

(b) The base populations in Asia are so huge and the rates of population growth are so high that European size movements would have little demographic effect, even if they were possible. The United States received 34 million migrants from Europe in the years from 1820 to 1955. This number of migrants would represent less than a single year's population growth in Asia.

(c) The nationalism of the current period is a barrier both to the movement of emigrants and to the willingness of countries to receive immigrants.

(d) Emigration can be a demographic safety valve for countries in process of modernization, with increasing industrialization and urbanization, expanding education, and declining birth rates. It offers only transitory relief to the premodern country where modernization is hope rather than ongoing process and birth rates are intact at ancient levels.

TABLE VIII.

Projected populations of Java and Sumatra, 1950 and 1980

Age	Numbers (in thousands)				Increase, 1950 to 1980			
	Java		Sumatra		Amount (in thousands)		Percent	
	1950	1980	1950	1980	Java	Sumatra	Java	Sumatra
Populations without migration [1]								
Total	50,000	92,261	12,000	22,200	42,261	10,200	84.5	85.0
0 to 14	17,899	36,353	4,665	8,993	18,454	4,328	103.1	92.8
15 to 59	29,582	50,155	6,732	11,892	20,573	5,100	69.5	76.6
60 plus	2,519	3,753	603	1,315	3,234	712	28.4	118.1
Populations with transfer of 20,000 households a year from Java to Sumatra [2]								
Total	50,000	86,999	12,000	27,462	36,999	15,462	74.0	128.9
0 to 14	17,899	34,015	4,665	11,331	16,116	6,666	90.0	142.9
15 to 59	29,582	47,391	6,732	14,656	17,809	7,924	60.2	117.6
60 plus	2,519	5,593	603	1,475	3,074	872	122.0	144.6

[1] Conservative projections of the population.

[2] The net transfer of 20,000 households each year from 1950 to 1980 would reduce the increase of the population of Java during this thirty-year period from 42.3 to 37.0 millions. It would raise the increase of the population of Sumatra from 10.2 to 15.5 millions. Source of data: United Nations. Department of Economic and Social Affairs. "The Population of southeast Asia (including Ceylon and China: Taiwan), 1950–1980." Future Population Estimates by Sex and Age, Rept. III. Population Studies No. 30. ST/SOA/ /Series A/30. New York, 1958. Section VII, "Effects of Internal Migration on Population Distribution and Growth." Especially pp. 85, 87, 89, and 90.

9. Given the absence of international boundaries, there would be major migrations and population redistributions within the Asian region. The potentialities of the slightly used river deltas of southeast Asia and the fabulous resources of the outer islands of Indonesia would not long remain simply potentialities to be developed at leisure by their present holders.

10. The greatest of the many "danger spots" in the world population of the coming century is the long, fortified, and already vacated frontier zone that separates the Asian peoples of the southern portion of the geographic continent of Asia from the European peoples of the northern portion of that continent. The wall against migrants from a developing Asia is already erected by the Soviet Union; the critical confrontation is already fact. The shape of the outcome depends on the rate of development of the Asian peoples.

11. Expansionism, militarism, and the associated migrations of peoples have characterized nations midway in their modernization. This which has been true of the European and the Japanese pasts may also be true of the Asian futures.

IRENE B. TAEUBER, Ph. D., LL D., has been demographer and sociologist with the Office of Population Research, Princeton University, since 1936. She is currently consultant in demography to the Pacific Science Board of the National Academy of Sciences, a Member of the Sub-Committee on Chinese Society of the Joint American Council of Learned Societies – Social Science Research Council Committee on Contemporary China, and Vice-President of the International Union for the Scientific Study of Population. Dr. TAEUBER was Secretary of the American Sociological Society in 1949 and President of the Population Association of America in 1953–54. Her publications in book form include, as author, The Population of Tanganyika (1949) and The Population of Japan (1958); as coauthor, Public Health and Demography in the Far East (1949), and The Changing Population of the United States (1958).

Quotations from Indian Authorities

SHRI RABINDRA NATH TAGORE

"The Birth Control movement is a great movement not only because it will save women from enforced and undesirable maternity, but because it will help the cause of peace by lessening the number of surplus population of a country, scrambling for food and space outside its own rightful limits. In a hunger-stricken country like India it is a cruel crime thoughtlessly to bring more children to existence than could properly be taken care of, causing endless suffering to them and imposing a degrading condition upon the whole family. It is evident that the utter helplessness of growing poverty very rarely acts as a check controlling the burden of overpopulation. It proves that in this case nature's urging gets the better of the severe warning that comes from the providence of civilized social life. Therefore, I believe, that to wait till the moral sense of man becomes a great deal more powerful than it is now and till then to allow countless generations of children to suffer privations and untimely death for no fault of their own is a great social injustice which should not be tolerated."

SHRI JAWAHARLAL NEHRU

"It is of the highest importance that we should make progress in this country and that we should raise the standards of life in this country. There are many other things coming in the way of the standards being raised but one is obviously the growth of population which tends to keep down the standards necessary. So that whether it is from a political, economic or social point of view, all these problems drive us to the conclusion that we must take up this question of family planning and press it forward with vigour and with intelligence.... I have no doubt that vast numbers of people in India would welcome family planning and population control from every point of view."

Rajkumari Amrit Kaur

"A planned and scientific approach towards the solution of the problem of family life should be the main objective which a national campaign for family planning must keep in view. The task that lies ahead is colossal and the path to success is by no means easy but even then there should be no room for despair, as the people in India are alive to the problem and are anxious to be helped and educated. It is necessary for the economic uplift of the country that the work be carried on with missionary zeal."

Shrimati Dhanvanthi Rama Rau

"Planned parenthood, has long been recognised as an important factor in preventing unhappiness and misery by providing married couples with the knowledge of safeguarding unwanted pregnancies, and spacing births in a manner that will result in the maintenance of the good health of both mother and child and imposing on the parents the responsibility of providing the basic requirements of healthy living to which each child is inherently entitled."

Extracts from an Inaugural Address to the Third International Conference on Planned Parenthood (Bombay: Family Planning Association of India) in 1952

by

S. RADHAKRISHNAN
Then Vice-President, now President of India

An advice given to students in our country according to tradition is – I will give you the Sanskrit first: '*matr devo bhava, pitr devo bhava, acarya devo bhava, atithi devo bhava, prajatantum mat vyavacchesih*" – "do not cut off the thread of offspring". Students, when they complete their careers are called upon to enter the state of the householder and there the advice given to them is "do not cut off the thread of offspring." In other words, they are called upon to marry and produce offspring. We never regard sex as something impious or obscene. It is the duty, normally speaking – we are not making laws for exceptional cases – of young students when they leave the universities to enter into the state of marriage, and there the main purpose of marriage is inculcated as the production of offspring. Marriage is the union of man and woman, and family life is enlarged and completed by the arrival of children.

Those who wish to avoid children for personal reasons, or for reasons of comfort, or for reasons of leading independent lives, are not encouraged. All the same, if you subject women to frequent childbirths, you will be guilty of cruelty to human beings, you will undermine their health, you will impair family happiness, you will be making difficult, marriages which otherwise might have been successful. If, therefore, your intention is to safeguard the health and happiness of family life, you must determine the time of childbirth, space the arrival of the children. I take it, to determine this, is to plan a family. If, therefore, your main interest is to secure the health and happiness of both mothers and children, if your main interest is to bring down the infant and maternal mortality in this country which is so ruinous, it is essential for us to adopt a system of family planning. I appeal for that in the name of social welfare of both parents and children. I do not think it is anybody's view here that we should overstrain and tax the health of mothers, and bring into being weaklings who are not able to stand the strain of life, people whose bodies are crippled from the very start. It is, therefore, essential that there should be some system of planning of families.

There is a social aspect to this problem also. We have today two and a half billion human beings in this world. We now talk about human rights. The Declaration of Human Rights has been adopted by the United Nations and the UNESCO. In other words, we wish to provide for children all facilities of food, clothing, shelter, medicine, education, etc. We have committed ourselves to this doctrine of human rights. There was a time when we regarded human beings as so many chattels; human beings were poor, ignorant, illiterate, diseased and crippled. Those days are over. People are not prepared to accept as axiomatic, poverty, misery, starvation and the like. We are committed to a social welfare state. It is our aim in this country to see to it that our children are given every kind of facility to grow into healthy, happy, responsible citizens of our community. Are we in a position to do so at the present moment? Are we doing it? On every side I turn, there is discontent, dissatisfaction, and everybody thinks that every child however humble it may be, has a right to grow up in peace ahd security, has a right to be treated when it falls ill, has a right to be educated. We are not in a position even with our present population to give that kind of assistance to our people. So it seems that where other countries like Russia, or New Zealand or Australia encourage larger families, there is a feeling that in our country we must try to do something to limit population. The Planning Commission speaks of it; as a recent message of the Prime Minister says, we must try to reduce population, to limit population, and we are not committed to any one method. MAHATMA GANDHI said that by means of abstinence, you must try to bring down population; he did not want so many people brought into existence who could not be cared for properly. That is the conviction of many of the leaders of our country.

The question is sometimes raised whether it is not true that God sends children into this world and we should not interfere with the Will of God – that is the way in which it is put. I may tell you that if God has given us any intelligence, he has given it to us to be used. Intelligence is a Divine gift, anticipating consequences and planning with special relevance to the facts. These are things which we are called upon to adopt because the human mind is a gift of the Divine. We have had infanticide, we have had pestilence, we have had floods and earthquakes, and we have been acquiescing in all sorts of evil practices in this country. We have inherited not only great areas of light, but we have inherited large tracts of darkness and ignorance.

What is civilization? It is a progressive control of nature. While in the animal world it is the environment that selects who survives and who does not survive, man is given intelligence to adapt himself to the environment. The duty which human individuals have, is to find out what the social needs are, what the physical needs are, what the spiritual needs are, and strive to fulfil them. God is not an external despot. He is there in the innermost depth of our being, and when the still, small voice prompts us, asks us to use our intelligence in a fairminded, objective, honest way, we are using the gift of God for purposes of human welfare. That is how we have to employ our intelligence to achieve human welfare.

We have various ideas as to how there can be limitation of population. There are some who tell us that if we raise human standards, there will be a fall in the birth rate – look at some of the advanced Western countries. There are others who tells us that by the application of modern science and technology we can improve the world's yield of food, so that the increase of population will never outrun the subsistence level. There are still others who tell us that if we only change our economy, if our whole social structure is altered, then we can go on producing as many as we please with no disastrous results. These are all different ways in which we are called upon to look at this problem of family planning. I want to say that these are long term remedies. Our need is desperate, the claims of humanity appeal to us, and it is essential that we should do something for regulating population. We have interfered with nature, we have controlled nature in lowering the death rate, postponing death, combating disease, prolonged human life to preserve ourselves from floods and earthquakes. In all these matters, we are using human intelligence – to prolong the life of human beings and to preserve them for a higher purpose – that is what we are attempting to do. But we are called upon, just when it comes to limitation of population, that we are interfering with the drift of nature. The drift of nature is excessive production. The poorer we are, the more ill-nourished we are. Sex is the only indoor sport open to us, and large families are produced. It is the poor people that produce large families and not the rich ones.

Now, how can we best bring about limitation of population? We are told that GANDHI is our greatest authority here. He said "I want limitation of population, but the method which we should adopt is the method of abstinence, austerity and self-control." There is no doubt that it is the best method but I should like to ask, whether it be self-control or abstinence or austerity of living by which limitation of population is brought about, is that not an interference with nature? If we do not control ourselves, we will produce more, and if we do control ourselves we will produce less. Well, there is an interference with nature even there, and so far as we are concerned, most of us are human beings striving to be saintly, but have not yet become saints. There is another method which is called the "rhythm method." There are safe periods and there are unsafe periods. In unsafe periods, abstain. In safe periods it does not matter what we do. Well, this method makes out that we can interfere with nature. That is what they tell us. It also recognises that marriage has got its own justification apart from parenthood because we are allowed to use sex for purposes of mutual satisfaction without any expectation of producing offspring. So, here again, there is this method of abstinence for certain periods, but indulgence for certain other periods, and so, this method also is an interference with nature and at the same time admits that marriage has its own value apart from parenthood. That is what it comes to, but here we avoid the application of mechanical and chemical means. We have that next. There again, there is interference with nature and we also have a recognition that marriage has its justification apart from parenthood.

There is a journal called *Science* published by the American Association for the Advancement of Science. That journal points out that scientists are experimenting with an antifertility drug which is to be administered orally which has got all the value without the disvalue of other methods which are now being adopted. Science, I may tell you, will go on advancing and will give us all sorts of methods which are bound to be used for the use of man. All knowledge is a double-edged sword, whether it is atomic energy or whether it is contraceptives. It all depends on the purpose for which this knowledge is employed. If we employ it for preserving health and happiness for medical, scientific, social or economic reasons, we cannot ban it. If we use these methods for illicit gratification of our appetites or for evading the consequences of our acts, it is to be deprecated. So, whether we use it for (a) or (b) depends entirely on the frame of mind or the purpose for which we use it. In this world, there are no absolutes, except the well-being of man. The world is one of perpetual movement. We call it the world of sansara.

St. Paul thought celibacy was the highest ideal but then found that those who were celibates were getting disturbed, disorganized and dis-integrated in their minds. So he said: "It is better to marry than to burn." Instead of burning by the effects of a single life, if our development requires marriage, go and get married.

We know that Gandhi himself was a philosophical anarchist who be-lieved that individuals must be self-regulated, self-controlled; but in view of the circumstances of the world, he acquiesced in social regulations, prisons, police, etc. He taught us to resist evil by non-violence and added, "but if you can't resist evil by non-violence, cowardice is worse than violence. But resistance to evil is essential. Never submit to evil." The ideal is non-resistance, resistance by non-violent means but resistance by violent means is not to be ruled out if we are incapable of spiritual resistance. He made a distinction between what may be regarded as the ideal and what is to be regarded as the permissible.

Now, when we have all these methods, when the Planning Commission has told us, when the leaders tell us that it is essential for us to control increase of population, it is open to us to find out, each for himself, what is best adapted to his own development. I may say, if the purpose is not wrong there is no ethical or spiritual harm done, and it is the purpose which determines the use or abuse of these modern inventions. If a surgeon inflicts pain to heal he is not wrong: if a murderer inflicts pain to kill he is guilty of the greatest crime.

I am not an authority on these matters but I have heard these things talked about and I was trying to think for myself what exactly should be the attitude so far as our country is concerned. This attitude of the ideal and the permissible has come down to us from ancient times. There is a verse which says: "we have the vedic methods, the brahmanical methods of fighting evil with spiritual weapons. If we are unable to do it, we must fight evil with military weapons. Both are permissible, but spiritual resistance is higher than military resistance." That is how the ancient scriptures put it.

Sir SARVEPALLI RADHAKRISHNAN, Kt, O.M., M.A., Litt. D., D.C.L., LL.D., F.B.A., has been President of India since 1962. Dr. RADHAKRISHNAN was Spalding Professor of Eastern Religions and Ethics at Oxford University 1936–1952; Vice Chancellor of Benares Hindu University 1939–1948; Chairman of Executive Board of UNESCO in 1947 and President in 1952; and Chancellor of Delhi University 1953–1962. Dr. RADHAKRISHNAN was Vice-President of the Republic of India from 1952–1962. He is author, among other works, of the Reign of Religion in Contemporary Philosophy (1920); Indian Philosophy (1923 and 1926); The Hindu View of Life (1927); India and China (1944); East and West (1956); Brahma Sutra (1960).

The Population Crisis in India*

by

Ambassador M. C. Chagla

I might refer to three different expressions – birth control, prevention of population explosion and family planning; in essence they mean the same thing. We use them according as to whether we are courageous or timid advocates of the same cause, whether we like to speak sotto voce or shout our faith and our creed from the house tops.

Let us remember how the thinking on the subject has changed in the United States in the last thirty or forty years. There was a time when to mention birth control was considered not respectable. Not only that, it was considered immoral and it was sometimes even illegal. Such a subject was supposed to be discussed in small esoteric circles where doubtful intellectuals and high browed people met to exchange ideas about matters which were not supposed to be the concern by and large of the people of this country. The population explosion which was taking place was hardly heard on these shores. In any case, it was something completely remote and far away.

Birth control or family planning was not supposed to be a necessity here. This was a large and flourishing country with wide open spaces, indeed a truly affluent society. Hunger was no problem, so much so that the real problem was not shortage of food but excess of it with the result that food had sometimes to be burnt and in any case it could always be given away. The threat of Communism had not yet arisen in acute form and people did not have to think of what growth of population meant when it added millions of unemployed, starving and frustrated people to the world. Mrs. SANGER preached her message with a deep insight into the future. As all great people, she had a prophetic vision and long before others she saw the dangers of population explosion, as scientists saw the terrible and ghastly possibilities of atomic explosion.

I would like to look upon this problem of birth control as a human problem, shorn of its technicalities and the impressive statistics which are always brought up when this subject is discussed. Our sympathies are

* Address at Testimonial Dinner in honor of Mrs. MARGARET SANGER, New York, May 11, 1961, marking opening of Conference on the World Population Crisis.

always excited when we hear of disease, famine, epidemic or suffering. We think of death and death is always a frightening thought, although it is the only certain thing in this uncertain world. We are always anxious to fight death and if we cannot succeed in conquering it, we want at least to postpone it as long as possible; and, may I say so, that no country has done more, has shown greater missionary zeal, than the United States in trying to abolish sickness and disease. There are large and important national institutions of research which every day are discovering new and cheaper cures for different diseases. The Government here spends millions of dollars to finance these institutions and support their research. But strangely enough, people here turn away with indifference from the most terrible malady from which humanity is suffering today.

We are glibly told that birth control means prevention of births not deaths, that it is irreligious and immoral to interfere with the ways of Providence, that we must trust a benevolent Providence to look after the increasing population and that God will feed every mouth that is brought into this world.

I wish to say this emphatically that there is no more wicked or cruel belief than this. Today two-thirds of the world's population is underdeveloped and population in those areas is increasing at a faster rate than in developing countries. Is it true that every young mouth in these underdeveloped countries gets sufficient food?

But food is not everything. Even stray dogs on the road find some garbage to satisfy their appetites. If you bring human beings into this world, you must invest them with human dignity. We all proudly believe that man is the lord of creation. If that is so, then he must live according to the stature he has given to himself. Not only must he have food, he must have shelter, he must have education, he must have gainful employment. How many of the children who are being born this very minute will have all these?

By this terrific and explosive increase in population, not only are we bringing into this world children who will never have the minimum benefits and adventages to which every human being is entitled, but we are increasing tensions and conflicts and political problems from which the world is suffering. By uncontrolled population increase we are increasing the sense of bitterness and frustration. We are making people lose faith in democracy and we are jeopardizing freedom and we are exposing millions to the will of the wisp of totalitarian doctrines. It is apt to be forgotten that democracy and freedom do not function in a vacuum. It will need strong hands to maintain them and it is absurd to expect that they can be safe with people whose primary concern is how to fight hunger and how to get at least one square meal a day. It is indeed ironical to build up military bases and enter into military alliances in defence of democracy when you allow the barricades to be overrun by advancing population.

The role of civilization in underdeveloped countries is a subject over which we may well ponder. To my mind, it has advanced only on one front. It has brought about improvement in medical science and public health. It has advanced the age of expectancy of life, it has reduced child mortality. The inevitable result is that more children live after child birth and people live longer than they used to. Civilization has in effect prevented nature from dealing with the increasing population. Nature in her ruthless and amoral way used to redress the balance by plagues and epidemics and men used to help her by having small wars on their own. Plagues and epidemics have gone and small wars have become out of fashion; the only war we want to wage is an atomic war which will solve the problem of population control for all time. But civilization has interfered with nature and having brought great boons to people has refused or has hesitated to play the other role of nature. That role should be to restrict birth by artificial means. In doing so, we are undoubtedly interfering with the laws of nature. But we are not doing this more than when we improve and increase life by means of modern science and technology.

The situation today is that to prolong life has become cheap and easy, such great strides have been taken in medical science. But to prevent superfluous births – a source of great danger and explosive potentially – is difficult and expensive. It is difficult and expensive because we do not attach as much importance to the latter as we do to the former.

Turning to my own country, the increase in population has been immense. In 1911, it was 250 million, in 1951, 356 million and; as the census which was recently taken shows in this year, our population has reached 438 million in the last decade, 1951–1961. The increase has been approximately 25%. The rate of population growth in this decade has been 61% faster than the rate in the previous decade. It is not as if we are not conscious of the tremendous problem these figures pose for us. Our Government has officially supported the policy of birth control. The birth control clinics have risen from 147 in 1956 to 3,000 today. There were 7,823 sterilizations in 1956 and 41,091 in 1960. The sale of contraceptive goods has gone up six times from 1956 to 1958. Contraceptives are given free to people with an income of $60 a month. But all this is not enough.

We have received from the United States foreign aid to the extent of 3 billion dollars since our independence. It was a generous gesture on the part of this country. It was also wise and statesmanlike because this country realized the importance of economic advance in India in a democratic set up. India was trying to demonstrate to the world that a poor underdeveloped country can become prosperous without sacrificing freedom or democratic institutions. But the effect of this aid is, to a large extent, being nullified by the increase in population. Look at what has happened recently. We have just launched our third Five Year Plan. All our calculations and our projects were based on the assumption that in 1961 our population would be 430 million but in the census figures that were published, we found that we had gone wrong because the population was 438 million and not 430 million. Can you imagine what it means to provide food, employment, education to 8 million more people?

It is said that proper and human remedies for overpopulation are not birth control but increase in food production and industrialization. We are doing both but that is not enough. We cannot allow our increase in population to catch up with whatever advance we might make on the food and industrial fronts. All the time we cannot be looking behind us watching the spectre at our heels trying to frustrate whatever we might seek to achieve.

I think there is no public in any country, once its conscience is aroused, which will fight evil with a greater sense of dedication than the public of the United States of America. I want to convince the public that overpopulation is an evil, a terrible evil and it has to be fought with the same zeal with which we have fought maladies like malaria, cholera and plague. I want the national health institutions to carry on research on how to fight this evil, how to find ways and means to prevent this population explosion. We must get the United Nations interested in this global problem. The United Nations has realized the danger of atomic explosion. Let it realize the danger of the other explosion. The atomic explosion may blow up the world, but we can still trust in the wisdom of our statesmen to arrive at some agreement to control atomic armament; but the population explosion which goes on every day and every minute is serious, sinister and malignant. It cannot be stopped by agreement or treaties but only by a great act of faith, followed by a determination to see that the faith is justified by determined and immediate action.

Hon. MAHOMEDALI CURRIM CHAGLA, B.A. (Oxon), Bar-at-Law; High Commissioner for India in U.K.; educated: St. Xavier's High School and College, Bombay, Lincoln College, Oxford; graduated at Oxford in Honours School of Modern History, 1922; President, Oxford Asiatic Society 1921; President Oxford Indian Majlis 1922; called to the Bar, Inner Temple 1922; Prof. of Constitutional Law, Government Law College, Bombay 1927–30; Hon. Secy. Bar Council, High Court of Judicature, Bombay 1933–41; Puisne Judge, High Court Bombay 1941–47; Delegate to U.N.O. to fight the cause of Indians in South Africa 1946; Vice-Chancellor, Bombay University 1947; Fellow, Bombay University; Chief Justice, High Court Bombay, 1947–58, President Asiatic Society of Bombay 1947–58; Chairman, Legal Education Committee 1948; Member, Law Commission 1955–58; delivered Shri Krishnarajendra Silver Jubilee Lecture on Individual Freedom and Welfare State, under the auspices of the Mysore University on August 7, 1954; Governor of Bombay, October-December 1956; Ad Hoc Judge, International Court of Justice, The Hague 1957–60; Chairman, Life Insurance Corporation Enquiry Commission, 1958; Ambassador of India in U.S.A., Mexico and Cuba 1958–1961; Hon. LL.D., University of Hartford, 1959; Temple University 1960; Boston University 1960; Dartmouth College 1960; Hon. Fellow Lincoln College, Oxford 1961; Member, Sikh Grievances Enquiry Commission 1961. Publications: The Indian Constitution; Law, Liberty and Life; the ndividual and the State; An Ambassador Speaks.

The Family Planning Program in India*

India ranks second in the world population next only to China with an area of little more than 2% (2.4%) of the total land area of the world. India has to support about 14% of the world population. If the death rate in India could be lowered to that of the United States of America, the present birth rate unchecked may result in a single century in population five times that of the present population. In 1901, the total population in India was 225 million. The 1961 Census figure is 438 million. The increase during the last ten years has been 21.49%. The anticipated figure in 1976 is 625 million.

IMPACT ON RESOURCES

The demographic situation varies in different States. During the last 60 years the increase differs from over 21.9% in Assam to 51.1% in Uttar Pradesh. There is no doubt that a family planning program must be conducted in all the States in India, but each State requires a different treatment.

The impact of the population problem on resources is alarming. For example the back-log of unemployment at the end of the Second Five Year Plan Period was about 9 million and under-employment was estimated to be 15–18 million. The addition to the labour force during the Third Five Year Plan period may be about 17 million. The plan envisages that the Third Five Year Plan program will provide about 14 million additional jobs. During the last 10 years the increase in the aggregate national income was only about 42% but the increase in per capita income is only about 16%. Strenuous efforts are being made to increase the resources. A large portion of the saving should be diverted to capital formation which should increase productivity and not just maintain old levels.

Public Health measures have led to a decrease in the death rates, especially infant mortality. Death rates have been lowered from 27.4 (1941–1951) to 21.6 (1956–61). They will be still lowered. Expectation of life has also in-

* Release by the Information Service of India. August 1962.

creased. The rate of increasing numbers seem to threaten us to run fast to remain at the present level of living. The Planning Commission has, therefore, stated that "the objective of stabilising the growth of population over a reasonable period must be at the very center of planned development. In this context the greatest stress has to be placed in the Third and subsequent Five Year Plans on the program of family planning...."

MOMENTOUS DECISIONS AFTER INDEPENDENCE

The family planning program launched by the Government of India is really a culmination of efforts of a large number of people over several years. The National Planning Committee under the Chairmanship of Prime Minister NEHRU, formed by the Indian National Congress in 1935, strongly supported family planning. The Health Survey & Development Committee appointed by the Government of India recommended provisions of birth control services but mainly for health reasons. Soon after Independence momentous decisions were taken to raise the standard of living of the people and the Government of India appointed a Planning Commission in March, 1950.

During the First Five Year Plan period family planning emerged as a Governmental program. A great deal of emphasis was given to research. During the Second Five Year Plan period the family planning program was developed as an action-research program on an extensive scale. Efforts were made to set up an organisational base over which to build a fourfold Education, Service, Training and Research program. It was soon evident that emphasis should be on Education and action research. The Central Family Boards were formed in various States. The next step was to form District Committees in each State, with Government of India assistance. Family Planning Officers have been appointed in most States. Some still work part time for family planning in addition to their other duties.

There are three expert committees in the Union Ministry of Health, viz., the Demographic Advisory Committee, the Committee on Scientific Aspects of Family Planning of the Indian Council of Medical Research (which deals with the medical and biological aspects) and the Communication Motivation Action-Research Committee. Ad hoc committees are formed for special subjects like oral contraceptives, the Third Five Year Plan, Competitions and Awards, etc.

SURVEY ON FAMILY PLANNING

In the field of education, an attempt was made to collect information of factors which were responsible for community attitudes, beliefs and behaviour pattern, to identify natural group leaders and use them as channels of communication, and to test and prepare basic materials and methods for the mass, community groups, and individuals. The studies at Raman-agaram and Delhi showed that 70.5% to 75.8% persons were in favour of Family Planning. The Bangalore Study indicated that 32.8% males and 27.6% females knew one or the other methods of family planning. They did not seem to have adequate knowledge of physiology of human reproduction and family limitation. Some studies showed that they did not have a sufficiently strong motivation to continue an initially accepted method. Well designed studies without an education program did not yield the desired results. This led to the formation of the Family Planning Communication Action Research Program.

The Ford Foundation has offered assistance for communication research and training. The general goals of this program are to provide better understanding of the basic factors which influence the acceptance of family planning and the use of this understanding plus the educational knowledge and skills already available to develop a more effective family planning program.

The methods which are being used to promote the movement vary in scope from simple talks with friends and neighbours to group meetings, film shows, advertisements and more elaborate family planning clinic services. Among the methods which have been used one which has appeared to be of a considerable value is family planning orientation camps. After a number of pilot studies with orientation camps which have turned out favorably, the Government of India recently has offered financial help and assistance for the holding of such camps throughout India.

Honorary Family Planning Education leaders have been appointed. Such group leaders help considerably in creating the background of acceptance of Family Planning. They address meetings, arrange group discussions, motivate people, mobilize public opinion and form a network of local voluntary groups in different places to carry the message. They have done a valuable work. The response is enthusiastic and exhilirating. A stage has been reached where such leaders may be appointed at the District level. It is proposed to have voluntary Family Workers (PARIVAR KA LYAN SAHYAKS) in each village.

TRAINING PROGRAM

The training program began with ad hoc courses. There are training centers directly under the Government of India and also regional training centers under the State Government. Touring Training Teams are being posted to each State. They should be fully utilised for training doctors and medical auxiliaries in their respective Stations. The Second Plan was started with 67 persons trained in ad hoc courses. Since 1956, 4103 persons have been trained (October 1961).

In the field of services, a start was made with research of safe periods.

Soon after foam tablets were offered. Now all available methods including sterilization are offered. The decision to accept one or the other methods is left entirely to the discretion of the individual family. The point of view of conscientious objectors is respected and appreciated. The program is developed as a peoples program with Government assistance seeking the co-operation of all parties and religious groups and steering clear of religious, ideological and political controversies. The demand for contraceptives has increased considerably, at one time heavy demands created a shortage in supplies, orders had to be placed abroad in bulk. Their manufacture in the country has been expedited. Foam tablets, jellies and sheaths are now manufactured in India.

The Second Plan was started with 20 rural and 125 urban clinics. By October, 1961, there were 3125 rural and 1024 urban centers where contraceptives could be obtained. The number of rural and urban family planning centers and other medical and health centers giving advice in family planning proposed to be opened up to 1966 is as follows:

| | Regular Clinics | | Other Medical Health Clinics giving advice in Family Planning | Target for Third Plan | Total at the end of Third Plan 1966 |
	First Plan	Second Plan (1956 to 1961)			
Rural	20	1079	1864	6,100	9,063
Urban	125	421	330	2,100	2,976
Total	145	1500	2194	8,200	12,039

At present (1962) the total number of clinics in rural and urban areas is 42,000.

Contraceptives are offered free as well as at subsidised rates. Those who receive contraceptives free, can contribute to a Welfare Voluntary Contribution Box which can be kept in each clinic. Funds thus collected can be utilised for the welfare of mothers and children. All types of contraceptives can be distributed free in rural areas irrespective of income. Sheaths can be issued by non-medical personnel and foam tablets can be distributed through Public Health Nurses, Health Visitors, and Auxiliary Nurses. It has been recommended that the family planning services should form an integral part of the medical, health and welfare services. National Extension and Community Development Organizations are gradually covering the entire country and each block will have a primary health center. In rural areas the clinics are, therefore, being mainly associated with primary health centers.

STERILIZATION OPERATION

The Central Family Planning Board recommended the inclusion of a sterilization operation in the family planning program, on the merit of each case, after careful examination by a qualified doctor, with the consent of both husband and wife. In hospitals and institutions where facilities exist the Government of India have sanctioned extra personnel to strengthen the staff of some of the hospitals directly under them, and the grant of special casual leave, not exceeding six working days to Government servants who undergo a sterilization operation. It has also offered assistance to State Governments to strengthen the staff of hospitals up to the taluk level for a sterilization operation, for training and for medical units.

It is visualised that during the Third Plan facilities for sterilization will be extended to district hospitals, subdivisional hospitals and to such primary health centers as have the necessary health facilities for surgical work. With the help of mobile units, these facilities can be extended further. 7823 sterilization operations (2,333 males and 5,490 females) were performed during 1956. This number increased to 46,265 (31,067 male and 15,198 females) in 1960. The number of sterilization operations conducted since 1956 as per information available is as follows:

	Year	Male	Female	Total
	1956	2,333	5,490	7,823
	1957	3,671	9,859	13,530
	1958	9,072	16,801	25,873
	1959	13,925	21,797	35,722
	1960	31,067	15,198	46,265
Oct.	1961	18,184	6,616	24,800
Total		78,252	75,761	154,013

RESEARCH IN VARIOUS FIELDS

Research in medical and biological fields, demography and communication, is in progress. The Director, Indian Council of Medical Research has requested all members of the Advisory Committee on Scientific Aspects of Family Planning, Officers in charge of the Indian Council of Medical Research Institutes and Universities, Administrative Medical Officers and Medical Associations and Societies in India to send research schemes for consideration on (1) development of suitable oral contraceptives either synthetic or extracts from indigenous plant material, (2) development of more effective local contraceptives, (3) follow up of sterilization cases both male and female to investigate possible after-effects in such cases, (4) investigation of the mechanism of spermatogenesis and ovulation, fertilization and cytological studies, (5) other studies in the physiology of human reproduction such as fertility, and (6) development of studies of human genetics and (7) investigations in sterility.

The much debated subject of the use of progestational steroids has also been considered. An Expert Committee on oral contraceptives makes recommendations to the Government of India regarding the action that may be taken for their research and use in the country. This Committee has made various recommendations. Demographic Training and Research Centers have been established. The Ford Foundation and the Population Council, New York is giving valuable assistance. The effect of the program on birth rates is not likely to be evident still for a number of years. But a study of Contributory Health Scheme Clinics patients of Delhi by the Demographic Research Center, Delhi University, has shown that the pregnancy rate for non-contraception-use period ranged between 62 and 66; for contraception-use period without clinics service was 35.2 and for the post-clinic contraception-use period it was 10 for the diaphram and jelly and 12.6 for all the prescribed contraceptives. This shows that by using contraceptives under clinic guidance, it is possible to reduce expected pregnancies by 80%.

ENCOURAGING PROGRESS

The Family Planning Program, implemented during the First Two Plans, which may justifiably be considered as a preparatory phase for a more extensive approach beginning with the Third Plan, provides "for (a) education and motivation for family planning, (b) provision of services, (c) training, (d) supplies, (e) communication and motivation research, (f) demographic research and (g) medical and biological research." The program as approved, involves a total outlay of $10.5 million. Various other aspects are also being investigated:

  (i) Development of studies of human genetics.
 (ii) Studies in the physiology of reproduction.
(iii) Development of more effective local contraceptives.
(iv) Development of suitable oral contraceptives.
 (v) Follow up of sterilization cases, both male and femal, to investigate
     possible after-effects in such cases.

The progress made so far is significant and encouraging, but it is just a beginning. The results achieved are not only due to the efforts of the Governmental and non-Governmental Organisations but to a great extent due to the acceptance of the program by the people. To make family planning a way of life of the people requires a great deal of further effort and participation of the people, which is gradually increasing. The task of planning and development is enormous. But as stated by the Planning Commission, "Given a sense of urgency and a spirit of dedicated endeavour, it is fully within the capacity of the nation to achieve the goals it has set for itself."

Address at the Conference on the World Population Crisis New York, May 11, 1961

by

SAID HASAN
Ambassador of Pakistan to the United Nations

Population explosions become a problem and a matter of concern when the economic and social resources of a country are unable to cope with increasing numbers. I shall attempt to demonstrate the nature and dimensions of the problem by reference to my own country, Pakistan.

The provisional figures of Pakistan's second decennial Census, issued on 4th March, 1961, showed that the population of the country has now reached a figure of 93.8 million, as compared to 75.86 million in 1951. Pakistan accordingly ranks at present as the sixth most *populous* nation of the world after People's Republic of China, India, USSR, U.S.A. and Japan.

The most alarming feature of the Census figures is the fact that the population of the country has increased by 23% over the last decade, i.e., at an average of 2.3% per year. This is a much higher rate than we had anticipated. The rates of increase during previous decades had been much slower – 4.9, 6.7 and 8.8% during the decades 1901-11, 1911-21, and 1921-31 respectively. If the trends revealed in the 1961 Census continue, then the population of Pakistan, which doubled itself in 60 years between 1901-1961, is likely to repeat the performance in half the time from 1951. The rapid increase in population growth has been brought about by a fall in death rates. Improved health measures have played a large part in this regard – a role which is likely to be enhanced in the years to come. If this happens, the growth rate will be further distorted and the population curve given a sharp upward incline. The population of Pakistan which increased by 4, 5, 6, 7 and 8 million during the decades 1901-11, 1911-21, 1921-31, 1931-41 and 1941-51, and by 18 million during the last decade, would experience a much faster rate of acceleration. In fact, according to an expert U.N. estimate, the population of the country, given the existing levels of fertility and a moderate to rapid decline in mortality, would reach 150.8 million by 1981 – a catastrophic level.

The 1961 Census figures show that the density of population for the whole country is 257 persons per square mile as compared to 208 in 1951. The Eastern wing of the country has, however, a density of 922 persons per square mile as against 136 persons in West Pakistan, and 256 persons in the metropolitan area of Karachi. Ten out of the seventeen districts of East Pakistan show a density of more than 1000 per square mile, while two districts lead with a density of 1761 and 1683, respectively. For a predominantly agricultural economy, these figures are amongst the highest in the world.

The figures of population have importance only in relation to economic data. In Western countries the growth of population is not a problem. In the U.S.S.R. there is a shortage of man-power. West Germany imports labor from Italy. But in undeveloped countries with a per capita income of around $100 a year as against $2000 in U.S.A., $875 in Britain and $550 in the U.S.S.R., these differences tell a story of human misery which the world of today cannot ignore. For one thing, the peoples of the underdeveloped countries no longer accept poverty as a part of inexorable destiny. On the one hand, they have reached the very edges of starvation; on the other they are today exposed to the ideas and aspirations of peoples who live in the more developed countries. New vistas have opened up before them giving shape to their suppressed longings. The age of despair imposed on them for so long by colonial rule and domination has given way to an age of expectation and demand. This phenomenon presents a unique opportunity and a great danger. It could be harnessed to the accomplishment of the great constructive tasks that face less developed countries. On the other hand if the economic gulf between the advanced and the under-developed countries keeps steadily widening as at present, the resultant frustrations could only heighten world tensions. We are living in times when conflicting ideologies, economic no less than political, are competing for the allegiance of men. It is a matter of concern to us that the challenge implicit in this situation, so pregnant with peril, has not as yet received that wide understanding and acceptance which is its due.

It is in this context of the need for rapid economic development that the population problem must be viewed. Viewed as such, an accelerated rate of population growth has manifold consequences for an under-developed country, such as Pakistan. It is reflected, in the first place, in a chronic shortage of food supply. Pakistan which was a food surplus country with a favorable balance of trade on commodity account has passed within the last decade to sizeable deficits on both counts.

There are also other costs which a country passing through a phase of high birth and low death rates has to pay. There is, for instance, the cost of supporting minor children under 15, who do not by definition contribute to the national product. The percentage of the population of such children, which is about 20 in countries like Great Britain, is as high as 40 in Pakistan. This adds to the total burden of dependency. Whereas in the United States the dependency burden does not exceed about 43% of the total population, in my country approximately 47% of the population is supporting a de-

pendent population of about 53%. This population also suffers from a high
rate of morbidity. Not only is the average life expectancy low, but those
who live suffer in "productive efficiency" due to weak health and malnutrition. Between 1/3rd and half of the total population is believed to be
undernourished and prey to a high disease rate, necessitating in turn
enormous expenditures on medicines, treatment and health services for
both individuals and public authorities. Needless to say that such expenditures are a high depressing burden on the limited resources of the country.
Furthermore, high population pressure requires concentration of resources
on food crops for sustenance rather than on export crops for investment
surplus. Even where cash crops are raised, the economy as a whole becomes
overwhelmingly dependent on primary agriculture, which gradually tends
to make the economic framework rigid and causes excessive pressure on
land. Increasing pressure on land results in sub-division and fragmentation of land until broken into small, uneconomic units. By and
large, agrarian economies get adjusted to a "low-income equilibrium,"
and develop a reactionary philosophy of life that suspects change,
resists reform, and tends to perpetuate a state of poverty. Over-populated peasant economies like these come to a breaking point when improved health preservation methods and facilities, like D.D.T. spray,
B.C.G. vaccines, cholera and typhoid injections, or anti-malaria operations, are introduced. Then, either these reforms and improvements
have to be rejected or some kind of development program becomes a
necessity. If the choice falls on development, the way is often found blocked
because, after accounting for all current expenditures and the bearing of
the heavy burden of social overhead, little or no surplus resources are
available for reinvestment.

The rate of population growth is one of the foundations of economic
planning, as a net increase in per capita income can only be calculated after
account has been taken of the increase in numbers. Pakistan's First Five
Year Plan, which had hoped to increase the national income to an appreciable extent by 1965, assumed a rate of 1.8%. The growth rate of 2.3%, revealed
by the 1961 Census figures, reduces considerably the margin of benefits
expected and adds immeasurably to the difficulties of the Plan. The Plan
provided for an increase of 20% in national income over a period of five
years. This would have given an annual average of 4%, which after allowing
for the assumed increase in population would have resulted in an increase
of 2% in per capita income. This rate of increase in per capita income was
considered to be the minimum required for achieving the stage of self-
sustaining growth, or in the language of Rostow, of the take off, in the
course of the next ten to fifteen years. The Plan also assumed that the
proportion of working population to total population would remain
constant during the Plan period and that the labor force would increase
from 28.3 million in 1960 to 30.8 million in 1965, that is by 2.5 million. It was

recognized that a very serious effort will have to be made to create enough job opportunities to absorb this increase in the labor force. In view of the data furnished by the 1961 census, the basic assumptions of the Plan about the size of the population and its rate of growth have turned out to be un-realistic. A greater effort than was envisaged in the Plan would be necessary to achieve the target of increasing the per capita income at an average annual rate of 2% and to provide employment opportunities for the in-creasing labor force.

To appreciate the problem we are facing it is necessary to get some estimate of the present rate of investment in the under-developed countries. Out of a total $120 billion income, all the under-developed countries combined together are able to devote approximately $6 billion to capital formation. To this may be added a yearly investment of $3 to $4 billion from all outside sources, private or public. The total amount of capital thus made available makes possible an annual average increase in the national incomes of the less developed countries of about 3%. Over against this figure we must set our statistics of population growth. A growth rate of 2.3% means in the case of Pakistan a net increase in national income of about 0.7% per year, or a net increase in personal living standards of about 0.45% per person.

What can be done to relieve the situation? The under-developed countries are engaged almost without exception in a massive struggle to improve their economic conditions. The struggle is hard, and what they can achieve through their own efforts is limited. Although not much information is available in this regard, a capital-output ratio of 3 : 1 would seem to be a fair approximation for most under-developed countries, including Pakistan. This means that in order to achieve a 3% increment, about 10% of the nation-al income has to be saved and invested. That is, with the rates of population growth of the order under consideration, Pakistan would need to invest between 6% and 9% of its national income just to hold its own after it has reduced death rates. All gains in per capita income must come from still higher levels of investment. Few under-developed countries have a net savings rate in excess of 10% of national income. In fact, the domestic savings rate in Pakistan has been estimated to be barely 6% to 7% at present. This is a reflection of the low margin between income and consumption in the country, which makes the capacity for savings practically non-existent.

These considerations show that the problem of economic development and the problem of population are essentially inter-related; that they are, in fact, two sides of the same equation. In order to achieve rapid economic and social development and reach the "take-off" or "self-generating" stage of economic growth, a combination of both accelerated technological progress and retardation of population increase is necessary. Population control is not a panacea. It cannot by itself solve the problem of economic development. As has been said, every man is born not only with a mouth but also with a pair of hands. A vigorous population can be a great asset to a developing country. What we are aiming at fundamentally is the conversion of a population load from being a liability to being an asset. It is the failure to do so which gives, as we have seen, varying rates of population growth a differential impact on prospects for economic development...

It is worth noting that a conversion of the nature I am speaking about is a direct function of the state of technological progress and know-how. When MALTHUS wrote his "Essay on Population" in 1798, European populations had reached the upper limits provided by the then available productive processes. Income had become stagnant, reacting almost exclusively to harvest fluctuations. Population pressure had forced wages down to subsistence, and economies towards a stationary state (where by definition savings and capital accumulation = zero). With the advent of the Industrial Revolution, which was at this time in the offing, the picture changed completely. How much it changed is reflected in the writings of the neo-classical school of economists. Technological progress during the 19th century was so remarkable that pessimism and concern over population growth came to be replaced by optimism, and emphasis shifted from growth to distribution and from macro to micro-economics. Today, the cycle has turned full circle again, and population problems are back in the lime-light of contemporary growth economics. One cannot help wondering, however, if we are not at the threshold of another New Age, the Atomic Age. The harnessing of atomic energy for the service of man may well lead to a massive and revolutionary break-through in technological progress. If this happens, the population problem, as we know it, may come to have a completely new dimension.

But we have to live with facts of life as they are. We are extremely backward technologically and we have a system of free enterprise and of complete individual freedom. The problem of population is therefore a grave one for us, and it is in recognition of this situation that my country has adopted a positive population policy as an essential part of a long-term development planning. The policy of the Government of Pakistan involves a major effort to spread practices of adaptative fertility. Fortunately, we have not encountered theological objection to family planning in Pakistan. Family planning will need a basic change in the social attitudes and traditions of our people, particularly in the villages where 85% of the people live. This is a complex and gigantic task which has to be approached from many different directions. The classical economists, such as MALTHUS, SENIOR, JOHN STEWART MILL, felt that literacy and education were of the greatest importance in changing social attitudes towards child bearing. MILL pleaded, in particular, for an extension of female education and also for the political, social and economic emancipation of women. Modern writers on the subject have emphasized the importance of the inter-action of various social processes, such as, industrialization, urbanization, social mobility, the introduction of mass media of information and entertainment, improvements in personal standards of living, etc. The fact is that such social processes are developing, acting and inter-acting continuously in any given economy: we intend to strengthen these trends. More immediately according to information available, it seems that given literacy, family planning may well catch the imagination of the people of Pakistan as a solution to a common and pressing problem.

Pakistan's Second Five Year Plan has strongly advocated a policy of family planning and has made provisions for a family planning program. The program does not envisage compulsion in any manner, but only the stimulation of motivation on a country-wide basis. It emphasizes widespread education and the provision of the necessary medical and other facilities. Family planning clinics will be established in government hospitals, dispensaries and maternity centers. The medical personnel such as doctors, nurses, health visitors and midwives will be trained in family planning methods. Publicity and information programs will also be organized. Research will be undertaken on the attitudes of parents for a large or a small family and on the acceptability and effectiveness of different methods of birth control.

Like the sun and the rain which shine and fall on the just and the unjust alike, the munificence of the United States of America benefits the friend and the foe and the indefinable in-between alike and equally. The United States feels a great concern for the welfare of the peoples of the underdeveloped countries and her multi-billion annual program of foreign assistance bears testimony to her solicitude. It is inevitable that arising out of this fabulous activity, there should be some quixotic ideas also and one hears of an experiment – what may be called Operation SHOW-CASE. It is intended to prove in one country the benefits of economic development coupled with democratic institutions. It is an amusing concept of a large continent at a standstill, sitting hand-folded to see the outcome of this experiment before determining its future allegiances. The concept has no doubt been drawn by persons who believe that Asia is even more static in its ways than it actually is. Asian countries in fact are not static at all. For evil or good, they are moving on rapidly and individually in different directions. They may flounder and meander for a little while, but they will reach certain goals and these goals will be determined by the pressures on their lives. One such great pressure is of population. If their population can be educated and trained so as to add to the national product and be an instrument of well-being of these nations, and if this can be done without compulsion, the goal will be a life of freedom and democratic institutions. But if the population of countries cannot be educated and trained without force, these countries will be driven to use methods of regimentation, because one thing is certain that no country can just be adrift and survive, and for their survival a full use has to be made of their labor force which is their greatest asset.

Hon. SAID MOHAMMAD HASAN, Ambassador of Pakistan to the United Nations, New York. Educated at Punjab University, Lahore, Aitchinson Chief's College, Indian Military Academy, Dehradun. After several years service in the British Indian Army from 1934 onwards, he was Indian Government Trade Commissioner in Teheran from 1944 to 1947, and served as Councellor in Pakistan Embassies in Iran (1947–1949), Turkey (1949), U.S.S.R. (1949–1951). In 1952 he became Deputy Secretary of the Ministry or Foreign Affairs and was Joint Secretary between 1952 and 1956. Before being appointed Ambassador to the United Nations, he was Ambassador to Turkey from 1957.

Population Growth and its Effects on Economic and Social Goals in The United Arab Republic

by

HANNA RIZK

The history of the Arab States in the last decade is characterized by a series of revolutions which brought in radical changes in the long established ways of life. Immediate causes of these revolutions and the means of bringing about the desired change may have been different in each country. However, the basic factors underlying them are identical. These are three-fold: The desire to achieve and maintain independence; realization of a higher level of material welfare for the masses and narrowing the wide social and economic gaps between individuals so that an integrated and strong society may emerge.

In each country where the revolution had won its first round politically, programs of action were launched to push the revolution into its economic and social ends. The experience of the United Arab Republic in this respect may reflect in general the pattern of goals, achievements, and problems of the whole area.

In the U.A.R. extensive measures have been taken since the outbreak of the revolution in 1952 to realize a decent level of living for all the people. These measures included redistribution of land,[1] reduction of land rent, and raising peasants' wages. The High Dam Project at Aswan and programs of land reclamations are under way to provide an additional two million acres for cultivation.

A number of new industries, including iron and steel plants, fertilizer plants, electric power and tire production have been established. Old industries have been enormously expanded. New laws were passed so that laborers may share in the net profit of the industries.

Programs of sanitation facilities and health improvement have been implemented. In the last 10 years the number of doctors has doubled, beds in government hospitals have tripled [2] and the supply of drinking water to the rural population has quadrupled.[3]

1. This law promulgated in 1952 and modified in 1961 restricting land ownership to 100 acres per family.
2. Basic Statistical Data. Misr Printing Office, 1962, p. 204.
3. Ibid, p. 208.

These revolutionary measures were necessitated by the acute economic problem of the country in which the per capita income was £.E. 35 ($98) in 1952 and the per capita share of the crop area in the year was 0.46 feddan.[4] The extent of success of these modernization programs in achieving the desirable social and economic objectives has been affected by the rate of population growth and the associated changes in the size and structure of population.

POPULATION GROWTH

Egypt passed through an era of modernization during the 19th century. The process was slow and intermittent all through the century. However, rudimentary improvements in security and economic conditions made possible a slow but steady increase in the population which grew from 3 million to 10 million during the century.

The annual rate of growth has continued at the rate of 1.2% from 1900 until the beginning of the Second World War. In the intercensus period 1937–1947, the average annual increase shot up to 1.9%; then up to 2.4 in the following decade, and up again to 2.6 in the last 3 years.

The average annual increase in population has been jumping in the last three decades from 170.000 in the first decade to 304.000 in the second decade and 540.000 in the third. Last year, the population increased by 760.000.

Since its first census in 1882, Egypt has quadrupled its population. If the present rate of growth is allowed to continue, the increase will be six fold by 1980, and the total increases in the century 1880–1980 will be matched in the following 20 years when the population will inch upward to 70 million by the year 2000.

The rapid growth of population and the imbalance in its age structure have occurred when the old balance between deaths and births was radically upset.

The Death Rate

Registration of births and deaths was not made compulsory in Egypt until 1912 and therefore there are no vital statistics for earlier periods. However, several estimates of death rate indicate that health conditions were extremely poor until the end of the 19th century. Malaria, dysentery and typhoid were endemic diseases. It was not unusual in the epidemic years to have a death rate of 70 per 1000 and an infant mortality rate of 500.[5]

The slight improvement in the economic and social conditions of Egypt in the early part of the 20th century reduced the frequency of epidemics

4. The Population Problem in Egypt, Report of the Economic Sub-Committee, Cairo Mondial Press, Cairo, 1962, p. 10–11.
5. GREATLY, ALI: Population and Economic Resource in Egypt, Misr Printing Office, 1962, p. 36.

and induced a definite decline in death rate. From 1912 to 1945, death rates ranged between 26 and 29 per 1000 of the population.

Significant measures have been taken for health improvement and advanced sanitation since 1923[6] when the country achieved the greater part of its independence and assumed responsibilities for its internal affairs. These measures made possible the prevention of epidemics. Between 1945 and 1960 the crude death rate declined from 28 to 16 per 1000, marking an improvement of 43% in 15 years. In the same period infant mortality was reduced from 153 to 110[7] per 1000. In 1945 the number of deaths was 512,000 while in 1960 with an increase of the population of 42%, the number of deaths was 74,200 less.

The reduction in infant mortality is reflected in an increase in the life expectancy at birth. Twenty years ago men could expect to live only 37 years and women 39 years. Today life expectancy is about 50 and 52 years for male and female respectively. This change has important implications for future population growth. The female age group 20–29 in 1980 will be twice as many as its number in 1960, and three times as many as in 1947.

The Birth Rate

Population growth in the United Arab Republic, as in most other developing countries at the present time, challenges the concept that reduced mortality automatically brings with it reduced fertility. Programs of modernization aiming at economic development and health improvement, have reduced death rates markedly in a short time. It is doubtful, however, if they have changed to any considerable degree marriage customs, attitudes and social values which throughout the centuries have served to maintain high birth rates. The frequent epidemics and the general high death rates, which prevailed until a few decades ago, required the highest possible fertility for the existence of the family and the nation.

A few years ago an empirical Study of the fertility patterns in Egypt was initiated and supervised by the Permanent Council for Public Services. The study included 6,067 women "ever married" from selected urban, semi-urban and rural areas. This study reveals the following facts:

I. a. In urban areas there was a pronounced decline in fertility rate among wives of university educated husbands, a definite but lesser decline among wives of secondary educated husbands, and no difference in fertility between wives of the primary or elementary educated and illiterate husbands. The number of live births per 100 "completed" (women 45 years of age or more) wives of each of these groups was found to be 394, 578 and 750, respectively. The same pattern is

6. The Unilateral declaration of independence of Egypt with four reservations was made in February 1922.
7. Basic Statistical Data, Central Committee for Statistics, Cairo 1962, p. 202.

true with respect to "incomplete" (women under 45 years of age) wives in these educational levels.

    b. In the rural sample where education is limited to primary and elementary schooling, there was no difference in fertility rate among wives, whether classified by education, occupation or religion. The rate of live births per 100 "completed" wives ranges between 760 and 790 in the three surveyed villages.

II. The study points to two causes which may have contributed to the differential fertility in the urban area, namely, birth control practices and mean age at marriage. Among the university-secondary educated group, 39% of the "completed" wives and 51% of the "incomplete" wives practiced birth control. In the primary-elementary educated, 19% and 23% practiced control in the "completed" and "incomplete" groups respectively. Among illiterates, 9% practiced control in these two groups. Age at marriage may have contributed slightly to the differential fertility. The average age at marriage was 22 years among the university, 19 years among secondary and 18 years among preliminary-elementary and 17 among illiterate.

    In the rural area wives scarcely practiced birth control. Only 3% of the literate and 1% of the illiterate ever made an effort to limit their families. The average age at marriage was 17 for the literate and 16 for the illiterate in the rural area.

III. The wives who practiced birth control among Socio-economic Class I had markedly lower fertility than the non-practicing. In Class II the fertility was barely lower among controllers than noncontrollers. In Class III the rates of the two groups are reversed with controllers having 803 births per 100 wives, while noncontrollers have 700 live births. It is evident that the controlling group in Class II and III are those whose fecundity allowed them to have excessively large families and whose social and economic circumstances made it difficult for them to achieve their desire to control.

It is apparent from the study that family limitation in Egypt has been fairly well established among the top educational class in the urban areas and has spread slightly among the secondary educated class but has been almost unknown or ineffective among the illiterate and the lower educational groups.

THE SOCIAL AND ECONOMIC CONSEQUENCES OF POPULATION GROWTH

The slower response of the birth rate to modernization has upset the old balance between birth and death and caused an unprecedented, rapid growth in population. During the last 25 years the population increased by 70%. Population density in the inhabitable area has jumped from 450 persons to 724 persons per square kilometer.

    The impact of population growth on the economic and social goals of the Revolution is already raising serious questions. In the last census the rural population constituted 65% of the total population. Therefore, two persons produce food stuff for three. Since the beginning of the century, irrigation projects have been in progress to increase the cultivable and the crop areas. During the last 60 years the increase in the cultivable area was 16% and that in the crop area was 50%. In the same period the population increased by 160%.[8] There is a heavy and increasing density in rural areas

8. GREATLY, ALI, Population and Economic Resource in Egypt-Misr Printing Office, 1962, p. 91.

in spite of the urbanization processes. While the percentage of rural population has decreased from 75% in 1937 to 62% in 1960, the actual number of
rural population has increased in the same period from 12 million to 16
million in 1960.[9]

The pressing need for expansion in agricultural land induced the High
Dam Project which will cost £.E. 200 million, for its building and an additional sum of £.E. 300 million, for land reclamation and irrigation projects.
When this great work is completed in ten years, Egypt will have added
2 million acres to its present cultivation area of 6 million. However, at that
time the rural population will have increased by six or seven million, and
therefore all the additional output will be hardly enough to maintain the
present levels of living.

During the last 10 years new industries have been established and old
industries have been expanded to alleviate the pressure of labor on land.
The increase of labor force in all industries which employ 10 persons or
more has been 53,000 from 1952 to 1960,[10] making a total employment of
326,936 persons. It is estimated that the annual addition to manpower is
180,000 which is 27 times the average number absorbed annually by industries.

The rapid growth of population is also reflected on the per capita income.
The national income has been estimated at £.E. 502 million in 1945 and
£.E. 1100 million for 1960. The per capita real income has been stationery at
the low figure of 32.5 Egyptian pounds from 1935 until the present time.

The increasingly large proportion of dependents to the total population
requires the diversion of a heavy investment from the national income for
services programs. In the last 10 years, the Ministry of Education expanded
its primary and elementary education. It added 949 schools, 34,953 classes,
and 6,695 teachers, and thus it was possible to double enrollment and
accomodate a total number of 3,056,000 students. To achieve this goal, the
Ministry had to raise its budget in one decade from £.E. 33 million to
£.E. 102 million. However, in spite of this great effort, there are still 38% of
children of compulsory school age (6-12) without schools.

The continuous stream of emigrants from villages to cities, under the
economic pressure, has created grave problems in housing, traffic and
public utilities. Cairo has increased its population in the last 20 years by
250% and Alexandria by 220%. A housing program had to be implemented to
meet the situation. The expenditure in the last two years amounted to
£.E. 50 million. In october 1962, the Minister of Housing announced that the
housing program for the next five years will cost £.E. 440 million.[11]

The high rate of population growth involves the problems of a higher
level of needed investment to achieve a given per capita output.[12] The

9. Basic Data-Control Commission for Statistics 1962, p. 20.
10. Basic Statistical Data, The Central Statistical Commission – 1962, p. 102.
11. Al Ahram Newspaper, Cairo, October 16, 1962.
12. COALE, ANSLEY J. & HOOVER, EDGAR M., Population Growth and Economic Development in Low Income Countries, Princeton University Press, Princeton, 1958, p. 20.

increasing proportion of dependents to the labor force has reduced the availability of capital for new investment.

There is no evidence yet that the fertility rates may decline in the near future. There is expectation that death rates will continue to decline particularly among children under 5 years of age due to the planned development of child welfare centers and expansion of medical service. The techniques of death control have been widely and effectively used, but the techniques of birth control have been limited to a small fraction of the urban population.

FAMILY PLANNING PROSPECTS IN U.A.R.

The history of family planning as a movement in Egypt took its roots in 1937 when a group of University professors organized a public forum to discuss necessity of family planning for the achievement of the happy family. In the same year this group was able to obtain a Fatwa (pronouncement containing an interpretation of a point in Islamic law) that birth control is permissible in Islam under certain conditions.

The next step forward was the formation of the National Population Commission toward the end of 1953. Under the auspices of the Commission, the first four planned parenthood clinics were opened in 1955. Today there are 14 clinics in urban areas and 14 in rural areas.

Until last spring the movement made little or no progress. The total number of visits to the clinics has not exceeded 6,000 in any one year, one-third of whom wanted treatment of sterility. Television, radio, and the press, as well as religious leaders, discussed the subject of birth control in a manner which confused the public.

The movement gained momentum last May when the Egyptian Medical Association organized a Conference on Social and Medical Aspects of Family Planning. The Press gave the Conference full publicity and emphasized the urgent need for birth control.

In the same week a decisive victory was gained for the cause of family planning when President NASSER announced in the National Charter that "The Population increase constitutes the most dangerous obstacle that faces the Egyptian people in their drive towards raising the standards of production in their country in an effective and efficient way." He added that "attempts at family planning with aim of facing the problem of increasing population deserve the most sincere efforts supported by modern scientific methods."[13] He added later that family planning necessitates changing the attitude of fatalism to that of responsibility.

These statements had strong repercussion all over the country and gave an impetus to a campaign led by the Press for Birth Control.

The Conference of the developing countries on the Problems of Eco-

13. Draft of the Charter (English Version) Information Department, Cairo May 1962, p. 53.

nomic Development held in Cairo last July, recognized the problem of Population Growth. In his opening address President NASSER stressed that "many of us are faced with the problem of increasing population at a speed which all but engulfs the rate of economic development... Indeed the problem of overpopulation in the whole world justifies the appellation given it by certain research specialists in the field who drew a parallel between the destructive power of the 'population explosion and that of the Nuclear devices.' While all efforts are being exerted to prevent the destruction caused by nuclear device explosions, it is imperative that even greater efforts be exerted to counter the problem of the lower standards of living which will occur universally as a result of overpopulation in excess of world food resources". The problem was recognized also in the Cairo Declaration which included the decision made by the Conference.

The first woman minister in Egypt, Dr. HICKMAT ABU ZAID, Minister of Social Services, assured me in a recent message that the Ministry considered family planning an important means for realizing a balance between the resources and the population, and that "spacing pregnancies would protect the health of mothers and the children and make possible a sense of security in the family."

The recognition of the population problem by the authorities is essential for action on a nation wide scale. However Egypt faces an acute population problem which needs undelayed action. Undiminished effort must be made on different fronts. Changes in family customs, values and attitudes must be sought through programs of education, religious teachings and health services. Research programs in the fields of demography, economics and medicine must be launched for the scientific study of the related aspects of the population problem. The program must go side by side with the efforts of industrialization and modernization for realizing greater per capita output.

This heavy task may be impossible to achieve without full international understanding and cooperation. The threats of the consequences of rapid population growth to national and international peace and prosperity are obvious.

HANNA RIZK, B.A., M.A., Ph.D., has been Director, Division of Public Services, and is now Vice-President of the American University in Cairo. He received his education in part at the American University in Cairo, The University of Chicago and Princeton University.

Communist China and the Population Problem

by

ROBERT C. NORTH

Human beings, in order to survive, must constantly adapt themselves to their environment – or alter the environment to meet their needs or to suit their purposes.

Whether a given population or society adapts relatively more or alters its surroundings relatively more will depend to a considerable degree upon the "hostility" or "friendliness" of the environment and also upon the level of organization the people have achieved when they confront it.

If the environment is extremely hostile the people will be engrossed in extracting a minimal living from it and will not easily accumulate the spare energy necessary for organizing themselves sufficiently to make large changes in their surroundings. On the other hand, if the environment is extremely benign, with fruit falling into the lap, so to speak, the people may perceive no need for changing the world about them, and consequently their efforts at self-organization are not likely to go beyond the minimal demands of the community.

Human beings living somewhere between such extremes of environment will be continually challenged by what appear to be the shortcomings or undesirable characteristics of the world immediately about them. Over the years and decades and centuries they will try to "reorganize" the environ- ment to suit their purposes, and these efforts, in turn, will stimulate them to devise more effective and efficient forms of self-organization.

This self-organization will tend to be political insofar as it involves relationships that are essentially interpersonal – and economic insofar as it involves the allocation and exchange of resources. The physical alteration, the re-shaping, the reorganization, and the transformation of the environ- ment, on the other hand, tends to be considered technological rather than political or economic.

Whether the alteration of the environment is relatively easy or relatively difficult will depend to a large degree upon the distribution of certain vital resources such as the proximity of fertile land and a supply of water or the sequential arrangement on the earth's surface of timber (or coal), a navigable river, and deposits of iron.

It is probable, therefore, that people in areas where the resources are easy – but not too easy – to obtain and conveniently – but not too conveniently – distributed will be stimulated to greater organizational effort than people elsewhere.

Whether a given environment is essentially "hostile" or "benign" will depend to some extent, of course, upon the ratio between the resources and the numbers of people. If the population is too small, there will not be the manpower to manipulate the environment, and if the population is too large, a mass of the population will be poor and there will be neither the reservoir of human energy nor the "capital" or minimal stockpile of resources necessary for reorganization of the surroundings.

It should be clear, however, that a highly organized people operating from a highly organized – or "reorganized" – base environment can move into an extremely hostile environment, a desert, for example, and reshape it. Also, a relatively unorganized people in a hostile environment can borrow organizational techniques and organized resources (tools, capital, and the like) from a highly organized people with a highly organized base.

Much of the world-wide conflict today concerns first of all the allocation of the world's resources and also the means by which relatively unorganized people in relatively "hostile" environments shall be equipped to alter and even transform, their surroundings.

In this conflict there is not much disagreement on the technical level, but in the political and economic spheres the controversy is heated and sometimes violent. What systems of allocation and exchange will bring about the necessary technological transformation most effectively and efficiently, and what patterns of interpersonal relationships are needed or best suited to ensure the economic and technological undertakings? It is over these issues that much of the cold war is being fought.

There is one problem, however, that appears to be political, economic, and technological all at once, and that is the population issue.

If the numbers of people are too large for the environment as it stands, what is the most effective course of action? Can the imbalance be redressed by a reorganization of the environment? In some circumstances the answer is clearly affirmative. A population problem in an arid region, for example, can frequently be solved by a large-scale importation of water.

But is it always possible to alter the environment rapidly enough and continuously enough to meet the needs of a population that grows rapidly and continuously? Or is it sometimes necessary – for sheer lack of resources or even space – to think about limiting the population? Can such an exploding population alter the environment to meet its requirements, or must the population adjust within certain limits of the environment?

This is a question which confronts many people in the world today, including Communist China, and it is in Communist China, perhaps, that the issue has been associated with the most bitter political controversy.

The usual Marxist-Leninist view has always been that a country or a region is "over-populated" only because of a gap between the technological level of the society and the appropriateness and effectiveness of the political and economic systems.

In capitalist society, therefore, the population difficulty is seen by communists as inevitably rooted in the conflict between capitalist production relations – how the economic system is organized – and the labor or productive force. This clash between capital and labor must inescapably give rise to a state of relative underemployment and over-population. The only solution for the population problem of a capitalist country is the seizure of state power by the proletariat.

But what about the population in a generally non-capitalist, pre-industrial society such as China?

The Bolshevik revolution in Russia was scarcely a test of Marxist-Leninist population theories. Even today the resources and vast spaces of the Soviet Union are being used by only about two hundred million people, and the problem is more of man power shortage than of over-population. It was the communist seizure of power in China that put Marxism-Leninism face-to-face with the challenge of a vast population.

At first the Chinese Communists seemed intent on controlling their rate of population growth, but then a number of ambiguities appeared in the official attitudes, and in time a loud and spirited debate ensued.

In dealing with Chinese population problems, the communists have identified two incompatible approaches – the Malthusian and the Marxist. According to Malthusian theory one might expect the needs of a rapidly expanding population to increase at a greater rate than production and supply. "But Marxists," according to WANG YA-NAN, the President of Amoy University, "do not approach the problem in this way. Marxists admit that in a certain stage of society the relatively large or small population produces a definite influence over the improvement of the economic life or the development of the economy of the society. But they first of all affirm that human labor, at any stage of society, remains the most valuable wealth, or the source of wealth."

The question hinges, according to WANG, on the capacity of the social system to make rational utilization of and arrangements for its existing labor power. Capitalism and private enterprise "waste" human labor power and thus render a given population "excessive." Under such circumstances a "population problem" is frequently inescapable. This injurious social system, moreover, and particularly the evil influences it leaves behind, cannot be wholly eradicated all at once, and hence a certain transition period is inevitable in a pre-industrial society such as China.

During this development from capitalism to Marxist-Leninist-Maoist socialism "millions and tens of millions of the laboring masses" may have been basically rid of poverty and exploitation, but it was inevitable that some of the disabilities of the earlier period of capitalism and imperialism should persist and that the people would have to endure great difficulties and sacrifices including even unemployment and severe food shortages. Yet these sacrifices were of a wholly different and fundamentally optimistic nature since they paved the way for new and unprecedented progress and development.

The surplus of population, according to the communist viewpoint, had been a dangerous phenomenon under conditions which existed previously in China. In those days vast numbers of people were unemployed, impoverished and destitute. There was wide-spread suffering from pestilence, and the mortality rate was high. Under such circumstances the rapid growth of the Chinese population had been a serious menace.

But the communist victory in China had created a wholly different situation, according to WANG YA-NAN. For once they had achieved power, MAO TSE-TUNG and his colleagues had been able to alter the proportionate shares of the different sectors of the economy. In short order the state sector was rendered significantly larger than the private sector, and the industrial sector was increased relative to the agricultural sector. Productivity could now be raised, and the living conditions of the people – even the living conditions of a population that was rapidly expanding – could be steadily improved. It was possible, now, to abolish unemployment, poverty, vagrancy, hunger, pestilence, war and untimely death and to put the increasingly numbers of people into productive work.[1]

Early in 1957 a controversy emerged between Chinese Communist spokesmen, on the one hand, and non-Party scholars and intellectuals, many of these "population experts" of many years standing. While confessing certain "errors" of the past and disassociating themselves from Malthusianism – or even the "New Malthusianism" of which they were charged – these non-Party intellectuals insisted that the rapidly rising population in China was still a serious problem. In presenting their arguments, these men differed somewhat among themselves, but it was clear that all of them were taking serious issue with the Party policy on population.

"In pre-liberation days I wrote many articles on the problem of the population of China," confessed WU CHING-CH'AO, professor in the China People's University and a member of the China Democratic League. A sociologist, WU had taken his Ph. D. at the University of Chicago years

---

1. WANG YA-NAN (President of Amoy University), "The Post-Liberation Population Problem of China," Ma Ke Su Chu I Ti Jen Kou Li Lun Yu Chung Kuo Jen Kou Wen Ti (Marxist Population Theory and China's Population, December, 1956), *Extracts from China Mainland Magazines (ECMM)*, No. 84, May 27, 1957, p. 2.

before. "When I go over these articles today, I immediately find that many of the points I brought up before were incorrect." [2]

Wu had maintained in the days of the pre-communist era that "the large population of China is the main cause of the poverty of the majority of people in China." Now it was clear, however, that poverty and the large population had been two different phenomena, and that there was "no connection whatsoever between them," or – if there had been any connection – it was entirely "accidental." The truth of the matter was that unemployment and poverty and misery and untimely death had been the consequence of the social system, and not of the expanding population.

Wu CHING-CH'AO now realized that he had been guilty of another error. "...I dreamed that China's birth rate would one day drop considerably... This is an idealist point of view. Experience teaches us that never in an industrialized nation has the number of population been reduced as a result of the practice of birth control." [3]

"The cause of my errors," Wu CHING-CH'AO admitted, "was that I did not study the problem from the standpoint and method of historical materialism." [4] As a consequence of this carelessness he had "covered up the crime of the reactionary ruling class and had confused the masses about the nature of the revolutionary struggle. The basic task is not to achieve birth control, Wu conceded, but to increase labor productivity – though "too high a birthrate," he insited, would impede capital accumulation even under socialism.

Honesty forced Wu CHING-CH'AO, after confessing his errors, to come back to the birth rate problem. On the one hand, China should undoubtedly strive to accelerate socialist industrialization so that the country's technical level could be steadily raised. On the other hand, however, it was inescapable that the rate of population increase should be kept down so that the number of people asking for employment should be reduced gradually. "In introducing birth control to China," he asserted, "our goal is to reduce the present birth rate of 3.7% to 1.7%." [5]

Having blurted out the unpleasant truth as he saw it, Wu hastened to disassociate himself from any taint of Malthusianism.

"There are among us those who are inclined to make criticism which is unwarranted," he complained. "The moment they hear people talk about birth control, they consider it an attempt to promote New Malthusianism ... [which] seems to have something in common with our policy. This view is incorrect... There is a fundamental difference between us and the New Malthusianists. In the first place, the New Malthusianists generally

2. Wu CHING-CH'AO, "A new Treatise on the Problem of China's Population," Hsin Chien She (New Construction), No. 3, March 3, 1957, translated in ECMM, No. 78, April 15, 1957.
3. Ibid., p. 1.
4. Ibid., p. 2.
5. Ibid., p. 12.

take a pessimistic attitude toward agricultural production, constantly worrying about food shortage for the population. We are not at all pessimistic about this point ... even if the present rate of population did not drop, we could still produce more than enough to feed our people. We promote birth control, not for the shortage of food."

The purpose of promoting birth control, according to WU CHING-CH'AO, was to improve the health of mothers and babies and to "make our production fall in line with the basic economic law of socialism and the law of development according to ratio and plan, so that we may fulfill without any difficulty the general task of the transition period." [6]

At the July 3, 1957 meeting of the fourth session of the First National People's Congress in Peking Dr. MA YIN-CH'U, a distinguished Chinese economist with a Ph. D. from Columbia University and the President of Peking University, issued a paper entitled "A New Theory of Population."

While carefully disassociating himself from the Malthusian approach, MA asserted that the biggest contradiction in China was between over-population and an inadequate supply of capital and identified the large population of the country and its rapid rate of increase as major problems and chief obstacles to economic development.

In order to improve living conditions, MA declared, it was necessary to increase the supply of capital as a prerequisite to production expansion. "As we have a big population," he pointed out, "our consumption expenditure is enormous and not much national income can be saved for capital accumulation, which must be distributed among many production departments. Thus the amount of capital a department can receive is too small." [7] China's vast population had become a stumbling block to the country's industrialization. The need was to bring the Chinese population under control in order to lower the ratio of consumption expenditure to capital accumulation.

Unless such measures were taken, MA warned, the drive for industrialization would move forward only at the extreme expense of the people, who might well retaliate by violence – as the people of Poland and Hungary had done, "...if we do not try to tackle the problem of population as soon as possible, the kindness we have rendered the peasants will inevitably be translated into disappointment and dissatisfaction. Although they will not follow the footsteps of the Poles and Hungarians, they will give the government a great deal of trouble." [8]

Communist spokesmen were quick to take issue with the proponents of birth control – even though the government had made extensive, though largely ineffective, efforts of its own to reduce the rate of population growth.

6. Ibid., p. *16*.
7. MA YIN-CH'U, "A New Theory of Population," Peking, Jen-min Jih-pao, July 5, 1957. Translated in *Current Background*, No. 469, July 25, 1957, p. *3*.
8. Ibid., p. *8*.

The "rightists," according to the Party, had intentionally taken advantage of the population problem "to oppose the Party and socialism." They had seized the problem as "an excuse for the restoration of the bourgeois sociology as well as of capitalism." These "rightists," in fact, "were really old hands in class struggle and, therefore, could avail themselves of this problem in the pitch of class struggle and political struggle." [9]

The theory which considers population a fundamental problem of the society, according to government and Party spokesmen, had been one of the most powerful weapons used to paralyze the revolutionary consciousness of the working class. Imperialism and the reactionary factions in China had used the problem all along, and now it was proving useful to the new group of rightists who wanted to prove that China, by the fact of its great population, could not be built into a socialist country. [10]

Perhaps the rightists would "craftily attempt to deny" their intent to cretae ideological confusion and to make the masses lose confidence in socialism and industrialization. "We have," they might say, "committed theoretical mistakes at most. Our intention is good. We act so only to popularize birth control." Yet the outcome of the rightist arguments, Party spokesmen declared, was to assert "that China is over-populated now and cannot be built into a socialist country." Beyond this, ". . . you yourselves understand clearly that birth control cannot be carried out immediately. Even though we may enforce it throughout China right now, in a perfectly strict way conformable to our ideal, it will take effect only after more than a decade." [11]

Perhaps the technical difficulties associated with attempts at population control lay at the heart of the Party attitude. Perhaps they were trying to hide a program that had failed, to make an asset out of a discouraging reality.

In any case, according to the Party viewpoint, the rightists wanted to take a capitalist road out of the population difficulty. (Even the Party admitted that there was a difficulty.)

"Opinion differs as to how the population problem of our country can be tackled and solved," an early 1958 Jen Min Jih Pao article asserted. "One kind of view is 'leftist.' Those who maintain this point of view think that our large population and high rate of population growth is positively a good thing. From their point of view, the birth control campaign is making mountains out of mole hills. When tackling problems and laying down plans they seldom based their thinking on the population of 600,000,000, but

9. Li Pu, "The Rightists Shall Not be Permitted to Take Advantage of the Population Problem for Political Scheming," Peking, Jen-min Jih-pao, October 14, 1957. Translated In Survey from China Mainland Press (SCMP), No. 1644, November 4, 1957, p. 2.
10. Ibid., p. 2.
11. Ibid., p. 3.

are often concerned with absolute magnitudes and speed with no regard whatever for reality." [12]

Opposed to this viewpoint, Party spokesmen charged, the rightists "think that our huge population and high rate of population growth are absolutely a bad thing. From their point of view, all difficulties may be attributed to the size of our population... They pin their hope on an unrealistic birth control program aimed to keep the population from going beyond the 600,000,000 mark." [13]

Both the "leftist" and "rightist" viewpoints were condemned as erroneous. Ideologically and practically both were absolutist from the Party standpoint. "To them a huge population is either absolutely good or absolutely bad." [14]

"Our Party has pointed out that our large population is a good thing..." one spokesman recalled. "But our Party has also pointed out the difficulties arising from a big population. These are difficulties of development, and we are already prepared for overcoming these difficulties." [15]

The correct Party way to solve the population problem was by means of a basically multi-pronged approach: "The concrete content of this way is to encourage planned birth-giving and propagandize and popularize birth control, and to make unified arrangements for production, labor and pay or allotment on the basis of 600,000,000 million people. The most fundamental means, however, is to develop vigorously our industrial and agricultural production and increase our social productivity." [16]

During the transition period the People's Republic – while encouraging birth control – must expand industrial and agricultural production as rapidly as. possible; allot rewards "according to labor," that is, lengthen apprenticeships and avoid excessive pay to young men in order to discourage early marriage and large families; and make unified arrangements for raising the level of technical capability in order to hasten the achievement of socialism.[17]

"The venerable Doctor MA always claims himself to be different from MALTHUS," two critics charged at a Seminar on the History of Chinese Revolutions at Peking University. "And we sincerely hope that he is not a Malthusian. Yet, in his masterpiece "The New Population Theory," the venerable Doctor MA did really and actually disseminate MALTHUS' views. This is indeed to be regretted." [18] Like MALTHUS, MA had perceived the population problem, as the "root of all social problems."

12. WANG CHO, "Way to Solve the Population Problem in China," Peking, Jen-min Jih-pao, February 1, 1958. Translated in SCMP, No. 1721, February 28, 1958, p. 2.
13. Ibid., p. 2.
14. Ibid., p. 2.
15. Ibid., p. 3.
16. Ibid., p. 3.
17. Ibid., p. 4.
18. CHOU CHIA-PEN & CHIANG CHUNG-HUA, "Comments on Ma Yin-chu's 'New Population Theory'," Peking, Kuang Ming Jih Pao, April 19, 1958. Translated in SCMP, No. 1763, May 2, 1958, p. 6.

The central problem, as the Party saw it, was this: "As our country is densely populated and has a weak economic foundation, can we rely on our own strength to build up socialism? Or can we rely on our own strength to guarantee a high rate of development of productivity in society?" [19]

A large population would be not only an outstanding, but also an advantageous characteristic of China with the potential for "generating a tremendous energy for the building of socialism." [20] But the bourgeois rightists, hitherto having nursed "an inveterate hatred" of the working people, did not miss an opportunity "to curse" the large population of China. Previously these mischief makers had held the large population responsible for evils actually emanating from imperialism. Now, hiding behind a new phraseology, they were insulting and slandering the Chinese people by contending that it would be exceedingly difficult to build socialism in the face of a rapidly expanding population.[21]

There was one basic difference between Malthusians and Marxists. "They [the Malthusians] regard the population problem as the fundamental problem underlying the solution of all the problems relating to human society: only if birth control is practiced, population is reduced and poor people are restrained from producing more children, then all the problems will vanish and society can make smooth progress. We believe that such a view is incongruous with the materialist conception of history. The fundamental problem of the development of human society lies in whether the nature of production relations meets the demand of productivity." [22]

Dr MA had failed to perceive these realities.

"Our point of view is dramatically opposed to his," wrote MIN TZU, putting forward the Party viewpoint a few weeks later. "We believe that it is a very good thing for China to have a large population. Since the liberation we have made extremely brilliant achievements in economic and cultural construction. The reason why we can do this is inseparable from the great creative labor of the 600 million people." [23]

"As all of us know, the national income is the material wealth newly produced by the toiling people in the process of production," MIN TZU wrote. "When the 600 million people give full play to their production enthusiasm, it will increase the national income considerably. When the absolute amount of national income is increased, it is possible for us to speed up capital accumulation, which in turn will guarantee the develop-

19. Ibid., p. 5.
20. CHU PAO-YI, "Refutation of Wu Ching-ch'ao's Slanderous Remarks Against The Chinese People on the Population Issue," Tsai Ching Yen Chiu (Finance and Economics), No. 1, February 15, 1958. Translated in ECMM, No. 128, May 12, 1958, p. 17.
21. Ibid., p. 17.
22. Ibid., p. 20.
23. MIN TZU, "It is Good To Have a Large Population," Ch'i Hua Ching Chi (Planned Economy), No. 6, June 9, 1958. Translated in ECMM, No. 142, Sept. 15, 1958, p. 25.

ment of the national economy, increase our consumption to a definite extent, and thus improve our people's livelihood." [24]

What should particularly be pointed out here, according to MIN TZU, is that "the labor of the broad masses is itself a kind of investment."

"Is a large population really contradictory to mechanization and automation?" asked MIN TZU. "MA's thesis was based on the following point: "What it took a thousand men to do before can now be done by, say, 50 after mechanization and automation. Then, what shall we do with the 950 persons who have been laid idle?" Obviously, he took mechanization and automation as the factor responsible for over-population and unemployment. Thus, to avert over-population and unemployment he thought it necessary for us to slow down mechanization and automation. This is an extremely erroneous theory which inflexibly applies to socialist society the law of relative over-population applicable under capitalist conditions." [25]

In contrast to the limited productive possibilities of capitalism, MIN TZU asserted, a socialist society would open up wholly new productive relations with the capacity for "infinitely broad" development of productive forces. "...the large population in China is not in contradiction with mechanization and automation, but instead may speed up mechanization and automation." [26]

"Why is there so big a difference between MA YIN-CH'U's view and ours?" MIN TZU asked. "This is because he took the bourgeois stand, observing problems in the light of metaphysics and through a non-realistic approach. Thus he failed to reflect upon the objective actuality, a fact which led his discussion in the wrong direction." [27]

Labor productivity, according to MIN TZU, is determined by the number of workers and output per worker. If we see more workers employed, but lose sight of their larger output, the conclusion is bound to be that the labor productivity tends to be lower with more workers employed. If we are aware that in this socialist society industrial and agricultural development is speedy, and becomes even speedier than the growth of population, we may understand that socialism can raise productivity to a high level." [28]

Any apparent similarity between Party policy and the New Population Theory was illusory and false, according to the Party viewpoint. "Our efforts to publicize and popularize birth control and to control appropriately the rate of increase of population aim at abating the difficulties confronting us in the large-scale economic construction resulted from the large population and the inherent economic backwardness. However, we

24. Ibid., pp. 25–26.
25. Ibid., p. 27.
26. Ibid., p. 28.
27. Ibid., p. 32.
28. Ibid., p. 29.

never regard the control of the rate of increase of population as the prerequisite for the construction of socialism. On the contrary, we believe that our 600,000,000 population is the capital for socialist construction, and we must rely on the mass of hard working and gallant people to erect a magnificent edifice of socialism." [29]

The official Chinese Communist attitude was summed up by LIU SHAO-CH'I, who made it clear that the population of China – in line with Marxist-Leninist-Maoist theory – was expected to transform the environment rather than to adapt itself through a limitation of its numbers.

"We have a population of more than 600 million," LIU told the Second Session of the C.C.P. Eighth National Congress on May 5, 1958, "and our Party has ties of flesh and blood with this vast population. By relying on this great force we can or soon can do anything within the realms of human possibility." [30] The vast population was an asset and not a liability. Man – Chinese man – need not limit his numbers. Chinese man could do anything.

LIU admitted that "for the time being" the people were economically poor and "culturally like a clean sheet of paper." But his colleague, MAO TSE-TUNG, had already described well the true implications of these circumstances: "Poor people want change, to work hard and to make a revolution. A clean sheet of white paper has nothing written on it and is therefore well suited for writing the newest and most beautiful words on it and for drawing the newest and most beautiful pictures." Precisely because the people were poor and unsophisticated, LIU maintained, they would exert the vigor to transform their environment into a proper place and find ways for developing its productivity faster than the needs and demands of the increasing numbers of people.

In mid-1962 these optimistic attitudes toward population were abruptly altered.

With the faltering of the Great Leap Forward, Chinese Communist leaders fell back on a "campaign against early marriages" and the discouragement of too many children in the early years as oblique approaches to the problem of birth control. The minimum age for marriage, according to the Marriage Law, was twenty for men and eighteen for women. "From a medical point of view," it was asserted, these ages were the absolute lower limit for "physical and intellectual growth" and "psychological well-being." [31] Later marriages were encouraged, and unmarried young people were especially cautioned against premature unions motivated by

29. WANT TSO & TAI YUAN-CHEN, "Criticism and Appraisal of the "New Theory of Population," Ching Chi Yen Chiu (Economic Research), No. 2, February 17, 1958, Translated in ECMM, No. 128, May 12, 1958, p. 5.

30. LIU SHAO-CH'I, "The Present Situation, the Party's General Line for Socialist Construction and its Future Tasks," NCNA, Peking, May 26, 1958. See Current Background, No. 507, June 2, 1958, p. 24.

31. "Early Marriage is Harmful, Not Beneficial," Canton, Nan-fang Jih-pao, May 15, 1962. Translated in SCMP, No. 2757, June 13, 1962, p. 11.

"bourgeois affection" and similar emotions rather than by the requirements of society. [32]

Under the new Chinese Communist policy "family planners" – themselves under attack only a few years ago – were also warning young wives against endangering their health and the effectiveness of their work by having too many children in the early years of marriage.[33]

In view of the total problem, however, these measures seemed scarcely adequate.

It remains to be seen whether, objectively, the Chinese Communists will be capable of their Herculean task or whether the plans of Liu, Mao and their colleagues emerge only as "most beautiful pictures" on a clean sheet of paper. In the meantime a bitter race continues between efforts to raise production, on the one hand, and the exploding population on the other. It is difficult to foresee a satisfactory outcome: with every advance – in food production, in sanitation, in housing – the population takes a further leap. And with each discrepancy between accomplishment and demand the society will be subject to further stresses and strains – no matter what the nature of the governing system.

ROBERT CARVER NORTH, Ph.D., has been Professor of Political Science, Stanford University, since 1962. He is author of Moscow and Chinese Communists, Kuomintang and Chinese Communist Elites; coauthor of Soviet Russia and the East.

32. "A Problem that Deserves Consideration by Unmarried Young People," Peking, Chung-kuo Ch'ing-nien Pao, May 10, 1962. Translated in *SCMP*, No. 2745, May 24, 1962, p. 15.
33. YEH KUNG-SHAO, "What is the Most Suitable Age for Marriage," Peking, Chung-kuo Ch'ing-nien Pao, April 12, 1962. Translated in *SCMP*, No. 2745, May 24, 1962.

Japan's Population: Miracle, Model, or Case Study? *

by

IRENE B. TAEUBER

I

The spectacular story of the decline in Japan's population growth continues with that regularity in the extraordinary which has characterized the country over the past hundred years. Death rates are low, but so are the birth rates. Growth continues slowly, but only because the age structure is inherited from a period when birth rates were higher. Official views remain pessimistic – no longer because of excessive growth, however, but because growth itself may cease late in the century and might then be replaced by a decline that eventually could reach 10% a generation. Quiet inquiries are already being made concerning the pursuit and the timing of policies to increase birth rates.

Feelings of wonder merge into awe as one watches this transformation in an Asian country. The Japan whose industrial potential was presumably destroyed only 17 years age has rates of economic growth that exceed 10% a year. Present economic targets involve a doubling of national income within a decade, together with a shift of 2 million people away from agricultural occupations. Already the limited land provides most of the rice needed for 95 million people, and hybrid varieties, improved fertilizers, and mechanization threaten to add food surpluses to Japan's many problems of foreign markets. There is no problem of surplus population here, though, for the movement off the land is so massive that in 26 of Japan's 46 prefectures the population declined between 1955 and 1960. The Tokyo-Yokohama metropolitan area contains 15.8 million people, that of Kyoto-Osaka-Kobe 10.2 million.

There are, of course, unanswered questions about this fabulous tale. In itself that is not surprising; periods of pessimism and grandiose delusion have succeeded each other in Japan's history. Projections of Japan's future

* Reprinted by permission from *Foreign Affairs* of July, 1962. This article is copyrighted by the Council on Foreign Relations, Inc., New York.

now are probably as hazardous as they were in the past; and we see today just how hazardous the earlier ones were, for it may be stated categorically that no students in or outside Japan predicted either the sharp drop in the birth rate or the high rate of economic growth. We study the Japanese phenomena, though, not because we know the answers but because Japan demonstrates the fact of Asian modernization and raises questions about the relevance of her experience for the billion or so people in Asia today who are approximately at the stage were 35 million Japanese were a century or so ago. It is in this context that it becomes particularly worthwhile to look briefly at what has happened in Japan's modern century and to raise questions that have not yet received, in Japan or elsewhere, the attention they deserve.

II

In the years from the Meiji Restoration of 1868 to the late 1930's, Japan seemed to be a perfect illustration of the classic assumptions about the interaction of demographic and economic factors – that is, birth and death rates declined as industrialization and urbanization proceeded. In the middle decades of the 19th century, population growth, if it occured at all, was slow and irregular. Then early economic growth was followed by a population increase. The concentration on the land remained unchanged as peasant sons and daughters beyond those needed for replacement moved from agricultural jobs to nonagricultural jobs in the cities. Death rates declined slowly, for incomes were low, nutrition was inadequate, and sanitation deficient. Birth rates also declined, initially in the urban areas and among the upper occupational and the educated groups, eventually throughout the nation. In the years from 1920 to 1940, fertility declined steadily in practically all prefectures, rural as well as urban.

The rate of the population increase was low: from 1872 to 1940 it never exceeded 1.5% a year. Yet over the decades this slow growth produced a massive total increase. Population became a national concern. In 1872 the total was 35 million; by 1940 it had more than doubled to 71 million. It seemed probable that the population would continue to increase throughout the 20th century, and that population problems would become more rather than less serious.

The pattern which emerges is a decline in birth and death rates in association with advances in industrialization, urbanization and education. The resulting population growth was never high; the social and economic problems produced were not major hazards to modernization.

Is this, then, the pattern that can be expected or imitated in other Asian nations? The answer is definitely in the negative, whether we base our conclusions on demographic, economic, or social factors. Japan's early modernization occurred prior to the availability of DDT and the antibiotics and consequently her death rates were high. To have reduced them substantially would have required major investments in public health and sanitation, in improving working conditions, and in raising nutritional levels. If she had made these investments, it is doubtful whether economic growth could have occurred as rapidly as it did, since on the one hand the rates of savings would have been curtailed sharply, while on the other the more rapid population growth resulting from reduced death rates would have required a major expansion of employment opportunities. If larger proportions of sons and daughters had survived in the rural areas, the exodus to the cities would have had to be much greater in order to prevent pile-ups of people on the land. Furthermore, increased consumption would have reduced the rural savings that contributed so substantially to urban development.

The conditions under which Japan achieved her economic and social development do not correspond to the situation today in the under-developed nations, where the "revolution of rising expectations" is a para-mount fact. There was universal education in Japan, but it included in-doctrination to accept one's role in life and one's duties to the state. Economic modernization took place in compartments : hand labor and traditional ways persisted in agriculture and small industries, while advanced technology was limited to those sectors related to international markets and military power. The state concentrated its resources on industrialization, expansion and power; it assumed no responsibilities for individual and family welfare.

A more serious question as to the relevance of Japan's experience lies in the fact that the population increase and the industrialization occurred in company with a drive for geographic expansion and political power. The advances of empire and the wars that led from easy victory in 1895 to costly defeat in 1945 need not be summarized or evaluated here. What does need to be asked is whether economic and military expansion is an inevitable con-comitant of modernization in a country where land is limited and people are many. Whatever the answer, it involves both the economic realities associated with population increase and the interpretation of those realities by makers of national policy. In Japan, the pressure of an increasing popu-lation was the major argument for expansion. Was it a genuine factor in forming the beliefs and decisions that led to militarism, imperialism and, finally war? Or was it simply used to support policies and actions that could not be properly defended on other grounds? One need not elaborate on the relevance of these questions in any assessment of the future of Japan's colossal neighbor on the mainland.

The last great period of Japanese expansion began with the movement into Manchuria in 1931. The military losses were slight, the presumed achievements substantial. Once they had conquered North China and achieved the goal of an Asian Co-Prosperity Sphere, the Japanese saw their population problem in a quite different light – now it was one of insufficient numbers. Japan's net human losses as a result of the Pacific war were limited by the fact that intensive efforts had been made to increase birth rates and reduce death rates.

Losses were nevertheless severe, for Japanese forces were often isolated in the islands of the Pacific and on the Asian mainland with little food and no medical supplies; and many civilians also died, particularly in the incendiary raids on cities. Total defeat and total surrender meant the liquidation of the colonial empire and the imperial structure. Some 7 million Japanese were returned to a country where cities had been devastated, industrial plants destroyed, and transportation disrupted.

The Japanese people and economy were so seriously injured that demographers forecast high death rates and a declining population. In fact, however, a rapid restoration took place, for the Japanese are an educated and disciplined people and the military occupation was both humanitarian and constructive. So while pessimism reigned and the ghost of MALTHUS hovered near, families were reunited, new families were formed, and a baby boom developed. And death rates dropped rapidly.

In 1947, the birth rate was 34.3 for each 1,000 of population, the death rate 14.6. In 1948 and 1949, birth rates were about 33, death rates below 12. The rate of growth rose above 2% a year for the first time in Japan's history. In numerical terms, births remained about 2.7 million a year while deaths declined from more than 1.1 million to less than 950,000. The natural increase was 1.5 million in 1947, 1.8 million in 1948 and 1949. Both the occupation authorities and the Japanese Government foresaw a soaring population. General MACARTHUR barred Mrs. SANGER and suppressed an American report on the natural resources of the country; the Japanese newspapers joined in the excitement; and birth control became a topic of conversation throughout Japan.

The most influential factors affecting population growth were not demographic. Revolutionary changes came in ways which were in some cases expected, in others rather weird. The Emperor became a man, like other men. Women became the equals of men – in the constitution – and the family system lost legal sanction. There was land reform. Many owned land, but few owned enough to live from its products. Primogeniture was abolished, and with the vanishing security of the eldest son went that of the family in perpetuity. A commission of the Diet recommended both contraception and emigration as government policies to help solve the population problem, but the Diet, which is democratically elected, ignored the report.

In this chaotic situation, the racially conscious Japanese worried that the unfit were multiplying and that the country's biological stock was deteriorating. Prohibitions adopted during the war barred sterilization as well as induced abortion. But in September 1949, the Diet revised the eugenics protection law so as to legalize sterilization and abortion for specific reasons, and it permitted contraceptive services in health centers. Proponents of contraception within and outside Japan were jubilant. They looked forward to a limited use of sterilization and abortion for eugenic reasons along with an extensive use of contraception for family planning.

Japanese ethics did not condemn abortion; the country's medical personnel were numerous and its technology was quite adequate for adapting scientific advances to the field of fertility control. Selected physicians received instructions and the public was informed as to when abortions should be performed. Operations were conducted under aseptic conditions, and the use of penicillin was routine. Since they were performed under medical insurance plans, the cost to patients was not a problem. The number of abortions reported moved swiftly upward, then more or less stabilized at something over a million a year. The government health services, alarmed at the threat to health presumably posed by such widespread resort to induced abortion, began actively training doctors, nurses, and midwives to give contraceptive advice.

These actions of the Japanese Government and people are still topics of controversy on many grounds, but the facts of the decline in fertility are demonstrable. The birth rate tumbled from 28.3 per 1,000 population in 1950 to 17.2 in 1957, and then remained approximately at this level. The death rate declined from 10.9 per 1,000 population in 1950 to 8.3 in 1957 and 7.6 in 1960. The population continues to increase, but at a slowing rate and with declining annual increments. If the birth and death rates of the last several years continue, the population will eventually decline.

Are we to assume that this rapid decline in Japanese vital rates in the last decade and a half will now serve as a model for the rest of Asia? Again the answer is negative. The Japanese who have achieved the low death rate and birth rate of a modern people are themselves modern. Their economy is industrial, their residence metropolitan. Education has been compulsory for more than three-quarters of a century; school attendance at the elementary level has been almost universal for more than half a century. Families have strong motives to limit the numbers of their children, and they do so.

No; Japan's experience is not directly transferable, for the conditions that were associated there with slow natural transitions of industrialization no longer exist in Asia. In Japan, industrialization and urbanization were aspects of a single process of economic growth; industries expanded and cities grew; the migration to the city was movement to a job – or, for a girl, to marriage. In contemporary Asia, great cities have grown without an adequate economic base. Some are products of economic failure; surplus people from the rural areas move to cities where jobs are insufficient, housing and amenities improvised, and schools are inadequate. The stimulation for mobility upward, the motivation for limiting the size of families, the aspiration for one's children – all are lacking. What is to be expected now in a Saigon, a Djakarta, or a Seoul cannot be equated with what occurred earlier in a Tokyo or an Osaka.

III

The great significance of Japan to Asia is the fact that Japan exists as it does – industrial, urban, modern, a "have" nation with a "have-not" background. Asian pride in the sprawling neon-lit expanses of Tokyo seems to begin in Istanbul and increases in depth across the continent. Among the sophisticated and the unsophisticated alike in many if not all the Asian countries, there is a deep interest in how Japan achieved the demographic breakthrough to completed modernization within a decade. Group after group visits the Institute of Public Health to study Japan's Government-sponsored activities in the field of contraception. In Tokyo, throughout Japan, and at scientific meetings elsewhere, private conversation turns to that topic which no government, either in Japan or in other Asian countries, will mention approvingly in public – induced abortion.

The only direct Asian imitation has occurred in the Peoples Republic of China, where visiting consultants on a friendship tour were queried unofficially, and where the law announced soon thereafter was almost a replica of that in Japan – although this is acknowledged neither in Tokyo nor Peiping. Other Asian countries are interested in Japan's pool of medical personnel as a possible source for technical assistance in their own family-planning programs. But there are limitations, since the Japanese Government obviously could not send abroad physicians who are specialists in induced abortion, nor could other countries accept them if offered. Neither would Japan admit officially that approval of contraception and the establishment of major public health facilities to spread its practice came only after the birth rate had been reduced dramatically by a nationwide resort to induced abortion.

Analysis of the steps in Japan's early development could nevertheless be helpful to planners in other Asian countries. Japan long ago made education through six grades compulsory for boys and girls alike, in rural areas and in cities. Did the resulting universal literacy and widespread elementary education lead to declining birth rates among village people? There were extensive household industries in Japan and small factories increased in number in rural areas. Was this a factor in reducing birth rates, or did it result only from industrialization in the large cities? Or, again, what were the levels and the changes in birth rates in those urban areas where families worked in their own homes under conditions of stability as great as those in the peasant village? Were these families "urbanized"? Were education, upward mobility, and the small family characteristic among the migrants themselves or only among the children of migrants? For a time at least, Japan has achieved solutions to problems of poverty and population which presumably are inherent in the ancient cultures of the rice lands of monsoon Asia. The quantitative record is long and diverse, and descriptive materials are plentiful; analysis of them might yield clues as to how to induce social change and declining birth rates among other crowded peoples.

Japan's experience in recent years contradicts the prevalent assumption that the lethargy of traditional societies of the East prevents rapid social change. Japanese culture has been persistent but ever changing. The values and institutions of the village society were aspects of this culture, and they sanctioned early marriage, large families, and a veneration for the lineage and property rights of elder sons. Yet the values and the institutions of the great cities and the modernizing villages of today are also aspects of this culture, and they sanction delayed marriage, small families and an emphasis on personal responsibility and achievement. At different times the values of the Japanese culture approved families of quite different sizes, and changes often came swiftly. There were alternatives, in Japanese culture, to demographic doom, and it may be presumed that there are such alternatives in other cultures. The projection of Japan's past into the future has never yielded a description of that future. The Japanese transformation occurred in a period of continuing advances in science and technology, and the changes which they brought were unforeseen. The importance of this fact to the rest of Asia is apparent.

IV

Today the problems created by rapid population growth are widely realized and even more widely discussed. Many people in many sectors of our diverse culture, with its differing traditions and customs, believe that something should be done. There is no concensus, however, for others believe that the doing would be unethical, unwise or simply ineffective. Given a consensus as to the desirability of taking some action, there still would have to be a selection among many possible lines of activity, and this would involve intricate considerations of international propriety. But, even assuming that we overcome our scruples on this score, is effective action in this field feasible? Would our policy be viewed favorably in other countries? Would any policies that we might adopt prove successful in slowing rates of population growth among the peoples of Asia and Africa? The difficulties in these continents seem minimal, moreover, as compared to those of Latin America, especially if family planning were included as an essential aspect of the social modernization that is demanded by the Alliance for Progress.

Glances backward in history or outward across the world provide few answers concerning policy and action in the population field. The areas that are developing today present problems that are new in their magnitudes and their urgencies. Almost the only relevant experience at our disposal has been in Japan, which had no announced policy to reduce birth rates, but which took measures that profoundly affected them. The fundamental lesson learned there merely corroborated a fact that was obvious: population policies concern or impinge on religious and ethical systems, values and the conflict of values, institutional tensions, political and ideological identifications, aspirations for strategic advantage, rationalizations for power drives, and many things more. Overt encouragement or sponsorship of the policies of other governments in this complicated and delicate field therefore requires the most careful assessment of conditions in each specific case – if, indeed, the occasion should arise when such sponsorship would be other than presumptuous on our part.

The decision as to U.S. policy is not therefore resolved, for what is in view is not our sponsorship but our cooperation or assistance – in personnel, training, facilities and the provision of means. The basic need is not to find a U.S. policy for the population problems of other countries but a U.S. policy for the cooperation in population policies that other countries themselves have adopted – or wish to adopt. Our critical foreign-policy decision therefore involves a solution of our own internal difficulties and hesitations with reference to population policies in general and birth control in particular. Our dilemma is posed by the deep, divergent religious beliefs and the disparate cultural and social values of our people. It will not be resolved simply or quickly if it is posed in terms of harsh alternatives.

Among American Negroes, birth rates are substantially higher than they were in prewar Japan. The associated problems of limited education, low incomes, high fertility, disorganization, and delinquency are as real for us as for the Japanese. And however we may estimate our international obligations, we cannot deny our responsibilities for the Navajo on the reservations. A positive approach to the world's population problem, then, requires that we view the many related problems within our own society with the same frankness with which we approach those of other countries. We have the responsibility for whatever actions are needed in our own country, just as others bear it in theirs. And we should remember what our experience in Japan has taught us: that the fundamental problems and policies in the population field may not be demographic in nature, but social, political, and economic.

Finally, we should do well to bear in mind that forecasting in this field has been notably unsatisfactory. Projections of future populations made in the years prior to 1947 involved an implicit assumption that death rates were tied necessarily to ways of living. The numbers expected by the year 2000 were scarcely larger than the numbers that now exist in 1962. Many projections are made today on the implicit assumption that death rates have self-perpetuating downward mechanisms while birth rates retain their inexorable ties with ancient traditions and values. Perhaps so, perhaps not. Projections made prior to the revolutionary technological advances in control over mortality became archaic within a decade. Projections prior to comparable technological advance in control over fertility may become similarly archaic. This is a period of vulnerability and crisis, and we cannot know what the resolution of the conflicting factors will be. It is with an acknowledgement of this uncertainty that we can best proceed to assess the Japanese experience and evolve our own proper policies.

The Population Explosion in Latin America

by

RONALD HILTON

Much has been made, and rightly, of the population explosion in Latin America. As recorded in the attached bibliography, there is an abundant literature on the statistical aspects of the problem, together with the usual sociological considerations.[1] This paper will, therefore, concentrate on some highly significant but neglected aspects of the question.

A glance at the map of Latin America shows that the population is concentrated in the highlands, or temperate zone, and along the coastlines. The deep substratum of the population in the highlands is Indian, although the top layers may, to varying degrees, have been modified by miscegenation with white immigrants, and in very rare cases with Negroes who have wandered up from the coastal areas. These areas have a population which is primarily white south of the Tropic of Capricorn, Negro in the areas such as northeastern Brazil where a plantation economy flourished, and mixed Indian, white and Negro in the remaining sectors. In general the highlands provided a better environment than the lowlands for the development of Indian civilizations. The Indians who lived at sea level were usually the victims of internecine warfare. While it is absurd to repeat that the Spaniards killed off literally all of the Indians in the Caribbean islands, it is true that they virtually annihilated them and completed the "destruction of the Indies" with even more success than the Caribs, who were busy annihilating the Arawaks when the Spaniards arrived.

From this general description several considerations derive. The first is that, conspicuously in South America, there is a large empty area between the coastal zone and the highlands. The immediate response is to say that this area should be filled up and that it provides a built-in safety valve for the continent's population explosion. This is largely the motivation behind the transferral of Brazil's capital from Rio de Janeiro to Brasília. It remains to be seen whether the creation of Brasília will lead to the opening up of

1. See T. LYNN SMITH, *Latin Americas Population Studies*, University of Florida Monographs, Social Sciences No. 8, Fall 1960.

the Brazilian plateau, which has a much better climate than the coastal
zone but which seems to have been denuded by centuries of destructive
fire-agriculture. Moreover, the soils in the Brasília area are not in general
satisfactory for agriculture, and the Belchers Associates of Ithaca, New
York, the consultants for the Brasília project, did not answer satisfactorily
the questions on this subject asked by the *Hispanic American Report*.

Indeed, much of the unoccupied area of South America suffers from
edaphological difficulties. The Guianese and Brazilian shields have practically no humus. In the Guianas there is a fertile strip of alluvial soil along
the coast, but the forests of the interior hide extremely poor soils. Where
the rains are excessively heavy (and a characteristic of Latin America is that
most areas suffer from an extremely high or conversely an extremely low
rainfall), the soils are leached, and even apparently good grazing land lacks
mineral content and can support only the most miserable herds of cattle.
These considerations were the basis for the pessimism expressed by ISAIAH
BOWMAN in his *Limits of Land Settlement* (*New York*, 1937).

Then there is the basic fact that the tropical rivers of South America still
do more harm than good. It has been calculated that the Amazon alone
provides about one-fifth of all the water entering the world's oceans. The
damp winds from the Atlantic striking against the Andes produce three
great river systems – the Amazon, the Orinoco, and the Magdalena – and
if one sees them on a rampage one can realize why in classical antiquity
the bull was the symbol of a roaring torrent; Hercules wrenching off a
bull's horn, out of which flowed water producing the cornucopia or horn
of plenty, is a symbol of man's conquest of rivers. Latin America needs lots
of Hercules to bring the Amazon, the Orinoco, and the Magdalena systems
within fixed channels, just as at long last the United States is finally taming
the Missisippi system.

There still remain in the interior of South America certain fairly fertile
highland areas which would be excellent centers of colonization providing
the difficult problem of communications could be overcome. In an un-
pretentious book, *The Conquest of Brazil*, which has become a classic and has
been translated into Portuguese, ROY NASH has expounded the thesis that
these highland areas must be colonized first and that from them the great
river basins, especially Amazonia, can slowly be reduced to submission.

Is it possible then to make Amazonia an effective center of human
activity? There is a manic-depressive answer to this question. ELLSWORTH
HUNTINGTON said no, since the area does not provide the climatic stimuli
without which no civilization can develop. PRESTON JAMES believes that this
is an old wives' tale, with about as much substance as the belief of ancient
geographers that Germania could never become civilized because of the
excessive cold. It may be that, just as developments in heating made Germania habitable, so progress in airconditioning will make life in Amazonia
tolerable. In any case, no spot in Amazonia has a climate as unbearable as

New York or Washington in summer. Some Latin American writers, like the Mexican José Vasconcelos and the Colombian Luis Enrique Osorio, have developed an almost mystical theory according to which civilization, which began in the tropics, will return there in due course, and Amazonia will become a great center of culture. This area of conjecture does not lend itself to scientific speculation, but rightly or wrongly most disinterested observers state that there is little likelihood of Amazonia becoming a center of dense population and creative activity in the foreseeable future.

Indeed, who will inhabit regions like Amazonia? In *La raza cósmica*, Vasconcelos expresses the idea that Latin America's lack of racial purity, far from being a handicap as was earlier thought, may allow Latin America to create the "cosmic race," the mixture of white, Indian, and Negro, which will represent the culmination of human evolution. Miscegenation, regarded in the past as creating half-breeds, who combined the defects of the racially "pure" parents and in some mysterious way destroyed their qualities, will, according to modern genetic theories, create new and superior types, just as hybrid maize is superior to more elementary species.

This theory may appear to be attractive scientifically and even philosophically, but who indeed is peopling the empty spaces of Latin America? The hard fact is that the present occupants are tending to move off the land and to add to the population of the capitals, making Latin America a continent of megapoles.[2] As typical manifestations of macrocephalia, greater Buenos Aires has about a quarter of Argentina's population, while Montevideo comprises almost a half of the population of Uruguay. It is common to lament this trend, but the economist Lauchlin Currie has propounded a scheme by which much of the population of Columbia would be moved off the land and established in the big cities to make possible a rationalization of Colombian agriculture.

It is, in fact, becoming harder and harder to find immigrants who will settle on the land and face the conditions prevailing there. The Italians who opened up the countryside of southern Brazil, Uruguay, and Argentina have been succeeded by a generation which can find good jobs in the area of the European Common Market. Many of those who migrated to Brazil, revolted at being expected to undertake tasks the Brazilians themselves would not do, demanded that they be repatriated to Italy. There was in the past century a free migration of Spaniards to and from Latin America, but, despite the population pressure resultant from the rise of the Spanish population to 30 million, the Franco government discourages this loss of manpower. In any case, Spaniards like Italians today prefer to find work in France, Germany, or one of the other Common Market countries. The Chinese and Syrian-Lebanese are not wanted in Latin America since they

2. See W. Stanley Rycroft & Myrtle M. Clemmer, *A Study of Urbanization in Latin America* (1962).

tend to congregate in the cities as small tradesmen. It is startling, for example, to see how much of the trade of Paramaribo, Surinam, is in Chinese hands.

By the default of others, the Japanese have become priority immigrants. Not only do Brazil and Paraguay in particular welcome them, but the Japanese Government, determined to maintain the island's population at 90 million, regards migration to South America, in addition to birth control and abortion, as being an important means to this end. Although nationalism and terrorism still infect the Japanese colonies in Brazil, the Japanese immigrants are welcomed, but it remains to be seen if the second generation of Japanese will be content to stay on the farm as their fathers did. Be that as it may, it was the Japanese farmers who opened such important areas as western São Paulo and Paraná. In any case, the population explosion of Latin America is the result of internal growth rather than of immigration.

Why should there be a startling growth of the native population? Undoubtedly the elimination in large areas of such diseases as malaria and yellow fever has been a contributing factor, as has the decline in the death rate and especially in the infant mortality rate because of generally improved health conditions. While such improvements would benefit primarily the underprivileged Indians and Negroes, it would seem correct to say that the greatest increase occurs among the mixed breeds, whose dynamism and fertility contrasts with the lack of will to live and reproduce among the pure Indians. In countries like Haiti there is a sharp rivalry between the mulattoes and the pure Negroes; it appears that the former are reproducing more rapidly.

Two other explanations of the population increase in Latin America deserve to be examined more critically. The first is that the Catholic Church has effectively banned birth control. It is true that Latin America is rapidly becoming the greatest concentration of Roman Catholics in the world, thus establishing an embarrassing correlation between Catholicism, backwardness, and social unrest. It is equally true that the Catholic Church is promoting rather grotesque methods of birth control and is playing Russian roulette with fertility. It is a fact that Argentina, officially a Catholic country which has presented such a disgraceful spectacle of military and ecclesiastical tyranny, has felt moved, through its delegation in the United Nations, to fight any attempt to promote the study of birth control as being incompatible with the Latin American heritage (from which may the Good Lord preserve civilization). It is a fact that the United States Government, in the whole of the Alliance for Progress program, has not felt free to make any serious reference to the problem of birth control.[3]

3. For a hard-hitting attack on the failure of the Alliance for Progress to face up to the birth-control issue, see "Latin America and Population Growth. What Price Evasion?" *Population Bulletin* (Washington: Population Reference Bureau Inc.), XVIII, No. 6, October 1962.

At the same time, Catholic Argentina which so vigorously fights birth control, has about the lowest birth rate in Latin America. Many nominal Catholics pay about as much attention to the Catholic Church's stand on birth control as Baptists and other low church groups in this country do to the prohibition against liquor. Indeed, it has been suggested that just as prohibition did much to undermine Fundamentalist Protestantism in this country, so hostility to effective birth control will undermine fundamental Catholicism in Latin America. This is already happening in Puerto Rico, where the supposedly Catholic women of the people would sooner face the ire of the priests than a lifetime of misery brought about by the bearing of excessively large families.[4]

Among the intellectuals and government officials, there has been a growing willingness to disregard the Church's interdiction of a serious discussion of birth control problems. The liberal, anti-clerical Mexican publishing house, the Fondo de Cultura Económica, took the lead a few years ago when it translated MALTHUS into Spanish. Since then there has been an increasing candor regarding this controversial issue. The military dictatorships which plague Latin America willingly ally themselves for practical reasons with the Catholic Church, which can so easily become an instrument of thought-control, yet they usually do not share the Church's puritanical attitude in sexual matters. With a strange and picturesque inconsistency, at the same time as Argentine dictator JUAN PERÓN was promoting his claim that his dead wife EVITA should be made a saint, he was sponsoring legalized prostitution, which the Catholic Church disapproves of, although with none of the vigor it displays in fighting birth control. El Salvador is one of the most Catholic countries in Latin America, but it is reported that the military clique at present ruling El Salvador is quietly promoting birth control to fight the problems brought about by El Salvador's population density, one of the highest in Latin America.

Whatever the actual influence of the Catholic Church may be in these matters, it is certain that the Church's vehement stand on this issue, in sharp contrast with its indifference to matters of poverty, tyranny, and social injustice, is undermining the prestige of the Catholic Church in Latin America. Indeed, the feeling is spreading that the Catholic Church is a nuisance and a hindrance to the development of decent living standards in Latin America.

Besides the theory that the Catholic veto on birth control is an important factor in the population explosion of Latin America, we should mention the explanation given by the Brazilian JOSUÉ DE CASTRO in his *Geography of Hunger*. DE CASTRO is a nutritionist whose theories have won him such wide respect that he was appointed director general of the United Nations Food and Agriculture Organisation. Baldly stated, his theory is that mammals,

4. The Family Planning Association operates clinics throughout Puerto Rico, distributes contraceptive pills free and has legally sterilized some 100,000 men and women.

and indeed other organisms, when they are starved, become unusually fertile and reproduce vigorously, as a biological assertion of the need to survive. Thus it is, according to JOSUÉ DE CASTRO, that there is a population explosion among the starving people of Brazil's Northeast.

This theory is ingenious and attractive, but obviously it involves some highly technical biological considerations. The distinguished biochemist Professor JAMES MURRAY LUCK does not hesitate to dismiss JOSUÉ DE CASTRO's thesis as worthless. According to Professor LUCK, it is based on deductions irresponsibly drawn from unverified experiments carried out years ago at Stanford.[5]

It has not been suggested elsewhere, but it seems evident that population concentrations in Latin America are the result of economic activities. Once these activities decline, the population may not be reduced as fast as the circumstances would warrant. While this may be a universal law, it would seem to be especially applicable to Latin America, where national boundaries prevent free migrations. The population density of Haiti, where there are almost twice as many people as in the Dominican Republic, which has almost twice the area of Haiti,[6] is in part the result of the former prosperity of the French plantations, which were wrecked during the wars of independence. The result has been a phenomenon similar to that of the wetbacks coming from Mexico into the United States. Haitians moved in as farm workers onto the Dominican sugar plantations. In part because of cultural differences (the Haitians speak creole French patois, the Dominicans, Spanish), tensions built up to such a point that dictator TRUJILLO in 1932 ordered the massacre of the Haitian immigrants. In this disgraceful episode, which ALBERT C. HICKS has described in *Blood in the Streets*, some 30,000 were killed, a small indication of the dangers with which the population explosion is fraught.

A geographical inspection of Haiti and the Dominican Republic provides no clues as to the population distribution. Indeed, geographically one would expect the Dominican Republic, which has some excellent farmland, to have a much greater population than eroded, worn-out Haiti. Some suggest that the rate of reproduction is larger among the relatively pure Negroes of Haiti than among the light mulattoes of the Dominican Republic. It is impossible to provide scientific evidence for this hypothesis. It might be argued that, perhaps in accord with the theories of JOSUÉ DE CASTRO, the impoverished Haitians breed faster than the somewhat less

5. Yet, whatever the explanation, and with the exception of Costa Rica, the population explosion is concentrated in the areas where the living standards are lowest. See CARR B. LAVELL, *Population Growth and the Development of South America*, Population Research Project of the George Washington University (1959). See also in the same series HAROLD L. GEISERT, *Population Problems in Mexico and Central America* (1959).
6. The population of Haiti, already hungry and crowded, will probably double to 8 million in 18 years.

poor Dominicans. A differential in birth rate based on income levels would be hard to verify, since the Dominicans have not reached the economic level at which the rate of reproduction seems to decline.

The answer seems to be historical and to be related to the economy of coffee plantations which require an unusual number of workers – far more than do sugar or other plantations. For geographical reasons, Haiti has produced primarily coffee, the Dominican Republic, sugar. During the colonial period, the French ran Haiti with remarkable efficiency, and its plantations made it possibly the wealthiest agricultural community in the New World – what a far cry from present-day Haiti! These efficient plantations attracted large numbers of farm workers. When, with independence, the plantation economy collapsed (what a lesson for those who believe that independence from "colonialism" is the solution to the woes of tropical countries!), the population remained, and indeed went on breeding, even though there was now no economie basis for the numerous population. It would seem that economic activity stimulates population growth which continues under its own momentum after the need for the population has disappeared.

There is a similar case in Central America. El Salvador, with a very high density of population, is surrounded by three countries with much lower population densities. In particular, there is a striking contrast between El Salvador and the adjoining areas of Honduras, which are almost empty. Racially the Salvadoreños are mestizos pretty much like the Hondureños, so that a differential in reproduction rate based on race would seem to have no basis.

The only satisfactory explanation is that El Salvador, like Haiti, is for geographical reasons good coffee country. The plantation economy has attracted a dense concentration of farm laborers, who have reproduced more than the local economy will justify, with the result that recently Salvadorean peasants began to settle on the Honduran side of the boundary, creating an international issue between the two Central American republics.

The most peculiar case is that of Costa Rica, which has today the highest annual rate of population growth in the world. It was recently placed at 4%, as opposed to 3.6% for Communist China and 2.6% for Latin America as a whole. Costa Rica is, however, a very special case. Whereas it is estimated that a third of the population of Paraguay has left the country because of a series of dictatorships culminating in the STROESSNER regime, Costa Rica is a peaceful democracy which attracks the victims of neighboring dictatorships. We hear much of the conflict between the oligarchy and the masses in Latin America, but Costa Rica has a classless society without grinding poverty and with a very low death rate. In much of Latin America life is a continual struggle between man and his telluric environment. Costa Rica is one of the few countries about which one may properly use the trite expression "eternal Spring." Costa Rica has a combination of plantation agriculture and small industries which together provide a good economic basis for a growing population. The Pan American Highway is opening up the western section of the country, and a startling development is taking place there. In brief, it would be as incorrect to regard Costa Rica as being typical of Latin America as it would be to view Florida or California as typical of the United States.

A variety of factors, including geographical barriers and the lack of social cohesiveness in the traditional Spanish way of life, brought about the fragmentation of Spanish America into 18 republics. Improved communications and increased travel are bringing about a common realization of their cultural unity. There is a growing linguistic unity, and even those who hate the Spanish tradition are attempting to spread, together with literacy, the use of the Spanish language. American anthropologists are trying to push the study of Indian languages on the grounds that the population of "Indoamerica" is increasing, but the argument is almost certainly fallacious. Those who know Paraguay, for example, can testify to the decline in the use of guaraní over the past twenty years.

Regardless of these considerations of detail, it is evident that there is a population explosion in Latin America. There is wide discrepancy among anthropologists about the Indian population of the New World at the time of the Conquest. Certainly the Peruvian JULIO TELLO, who was both an Indian and an Indianist, was being romantic when he placed the population of the Inca empire at 80 million. Anthropologists tend to be pro-Indian and anti-Spanish, and this should be taken into account in assessing their estimates. The present trend is to raise the earlier calculations of the Indian population at the time of the Conquest and to suggest that war and disease decimated it. Then, according to the calculations of SHERBURNE F. COOK & LESLEY B. SIMPSON, the population began to rise slowly until, in the 18th century, it reached the level of the late 15th century. Since then, at first by immigration and more recently by the rapid growth of the mestizo group, the population has risen rapidly, and today "Latin" America has more people than "Anglo" America. Population projections have in general proved quite inaccurate, but it has been calculated that eventually Latin America will have double the population of Anglo America.

This is hardly a reason for saying "The more, the merrier." This juxtaposition of Anglo and Latin America will probably produce the same degree of cordiality which Russia displays toward China. There is already evidence that the spectacular anti-American demonstrations in Latin America are matched by a dour and growing if undemonstrative hostility toward Latin America in the United States. Gone are the silly days of facile declarations of Pan Americanism. There will be a continuing flow of migrants to the United States from a Latin America strained by population pressures and by political strife. In the eastern part of the United States the Puerto Ricans occupy the lowest social level. Even though they are white, they are outranked socially by the Negroes. The bitterness which this produces is kept in check by the realization that Puerto Rico enjoys an artificially favorable economic status.[7] On the side of the native Americans there is one significant demonstration of a hostility to Latin America sparked by the dislike of Puerto Ricans: it is almost impossible to sell movies, TV programs, or radio programs with a Latin American theme. This is presumably the reason why American financiers have dropped a much publicized plan to make a movie about the life of SIMÓN BOLÍVAR. It is not without significance that a movie about the Spanish hero, the Cid, was given a wide and successful circulation and that all kinds of Puerto Ricans, Mexicans, and Cubans in the United States, as protective coloration, spread the story that they are really Spaniards. This will probably change with time, but it is too early to say what position the Puerto Ricans will finally occupy in the U.S. social structure.

In the western part of the United States there is a curious coincidence in that the area where the Bircher movement is strong – Southern California, Arizona, New Mexico, and Texas – has the highest concentration of Mexican population. There are significantly well-documented cases of teachers in that area being pressured by the Birchers into giving a strictly U.S. interpretation of the war with Mexico. Just as in the East, Puerto Ricans like TEODORO MOSCOSO have risen to positions of prominence, so RAYMOND L. TELLES was the first Mexican to become mayor of El Paso and to serve as a U.S. Ambassador. The Bircher movement in the West seems to have been stimulated by the uneasy feeling of the native American population that they are being pressed from below by the Mexicans.[8] It is significant that Birchers favor dictatorships in Latin America which will keep the people in their place and make them subservient to the United States. The Spaniards and the Portuguese in the area of high Mexican concentration often proclaim their admiration for FRANCO and SALAZAR in order to make it clear that they are Europeans not to be confused with Latin Americans.

One odd relic of the old Pan Americanism is that the United States set up a quota system after World War I to avoid an excessive migration of Latins from Europe and to preserve the north European character of the American population. The quota system was not applied to Latin America, but it is now apparent that the threat of "Latinization" comes not from the East but from the South. In the absence of a quota system a variety of economic tests are applied.

7. Puerto Rico, with a population density of 702 per square mile, would collapse economically were it not for the built-in subsidy implicit in the so-called "Commonwealth" status.

8. The population pressure on the Mexican border will increase. Between 1920 and 1962 the population of Mexico increased from 14.5 million to 34.5 million. IRENE B. TAEUBER of Princeton University estimates that in 1980 there will be 64.4 million Mexicans and it is most unlikely that the land will be able to feed them.

In view of the end of isolationism and the development of a global U.S. policy, this double standard should be abandoned, and immigration from all over the world strictly controlled. In the past, free international migration helped to open up empty areas of the globe. The problem now is not to fill up empty areas but to stabilize the population. The liberal dream of free migration is dangerously romantic. Because, for example, China fails to control its population, there is no reason why other countries should be asked to suffer the consequences and allow minorities to develop which will be a perennial social problem. Countries can function harmoniously only if they have a more or less homogeneous population. Immigration controls alone can make this possible, and countries like Haiti will simply have to accommodate their population realistically to the land and resources they have available. Only then can we have peaceful communities, and any institution which impedes this is a force for evil.[9]

BIBLIOGRAPHY

AGRICULTURAL GEOGRAPHY OF LATIN AMERICA (Washington, D.C.). "Population," Foreign Agricultural Service U.S. Dept. of Agriculture, May 1958, pp. 25–30. Rural and urban population of Latin American Nations in 1956. Maps showing population density per square mile, trend of population in selected Latin American Republics.

ALMOND, GABRIEL A. & JAMES I. COLEMAN, editors. The Politics of the Developing Areas. Princeton: Princeton University Press, 1960. Pp. 591. Examines the implications of the population problem in Latin America. "The population figures suggest that, even if there were no European immigrants in the area, with each succeeding generation, the proportion of Indians would become smaller."

9. For a protest against the Latin American conspiracy of silence on the population explosion, see ESTANISLAU FISCHLOWITZ, "Latinoamérica ante el vertiginoso crecimiento demográfico," Combate (San José de Costa Rica), July–August 1962, pp. 39–43.

In 1962, the population of the world was estimated to be about 3 billions, that of Latin America 206 million–75 million more than two decades earlier. The population of Latin America is increasing at about 2.6% annually (or 5.3 million), while the gain in Africa is 2.2% and in Asia 1.9%. Per capita output of goods and services increases by only 1.6% annually. See United Nations Demographic Yearbook, 1962. With the restrictions on immigration imposed by the British Government in 1962, islands like Jamaica and Barbados will cease to have a convenient safety-valve, and population specialists like Dr. RICHARD THOMAN of Queen's University (Kingston, Ontario) have warned them that they must take immediate steps to curb the birth-rate. The Catholic Church is not dominant in those islands and so could not block action easily.

AMERICAN PHILOSOPHIC SOCIETY. Problems of Development of Densely Settled Areas. New York: *Amer. Philos. Soc. Proc.* 95, 1, 1951. Special references to Central and South America.

AMUNDSON, R. H. "Population Explosion," *America Press* (New York), April 30, 1960, *192–95.* Central and South American areas specifically referred to.

AVERANGA, ASTHENIO. "Síntesis panorámica de la situación demográfica de Bolivia: Censo nacional de 1950," *Estadística* (Washington, D.C.), March 1955, *18–24.* A summary analysis of the structure of the Bolivian population, and summary tables on the principal characteristics investigated in the 1950 census.

BARRETTO CASTRO. Estudos brasileiros de população. 2nd edition. Rio de Janeiro. 1947.

— Povoamento e população, política populacional brasileira. Rio de Janeiro. 1958.

BASTIDE, ROGER. "Race Relations in Brazil," *UNESCO Int. Social Sci. Bull.* (Paris), IX, No. 4, 1957, *495–512.*

BASTOS DE ÁVILA, S. J. Rev. FERNANDO. "The Future of Immigration to South America," *Int. Labour Rev.* (Geneva), July 1957, *30–46.*

— "Immigration, Development and Industrial Expansion in Brazil," *Migration* (Washington, D.C.), Intergovernmental Committee for European Migration, January-March 1961, pp, *21–31.* The effect of immigration on development and industrial expansion in Brazil.

BATES, M. J., editor. Conference on the Migration of Peoples to Latin America. Migration of Peoples to Latin America. Washington, D.C.: Catholic University of America Press. 1957. Pp. 113. A colloquium dealing with the migratory influences on population in Central and South America.

BERGMANN, ANTONIO MARÍA. Inmigración para Colombia. Bogotá: Departamento Administrativo, Sección de Información y Publicaciones. August 1954. Pp. 88.

BLACK, E. R. "Warning to Have Not Nations," *U.S. News and World Report,* May 8, 1961, pp. *82–3.* Excerpts from address April 24, 1961.

BLANC, R. Handbook of Demographic Research in Underdeveloped Countries. New York: Institute of Public Service. 1961. Facts and figures on the most recent analysis of population figures in Central and South America.

BROWN, HARRISON, JAMES BONNER & JOHN WEIR. The Next 100 Years. New York: The Viking Press. 1957. Pp. 193. Technical manpower present and future, world food production, caloric intake, demands for raw materials in an industrialized society. Extensive bibliography.

BUITRÓN, ANÍBAL. Exodo rural en Venezuela. Washington, D.C.: Pan American Union. 1955. Pp. 272.

BULLETIN OF THE WORLD HEALTH ORGANIZATION (Geneva). "National Administration Responsible for Vital Registration and Vital Statistics," II, No. 1–2, 1954, *163–76.*

BURCH, T. K. "Facts and Fallacies about World Population Growth," *Catholic World* (New York), March 1960, *345–51.* References to Central and South America.

CAIGNARD, ROMAIN. "La montée démographique argentine: le recencement du 30 septembre 1960," *Cahiers d'Outre-Mer* (Paris), January-March 1961, *14, 53, 85–97.*

CALDEIRA, CLOVIS. "The Parched Land: Northeastern Brazil." *Americas* (Washington, D.C.), November 1961, *13–20.* The problem of internal migration; economy.

CÁRCANO, MIGUEL ÁNGEL. Proposiciones sobre inmigración sometidas a la conferencia económica nacional. Buenos Aires: Imprenta Mercatalí. Pp. 548.

CARVALHO, A. V. W. DE. A população brasileira: estudo e interpretação. Rio de Janeiro: Conselho Nacional de Estatística, I.B.G.E. 1960. Pp. 148. Detailed presentation of demographic problems, with statistics, in Brazil.

CASTRO, JOSUÉ DE. The Geography of Hunger. Boston: Little, Brown and Company. 1952. Pp. 286.

— Le livre noir de la faim. Paris: Les éditions ouvrières. 1961. Pp. 124. Deals with the campaign launched by the FAO. CASTRO exposes the physiological, economic and political consequences of hunger. He does not feel that the solution lies in birth control. To support his theory he details a program of protein production for Latin America.

CENSO DE POPULACIÓN: Estudios sobre métodos y procedimientos. Washington, D.C.: Pan American Union. 1960. A monograph dealing with the methods and procedures of census-taking in Central and South America.

CLARK, C. "Do Population and Freedom Grow Together?" *Fortune* (Chicago), December 1960, *136–39*. Special references to Central and South America.

COALE, A. J. and E. HOOVER. Population Growth and Economic Development in Low Income Countries. Princeton: Princeton University Press. 1959. Mexico and India.

COOK, ROBERT. "A Catholic Looks at the Population Problem," *Population Bull.* (Washington, D.C.), March 1962, entire issue.

CORCORAN, THOMAS F. "Crecimiento de la población de la República de Panamá," *Estadística* (Mexico), June 1945, *210–17*. The four periods of intense activity in relation to the large influx of foreigners who emigrated when employment opportunities decreased.

DARWIN, C. G. & J. J. SPENGLER. "Standing Room Only in the World?" *U.S. News and World Report* (Washington, D.C.), November 23, 1959, *80–84*. Central and South America are referred to.

DEMOGRAPHIC YEARBOOK. Published yearly since 1948 by the Statistical Office of the United Nations, Department of Economic and Social Affairs, New York.

DESMOND, A. "Fountain of Youth Overflows," *Americas* (Washington, D.C.), November 1959, *34–7*. A discussion of the increase in population in Latin America.

DIEGUES, JNR. MANUEL. "Experiences and Prospects of the Cultural Assimilation of the Immigrants in Brazil," Proc. World Population Conference, 1954, Vol. II, (New York), 1955, pp. 357–72 (United Nations Publication E/CONF. 13/414).

DUCOFF, LOUIS J. Human Resources of Central America, Panama and Mexico, 1950–1980, in Relation to Some Aspects of Economic Development. New York: United Nations Economic Commission for Latin America. 1960. ST/TAO/K/LATl (catalogue No. 60.XIII.1). Pp. 155.

DUCOFF, LOUIS. "The Future Population and Labor Force of Mexico, Central America and Panama: Some Implications for Economic Development," *Estadística* (Washington D.C.), June 1959, *315–24*. The economic consequences that may result from the increase in population up to 1980.

DURÁN OCHOA, JULIO. "El crecimiento de la problación mexicana," El trimestre económico XXII Num. 3, July-September 1955, pp. 331–49.

— Población. Mexico: Fondo de Cultura Económica. Pp. 300.

ECONOMIC BULLETIN FOR LATIN AMERICA. Santiago, Chile: Secretariat of the Economic Commission for Latin America (ECLA). First published 1956. Biannual publication.

— "The Economic Development of Bolivia," Vol. II, October 1957, p. 19. How to find employment for increasing population within the economy and the effect of the demographic pressure on the agricultural zones of the *altiplano*. Demographic data on p. 71.

ECONOMIC POLICIES AND PROGRAMS IN SOUTH AMERICA. Washington, D.C. Subcommittee on Inter-American Economic Relations of the Joint Economic Committee of the United States, 87th 2nd Session, U.S. Government Printing Office. 1962. Pp. 123.
Commodity and trade problems, agricultural problems and land reform. Alliance for Progress, GNP, and national growth, agricultural labor as a per cent of total labor force in 1950, population density 1958–59 per square mile.

ELABORACIÓN MECÁNICA EN LOS CENSOS GENERALES EN LATINOAMÉRICA. Washington, D.C.: Pan American Union. 1960. Monograph dealing with the mechanics of census taking in Central and South America.

ELLIS, CECIL A. Public Utilities in Colombia. New York: United Nations Technical Assistance Administration. 1953. ST/TAA/K/Colombia/1. II. H.2 Pp. 65. Discussion of demographic growth and urgent need for expansions of electrical facilities.

ESTADÍSTICA. (Washington, D.C.). "Censuses of the American Nations: Selected Information on Population (Including Illiteracy) and Housing," June 1954, *282–93*.
— "Empadronamiento individual de todos los habitantes de la República," March 1961,
136–38.
— "Honduras: Autorízase levantamiento de los censos nacionales de población y
vivienda," March 1961, p. 134. Decree no. 34 which provides for the taking of the census
in Honduras.
— "Levantamiento de censos en el Perú," September 1959, *510–11*. Law no. 13248 which
provides for the taking of Peru's census.
— "Statistical News," June 1945, *288–91*. In Argentina, decree law 24, 883/944, and decree
law 13,940 provide for the creation of the National Council of Statistics and Censuses
and that future censuses be taken every ten years, in the years ending in zero.
— "Venezuela: Decreto por el cual se fija el día del censo nacional," March 1961, *134–36*.
ESTRUCTURA DEMOGRÁFICA DE LAS NACIONES AMERICANAS: ANÁLISIS ESTADÍSTICO-CENSAL DE
LOS RESULTADOS OBTENIDOS BAJO EL PROGRAMA DEL CENSO DE LA AMÉRICA DE 1950 (COTA-
1950) (Washington, D.C.). "Características combinadas de la población económica-
mente activa," 1959, Vol. II, Tome II. Pp. 282. Detailed presentation of demographic
problems in Central and South America.
— "País de nacimiento, nacionalidad y lengua," June 1960, Vol. I, Tome III. Total population by place of birth and sex according to age: population born in foreign countries
by sex, according to place of birth; population by nationality and sex according to
age; foreign population by sex according to specific nationalities; population by sex
according to language.
FARLEY, RICHARD M. The Population Explosion and Christian Responsibility. New York:
Oxford University Press. 1960. Pp. 260. Bibliography.
FAMILY FARM POLICY. Chicago: University of Chicago. 1957. Pp. 516. Proceedings of a
conference on family farm policy attended by participants from the British Commonwealth, Northern Europe, Central Europe, Latin America, and the United States.
FENSTER, L. F. "Population Explosion," *New Republic* (Washington, D.C.), September 18,
1961, *30–31*. Special reference to Central and South America.
FERGUSON, J. HALCRO. Latin America: The Balance of Race Redressed. London, New
York: Oxford University Press. 1961. Pp. 101. Bibliography. The racial question and how
it affects population growth in Central and South America.
FISCHLOWITZ, ESTANISLAU. "Manpower Problems in Brazil," *Int. Labour Rev.* (Geneva),
April 1959, *398–417*. Because of rapid industrialization, there is a shortage of skilled
workers and underemployment of the unskilled. Demographic trends; internal
migration.
FORREST, FREDERICK AUGUST. Immigration as a Factor of Progress in Argentina, 1536–1853
Stanford, California. 1948. Pp. 118. A. M. Thesis.
GARCÉS, GABRIEL. "Immigration and Indian Policy in Latin American Countries," *Int.
Labour Rev.* (Geneva), January 1954, *18–30*. Theme: the Indians should be associated in
any national effort for economic development.
GARCÍA-FRÍAS, ROQUE. "Utilización de los censos para probar la integralidad del registro
de nacimientos," *Estadística* (Washington, D.C.), March 1955, *91–113*. During the census
the enumerator fills out an "infant card" which is later compared with birth records
to estimate the underregistration of births; comparison of the items matched by the
six American countries conducting tests of this character.
GEISERT, H. L. Population Problems in Mexico and Central America. Washington, D.C.:
Population Research Project, the George Washington University. 1959. Pp. 48. Bibliography.
GEORGE, PIERRE. Introduction à l'étude géographique de la population du monde.
Paris: Presses Universitaires de France. 1951. Pp. 278.
GONZÁLEZ, GALE, EDUARDO A. COGHLAN & CARLOS CORREA AVILA. "El analfabetismo en

la Argentina: Estudio comparativo desde 1869 a 1943," *Estadística* (Mexico), September 1945, *323–37.* Illiteracy now affects only one-sixth of the total population. A low standard of living always accompanies a high proportion of illiteracy. Regional differences. Tables and charts.

GOODE, WILLIAM J. "Illegitimacy, Anomie, and Cultural Penetration," *Amer. Sociol. Rev-* (New York), December 1961, *910–25.* An examination of the cultural conditions under which high illegitimacy rates occur. New World Indians and slaves are viewed as having been neither culturally nor socially integrated in their communities and into the national life.

GRACE, JOSEPH PETER. It's Not Too Late in Latin America: Proposals for Action Now. 1961. Pp. 74. 40% of Latin American population under 15 years of age, median age only 21.5 years, youth emerging as its dominant force.

GREVILLE, T. N. E. & NELSON LUIS DE ÁRAUJO MORAES. "Life Tables Studies in Brazil," *Estadística* (Washington, D.C.) June 1955, *264–68.*

GUTIÉRREZ, EMILIA DE. "Los hijos del azar," *El Tiempo* (Bogotá), June 5, 1962. The demographic explosion and illegitimate children.

HARREWOOD, JACK. "Overpopulation and Underemployment in the West Indies," *Int. Labour Rev.* (Geneva), August 1960, *1030–37.* Information on the economy, population, migration, employment, unemployment, underemployment, wage structure and hours of work in the most important islands of the West Indies Federation.

HAUSER, PHILIP MORRIS. "Demographic Dimensions of World Politics," *Science* (Washington, D.C.), June 3, 1960, *1641–47.* References to Central and South America. [See also this volume, p. 109.]

— editor. Population and World Politics. New York: Free Press. 1961. References to Central and South America.

— Population Perspectives. New Brunswick: Rutgers University Press. 1960. Pp. 183. Estimated population growth of Latin America between 1950–75, 3.4%. Present fertility rates will produce fantastic rates of growth following the decrease in the mortality rate.

— Urbanization in Latin America. New York: Columbia University Press, International Documents Service. 1961. Pp. 331. Edited by the chairman of the Department of Sociology of the University of Chicago, this volume contains the proceedings of a seminar sponsored jointly by the Bureau of Social Affairs of the United Nations, the Economic Commission for Latin America, and UNESCO (in cooperation with the International Labor Organization and the Organization of American States) on urbanization problems in Latin America. The seminar was held in Santiago de Chile from July 6–18, 1959.

— and O. D. DUNCAN, editors. The Study of Population: An Inventory and Appraisal. Chicago: University of Chicago Press. 1959. Pp. 864. A detailed study of the population situation with sections on Central and South America.

HEARE, GERTRUDE E. Brazil. Washington, D.C.: U.S. Department of Commerce. Pp. 214. Part II. Land and people of Brazil and expansion problems. Migration, etc. pp. *41–59.*

HENRY, L. "Analysis and Calculation of the Fertility of Populations of Under-Developed Countries," *Population Bull. United Nations* No. 5 (New York), July 1956, p. 51. Paper prepared for the seminar on population problems in Latin America.

HERTZLER, J. O. The Crisis in World Population. Lincoln: University of Nebraska Press. 1956. Pp. 279. A sociological examination, with special reference to the under-developed areas. Revolutions that have affected the demographic evolution. Bibliography.

HILL, G. W. "Achievements and Objectives of Recent and Current Immigration Plans in Latin America with Particular Reference to Economic Factors," Proc. World Population Conference, 1954. (New York: United Nations), 1955, pp. 437–454. E/CONF. 13/414. Two factors decisive in generating the era of immigration to Venezuela in the 1940's: the rapid transformation of pastoral-agricultural economy under the influence of the expanding petroleum industry; Venezuela's response to the pleas of the war refugees of Europe.

HILL, REUBEN, et. al. The Family and Population Control: A Puerto Rican Experiment in Social Change. A detailed exposition of a demographic experiment in Puerto Rico.

HUTCHINSON, BERTRAM. "Fertility, Social Mobility and Urban Migration in Brazil," *Population Studies* (New York), March 1961, *182–189*.

EL IMPACTO DEL INDUSTRIALISMO EN LA POBLACIÓN. Num. 2, Vol. VI. Mexico, D.F.: Fondo de Cultura Económica. Part of a series of documentary monographs dealing with population and other socio-economic problems. Contains detailed information with specific reference to Mexico.

INFIELD, HENRIK F. People in Ejidos. New York: Frederick A. Praeger Inc. 1954. Pp. 151.

INSTITUTO INTERAMERICANO DE ESTADÍSTICA (Inter-American Statistical Institute). La estructura demográfica de las naciones americanas. Washington, D.C.: Organization of American States. Vol. I, No. 1. April 1960. Pp. 125. Statistical analysis of the 1950 census with special reference to: basic groups, urban and rural distribution, private housing, type of family housing and number of occupants per unit, housing with running water.

— La estructura demográfica de las naciones americanas. Washington, D.C.: Organization of American States. Vol. I, No. 2. February 1960. Pp. 96. Distribution of the married population by age and sex.

— La estructura demográfica de las naciones americanas. Washington, D.C.: Organization of American States. Vol. I, No. 4. July 1960. Pp. 153. General characteristics of the population. Statistical analysis of the 1950 census. Population by age and sex according to educational level.

— La estructura demográfica de las naciones americanas. Washington, D.C.: Organization of American States. Vol. II, No. 1. June 1959. Pp. 236. Analysis of 1950 census. Economically active and noneconomically active population. General characteristics of the economically active population.

INTERNATIONAL LABOUR REVIEW. Published monthly from 1921 by the International Labour Office, Geneva.

— (Geneva). "Immigration and Settlement in Brazil, Argentina, and Uruguay: I," February 1937, *215–46*. A summary of Brazil's immigration policies and the possibilities that the country afforded for immigration and settlement.

— (Geneva). "Immigration and Settlement in Brazil, Argentina, and Uruguay: II," March 1937, *252–383*. Argentina: immigration policy; failure of private settlement schemes; state action in regard to settlement; possibilities of settlement. Uruguay: immigration and agriculture; state assistance for settlers; possibilities of settlement. Conclusions.

— (Geneva). "Vocational Training and the Establishment of Service Workshops in a Poor Rural Area. The Experience of the Andean Indian Programme," February 1962, *129–47*. Organisation of workshops, courses offered, problems encountered, the results of operations.

IRAGORRI, V. J. M. Evolución demográfica colombiana. Bogotá: Editorial Universitaria. 1959. Pp. 76. A detailed report on the demography of Colombia.

IZUMI, S. "Acculturation among the Japanese Agricultural Immigrants in Brazil," Proc. World Population Conference, 1954, Vol. II, (New York), 1955, *467–78*. (United Nations publication E/CONF. 13/414).

JAMES, PRESTON E. "Implications of the Race between Economics and Population in Latin America," *Ann. Amer. Acad. polit. Soc. Sci.* Study of the relationship between economics and population in Latin America.

JARDIM, GERMANO. "Subsídio para o estudo dos fatôres determinantes e conseqüências das variações demográficas no Brasil," *Estadística* (Washington, D.C.), September–December 1955, *435–43*.

JEFFERSON, MARK SYLVESTER WILLIAM. Peopling the Argentina Pampa. New York: American Geographical Society. 1962. Pp. 211.

LAMBERT, J. "Caractéristiques démographiques du Brésil contemporain," *Population* II, I (Paris), January–March 1947, *93*.

LANDIS, PAUL H. and PAUL K. HATT. Population Problems, a Cultural Interpretation. New York: American Book Company. 1954. Pp. 554. Special references to Central and South America.

THE LANDLESS FARMER IN LATIN AMERICA. Geneva: International Labour Office. 1957. Pp. 117. Conditions of tenants, share farmers and similar categories of semi-independent agricultural workers in Latin America; systems of land tenure, legislation and practice on agricultural leases. The family patrimony system, living conditions, contrast between ejidos in Mexico and colonos in Cuba. Alternatives of landless peasant.

LAVELL CARR B. Population Growth and the Development of South America. Washington, D.C. Washington Population Research Project, the George Washington University. 1959. Pp. 48. Bibliography.

LIEUWEN, EDWIN. Arms and Politics in Latin America. New York: Council on Foreign Relations. 1961. Contains a detailed analysis of population statistics on Latin America. "...Latin America's entire population is increasing at the extraordinary rapid rate of 2.5% annually, faster than any other area in the world."

LOEHNBERG, ALFRED. "Water and Economic Development," *Impact of Science on Society*, (Paris), January 1958, pp. *23–44*. Water supply and its relation to population growth in various parts of Latin America: Mexico and Brazil. In particular, developments in the valley of Mexico are discussed.

LOPES, R. PAULA. "Land Settlement in Brazil," *Int. Labour Rev.* (Geneva), February 1936, *152–184*.

— "Social Problems and Legislation in Brazil," *Int. Labour Rev.* (Geneva), November 1941, *493–537*. The situation of the rural population as mainly agricultural; sparseness of population; internal migration; unsatisfactory distribution of the population.

MCKERNAN, L. "Population Bomb," *Catholic World* (New York), May 1959, *124–29*. Central and South America are mentioned.

— "Population in a Changing World," *Catholic World* (New York), February 1960, *286–93*. Special references to Central and South America.

MARSAL, J. F. "Argentina as an Immigration Country," *Migration* (Washington, D.C.), October–December 1961, *17–35*. The River Plate sub-region zone; homogeneity of Argentina since European immigration ceased in 1930; good assimilation of migrants, mixed marriages; graphs on immigration and emigration of nationals from other South American countries; urban and rural distribution of the population; nationality of immigrants.

MENDIETA Y NÚÑEZ, LUCIO. "Racial and Cultural Tensions in Latin America," *Int. Sci. Bull.* (Paris), IV, 3, 1952, *442–50*.

MÉTRAUX, ALFRED. "The Incas of Today," *The UNESCO Courrier* (New York), February 1962, *15–21*.

— "The Racial Landscape of Latin America," *The UNESCO Courrier* (New York), October 1960, *21–3*.

— "The Social and Economic Structure of the Indian Communities of the Andean Region," *Int. Labour Rev.* (Geneva), March 1959, *225–43*. The political, economic, and social make-up of the Indian community. Internat. migration.

MÍCHALUP, ERIC. "The Construction of the First Venezuelan Life Tables 1941–1942," *Estadística* (Washington, D.C.), March 1951, *61–78*.

MIGRATION. Published every two months since January–February 1952 by the International Labour Office, Manpower Division, Geneva. Later published by the Intergovernmental Committee for European Migration, Washington, D.C.

MIGRATION (Geneva). "Agreement Between the United States of Brazil and the Kingdom of the Netherlands Regarding Immigration and Land Settlement," Vol. I

No. 4, July–August 1952, *67–79*. The complete text of the agreement. Promulgation Decree No. 30.692 of March 29, 1952.

— (Geneva). "Dutch Settlement at Campinas, State of São Paulo," Vol. I, No. 2, March–April 1952, *15–22*. The planning organization and operational problems of the Dutch co-operative "Holambra" founded in 1948, settling Dutch farmers in Brazil.

— (Geneva). "Italian Projects in Latin America," Vol. I, No. 1, January–February 1952, *69–73*. Explains the functions and responsibilities of the Italo-Chilean Land Settlement Corporation and tells about progress of settlements.

— (Geneva). "Italo-Brazilian Migration Agreement," Vol. I, No. 1, January–February 1952, *45–56*. Complete text of the agreement signed on July 5, 1950. All phases of migration are covered.

— (Geneva). "Settlement of 20,000 Families in Brazil," Vol. I, No. 1, January–February 1952, *64–68*. Swiss Aid to Europe, a federation of Swiss agencies for mutual aid at the international level, prepared a settlement scheme with Brazil in August 1950. Five villages comprised of 450 farming families, 50 families of craftsmen and the appropriate medical and administrative staff and ecclesiastics were planned and under construction.

— (Washington, D.C.). "Immigration in Argentina," October–December 1961, *54–64*. Would-be European immigrants now attracted by labor-starved factories of West Germany. Decline in numbers of immigrants from Europe. Neighboring republics provide immigrants to give Argentina a slightly favorable balance of immigration over emigration.

— (Washington, D.C.). "Immigration in Venezuela in 1960," October–December 1961, *80–82*.

— (Washington, D.C.). "The problem of Immigration in Brazil," July–September 1961, *54–56*.

— (Washington, D.C.). "Recent Trends in Paraguayan Immigration and Pioneer Settlements," October–December 1961, *77–78*.

MIGRATION FACTS AND FIGURES (Geneva: International Catholic Migration Committee). "Immigration into Latin America," January–February 1958. With the aid of charts, the article comments on the population, industrialization, housing, and human-element factors involved in migration to South America.

— "Re-migration," November–December 1956. Charts on re-migration from some Latin American countries, especially Venezuela and Brazil. The reasons for re-migration and means of preventing it.

— "Re-migration," November–December 1956. Charts on re-migration from some Latin American countries, especially Venezuela and Brazil. The reasons for re-migration and means of preventing it.

— "Spanish Overseas Migration," July–August 1956. A chart on post-war trends of Spanish Migration (1946–1954) to the United States, Canada, and Mexico, Middle America, and South America.

MINTZ, S. W. "Puerto Rican Emigration: a Three-fold Comparison," *Social and Economic Studies* (Kingston), December 1955, *311–325*.

MIRÓ, CARMEN A. "Vital Statistics of Panama," *Estadística* (Washington, D.C.), September–December 1955, *458–62*. Lists the succession of agencies and reports concerned with births, deaths, stillbirths, marriages, and divorces of Panama.

MORTARA, GIORGIO. "Estudios demográficos relativos a una política de población en los países latino-americanos," *Estadística* (Washington), December 1960, *664–82*. Analyzes the geographic distribution, natural and migratory increase, racial composition, and demographic growth of the population. The main part of the article deals with demographic studies and their utilization.

— "O maior nucleo japonês no Brasil: os amarelos em Marília," *Estadística* (Mexico), September 1944, *367–74*.

NATIONAL BUREAU COMMITTEE FOR ECONOMIC RESEARCH. *Demographic and Economic Change in Developed Countries*. Princeton: Princeton University Press. 1960. Detailed references to Central American and South American nations.

NATIONAL CATHOLIC ALMANAC – *1959*. Saint Anthony's Guild. Garden City, New York: Doubleday and Co. (distributor). 1959. Contains information on the Catholic church in Latin America during 1958. The pastoral care of Spanish-Speaking Catholics in the United States, the problems of Spanish-speaking immigrants to the United States from Latin America, especially Puerto Rico.

NEIVA, ARTHUR HEHL. "The Importance of Immigration in the Development of Brazil," *Migration* (Washington, D.C.), January–March 1961, *41–52*.

NOTESTEIN, F. W. "Poverty and Population," *Atlantic Monthly* (Boston), November 1959, *84–87*. Special references to Central and South American areas.

NUNLEY, R. E. The Distribution of Population in Costa Rica. Washington National Academy of Sciences. National Research Council. 1960. Pp. 71.

O'GARA, J. "Catholics and Population," *Commonweal* (New York), December 18, 1959, *339–42*. Particular references to Central and South America.

OSBORN, FREDERICK. Population: An *International Dilemma*. Princeton: Princeton University Press. 1958. A summary of the proceedings of the committee on population problems 1956–57. The Population Council, 230 Park Avenue, New York, 17, N.Y. Urban regions of Southern South America show declines in fertility. Largely agricultural areas of Northern South America, Central America, and the Caribbean with widespread illiteracy and low per capita incomes show increases.

PAN, CHIAN-LIN. "Effects of Recent and Possible Future Migration on the Population of Argentina, Brazil, Italy, and India," Proc. World Population Conference, 1954. Vol. II, New York, 1955, *131–66*. (United Nations Publication E/CONF. 13/414.) Net immigration of 100,000 per year during 1946–52 in Argentina increased male population under 45 years of age by 6% and reduced the population of age 55 and over by 6%. Brazil was not noticeably affected by the immigration of 300,000 from 1940–1950.

PEREIRA, J. DOS SANTOS. A previsão do crescimento das populacões urbanas. Bahía: University of Bahía. 1958. Pp. 100.

PERPIÑÁ, ROMÁN. Corología de la población de Nicaragua. Madrid: Instituto "Balmes" de Sociología. 1959. Pp. 121.

PETERSON, WILLIAM. Population. New York: The Macmillan Company. 1961. Pp. 621.

POBLETO TRONCOSO, M. "Too Many People," *Américas* (Washington, D.C.), September 1960, *11–15*. A Latin American discusses with disarming frankness the implication of the population explosion in Latin America.

POPULATION BULLETIN (Washington). Vol. XVIII, No. 6, October 1962, entire issue. Pp. 135.

THE POPULATION OF CENTRAL AMERICA, 1950–1980. New York: United Nations, Population Studies 16.

PRICE, PAUL H. "The Brazilian Population at Mid-Century," *Inter-American Economic Affairs* (Washington, D.C.), Vol. X, No. 1, Summer 1956, *66–78*.

PRICE, PAUL H. and J. V. FREITAS MARCONDES. "A Demographic Analysis of the Population of the State of São Paulo, Brazil," *Social Forces*, XXVII, 4, May 1959, *381–91*.

PROBLEMAS DEMOGRÁFICOS Y AGRARIOS DE MÉXICO. Mexico: Fondo de Cultura Económica. Part of a series of documentary monographs dealing with population and other sociological and economic problems. Contains specific information of value.

PROUDFOOT, M. J. "Demographic Aspects of Migration in the Caribbean," Proc. World Population Conference, 1954. Vol. II, New York 1955, *179–88*. (United Nations Publication E/CONF. 13.414.) The population problem is serious. Agriculture needs fewer workers and there is not enough industry to absorb them. Birth control is a problem. Prospects for reducing population pressure are poor, yet people demand a higher standard of living.

RIBEIRO, DARCY. "The Social Integration of Indigenous Populations in Brazil," *Int. Labour Rev.* (Geneva), April 1962, *325–45*.

— "The Social Integration of Indigenous Populations in Brazil: II. The Indian Problem in Brazil," *Int. Labour Rev.* (Geneva), May 1962, *459–77*.

ROBERT, G. W. "Recent Demographic Trends in Cuba, Haiti, and the British Caribbean," *Population Bull. United Nations* No. 5 (New York), July 1956, *42*. Population in the sugar colonies. Currents of migration: inter-island, from Asia and Africa, to the United States. Trends in mortality. Trends in fertility.

ROIG OCAMPOS, JORGE & CHARLES G. BENNETT. "Prueba de registro de nacimientos en Paraguay," *Estadística* (Mexico), March 1946, *111–16*.

SAUNDERS, J. V. D. La población del Ecuador: un análisis del censo de 1950. Quito: Casa de la Cultura Ecuatoriana. 1959. Pp. 118.

— The People of Ecuador, a Demographic Analysis. Gainesville, Florida: University of Florida Press. 1961. Pp. 61.

SAUVY, ALFRED. Fertility and Survival. New York: Criterion Books Inc. 1961. Pp. 230. Short discussion of Latin America's demographic prospects (pp. *61–64*). Contrasts 1950 data against probable data for 1980. Predicts on this basis the rate of increase between temperate zone (minus Paraguay) and the tropical zone (plus Paraguay). Tropical zone in 1980 will have population four times as large as that of the temperate zone, and Brazil will have a greater population than France and England together. Tables and maps.

SCHAUFF, J. C. Immigrant Colonization in Brazil as seen by European Experts. Geneva: International Catholic Migration Commission. 1956. Pp. 36.

SENIOR, CLARENCE. "Puerto Rican Migration: Spontaneous and Organized," Proc. World Population Conference, 1954. Vol. II, New York, 1955, *209–20*. (United Nations Publication E/CONF. 13/414.) Puerto Rican migration to the United States. A citizen, but culturally resembles an immigrant. Problems of adjustment to a new social atmosphere.

SHIMM, MELVIN G. Population Control. New York: Oceania Publications Ind. 1961. Pp. 254. Originally published in the summer of 1960 by Law and Contemporary Problems, Duke School of Law. Population projection to the year 2,000 for the world, continents, and regions. Population control in Puerto Rico. Excellent bibliography.

SIEWERS, ENRIQUE. "The Organization of Immigration and Land Settlement in Venezuela: I," *Int. Labour Rev.* (Geneva), June 1939, *764–72*.

— "The Organization of Immigration and Land Settlement in Venezuela: II," *Int. Labour Rev.* (Geneva), July 1939, *32–55*

SIGMAN, R. "Overpopulation Threatens the World," *Science News Letter* (Washington, D.C.), February 28, 1959, pp. *139*. Central and South American areas cited.

SIMONSON, ROBERTO C. "Economic Sources and Population Shifts," *Estadística* (Mexico), December 1944, *526–59*. The country treated is Brazil.

SIREAU, A., ZANARTU, M. and R. CERECEDA. Terre d'angoisse et d'espérance. L'Amérique Latine. Paris: Editions Universitaires Chrétienté Nouvelle. 1959. Pp. 168. Designed to draw Roman Catholic attention to the problems of Latin America resulting from its demographic expansion. Places special stress on the religious aspect.

SMITH, T. L. "Changing Image of Latin America," *Catholic World* (New York), February 1961, *272–77*. The population increase in Latin America.

— Latin American Population Studies. Gainesville, Florida: University of Florida Press. 1961. Pp. 83. University study of Central and South American demography.

STABILE, BLANCA. "The Working Woman in the Argentina Economy," *Int. Labour Rev.* (Geneva), February 1962, *122–28*. The situation of women workers in Argentina with regard to equality of remuneration, employment opportunities, standards of skill and maternity protection.

STEWARD, JULIAN H. "The Native Population of South America," Handbook of South American Indians. Washington, D.C.: Smithsonian Institution, U.S. Bureau of American Ethnology, Bulletin 143, U.S. Government Printing Office. 1949. Vol. V, part 3. Pp. 657.

STUART, ALEXANDER, J. Overpopulation: Twentieth Century Nemesis. New York: Exposition. 1958. Pp. 240. Central and South American nations are referred to.

SULLOWAY, ALVAH W. Birth Control and Catholic Doctrine. Boston: Beacon Press. 1959. Pp. 257. Introduction By Aldous Huxley.

TAUBER, ARNOST. "Social and Economic Aspects of World Food Production," *Impact of Science on Society* (Paris), January 1962, *39–59*. Tables illustrating South American development and problems as opposed to the rest of the world.

THOMPSON, WARREN. Population Problems. New York: McGraw-Hill. 4th edition 1953. Pp. 488. A discussion of the population problems of Central and South American nations is included in this comprehensive study.

TIETZE, CHRISTOPHER. "La fecundidad humana en América Latina," *Estadística* (Washington, D.C.), September 1959, *497–509*. The levels and trends of human fertility in Latin America; differential fertility; social and psychological factors associated with patterns of reproduction; implication for further population growth; prospects for a decline in fertility.

UNITED NATIONS DEPARTMENT OF ECONOMIC AND SOCIAL AFFAIRS, ECONOMIC COMMISSION FOR LATIN AMERICA. Análisis y proyecciones del desarrollo económico V: El desarrollo económico de la Argentina II. Los sectores de la producción. México. 1959. Pp. 259. II. G. 3. Vol. II E/CON. 12/429/Add 1/Y2/Rev. 1. Realization of human potential in regard to increasing production.

— Analyses and Projections of Economic Development III: The Economic Development of Colombia. Geneva. 1957. Pp. 454. II. G. 3. E/CN. 12/365/Rev. 1.

UNITED NATIONS ECONOMIC AND SOCIAL COUNCIL. Draft Annual Report of the Commission to the Economic and Social Council. Part I. (30 March 1960–15 March 1961). 1961. E/CN. 12/573. Demographic research *55–58*.

— Draft Report to the Economic and Social Council on the Eleventh Session of the Population Commission. New York. E CN. 9/L. 71/Add. 5. No. 3: regional; No. 4: Improvement of Demographic Statistics; No. 5: Program of work for 1961–62 in the field of population.

— Population Trends in Latin America in Relation to Economic and Social Policy. New York. 1961. Pp. 26. E/CN. 12/583.

— Preliminary Study of the Demographic Situation in Latin America. New York. 1961. Pp. 108. E/CN. 12/604.

UNITED NATIONS DEPARTMENT OF SOCIAL AFFAIRS. Multilingual Demographic Dictionary. June 1954. Pp. 73. Population Studies No. 19. St/SOA/Ser. A/19.

— Population Growth and the Standard of Living in Underdeveloped Countries. New York. October 1954. Pp. 9. Population Studies No. 20. St./SOA/Ser. A/20.

— The Population of South America 1950–1980. New York: Columbia University Press. 1955. Population Studies No. 21. St/SOA/Ser. A/21.

— Sex and Age of International Migrants; Statistics for 1918–1947. New York. January 1953. Pp. 281. Population Studies No. 11. St/SOA/Ser. A/11. Contains maps and tables for all countries, emigration figures vary from country to country. Some count aliens departing permanently, others include aliens and nationals leaving seaports and airports, etc.

— World Population Trends 1920–1947. New York. December 1949. Pp. 16. Population Studies No. 3. St/SOA/Ser. A/3. Population estimates in Latin America by age group, reliability of figures – fair for Latin America, rate of increase in Latin America averaging 2% per annum over the most recent years.

UNITED NATIONS POPULATION BULLETIN. Published since December 1951 by the Population Division of the U.N. Department of Social Affairs, New York.

UNITED NATIONS TECHNICAL ASSISTANCE ADMINISTRATION. Report of the United Nations of Technical Assistance to Bolivia. New York. 1951. Pp. 128. St/TAA/K/Bolivia/1. Brief section on colonization of the Oriente of Bolivia by inhabitants of the Altiplano p. 57. An evaluation of social developments in Bolivia and demographic problems, *89–111*.

UNITED STATES DEPARTMENT OF LABOR. Bureau of Labor Statistics. Migration and Population Growth for Puerto Rico: 1954. Puerta de Tierra, Puerto Rico. 1955. Pp. 7. Population growth by sex, birth rate, mortality rate, unemployment in the U.S. Tables on estimated population 1950–1955, estimated age and sex composition of the migrants during 1954, estimated age and sex composition of the migrants during 1953.

URIBE, ROMO EMILIO. "México y las implicaciones demográficas de la post guerra." Rev. Mexic. Sociol. (Mexico), September–December 1947, p. 315.

VAN DEN HAAG, E. "Demographers Go to New York," Saturday Review (New York), June 20, 1959, p. 24. Special references to Central and South American areas.

VANZETTO, CARLO. Land and Man in Latin America. Rome: Società Italiana di Sociologia Rurale. 1961. Pp. 33. Heterogenous composition of Latin America, distribution of arable land, animal species raised per square mile, tables on estimate of areas occupied by the different types of entrepreneur in millions of hectares and percentages of total area of Latin America. Tables on population density and estimates of size and racial composition.

THE VISION LETTER (New York). "Chile Has Become the First Latin American Nation to Take Stock Officially of the Critical Problems of Overpopulation," June 19, 1962, pp. 2–3.

VIVES, AUGUSTO. "Life Tables for Panama 1941–1943," Estadística (Washington, D.C.), March 1949, 113–19.

VOGT, WILLIAM. People. New York: William Sloane Associate. 1960. Pp. 257. Excessive population growth, ethics of parenthood, bibliography.

— "People: Challenge to Survival," Saturday Review (New York), January 14, 1961, p. 30. References to Central and South American areas.

WATERLOO J. and A. VERGARA. "La malnutrition protéique au Brésil," Bulletin of the W.H.O. (Geneva), XV, 1956, 165–201. Tables and charts, discussion of socio-economic aspects of the problems.

WHITLOCK, RALPH. "Leaf Protein-Food of the Future," Impact of Science on Society (Paris), December 1956, 225–33. An interesting if somewhat unusual article involving the problem of the low standard of living in the Amazon basin and the possibility of the use of Amazonian vegetation as a source of food for the swollen population of Brazilian cities.

WHY LABOUR LEAVES THE LAND. Geneva: International Labour Office. 1960. 143–59. Brazil – currents in migration, agricultural labour force trends, social causes of the movement out of agriculture, effects of the movement. Venezuela – decline in agricultural labour force from 1941–1950, pull forces and push forces in declining rural population.

WYTHE, GEORGE, with the assistance of ROYCE A. WIGHT and HAROLD M. MIDKIFF. Brazil an Expanding Economy. New York: The Twentieth Century Fund. 1949. Pp. 412. Basic information regarding Brazil's population.

WOYTINSKY, W. S., and E. S. World Population and Production: Trends and Outlook. New York: Twentieth Century Fund. 1953. Pp. 1268. Special references to Central and South America.

YOUNG, CHESTER W. "Some of Haiti's Population and National Territory Significant in Census Consideration," Estadística (Washington, D.C.), December 1949, 516–29. Data on the origin of the population of Haiti.

— "Some Aspects of Haiti's Population and National Territory Significant in Census Consideration," Estadística (Washington, D.C.), March 1950, 69–86. Population characteristics: distribution and movement; composition of population; religious adherence; educational condition; occupational status; tables and charts.

— "Some Aspects of Haiti's Population and National Territory Significant in Census Consideration," Estadística (Washington, D.C.), September 1950, 388–99. The nature and relationship of settlement patterns and population groupings.

ZUCKERMAN, SIR SOLLY. "The Control of Human Fertility," Impact of Science on Society (Paris), February 1958, 61–78. Deals in particular with Puerto Rico and Barbados.

Addendum

ERICKSON, E. GORDON. The West Indies Population Problems: Dimensions in Action. Lawrence: Univ. of Kansas Social Sci. Studies, 1962. Pp. X, 194. Maps. Charts. Diagrams. Graphs. Tables. Demographic problems from 1956 to 59, with special reference to the British islands.

RONALD HILTON is Professor of Romanic Languages and Director of the Institute of Hispanic American and Luso-Brazilian Studies at Stanford University. He is the founder and editor of the Hispanic American Report, a monthly analysis of developments in Spain, Portugal and Latin America. He is the author of numerous books and articles on Spanish and Latin American subjects, among them the *Handbook of Hispanic Source Materials in the United States, Campoamor Spain and the World,* and *Four Studies in Franco-Spanish Relations.* He is also the editor of *Who's Who in Latin America.*

Housing and Population Growth in Africa, Asia, and Latin America

by

ROBERT C. COOK & KAVAL GULHATI

INTRODUCTION

This paper discusses the housing problem in Africa, Asia, and Latin America in relation to population growth and urban expansion. The main emphasis is on the present housing deficit and on the population growth which is likely to increase this deficit, especially in the urban areas.

THE PROBLEM OF THE HOUSING DEFICIT

An accumulated housing deficit exists in African, Asian, and Latin American countries. This deficit is a reflection of the low standards of living and the high rates of population increase in these areas.

Most African, Asian, and Latin American countries have a small group of high-income families who occupy spacious – or at least modern – housing units. This tiny, well-housed minority is not the focus of the discussion that follows. The emphasis here is, necessarily, on the great majority of the population living in overcrowded, often primitive and unhygienic, conditions.

Millions of these low-income or "no income" persons in these areas who do not occupy conventional housing units live in "makeshift (improvised, rustic, nonpermanent) structures..... made of such materials as mud, old boards, straw, scrap metal, etc." Others dwell in housing units which are dilapidated or which lack basic facilities, such as piped water, sanitary service, etc. Still others have no private dwelling and literally live on sidewalks or other public places, as in Calcutta or Hong Kong. According to a United Nations report, these persons are probably left out from both the housing and population censuses, and to make even an approximate estimate of their number is almost impossible. (4A).

However, a large proportion of those that do get enumerated are inadequately housed. A recent United Nations report on world housing estimated that over 900 million persons in Africa, Asia, and Latin America are without proper housing. More than 700 million of these people live in Asia. At a low estimate of $500 per unit, the total cost to eliminate this shortage in Asia would amount to $70 billion.

In the past, little or no gain was made in meeting the deficit. The reason for this is the economic inability of the nonindustrial nations to provide enough housing for their expanding populations. In the large-population countries, this is an enormous problem. As these populations grow bigger, the already appalling housing situation is likely to get worse.

THE RATE OF POPULATION GROWTH IN RELATION TO THE HOUSING SITUATION

The impact of the high rate of population growth on the housing deficit is threefold:

(1) High birth rates and falling death rates result in larger family size. More babies mean more overcrowding in the already cramped dwellings of many Asian and Latin American countries. In Panama, for example, where the birth rate is about 40 [1] and the death rate 18, the average number of persons per room is almost 3. Denmark, with a birth rate of only 16.6 and

TABLE I

Number of persons per dwelling and per room in selected countries for latest available year

Country	Average number of persons per dwelling	Percentage of dwellings with following number of rooms			Percentage of dwellings with following number of persons per room			
		1–2	3–4	5 plus	Less than 1.5	1.5 and over	2 and over	3 and over
Argentina	5–6	63	27	10	19	81	63	36
Panama	5	82	14	4	27	73	66	46
Trinidad-Tobago	4–5	57	36	7	42	58	48	24
Mauritius	5	74	18	8	28	72	62	33
Ceylon	5–6	76	19	5	....	....	....	....
United States	3. 3	8	33	59	....	....	....	....
Denmark	3. 1	4	58	38	96	4	1	0
West Germany	4. 0	17	58	26	83	17	7	1

NOTE. – The data refer to dwellings only. A dwelling is a room or a suite of rooms and its accessories intended for private habitation with a separate access to the street. In some countries, the data include nonpermanent structures and improvised shelters. Source: United Nations. Statistical Yearbook, New York, 1961.

1. Birth and death rates are in terms of 1,000 of the population per year.

a death rate of 9.5, has just about one person to every two rooms. These high rates of growth in Africa, Asia, and Latin America have resulted in a larger proportion of children in the population. For example, in the industrial countries where the low birth- and death-rate pattern is established, the ratio of children under 15 years to the total population is only about 20–30%. In the underdeveloped areas, this proportion is 40% or more of the total population. Table I gives statistics on the crowded housing conditions of some countries in the underdeveloped areas.

The table shows that these African, Asian, and Latin American countries average five to six persons per housing unit, whereas in the United States and Europe the average is about three to four persons. Further, about three-fourths of the dwellings in the underdeveloped countries have less than two rooms. And in three countries, Argentina, Panama, and Mauritius, nearly two-thirds of the dwellings have more than two persons per room. In contrast, the United States, Denmark, and Germany have over three rooms to almost every dwelling. And the overwhelming majority of dwellings have less than three persons to every two rooms.

(2) High birth rates and large family size mean more babies and more family expenditure. This adversely affects (a) the rate of family savings, and (b) the rate of increase of the national per capita income.

Unless these low-income families save, they cannot invest in private houses or hope to pay higher rents for better housing.

As it is, the current per capita income levels in Africa, Asia, and Latin America are extremely low. The average per capita income for Asia is a little over $100, and in India and Pakistan it is as low as $70–$80. The Latin American average of $298 is somewhat better... The faster these income levels rise, the quicker will be the effect on living conditions. But, in the past, population increase has been so rapid that the relative increase in per capita income has been slight. (For data on income levels, see table III.)

(3) Future population growth: The current situation with respect to population growth and housing conditions is complicated. The prospect for future rapid growth adds to the gravity of the problem.

In terms of housing needed or of new housing required in the future, the rate of growth of the adult population (that is, changes in birth and death rates in prior periods) is the most relevant factor. By studying the age distribution of a population (and relating this to marriage, divorce, and widowhood rates, that is, rates of household formation), an estimate can be made of the number of housing units needed in the future.

Table II gives the population of Latin America by age for 1960 and projections to 1975. (See appendix table I for percentage age composition of India.)

The striking facts that emerge from the table are:

(a) In absolute numbers, the age group 0–19 outstripped all other age

TABLE II

Estimated population of mainland Latin America, by age, 1960

POPULATION

[In thousands]

Age	Mainland Latin America	Mexico	Central America	Tropical South America	Temperate South America
0 to 4	31,147	6,068	2,101	18,735	4,243
5 to 14	46,570	9,181	2,992	27,942	6,455
15 to 19	18,223	3,402	1,196	10,886	2,739
20 to 44	61,280	10,452	3,786	35,494	11,548
45 to 64	23,282	4,036	1,303	12,444	5,499
65 and over	6,040	981	359	3,070	1,630
Total population, 1960	186,542	34,119	11,737	108,572	32,114

PERCENT INCREASE, 1960–75

Age	Mainland Latin America	Mexico	Central America	Tropical South America	Temperate South America
0 to 4	50.2	63.1	53.9	53.8	14.0
5 to 14	55.4	59.4	62.8	58.2	33.5
15 to 19	58.5	66.3	59.9	58.0	50.6
20 to 44	45.0	61.5	52.0	48.0	18.4
45 to 64	44.1	38.2	52.1	49.1	34.9
65 and over	72.3	84.8	70.2	69.4	70.5
Total increase, all ages	50.5	59.6	56.4	53.4	29.0

Source: Population Reference Bureau, *Population Bulletin*, Vol. XVIII, No. 6, October 1962.

TABLE III

Population and per capita gross national product in 1960

Region and country	GNP per capita (U.S. dollars)	Mid-1960 population (millions)	Region and country	GNP per capita (U.S. dollars)	Mid-1960 population (millions)
Total free world	558	1,968	Latin America–Con.		
Africa	128	225	Bolivia	62	4
Asia	111	969	Mexico	310	35
India	81	433	Northern America	2,720	199
Pakistan	68	92	United States	2,791	181
Japan	413	94	Canada	2,009	18
Philippines	144	28	Western Europe	917	354
Latin America	298	204	France	1,267	46
Argentina	439	21	United Kingdom	1,347	53
Brazil	196	66	Oceania	1,259	16

Source: U.S. Department of State, Agency for International Development, Statistics and Reports Division. "Estimates of Gross National Product," March 1962.

groups in 1960. The current household forming age group of 20–44 was about one-third of the population;

(b) A little over half of the total population was under 19 years. These are the youngsters who will need independent housing during the next decade; and

(c) The expected percent increase during 1960–75 in all age groups is 50. In the age group 5–19, the expected increase is over 55%.

This mushrooming growth of young people who will soon be forming their own families will add more pressure to the current housing situation. Thus, any planning for housing programs must take into account the housing needs of the present population (that is, the current housing deficit), plus a continuing increase of these needs due to population growth.

A quotation from Dr. IRENE TAEUBER in a recent paper published in the *Population Bulletin* sums up the demographic outlook for Latin America:

"Increase is rapid in all age groups. Any planning in any aspect of social and economic development must involve a present population plus a continuing increase of that population.....

If age at marriage remains unchanged, new families formed in 1975 will be three-fifths again as numerous as those formed in 1960. There are potential markets here – but there are also major requirements for employment, and for investment in housing, equipment, and facilities.....

If fertility remains unchanging, the analysts of 1975 will compute ratios of growth from 1975 to 1990 as high as those that we have computed for the years from 1960 to 1975."

Calculations made by the United Nations show that in Africa, Asia, and Latin America, construction of over 7 million dwelling units is needed in 1960 to accommodate new households formed as a result of population increase. By 1975, the rate of construction must increase 75% over 1960 on account of accelerated population growth and associated changes in the age composition.

POPULATION GROWTH AND URBAN EXPANSION

The urban populations of Africa, Asia, and Latin America are growing at rates that are almost twice as high as the over-all population growth rates. The estimated rate of growth for urban Latin America is 4.2% per year. Urban Africa and urban Asia each has an annual rate of 4%.[2] (European urban growth is at the rate of 1.6% a year.) These staggeringly high growth rates mean the addition of an increasingly larger number of people to the already overpacked, underhoused city populations.

Table IV shows that in 1960 an estimated 275 million Africans, Asians, and Latin Americans were living in cities of over 100,000 people. (This figure is over 50% higher than the entire 1960 U.S. population of about 180 million.)

The annual rural growth rates are: Africa, 1.7%; Asia, 1.5%; Latin America, 1%.

And by 1975 the number will more than double. Further, the proportion of the populations living in urban areas of 100,000 and over will be twice as high for Africa, almost twice as high for Asia, and about three-fifths as high for Latin America in 1975.

TABLE IV

Estimated and projected urban population, by size groups, for Africa, Asia, and Latin America, 1960 and 1975

	Population in places 100,000 and over (millions)	As percent of total population	Population in places 1,000,000 and over (millions)	As percent of total population
Year 1960:				
Africa	20	8	6	2
Asia	204	12	102	6
Latin America	51	25	25	12
Year 1975:				
Africa	48	16	12	4
Asia	486	22	221	10
Latin America	118	39	61	20

Source: Urban Land Institute, World Urbanization, Technical Bulletin No. 43, April 1962.

The reasons for growth rates of these proportions are: (*a*) The migration of large numbers of rural people from agriculture to industry, located in urban areas; and (*b*) the high rates of natural increase, that is, births minus deaths, of the city populations.

The report of the United Nations Economic Commission for Europe Seminar on housing in October 1961 makes this comment:

"While the housing requirements of developed countries originate in a normal population development and the need for a renewal of housing stock, those of countries in the process of rapid industrialization arise mainly from large-scale and intense urbanization."

Table II in the appendix shows Latin American rural-urban population growth in 1950–60 and projections to 1970. This table indicates an urban population increase of 30 million (or about a 45% increase) in 1959–60. The estimated urban population of 138 million for 1970 will be more than double the 1950 figure of 66 million. In rural Latin America, the 1950–60 population growth was less than 15% .The estimated increase in rural numbers between 1950 and 1970 is about 29 million. The most striking fact is that, by 1970, Latin America's total population will jump by 60% over the 1950 figure. And over 70% of this increase is expected to be in urban areas.

In Asia, between 1900 and 1950, the population living in cities of 100,000 or more mounted from about 20 million to nearly 106 million (a gain of

444%). In Africa, there was a gain of 629%, from 1.4 million to 10.2 million.

A unique feature of Latin American urbanization is that about 10% of the total population in 13 out of the 20 countries lives in the largest city or metropolitan area, usually the capital city. In six countries, the largest city contains one-fifth or more of the population.

If 20% of the U.S. population lived in Washington, D.C., the Capital would have 36 million people.

These statistics explain why so much attention is directed to the urban housing situation. While rural housing, no doubt, poses problems, they remain pale in intensity as compared to urban conditions. Firstly, densities are less in rural areas and a lot of housing is put up on a self-help basis. And, secondly, the rural exodus to urban areas relieves some of the pressure on the land.

In the cities, land prices are prohibitively high and most people cannot afford to own their homes. For example, in Manila, an acre of land costs $25,000 to $30,000. Some Asians and Latin Americans can pay the high rent for a decent house, but the vast majority who cannot, live in filthy concentrations of rubble, scrap, and human beings. These are the urban slums, a selected few of which are described below.[3]

Bombay. – The population of Bombay grew by almost 70% during 1950–60.

About one-half of the population lives in substandard housing and a large number live on footpaths. Bombay's slums contain over half a million persons living in 9,000 dilapidated units. Another million live in 200,000 single-room tenements scattered over the city. In some cases, 7 to 10 persons consisting of 2 or 3 families share 1 room.

Calcutta.[4] – With a population of nearly 6 million. Calcutta is one of the largest cities in the world. Between 1950 and 1960, Calcutta's population increased by 2.3 million.

About one-fourth of the total population lives in one-eighth of the city's land which constitutes the Calcutta slums. Nearly two-thirds of these slum families have no water supply and no proper lighting or ventilation. In some cases, as many as 45 persons share 1 latrine.

Hong Kong. – A population of 2.9 million, increasing at a rate of 4.1% a year, gives the island a density of over 7,000 persons per square mile. In 1957, a survey of regular housing showed that 79% of the households shared

3. There is very little information available for individual African countries. In urban Africa as a whole, about 50% of the total population "live in improvised housing, in slums, under bridges, and in all kinds of other shelters as well as overcrowded dwellings." The 1957 United Nations Report on the World Social Situation states: "While . . . . . in many African cities low-rent housing programs have been put into operation in recent years, formidable obstacles are created by the rapid increase of urban population. the limited capacity of Africans to pay even minimal rentals, and the rising cost of land and building materials."

4. The Ford Foundation has recently sponsored a project for improving conditions in this city.

common facilities. About 40% were living in "cubicles, bedspaces, cocklofts, and on verandas." Only 7.5% had a living room not used for sleeping.

The new resettlement blocks provide low-rent accommodation averaging 24 square feet per person.

Rio de Janeiro. – By 1960, Rio's population had added nearly 1 million people to the 1950 total of 3 million. In 1950, Rio's slums, known as "favelas," contained about 14.3% of the population. A 1948 survey showed that two-thirds of the "houses" were worth less than $108. Three-fourths had no toilets and about 90% had no piped water.

Mexico City. – The population of the federal district surrounding Mexico City grew by 160% between 1940 and 1950. The city proper grew by 53% during the same period.

A citywide housing survey in 1952 showed that 34% of the population lived in "turgurios" – one-room apartments opening on a courtyard or passageway. Another 11% were living in rented "jacales" – shacks made from scrap materials. The jacales had about 34 persons per toilet but most of the toilets were out of order and the jacale dwellers used the waste land around their shacks.

Altogether in Latin America an estimated 70% of existing urban housing units require rebuilding. In urban India alone, a shortage of nearly 5 million houses leaves 20 to 30 million people (equivalent to the combined population of New York and California) in need of proper housing.

According to one United Nations estimate, the increase in African, Asian, and Latin American urban households would mean a 133% step-up in urban construction 15 years from now. In Asia, urban construction would be 250% more; in Africa, 133%; and in Latin America, almost 100% more.

CONCLUSION

The housing problem in the underdeveloped areas has three dimensions: (1) The accumulated housing deficit and replacement of existing stock, (2) the critical situation in urban areas, and (3) the new housing required for population increase.

If, as the United Nations recommends, 30 years were taken as the target to meet the housing shortage, and the average life of a house taken as about 25 years, then annual construction needed for these two factors plus that required by population growth, would be nearly 22 million units in 1960. By 1975, annual construction needs would be almost 28 million units. Population increase alone would require over 45% of these units. (See table V.) The urban areas of Africa, Asia, and Latin America constituting less than 30% of the total population, would account for over half of the recommended construction.

Unless population growth slows down and income levels rise rapidly, the housing situation in the underdeveloped areas is not likely to improve.

TABLE V

Estimated annual housing needs in Africa, Asia, and Latin America, 1960 and 1975

[In millions of dwelling units]

	1960	1975		1960	1975
Due to population increase:			To replace the stock: [1]		
Africa	0.84	1.50	Africa	1.03	1.03
Asia	5.30	9.40	Asia	7.10	7.10
Latin America	1.10	1.70	Latin America	.90	.90
To eliminate the deficit or			Total new housing needed:		
shortage in 30 years:			Africa	2.60	3.26
Africa	.73	.73	Asia	17.20	21.30
Asia	4.80	4.80	Latin America	2.60	3.20
Latin America	.60	.60			
			Total	22.40	27.76

1. Average life of a dwelling unit is assumed to be 30 years in urban and 20 years in rural areas. The 1975 figures do not take into account increments of stock between 1960 and 1975.

Source: United Nations, "World Housing Conditions and Estimated Requirements," July 1962.

Small-scale, low-income, public housing projects can hardly do more than keep a deplorable situation from getting worse. A United Nations report which reviews the social problems of urbanization in economically underdeveloped areas highlights these points:

"The housing problem cannot be solved simply by concentrating on construction of houses..... the rapidity of city growth..... can overwhelm even the most ambitious housing program. It has been reported that new construction for low-income groups sometimes encourages a large flow of (rural) migrants and, thus, diminishes the slum population not at all......

The housing problem goes beyond the question of construction..... because much of the population now living in the city slums is poorly adapted to urban life, economically, socially, and psychologically. These groups not only need an opportunity to move into better housing; they also lack...... incomes permitting them to maintain these standards without depriving themselves of other necessities. If these conditions are not met, new housing is likely to deteriorate rapidly through lack of maintenance, and the occupants will smuggle in lodgers to supplement their incomes and, thus, reproduce the former overcrowding."[5]

The housing crisis is part of the economic and social crisis which is sweeping across the underdeveloped nations today. Checking rapid growth by bringing high birth rates into line with modern low death rates is a prerequisite to coming to grips with the problem. Growing recognition of this fact is encouraging.

5. See bibliography, item 5 A.

APPENDIX

TABLE I

Percentage age composition of India's population, 1951, 1961, and 1981 [1]

Age	1951	1961	1981
Total	99.9	100.0	99.8
0 to 14	38.8	39.7	41.9
15 to 19	27.2	26.3	25.7
20 to 44	18.3	18.0	16.0
45 to 59	10.8	10.8	10.4
60 to 74	4.3	4.6	5.0
75 and over	.5	.6	.9

1. On an assumption of constant fertility.

Source: United Nations, "The Population of Asia and the Far East, 1950–1980," New York, 1959.

BIBLIOGRAPHY

1. BUTLER, WILLIAM F., Vice President of the Chase Manhattan Bank, an address, "Housing in Latin America," at the Latin American Housing Symposium, New York, April 1962.
2. Population Reference Bureau, *Population Bulletin*, volume XIII, No. 8, December 1957; volume XVIII, No. 6, October 1962; and volume XVIII, No. 8, December 1962.
3. United Nations.
   A. Economic Commission for Asia and the Far East: "Urbanization and Housing in Asia and the Far East," June 1962.
   B. Economic Commission for Europe: "Report on the Seminar on Housing Surveys and Programs," October 1961.
4. United Nations.
   A. Demographic Center for Latin America: "Demographic Information Required for Housing Programs With Special Reference to Latin America," July 1962.
   B. Housing, Building, and Planning Branch, Bureau of Social Affairs: "World Housing Conditions and Estimated Housing Requirements," July 1962.
5. United Nations, Department of Economic and Social Affairs.
   A. "Report on the World Social Situation," New York, 1957 and 1961.
   B. "The Population of Asia and the Far East, 1950–1980," New York, 1959.
   C. "The Future Growth of World Population," New York, 1958.
6. United Nations, Statistical Office.
   A. Demographic Yearbook, New York, 1961.
   B. Statistical Yearbook, New York, 1961.
7. Urban Land Institute: "World Urbanization," Technical Bulletin, No. 43. Washington, D.C., 1962.

TABLE II

Latin America: Estimates and projections of the total, urban and rural population by country, midyear 1950, 1960, and 1970

Country	Number (in thousands)									Decennial percent change					
	Total			Urban			Rural			Total		Urban		Rural	
	1950	1960	1970	1950	1960	1970	1950	1960	1970	1950-60	1960-70	1950-60	1960-70	1950-60	1960-70
Total	155,570	199,235	257,040	65,469	95,870	138,300	90,101	103,365	118,740	28	29	46	44	15	15
Argentina	17,190	21,000	24,990	11,040	14,205	17,485	6,150	6,795	7,505	22	19	29	23	10	10
Bolivia	2,930	3,600	4,540	1,015	1,380	1,980	1,915	2,220	2,560	23	26	36	43	16	15
Brazil	51,975	65,860[1]	84,440	18,815	27,380	39,780	33,160	38,480	44,660	27	28	46	45	16	16
Dominican Republic	2,130	2,845	3,895	505	865	1,480	1,625	1,980	2,415	34	37	71	71	22	22
Colombia	11,145	14,770	19,590	4,170	7,065	11,080	6,975	7,705	8,510	33	33	69	57	10	10
Costa Rica	800	1,145	1,560	265	460	685	535	685	875	43	36	74	49	28	28
Cuba	5,520	6,820	8,340	3,065	4,110	5,345	2,455	2,710	2,995	24	22	34	30	10	11
Chile	6,075	7,635	9,660	3,575	5,010	6,900	2,500	2,625	2,760	26	27	40	38	5	5
Ecuador	3,195	4,285	5,650	910	1,500	2,235	2,285	2,785	3,395	34	31	65	49	22	22
El Salvador	1,870	2,395	3,115	685	1,020	1,515	1,185	1,375	1,600	28	30	49	49	16	16
Guatemala	3,040	3,980	5,325	760	1,205	1,940	2,280	2,775	3,385	31	34	59	61	22	22
Haiti	3,110	3,725	4,620	380	710	1,290	2,730	3,015	3,330	20	24	87	82	10	10
Honduras	1,385	1,755	2,305	430	590	885	955	1,165	1,420	27	31	37	50	22	22
Mexico	26,435	35,115	47,330	11,265	17,510	26,900	15,170	17,605	20,430	33	35	55	54	16	16
Nicaragua	1,060	1,465	1,955	370	625	930	690	840	1,025	38	33	69	49	22	22
Panama	755	1,010	1,370	285	430	670	470	580	700	34	36	51	56	23	21
Paraguay	1,400	1,625	1,975	390	565	860	1,010	1,060	1,115	16	22	45	52	5	5
Peru	8,170	10,510	14,030	2,975	4,480	7,030	5,195	6,030	7,000	29	33	51	57	16	16
Uruguay	2,410	2,760	3,020	1,895	2,245	2,505	515	515	515	15	9	18	12	......	......
Venezuela	4,975	6,935	9,350	2,675	4,515	6,805	2,300	2,420	2,545	39	35	69	51	5	5

1. An estimate of Brazil's midyear population based on the provisional figure from the 1960 census is 70,600,000, or 4,700,000 greater than projected.

Source: United Nations, "Situación demográfica, económica, social y educativa de América Latina," Conferencia sobre educación y desarrollo económico y social en América Latina, Santiago de Chile, 5 a 19 de Marzo de 1962, ST/ECLA/CONF. 10/L. 4; 10 de enero, 1962, table 1, p. 8.

ROBERT CARTER COOK was Editor of the *Journal of Heredity* from 1922 to 1963 and Director of the Population Reference Bureau and Editor of the *Population Bulletin* from 1951 to 1958, the President of the Bureau since that time. He has been lecturer in Medical Genetics in the School of Medicine at George Washington University since 1944, and Lecturer in Biology there since 1946. He was a recipient of the Lasker Award in 1956. He is a contributor to technical and popular journals and author of *Human Fertility: The Modern Dilemma* (1951).

The American Fertility Cult

by

LINCOLN H. DAY

The United States is currently experiencing a most rapid rate of population growth. If such a rate were sustained for 356 more years, our country would have the population density of New York City. Ninety-eight more years at the average growth rate of the last five would bring our number up to one billion – *over a third of the present population of the entire world.*

The apologists for unchecked population growth, whoever they are and whatever country they refer to, overlook limitations in the earth's capacity to provide. Raw materials and the amount of land suitable for settlement are not infinitely elastic, and they contract to the extent that we continue to raise our level of living in the ways we have been doing. If the arguments in favor of population increase continue to prevail – even in this country – we must inevitably be faced with a choice between quantity and quality: vast numbers of people living poorly at necessarily low levels of living, or fewer people, but those fewer living well. We cannot have it both ways. Those who condone our continued growth in numbers – whether they realize it or not – have decided in favor of quantity. The choice is remarkable.

The arguments in support of our current population increase are of three general types: (1) Economic; (2) Scientific; and (3) Social.

The "economic" argument is that population growth is necessary for the maintenance of our current level of economic prosperity, and a requisite for any long-range prosperity, as well.

"Your future is great in a growing America," reads a so-called public service advertisement in the New York subway. "Every day 11,000 babies are born in America. This means new business, new jobs, new opportunities." And some weeks earlier the nation's most widely circulated weekly magazine had taken a similar tack with the cover title, "Kids: Built-in Recession

Reprinted from Columbia University Forum, Summer 1960. Copyright 1960 by the Reader's Digest Association, Inc.

Cure – How 4,000,000 a Year Make Millions in Business." Inside, it was "Rocketing Births: Business Bonanza."

Are such claims justified? Is economic prosperity in the United States a necessary result of population growth? Surely it was once. When a man's strength was an important source of energy and per capita consumption was at a low level, a growing population in a sparsely settled land could indeed be important in creating a high level of material living. More people meant more energy, a greater division of labor, and an expanding market for goods.

But today, the combination of increasing population and a generally rising level of living has revealed limitations in the supply of raw materials and increased the costs of developing them. All minerals and most of the sources of energy in current use are *non-renewable*. It has taken millions of years to create them. They represent capital. As we use them up we are using capital, not income. The fact that we have already had to resort to ores that are expensive to work and of relatively low grade is only one sign of approaching depletion. The predictions on copper, lead, tin, sulphur, and iron ore, among others, are that their real costs will increase in the near future (that is, their costs in hours of work and capital required per unit.)

The outlook is no brighter for *renewable* resources. The size and growth rates of our forests already limit the use of wood and wood products, whose real prices have approximately doubled since 1900. And despite greater development and conservation of water resources, our continued growth in numbers, combined with our rising level of living, has placed steeply mounting demands upon them. As ROBERT and LEONA RIENOW have noted:

"More than a thousand cities and towns [in the United States] already have been forced to curtail their water service. Near Chicago, where artesian wells flowed under their own pressure a hundred years ago, new wells must go down 2,000 feet to reach the water table. Dallas is already pumping the salt-tainted Red River into its main, and New York faces the likelihood that eventually it will have to purify the polluted Hudson to slake its growing thirst. In Missisipi, wells are now 400 feet deeper, on the average, than they were only ten years ago. Denver, eager for new industry, has been turning away manufacturers whose production processes involve a heavy use of water."

With our growing population and our high level of living we are borrowing on the future – our own and that of our posterity. It is not that we will suddenly find ourselves without resources. Long before we completely exhaust them the resources that remain will have become so costly as to be unobtainable.

To advocate American population growth as a means to economic prosperity is to be not only domestically shortsighted, but also ignorant of the realities of world political and economic conditions. Already, we

Americans, with but 6% of the world's population, consume half of the world's production of main minerals (iron, copper, lead, zinc); and we consume nearly twice as much commercial energy per person as Britain and eighty times as much as India. The imbalance between our numbers and our consumption of fossil fuels, metals, and so on highlights the fact that, important as the overpopulation – or threatened overpopulation – of much of the rest of the world may be, when it comes to depletion of the world's natural resources, it takes a lot of Asians or Africans or Latin Americans at *their* material levels of living to consume as much as one American at *his*. Any precise statistical comparison is impossible, yet it may not be far wrong to say that each year the average American consumes in natural resources as much as do twenty-five or thirty Indians. When we remember that because of a much greater life expectancy the American has more than twice as many years of consuming ahead of him, that bracing yearly addition of 4,000,000 American babies takes on new meaning indeed.

We know that part of the new nationalism in Asia, Africa, and the Near East expresses the desire of other peoples to live more decently – this can only worsen the situation. Even without improvement in their levels of living, the rapid population increases in these countries will place ever-mounting demands on the world's resources. To the extent these peoples attain the higher levels to which they aspire, the supply of raw materials will be depleted just so much faster. That fraction of the world's population which lives in the United States cannot for long continue to consume 40 to 50% of the world's resources.

The support for our present rate of population growth which is sup-posedly drawn from "science" (for which read: science-and-technology) rests on the assumption that scientific development will somehow keep up with any population growth we may experience (or perpetrate). Like other forms of utopianism, such a belief must rest ultimately on faith, not reason. On the one hand we hear claims that interplanetary transportation will solve all shortages of land and raw materials, and, on the other, declarations that God will provide for His flock no matter how large it becomes. But even if minerals were found on the moon, the costs of transportation to and from the earth would surely prohibit their use; while to assume that God will provide is to overlook the more than a billion already in the world who are currently umprovided for by even minimum dietary standards – they starve.

Those who put their faith in Science are merely replacing one deity with another. Obviously any solution to the problem of population growth will depend on further work in such specialties as physiology, agriculture, and economics. But science and technology in turn depend on existing re-sources. Moreover, further development in these fields will require substantial expenditures for education, training, experimentation, and research. Yet, the greater the difficulties created by a growing population, the more we shall have to spend simply to meet such fundamental needs of that population as food, housing, primary education, transportation, and medical care. The larger our population, the more capital we must invest (and the less we will have available for the purchase of consumer goods) and the more we must produce – in short, the faster we must run, just to stay in the same place.

Our population difficulty (and many other difficulties) would be solved – according to the "social" argument in favor of population growth – if we could but persuade *certain* segments of our society to have *larger* families. This view is often expressed by members of certain racial or religious groups whose preference for their own sort makes numerical increase seem desirable for its own sake: or who equate increases in size with increases in power. In more recent years this argument seems most convenient when one wishes to serve a specific class bias: a preference for the college graduate, the higher income group, the occupants of professional and managerial positions. The notion appears widespread that the quality of our society would be improved to the extent that family size in these groups equalled or exceeded that of the low income groups ,or of those with less schooling.

The assumption inderlying this view is, of course, either that the children of the former are inherently superior, or that their parents will offer them a superior environment. Those who have more of what the society values – material wealth, prestige, etc. – have always sought to justify their enviable position by boasts of innate or acquired virtue. Today, some support for the notion of upper-class superiority can be derived from a superficial reading of the results of various intelligence tests; for these show a rather consistent pattern of higher average group scores by the children of white collar and professional workers as against those of manual workers; by children of college-educated parents; by children from higher income families; by Whites as opposed to Negroes (although northern Negroes score higher, on the average, than do southern Whites); and by urban dwellers as against rural.

But these are only group averages. The degree of overlapping is considerable, and the extremes in each group approximate those of the others. Moreover, there is the more fundamental question whether these tests actually do measure intelligence. Aside from the well-founded uncertainty about just what intelligence is, various studies of these tests have concluded that of great importance in any particular test result are such matters as the number of years spent in school, prior experience with tests, and motivation to do well – not to mention the ability to understand the particular meaning attached to a given word or question used in the test by the psychologist who wrote it (himself likely to have been recruited from the more privileged classes). In short, non-hereditary characteristics are important, if not decisive. If the children of the upper classes have superior intellects, it has yet to be proved.

It is more plausible to say, as some do, that superior or not, the upper classes of our society are better able to *provide* for their children. This is not to claim that middle- or upper-class parents are better parents, but simply that they are better *able* to provide, leaving aside the question whether good provision is indeed made.

'You should have no more children than you can afford" is an admirable injunction. But does it follow that "couples who can afford them should have more?" Does anyone really bear all the costs of supporting his children? Perhaps the taxes paid by a few are substantial enough to meet the monetary costs of schooling, public health measures, roads, police protection, and the many other services a community must provide for its citizens. But what of the *social* cost? What of the crowded schools, the traffic, the vanishing countryside, the costs in time and peace of mind that additional numbers entail? This is a question that concerns none of the apologists for continued population increase. To quote the Roman Catholic Bishops of the United States:

"United States Catholics do not wish to ignore or minimize the problem of population pressure, but they do deplore the studious omission of adequate reference to the role of modern agriculture in food production. The 'population explosion' alarmists do not place in proper focus the idea of increasing the acreage yield to meet the food demands of an increasing population."

Man would appear to such apologists to be a strictly bread-and-potatoes phenomenon: let him increase as long as he can be fed.

Assume for a moment that by some miracle the world's supplies of resources were rendered inexhaustible and that, by a second miracle, international inequities were adjusted to the satisfaction of all concerned. Would the population problem have been solved? What, for instance, about land area? The increasing shortage of space is probably for the majority of Americans the most obvious consequence of population growth. Witness the traffic jams which beset all our major cities and most of our smaller ones as well. In some places this blight has afflicted us so long that it is now an accepted part of urban life. But the traffic jam is spreading to places where no one could have expected it ten or fifteen years ago: Yellowstone National Park and the mountains west of Denver, for example.

And then consider the crowded beaches, parks, and recreation areas; the cities and towns that run together, connected by a gum of suburbia and "highway culture": a picnic or a walk in the open country within easy motoring distance of home has become a virtual impossibility for a near-majority of our citizens. After reporting that once-green countryside is being bulldozed under at the rate of some three thousand acres a day, WILLIAM H. WHYTE goes on to say, "It is not merely that the countryside is ever receding; in the great expansion of the metropolitan areas the sub-divisions of one city are beginning to meet up with the subdivisions of another." Along the 600-mile strip of Atlantic seaboard from Maine to Virginia there are only two stretches – one of two miles and the other of seventeen miles – which are not parts of a metropolitan area. Like some dozen others scattered throughout the country, this area is in the process of becoming a strip city: 600 miles of Los Angeles on the Atlantic Coast!

Our national parks are the same. Visited by 7.4 million in 1940, their number of visitors had reached 19 million by 1955, more than double the number recommended by the Park Service. This is, of course, partly the result of higher levels of living – particularly the extension of paid vacations. But population increase *alone* would have brought the number of probable visitors up to the parks' capacity, had the level of living remained as it was in 1940. That levels of living have increased at the same time as population merely adds to the problem. It has now been proposed that certain roads in these parks be made one-way in order to handle the traffic!

The upper income groups may well pay higher taxes. But no group in our society can repay all of the social costs entailed by its excess reproduction – the rich probably least of all, for their style of life requires a much higher consumption of those very things upon which population increase – in whatever class – places a premium: raw materials and space.

If it is true that one must be born into a richer or better-schooled family in order to have the opportunity to develop his potentialities fully, an increase in family size among those segments of the population is hardly an adequate means to attain our ends. Must the right to bear children be distributed by the market mechanism? Would not a more efficient – and more democratic – approach be to raise the level of the less privileged?

Certainly the apologists for population growth are justified in claiming that much can be done with planning and scientific development to post-pone eventual reckoning with the consequences of population increase. A different solution to the pressure of population upon resources – one not seriously proposed as yet – would be a decrease in the levels of living. But under even our present economic conditions fully one out of four Americans lives in poverty or close to it, so any such belt-tightening would seem neither practical nor ethical. Besides, as already indicated, lower levels of living are likely to occur anyway as real costs increase. Temporary relief could be achieved without necessarily reducing the general level of living if we transferred a sizable proportion of our productive energies away from material goods (especially those which require non-renewable resources in their manufacture) and put them, instead, into education, social work, libraries, parole and probation systems, medical care, mental health facilities, music, art. Yet, continued growth in population makes more difficult the expansion of these services at the very time it makes them more necessary.

None of these arguments for continued population growth – singly or in concert – really faces up to the problem of such growth in a finite world. They are only palliatives, they are not cures. Some of the proposed courses of action could make life more enjoyable. Certain of them – better planned use of the land, for instance – are long overdue. But all are short-term measures at best.

Our population growth must be curbed or stopped in the very near future. But how? Any demographic change in a given area (the number of people, or their age or sex composition) occurs through the operation o: only three variables: migration, death, and birth. The proportion of our current annual population increase due to migration (that is, due to an excess of immigrants over emigrants) is very small: only 12%. And, our death rate was already so low by the end of World War II that yearly declines since then have added relatively little to our growth in numbers.

The major share, over 85%, of our increase is due to an excess of births over deaths. From an all-time low of 18.4 in 1933 and again in 1936, our birth rate climbed to 26.6 in 1947 and has since then fluctuated around 25.0, a higher level than in any other Western country. Without trying to assess the numerous personal decisions which produce it, we can say that such a birth rate has *not* been due to an increase in the proportion of couples having large families, that is, six or more children. In fact, since World War II, the rate for sixth and higher-order births has continued to decline while that for fifth births has remained about the same. The increase comes, instead, from the larger proportion with three and four children and the smaller proportion with no children or with only one. It also comes from a decline in the proportion who never marry. More of us marry; a greater proportion have between two and four children; and a smaller proportion remain childless or with but one child. The result is a slightly larger average family size and a rapidly growing population.

Can we halt population growth before the depletion of resources and the filling up of land area so reduce our level of living that such a question must be answered by a return of the high death rates of non-industrialized countries? Can we, that is, halt it while we still have a high level of living and before we lose control over our demographic destiny?

Emigration is no solution, for without a concurrent decrease in population growth it would merely spread the problem to more countries. Moreover, all the habitable areas in the world have been peopled, while the rise of the nation-state has tended to reduce the amount of freedom given an individual in choice of national residence. At best, migration is only a temporary expedient.

From both a pragmatic and an ethical standpoint, the only alternative is a decrease in fertility. Because our death rate is low and the proportion who marry is high, our population could be maintained at its present size if each family had on the average only slightly more than two children. The couple with more than three is contributing to the population disaster I have sketched. It is, in this sense, *socially irresponsible*, the more so the more numerous its children. For in this country the knowledge of how to control fertility is well known and widely diffused. A variety of means is available to us: late marriage, abstinence, abortion, *coitus interruptus*, contraception, sterilization. Aside from abortion, each is probably fairly acceptable to large numbers of people. Contraception appears the most widespread at the present time and probably presents the least psychological hazard. Sterilization may eventually become more common that it is now. But all means, so long as they are effective and do not endanger the well-being of the persons involved, must be considered.

The control of population by a check on fertility is the efficient way; it is the way most in keeping with our humanitarian and democratic values; and it represents the least social and ethical cost.

The best way for this control of fertility to come about is through the free decisions of individual parents. There can be no other way in a democratic society without serious loss to individual liberty. Let us hope that the current misuse of this most personal liberty by an unwittingly irresponsible portion of our citizenry can be halted before it jeopardizes any further the liberties of all of us.

LINCOLN HUBERT DAY, Ph. D., was Visiting Assistant Professor of Sociology, Princeton University, 1958–1959, and has been a Research Associate of the Bureau of Applied Social Research, Columbia University, since 1959. Dr. DAY has the position of Visiting Fellow at the Australian National University 1962–1964. He is author of the Age of Women at Completion of Childbearing, the American Fertility Cult, Status Implications of the Employment of Married Women in the United States, Divorce in Australia, the Measurement of Divorce, and co-author of two books: *Too Many Americans* (with ALICE TAYLOR DAY), Houghton Mifflin, 1964 (in press); and *Disabled Workers in the Labor Market* (with A. J. JAFFE and W. ADAMS), Bedminster Press, 1963 (in press).

Biology and Population

Current Approaches to the Biological Control of Fertility

by

Warren O. Nelson

The urgent need for man to recognize the necessity for achieving an equilibrium with his environment, both physically and biologically, is by no means a recent consideration. Nor are methods for achieving these ends new; excellent procedures for the control of fertility have been available for many years. It might, therefore, appear unnecessary to call attention to the requirement for more and better methods of effective, safe, acceptable and economical methods for the control of fertility. Those of us who are biologists might simply accept the existing procedures and pass to others the task of promoting their acceptance. However, in spite of their availability, it is obvious that the conventional contraceptives have failed to gain general acceptance. Objections are founded on economic, religious or cultural grounds, or on the basis that available agents are too technical and sophisticated for mass employment. Unquestionably, an additional factor is a lack of proper motivation.

These reasons for non-acceptance are acknowledged, but the hope remains that new techniques, involving a physiologic approach, may receive greater acceptance – and use. Even the simplest physiologic method however, will fall short of deserved success if obstacles, including lack of motivation, are present. The problem of educating and motivating people remains, and efforts toward these ends are imperative if people are to be made aware of the pressing need for fertility control.

In devising methods for the physiologic regulation of fertility, those reproductive processes susceptible to interference must be considered. At least 8 major areas exist in both sexes where physiologic reproductive mechanisms are vulnerable (1). Attention is being given to each of these by skillful investigators. Although studies are being made along many lines, in some instances, the possibility of practical application remains questionable. For the most part, this discussion will be confined to those physiologic procedures now used in man, or which show some promise of application in the relatively near future.

PHYSIOLOGY OF THE REPRODUCTIVE PROCESS

In the mammalian female, the reproductive process is a sequence of steps, each depending upon the successful fulfillment of the preceding one. In brief, these steps can be outlined as follows:

(1) production and release of the pituitary gonadotrophic hormones by way of hypothalamic mediation, (2) stimulation of egg and hormone production in the ovary by the gonadotrophic hormones, (3) ovulation and passage of the egg through the oviduct, (4) fertilization, (5) cleavage and early development of the fertilized egg during transport to the uterus, (6) entrance of the zygote into the uterus and formation of a blastocyst, (7) implantation of the blastocyst in the endometrium, and (8) maintenance of embryonic development.

The male, too, has a sequential progression of processes involved in reproduction. These are: (1) secretion and release of the pituitary gonadotrophic hormones, (2) production of spermatozoa and androgenic hormone by the testes under the influence of gonadotrophic hormones, (3) transport of sperm into and through the epididymis with concommitant physiologic maturation of spermatozoa, (4) passage of spermatozoa through the vas deferens to the ampulla, (5) suspension of sperm in the seminal plasma during ejaculation, (6) passage of sperm through the cervix, (7) ascent of sperm through the uterus and oviducts, and their capacitation, and (8) penetration of the ovum by a spermatozoon.

In both male and female it is possible to interfere with each step in the sequence of reproduction. Investigators in the field of reproduction are endeavoring to secure information enabling them to devise new methods for predictable regulation of one or another of the processes.

Inhibition of Ovulation

Gonadal hormones, estrogens and androgens have, for many years, been known to inhibit secretion of the gonadotrophic hormones, and as a consequence, to interfere with ovulation. During the past 8 years increased attention to the need for methods of regulating fertility, has led to a study of the effects of many new synthetic compounds on the occurrence of ovulation. Compounds having chemical similarity to the endogenous ovarian hormones received special attention, this being particularly true for those found to be effective when administered orally (2, 3, 4).

It is estimated that at least 1 and $\frac{1}{2}$ million women in the United States alone are using one of these agents, Enovid, as their sole method of contraception. It is probable that as many more women are using some similar type of available preparation. Enovid contains the synthetic progestin, norethynodrel, plus a small amount of the 3-methyl ether of ethinyl estradiol, an orally effective estrogen. One 5 mg tablet taken daily for 20 days, beginning on the fifth day of the menstrual cycle, inhibits ovulation and the normal cycle by suppressing secretion of the pituitary gonadotrophic hormones. Since the ingredients in the compound possess intrinsic ovarian hormone-like activities, artificial menstrual cycles are established. These cycles are, generally speaking, more regular than the subjects' spontaneous cycles would have been. Some women complain of gastro-intestinal disturbances resembling the "morning sickness" of pregnancy, or experience some degree of intermenstrual bleeding. These side effects as a rule, are of little consequence, and in most instances persist for no more than a month or two. If the dosage schedule is followed faithfully, this method can be regarded as absolutely effective. Enovid has been approved by the Food and Drug Administration for contraceptive use in doses of 10 mg and 5 mg per day and is now being considered at the 2½ mg level. Orthonovum, a related preparation, has also been approved for use in doses of 10 mg per day, and sanction for a 2 mg per day dose has been requested. These smaller doses are evidenced to be as effective as the higher ones and have the advantage of less cost to the consumer, as well as generally fewer side effects. However, concern exists on such matters as the ratio of progestin to estrin, incidence of breakthrough bleeding, and the possibility of non-physiological consequences which might result from their use. It is not clear as to exactly what these "non-physiological consequences" may be. Meanwhile, research on other synthetic progestins, usually in combination with estrogens, is being actively pursued. Some of the new preparations will undoubtedly be available in the relatively near future and may be superior to those currently available. At present, research is being directed toward substances which will cost less, have fewer side effects, and have a longer duration of activity. It would be highly desirable to have preparations which could be taken with less frequency than those now available, and efforts have been directed toward developing injectable substances with prolonged action. Preparations evolved thus far have been unsatisfactory because duration of activity has shown wide variation in different women. A solution for the problem may be achieved by proper exploration of a variety of doses and methods of preparation, so that a combination requiring administration only once every month or two can be secured. However, many women may very well question the acceptability of measures producing cycles of more than one month's duration.

In December, 1961 two women who had used Enovid as a contraceptive, died. These deaths focused attention toward the possibility that the drug may predispose women to thrombophlebitis, or to even more serious consequences. Other cases of thrombophlebitis and several additional deaths from pulmonary thrombosis have been reported to August 20, 1962. The total number of reported cases of both fatal and non-fatal thrombophlebitic and thrombotic diseases appears to have been no more than

100 of well over 1,500,000 women who have used Enovid, either for contraceptive or other purposes. So little is known of the casual incidence of thrombophlebitic disease and, more importantly, of fatal pulmonary thrombosis, that it is impossible to evaluate the extent of the problem. However, evidence collected from various sources suggests that the occurrence of these pathologic conditions in women using Enovid is no greater than that expected in the absence of any specific medication. At any rate, DE COSTA (5) has been unable to detect a definitive relationship between the use of Enovid and the occurrence of thrombophlebitis. Whether such a relationship actually exists, will continue to be a matter of great concern until a thorough study of all parameters of the problem has been made.

Detection of Ovulation

Every investigator interested in the physiological reproduction is cognizant of the importance of accurate methods for detecting ovulation. Even one method provided for predicting ovulation would be extremely valuable in making the rhythm method of contraception more dependable and, therefore, more acceptable to many people. Conversely, the ability to predict ovulation would have important application to the solution of some cases of infertility. Procedures now available reveal the *occurrence* of ovulation, but obviously these are not applicable to the pertinent need. Claims have been made for a chemical method (6) and for two methods of detecting incipient ovulation by use of "test" papers applied to the cervix or vagina (7, 8). Although other investigators have been unable to confirm these observations, studies now in progress may lead to more reliable methods for predicting ovulation. Perhaps the most promising of these involves application of immunologic procedures for discovering changes in levels of the gonadotrophic hormones. At least three groups of investigators have shown, independently, that immunologic methods can be employed to detect pregnancy (9). Since each of these procedures depends upon the presence of a gonadotrophic hormone (chorionic gonadotrophin) it is reasonable to anticipate that progressive refinement of techniques may eventually provide a method of foretelling ovulation.

Antizygotic Agents

These are substances which inhibit development of the very early embryo. There is considerable evidence showing the early fertilized ovum to be vulnerable to a variety of adverse circumstances, both spontaneous and induced. Death of early zygotes almost certainly occurs spontaneously at least as frequently as one in four instances. The causes for this fetal wastage are numerous. In some instances they are evident, but usually they are unknown. It is not surprising, therefore, that the early embryo is susceptible to extraneous influences and that some chemical substances have noxius effects. The antizygotic effects of MER-25, 1-(p-2-diethylamino-ethoxyphenyl)-1-phenyl-2-p-anisylethanol, have been described (10) and a second compound, MRL-41, 1-(p-B-diethylamino-ethoxyphenyl)-1,2-diphenyl-2-chloroethylene, was demonstrated to have even more potent activity (11). It is noteworthy that each of these compounds has been shown not only to inhibit development of the early zygote, but also to induce ovulation in some women with long histories of anovulation (12). Although these substances are known to be effective as oral contraceptive agents in animals, there is no more than indirect evidence to show that they have such activity in women. Clinical trials for this type of fertility control have their obvious problems, and before proper studies could be established, undesirable side effects emerged in the case of each compound. For MER-25 there was little reason to undertake serious clinical study in view of the fact that MRL-41 was found to have higher activity. When the latter compound was tested in animals over a long period of time, it was found to cause side effects which rendered its use unlikely.

A variety of substances apparently having the same antizygotic effect are now being synthesized and studied intensively. Such compounds include a series of 2,3-diphenylindenes reported by DUNCAN and his colleagues at Upjohn Laboratories (13). One of these (U-11555A), triethylamine 2-(p-[6-methoxy-2-(p-methoxyphenyl)-inden-3yl]-phenoxyl) hydrochloride, has been studied extensively in our laboratory. We found it to have approximately the same order of effectiveness which we had observed in the case of MRL-41. When the drug was administered in a single dose to mated female rats on any one of the four days occupied in passage of the egg to the uterus, pregnancy was prevented in every case. In animals where treatment was delayed until the 5th day after ovulation and mating, no influence on gestation could be detected. This observation is precisely the same as that made in similar studies with MER-25 and MRL-41. Although it may be too early to dismiss U-11555A as a human contraceptive, side effects have been observed. The probability exists that this agent will be numbered as another compound with a promising beginning, but not able to survive the rigorous testing necessary before a new drug can be released for general clinical use.

Other compounds with even more exciting promises are under intensive study in my laboratory. These have shown high orders of activity in animals and have caused no side effects in man. Of those examined, two compounds synthesized in the Upjohn Laboratories, and one synthesized in the Ortho Research Foundation Laboratories have been particularly impressive. Each one when given at a very low dose in a single oral treatment, is effective in suppressing development of the cleaving ovum during its passage through the oviduct. Such observations lead us to expect preparations which will provide effective oral conception control *after* coitus.

Antispermatogenic Agents

It has been known for about ten years that heterocyclic compounds of the nitrofuran and thiophene series (14, 15) are capable of inhibiting spermatogenesis in animals by halting the process at the primary spermatocyte stage. This is a completely reversible phenomenon and does not involve the endocrine functions of either the testes or the anterior pituitary gland. Inhibition of sperm production by this procedure has a distinct advantage over the spermatogenic inhibition induced by compounds preventing ovulation in females. Although the latter drugs are exceptionally effective contraceptives in males, they cannot be regarded as acceptable, since they inhibit secretion of male sex hormones (16).

The nitrofurans and thiophenes were not applied as contraceptives because the doses which were required for suppression of spermatogenesis also induced unpleasant side effects (17). More recently a series of bis (dichloroacetyl) diamine compounds have been synthesized by the Sterling-Winthrop Laboratories. Altough these compounds were evolved initially for their amebacidal activity, animal studies of the testes produced the same kind of effects that had be en observed earlier for the nitrofurans and thiophenes (18, 19). Studies in humans demonstrated that spermatogenic inhibition could be achieved, and that the effect was reversible (20). Sperm production returned to pretreatment levels about two months after treatment ceased. These observations, secured in two widely separated groups of prison inmates, were sufficiently encouraging to suggest clinical studies on the contraceptive effectiveness of these compounds. However, when the trials were made, an unexpected side effect became manifest almost immediately. Individuals ingesting the drugs experienced exaggerated responses to the peripheral effects of alcohol; although these effects were not serious, they were unpleasant enough to indicate that general acceptance of this form of contraception would be unlikely. Meanwhile, studies are under way in other laboratories, and are being continued by the Sterling-Winthrop Laboratories. Investigations have been directed toward development of compounds which will be effective antispermatogenic agents without possessing unpleasant side effects, and a number of preparations will probably be available for laboratory and clinical study. When one or more of these agents can be demonstrated to be effective, and to be without undesirable side effects, it will be exceedingly interesting to observe the degree of their acceptance as contraceptives by the human male.

Currently, the most promising of these is a group of dinitropyrroles prepared by the Ortho Research Foundation (21) Laboratories and investigated intensively in our laboratory. One of these, ORF-1616 (1-[N,N-diethyl-carbamylmethyl]-2,4-dinitropyrrole), has been highly effective as an antispermatogenic in rats. A single oral dose induces, after exhaustion of sperm already formed, a period of infertility lasting four weeks. An infertile state has been maintained indefinitely by administering single doses at four week intervals. The process of spermatogenesis is halted at the primary spermatocyte state and recovers when treatment is finally withdrawn (22).

Immunologic Control of Reproduction

As early as 1899, reports appeared in the literature on the immunologic response of animals to injections of sperm or testicular extracts. Beginning with the pioneer studies of LANDSTEINER, METCHNIKOFF, and METALNIKOFF, a large litereture has gradually developed on the subject of immuno-reproduction. TYLER (23) has recently reviewed both the earlier and more recent papers on this subject. During the past few years, interest in the possibility of controlling fertility by application of improved immunologic techniques has accelerated research on the subject, and some people optimistically believe that methods having human application will be found in the near future.

Perhaps the most advanced are those experiments concerned with active auto-immunization of the male with sperm or testes extracts. Although the concept that an animal is incapable of becoming immunized against components of its own tissues was generally accepted as a fundamental immunologic principle many years ago, it is now recognized that potential tissue antigens can assume antibody-inducing properties under certain circumstances. A report by FREUND (24) on the induction of aspermatogenesis in guinea pigs by administration of homologous material combined with an adjuvant, created great interest and stimulated other investigators to undertake related studies. It is now known that in addition to impairment of spermatogenesis, concurrent manifestations of generalized immediate hypersensitivity, as well as delayed skin sensitivity to testicular extracts, are present in animals treated by the Freund procedure. However, the severity of testicular lesions do not always correlate quantitatively with the levels of circulating antibodies. This lack of correlation between serum antibody titer and histologic damage to the testes, and failure to induce aspermato-genesis by serum antibody transfer, has led to the conclusion that genital lesions are indicative of a delayed type of hypersensitivity due to a cell-bound antibody. LAURENCE & PERLBACHS (25) have shown that aspermato-genic lesions from testes sensitive donors can be transferred to normal secondary recipients with mononuclear cells. The relationship between cell-bound antibody, humoral antibody and sequence of appearance of each type of immunological system is under investigation.

The testicular lesions resulting from this auto-immune phenomenon are limited to the germinal epithelium; the interstitial cells and other tissues of the reproductive tract are not damaged. Except for the granulo-matous lesion stimulated by the adjuvant material at the site of injection, the procedure causes no adverse effects. Current experiments with adjuvant agents, other than the Freund type, have been designed to determine whether lesions of the testicles can be produced without causing local effects at the inoculation site.

MANCINI of Buenos Aires has very recently secured results in human male volunteers duplicating those of the Freund procedures seen in animal experiments. While his observation suggests that the method may eventually be used to regulate fertility, additional studies are needed to assure that the testicular damage is controllable and reversible.

WEIL and his associates (26) have been concerned with a somewhat different approach to the problem of sperm antigenicity. This report holds that antigenic substances which stimulate the formation of sperm agglutinins in man arise from the accessory sex organs, rather than the testes, and become associated with spermatozoa only secondarily. On the other hand, there is evidence which indicates that antigenic factors occur primary to the spermatozoa (23).

These two concepts of sperm antigenicity actually may not be in conflict, but be concerned with different immunologic phenomena. In each case it is likely that application to fertility control is possible and may be achieved without causing serious testicular damage. Observations on the occurrence of sperm agglutinins in the serum of some infertile males (27) may be applicable in this regard. Testicular biopsies in such cases have usually revealed apparently normal spermatogenesis; sperm counts are frequently in the normal range, yet these men are infertile. Other instances of infertility are supposedly due to an antigen-antibody reaction in matings between blood type A fathers and type O mothers (28).

Some avenues of approach to the immunologic control of reproduction have been centered upon efforts to understand the nature, and possible significance, of sperm antibodies detected in the body fluids of both men and women (27), induction in the female of antibodies to sperm by inoculation with spermatozoa (29), immunization of the female against formation or survival of the placenta (30), and interference with the activities of the sex hormones by the formation of antihormones (31). It is reasonable to anticipate the development of several methods for the inhibition of fertility by inducing the formation of antibodies against one or another of the reproductive processes. In such cases, it would be possible for an occasional booster treatment to maintain an infertile state for any desired length of time. The possibilities are numerous and this area of investigation offers exceptional opportunities for the development of a new method of fertility regulation.

Another kind of immunologic research which has stimulated much interest is that concerned with the antigenic properties of pituitary gonadotrophins (32, 33). The possible application of such information includes control of fertility by neutralization of the action of gonadotrophic hormones, determination of ovulation time much more accurately than is presently feasible, and development of a simple test for pregnancy. At least three laboratories have now developed pregnancy tests based on immunologic principles. Although these are not yet as sensitive as available biologic methods, they have the advantage of being adaptable as office procedures and it is likely that greater sensitivity can be achieved.

Intrauterine Devices

Although intrauterine devices are scarcely a physiologic method for fertility control, they have an exceptionally good record for contraceptive effectiveness. Existing evidence suggests that they represent an exciting possibility for use as a relatively cheap and acceptable procedure. A variety of devices are available, including several constructed from plastic material, and rings formed from silk worm gut, nylon thread, and stainless steel. Some of these can be inserted into the uterine lumen without dilation of the cervix. The record for effectiveness, and acceptability of each device appears to be surprisingly good. For many years, the medical profession has held that intrauterine devices are dangerous, but such conclusions appear to have been based upon subjective considerations rather than objective evidence. Publications by ISHIHAMA (34), OPPENHEIMER (35), and HALL & STONE (36) suggest that further regard be given to this method of contraception. As a result, a conference of international scope on the use of intrauterine devices was organized and sponsored by the Population Council, on April 30–May 1, 1962. This meeting provided information encouraging enough to urge the undertaking of a vigorous study of the method for its efficacy, safety, acceptability, and mode of action. A preliminary report of the conference has been issued by the Population Council, and its full proceedings will be published by the Excerpta Medica Foundation (37).

Plant Extractives

During the last two decades a number of reports have suggested the presence of contraceptive substances in such plants as *Pisum sativum* and *Lithospermum ruderale*. Current evidence, however, is less hopeful, for there is no suggestion in any recent report that these plants, or, for that matter, any other plants are likely to yield substances having practical value in fertility regulation.

The Commonwealth Scientific and Industrial Research Organization of Australia has examined a variety of plants indigenous to Australia and New Guinea. Their studies indicate that a few of these may contain substances which do interfere with reproduction in rodents. This evidence, which has not yet been published, is more convincing than that offered for *Pisum sativum*, but thus far it is no more convincing than the evidence reported for *Lithospermum*. The possible existence of antifertility agents in plants cannot be denied, but available evidence for their presence is poor, and there is little to suggest their practical value. Perhaps the situation is one which should urge experienced plant chemists to recognize the challenge and apply their skills to the problem.

These remarks have been concerned with the status of research on physiological methods which are established as effective in the control of human fertility, or which have shown significant promise. Discussion of the subject well might be extended to include other areas of investigation less close to application, but of great interest to the subject of reproductive physiology. There is mounting evidence that attention to this field of investigation has increased progressively in recent years and that the importance of developing better methods of regulating fertility is beginning to be recognized in quarters where, until recently, the subject was studiously avoided.

The author wishes to acknowledge the editorial assistance of Miss JOAN H. HOFFMAN, B. A.*

BIBLIOGRAPHY

1. NELSON, W. O.: Status of Research on the Control of Fertility. *Fertil. and Steril.*, 12: *109*, 1961.
2. PINCUS, G., GARCIA, C. R., ROCK, J., PANIAGUA, M., PENDLETON, A., LARAQUE, F., NICHOLAS, R., BORNO, R. & PEAN, V.: Effectiveness of an Oral Contraceptive. *Science*, 130: *81*, 1959.
3. GOLDZIEHER, J. W., MOSES, L. E. & ELLIS, L. T.: A Field Trial With a Physiological Method of Conception Control. Research in Family Planning (edited by C. V. Kizer) Princeton University Press, Princeton, N.J., 1962.
4. TYLER, E. T.: An Oral Contraceptive – A 4-Year Study of Norethindrone. *Obstet. & Gynec.*, 18: *363*, 1961.
5. DE COSTA, E. J.: Those Deceptive Contraceptives. *J.A.M.A.*, 181: *122*, 1962.
6. SEVAG, M. G. & COLTON, S. W.: Simple Chemical Method for the Determination of Ovulation Time in Women. *J.A.M.A.*, 170: *13*, 1959.
7. DOYLE, J. B., EWERS, F. J. & SAPIT, D.: The New Fertility Testing Tape. A Predictive Test of the Fertile Period. *J.A.M.A.*, 172: *1744*, 1960.
8. BIRNBERG, C. H., KURZROCK, R. & LAUFER, A.: Simple Test for Determining Ovulation Time. *J.A.M.A.*, 166: *1174*, 1958.
9. WIDE, L. & GEMZELL, C. A.: An Immunological Pregnancy Test. *Acta endocr.*, 35: *261*, 1960.
10. SEGAL, S. J. & NELSON, W. O.: An Orally Active Compound With Antifertility Effects in Rats. *Proc. Soc. exp. Biol. Med.*, 98: *431*, 1958.
11. NELSON, W. O.: Current Research in the Regulation of Fertility. *J. Prosth. Dent.*, 11: *382*, 1961.
12. GREENBLATT, R. B.: Chemical Induction of Ovulation. *Fert. and Steril.*, 12: *402*, 1961.

* American Medical Writers Association.

13. DUNCAN, G. W., STUCKI, J. C., LYSTER, S. C. & LEDNICER, D.: An Orally Effective Mammalian Antifertility Agent. *Proc. Soc. exp. Biol. Med.*, 109: *163*, 1962.
14. STEINBERGER, E. & NELSON, W. O.: The Effect of Furodroxyl Treatment and X-irradiation on the Hyaluronidase Concentration of Rat Testes. *Endocrinology*, 60: *105*, 1957.
15. STEINBERGER, E., BOCCABELLA, A. & NELSON, W. O.: Cytotoxic Effects of 5-Chlor-2-Acetyl Thiophen (BA 11044) on the Testis of the Rat. *Anat. Rec.*, 125: *312*, 1956.
16. HELLER, C. G., MOORE, D. J., PAULSEN, C. A., NELSON, W. O. & LAIDLAW, W. M.: Effects of Progesterone and Synthetic Progestins on the Reproductive Physiology of Normal Men. *Fed. Proc.*, 18: *1057*, 1959.
17. NELSON, W. O. & BUNGE, R. G.: The Effect of Therapeutic Doses of Nitrofurantoin (Furandantin) Upon Spermatogenesis in Man. *J. Urol.*, 77: *275*, 1957.
18. DROBECK, H. P. & COULSTON, F.: Inhibition and Recovery of Spermatogenesis in Rats, Monkeys, and Dogs Medicated with Bis (Dichloroacetyl) Diamines. *Exp. & Molecular Path.*, 1: *251*, 1962.
19. NELSON, W. O. & PATANELLI, D. J.: Inhibition of Spermatogenesis. *Fed. Proc.*, 20: *418*, 1961.
20. Personal observations made in studies with C. G. HELLER and J. MACCLEOD.
21. Personal communication.
22. PATANELLI, D. J. & NELSON, W. O.: A Quantitative Study of Inhibition and Recovery of Spermatogenesis. Recent Advances in Hormone Research. Academic Press, Vol. 20, 1964 (In press).
23. TYLER, ALBERT: Approaches to the Control of Fertility Based on Immunological Phenomena. *J. Reprod. Fertil.*, 2: *473*, 1961.
24. FREUND, J., LIPTON, M. M. & THOMPSON, G. E.,: Aspermatogenesis in the Guinea Pig Induced by a Single Injection of Homologous Testicular Material With Paraffin Oil and Killed Mycobacteria. *Bull. N.Y. Acad. Med.*, 29: *739*, 1953.
25. LAURENCE, K. A. & PERLBACHS, M.: Studies on the Relationship of Delayed Hypersensitivity to Experimental Aspermatogenesis in Rats. *Bact. Proc.*, 88, 1962.
26. WEIL, A. J., KOTSEVALOV, O. & WILSON, L.: Antigens of Human Seminal Plasma. *Proc. Soc. exp. Biol. Med.* 92: *606*, 1956.
27. SEGAL, S., TYLER, E. T., RAO, S., RUMKE, P. & NAKABAYASHI, N.: Immunological Factors in Infertility. Sterility, Chap. 23, p. 386, Ed. E. T. Tyler, McGraw-Hill, New York, 1961.
28. BEHRMAN, S. J., BUETTNER-JANUSCH, J., HEGLAR, R., GERSHOWITZ, H. & TEW, W. L.: ABO(H) Blood Incompatibility As a Cause of Infertility: A New Concept. *Amer. J. Obstet. Gynec.*, 79: *847*, 1960.
29. MENGE, A. C., STONE, W. H., TYLER, W. J. & CASIDA, L. E.: Immunological Studies on Fertility and Sterility. IV. Fertility of Cattle and Rabbits Inseminated With Semen Treated With Antibodies Produced Against Semen, Spermatozoa and Erythrocytes. *J. Reprod. Fertil.*, 3: *331*, 1962.
30. COHEN, H. R. & NEDZEL, A. J.: Specific Action of an Antiserum for Placental Proteins on Placenta and Normal Progress of Pregnancy. *Proc. Soc. exp. Biol. Med.* 43: *249*, 1940.
31. LIEBERMAN, S., ERLANGER, B. E., BEISER, S. M. & AGATE, F. J.: Steroid Protein Conjugates: Their Chemical, Immunochemical and Endocrinological Properties. Recent Progress in Hormone Research, Vol. 15, p. 165, Ed. G. Pincus, Academic Press Inc., New York, 1959.
32. MOUDGAL, N. R. & LI, C. H.: An Immunochemical Study of Sheep Pituitary Interstitial Cell-Stimulating Hormone. *Arch. Biochem. Biophys.*, 95: *93*, 1961.
33. SEGAL, S. J., LAURENCE, K. A., PERLBACHS, M. & HAKIM, S.: Immunologic Analysis of Sheep Pituitary Gonadotrophin. *Gen. Comp. Endocr.*, (Suppl.), 1: *12*, 1962.
34. ISHIHAMA, ATSUMI: Clinical Studies on Intrauterine Rings Especially the Present State of Contraception in Japan and the Experiences in the Use of Intrauterine Rings. *Yokohama med. Bull.*, 10: *89*, 1959.

35. Oppenheimer, W.: Prevention of Pregnancy by the Graefenberg Ring Method. *Amer. J. Obstet. Gyn.*, 78: *446*, 1959.
36. Hall, Herbert H. & Stone, Martin L.: Observations on the Use of the Intrauterine Pessary, with Special Reference to the Graefenberg Ring. *Amer. J. Obstet. Gyn.*, 5: *683*, 1962.
37. Proceedings of the Conference on Intrauterine Contraceptive Devices (Edited by C. Tietze). Excerpta Medica Foundation, Amsterdam and New York (In Press).

Warren Otto Nelson, Ph. D., M. D. (hon., Giessen University, Germany), has been Medical Director of the Population Council since 1954. He was Professor of Anatomy, Wayne University, from 1936 to 1944 and Professor of Anatomy, University of Iowa, from 1944 to 1954. He has been a Consultant of the United States Public Health Service since 1951. He was President of the Endocrine Society 1955–56. Dr. Nelson has been a recipient of the American Urological Association Award (1952), Amory Award (1955), Lasker Award (1956) and is an Honorary Member of the Royal Society of Medicine, and the Argentinian Endocrine Society. Dr. Nelson is a distinguished student of endocrinology and the physiology of reproduction.

Research Involving Aspects of Mammalian Egg Development

by

Gregory Pincus

The development of the mammalian egg begins with the formation of the germ cells in the embryonic gonad. According to the best evidence presently available, the fetal ovary at birth contains all the ovocytes destined to last for the female's reproductive life. The slow maturation of the ovaries in prepubertal life involves chiefly the development of the follicular apparatus surrounding the egg until at puberty there is initiated the novel act of ovulation from ripe follicles. Thereafter ovulation occurs cyclically and the periodic production of eggs is halted only by pregnancy or by the quiescence of anoestrus. The ovulated egg is normally fertilized in the ampulla of the Fallopian tube, travels through the lower portion of the tube for some days, enters the uterus, and eventually implants in the uterine endometrium where its differentiation into a fetus takes place. I should like to consider experimental data concerned with: (a) the control of ovulation in animals and some applications to the human and (b) some aspects of the physiology of ovum development preceding implantation.

OVULATION

Ovulation in the mammal is not simply a cyclical or seasonal growth and rupture of ovarian follicles. This is immediately suggested when one considers that there are two categories of ovulators: those ovulating spontaneously such as the rat, the cow, the human and those that ovulate only after copulation such as the cat, the rabbit and the ferret. Among the latter, the need for a nervous stimulus to trigger follicle rupture is obvious. But similar nervous stimulus is needed to effect ovulation in the spontaneous ovulators. With the further development of our present-day information concerning the role of the nervous system in mammalian ovulation, a general concept of ovulation-controlling mechanisms may be framed. This is illustrated in Fig. 1 which indicates that a neurohumoral substance produced in the hypothalamus enters the

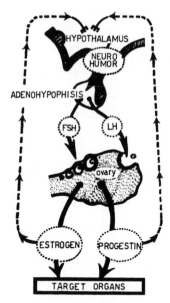

Fig. 1. Ovulation controlling
mechanisms.

anterior lobe of the pituitary via a portal circulation and acts upon the secretory cells of the pituitary to stimulate the secretion of a hormone generally called luteinizing hormone (LH), but also known (because of its action in the male) as interstitial cell stimulating hormone (ICSH). It is LH which enters the ovary from the circulation to stimulate the pre-ovulatory swelling and final rupture of the follicle. The corpus luteum formed from the ruptured follicle produces large amounts of progestational hormone exemplified by progesterone. Progesterone acts upon the hypothalamus to inhibit the production of the LH-stimulating neurohumor. Thus, since progesterone is secreted in large amount during pregnancy, ovulation during that critical period cannot occur as a complicating event. There are a number of variations to this general scheme but it is basic to the ovulation process in all mammals.

It is clear from the foregoing that there are four loci essential to ovulation and that each of these is open to experimental attack. As indicated in Table I, these loci are: (a) the hypothalamus, essentially a nervous structure,

TABLE I

Loci Essential for the Sequence of Processes Leading to Ovulation

Locus	Function
Hypothalamus	Production of LH-Stimulating Neurohumor
Anterior Pituitary	Receipt of and Response to Hypothalamic Neurohumor
Blood	Carrier of LH Secreted by the Pituitary
Ovarian Follicle	Swelling and Rupture in Response to Increased LH

(b) the anterior pituitary, essentially a secretory gland but containing in its stalk the hypothalamo-portal vessels, (c) the general circulation as a carrier of gonadotrophin (LH) and (d) the ovarian follicle. Experimental studies of ovulation control have largely centered on control of hypothalamic activity leading to ovulation. This has been due to the known inhibitory action of progesterone and to the finding that a number of centrally active drugs will also inhibit the production of ovulatory neurohumor. A list of such hypothalamic inhibitors is presented in Table II. You will note that ataractics are active as well as hypnotics, anticholinergics, antiadrenergics and anesthetics. The doses necessary for such inhibition appear to be rather high (*i.e.*, pharmacological), and this is prob-

TABLE II

Pharmacological Agents and Blockade of Ovulation

Antiadrenergics	Barbiturates
Dibenamine	Nembutal
SKF – 501	Dial
Anticholinergics	Ipral
Atropine	Amytal
Banthine	Barbital
Ataractics	Phenobarbital
Chlorpromazine	Prominal
Reserpine	
Anesthetics	
Morphine	
Ether	

ably why their experimental study in the human has not been carried on to any extent. Indeed, recent studies with therapeutic doses of chlorpromazine, reserpine, codein, phenobarbital and other drugs have given evidence of lack of effect on pituitary secretion (1). The situation is quite different with progesterone where we can clearly see ovulation inhibition at physiological doses.

Experimental work with loci other than the hypothalamus has been much more limited. Thus, direct inhibitors or stimulators of pituitary LH secretion have not been demonstrated. Several means of affecting circulating LH have been investigated. These are presented in Table III. None

TABLE III

Inactivators of Circulating Gonadotrophin

Source	Action
A plant – *Lithospermum ruderale*	Enzymatic Destruction?
A plant – *Lycopus virginicus*	Enzymatic Destruction?
Animal – Lysozyme	Enzymatic Destruction
Animal – Pituitary	Antigonadotrophin – perhaps competitive inhibitor
Animal – Fetal Serum	Antigonadotrophin – perhaps competitive inhibitor
Animal – Human Urine	Antigonadotrophin – against HCG *
Animal – LH Antibody	LH-Binding

* HCG = Human Chorionic Gonadotrophin

of these agents are chemically defined, and the nature of their action is often dubious. In the case of the LH antibodies, these have involved interspecific immunity in animals. While cross reaction has in some cases been clearly established, e.g., rabbit antiserum to ovine LH acting against endogenous LH in the rat (2, 3), much remains to be learned about long-range effects, the possibility of isoimmunity, sensitivity reactions and so on.

Concerning the fourth locus – the ovarian follicle itself – again there is only limited experimental work to consider. Curiously, the most effective drug which directly inhibits follicle rupture is reserpine (4). Certain steroids are active also, but again at what appears to be pharmacological doses. It should be emphasized, however, that animal work in this area is still embryonic and it may be predicted that interesting discoveries will come in the future.

Undoubtedly the most active experimental work has been with steroidal inhibitors of ovulation. Following our reinvestigation of progesterone inhibition of ovulation in the rabbit and the discovery of certain synthetic progestational 19-norsteroids as orally active agents (5, 6), a variety of animal studies have appeared. Indeed, no month passes without several publications on antigonadotrophic steroids. In a study of several hundred steroids in the rabbit, we have to date found 67 active compounds. In studies in the rabbit with a different series of steroids, KINCL & DORFMAN (7) have found approximately 50 active ovulation inhibitors. Actually only a few of these compounds exhibited marked inhibitory activity at signifi- cantly low dosages. In Fig. 2 are shown the four most active compounds

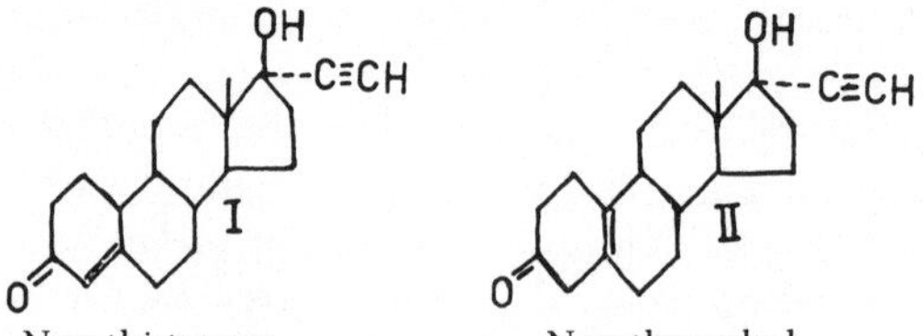

Norethisterone
MED [1] = 0.25 Mg

Norethynodrel
MED = 0.1 Mg

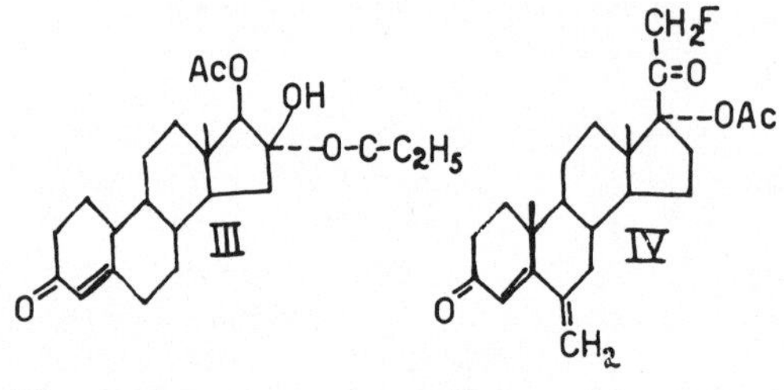

Norpropynone
MED = 0.08 Mg.

Fluormethypresgnone
MED = 0.02 Mg.

Fig. 2. Oral Ovulation Inhibitors.

1. MED = Minimal Effective Dose.

in our series. It will be noted that three of these four are 19-norsteroids. In Fig. 3 the four most active compounds of the KINCL & DORFMAN series are presented. These are all 6*a*-substituted derivates of 17-acetoxy-progesterone.

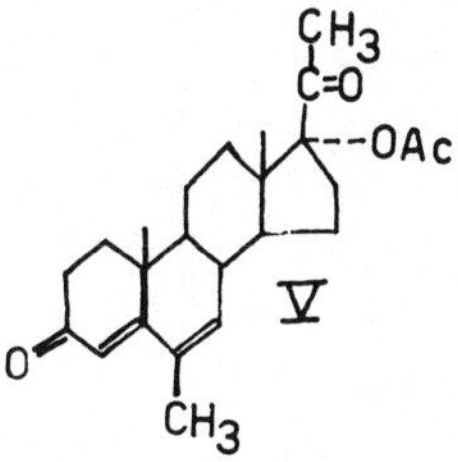

6–Dehydro-Methy-
pregnone R.P. = 5

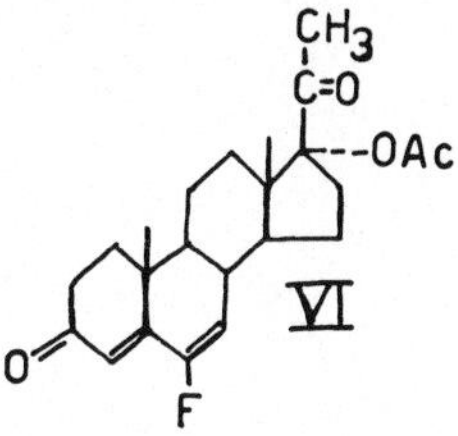

6–Dehydro-Fluoro-
pregnone R.P. = 9

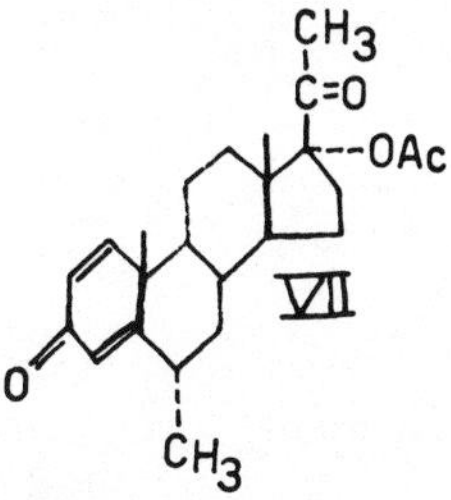

1–Dehydro-Methy-
pregnone R.P. = 10

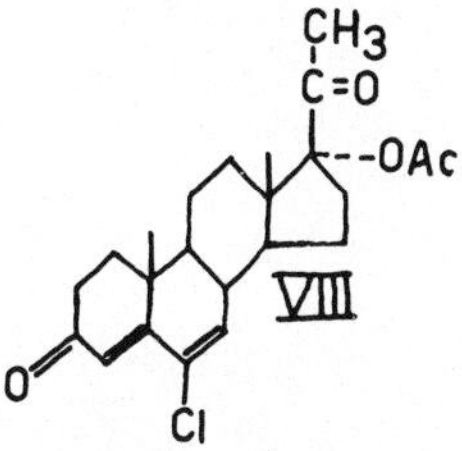

Chlormadinone
R.P. = 35

Fig. 3. Oral Ovulation Inhibitors. R.P. = Relative Potency Norethisterone = 1.

The comparative potency of these compounds as ovulation inhibitors in the human has thus far not been examined in detail, but we have had some evidence that substances more active orally than parenterally in the rabbit are excellent oral ovulation inhibitors in the human (8). In the human, the compound most extensively studied has been norethynodrel (Compound II in Figure 2). It is ordinarily administered in combination with an estrogen (in a preparation called Enovid), since the combination effects adequate control of the endometrial blood vessels, thus avoiding bleeding during medication. In turn, on withdrawing the medication, a menstrual flow followed in one to several days. Thus by employing a medication regime requiring the taking of a single tablet each day for 20 days beginning on day 5 of the menstrual cycle, an average cycle length of 28 days has been attained. Furthermore, with faithful following of this regime, a remarkable succession of regular menstrual cycles may be attained year after year. This is illustrated in Table IV which presents the percentage of cycles in which bleeding occurred during the taking of medication in a five-year period of study of volunteer subjects. It is clear that after the first few cycles of medication, presumably involving

TABLE IV

The Occurrence of Breakthrough Bleeding in Patients Taking Enovid *

Cycle No.	% with Breakthrough at		
	2.5 mg	5 mg	10 mg
1	28.3	13.4	6.4
2	23.4	11.9	4.2
3	20.8	7.4	4.3
4	20.0	6.6	2.4
5–9	17.5	4.7	2.9
10–19	13.1	4.7	2.2
20–29	13.5	3.7	1.5
30–39	11.2	2.8	3.0
40–49	12.3	2.8	⎫
50–59	4.7	4.0	⎬ 8.0
60–69	14.5	3.0	⎭
All cycles	16.2	4.9	3.2

* 10.4% of normal menstrual cycles show "breakthrough."

endometrial accommodation to the medication dosage, short cycles with premature bleeding are relatively infrequent, and their frequency is inversely proportional to the medication dose. It should be noted that when the 5 and 10 mg doses of Enovid are taken, the frequency of such short cycles is less than that observed in normally-menstruating women, *i.e.*, 3.2% for 10 mg, 4.9% for 5 mg and 10.4% in the non-medicated, normal menstrual cycles.

The volunteers in this project have employed this method of ovulation inhibition for purposes of contraception. The record from April 1956 to December 1961 of conceptions at the various dosages we have used is given in Table V (9). The conception rate is remarkably low, and control at the lowest dosage employed (2.5 mg per day) is just as effective as at the highest dosage (10 mg per day). We have several times pointed out that with faithful following of the medication regime, contraceptive efficiency is practically 100%. This is illustrated in Table VI which compares the conception rates for women allegedly missing no day of pill-taking during the

TABLE V

Fertility in Patients Taking Enovid

	10 mg	5 mg	2.5 mg
No. of pregnancies	22	15	3
Years of exposure	789.3	1579.1	217.8
Pregnancy rate per 100 woman years	2.8	0.95	1.4

TABLE VI

Fertility in Patients Taking Enovid

Number of Tablets Missed	Number of Pregnancies	Years of Exposure	Pregnancy Rate per 100 Women Years
0	4	2343.4	0.17
1–5	16	193.2	8.3
6–19	20	49.6	40.3
All Cycles	40	2586.2	1.5
Controls	124	59	210.0

20 days with those missing a few days and those missing more than five days. It is obvious that faithful tablet-taking gives practically complete conception control. But even with some tablet missing, a clear reduction in fertility occurs, for among these women the conception rate when no contraceptive is being used is 210 for 100 woman years of exposure. VENNING (10) has compared the conception rates reported for Enovid and for various other methods of contraception. This comparison is shown in Table VII; it is obvious that Enovid taken by mouth offers by far the most efficient method of conception control.

TABLE VII

Effectiveness of Different Methods of Conception Control, Taken from Seven Published Reports (10)

Method	Indiana- polis 1938[a]	BELAVAL et al. 1938[b]	MORGAN & BEEBE 1941[c]	TIETZE 1952[d]	Princeton 1957[e]	DUBROW & KUDER 1958[f]	Average Pregnancy rate per 100 Woman Years
Douche	21	—	—	36	41		31
Safe Period	—	—	—	14	38		24
Jelly Alone	—	28	—	4–38	—	7.6–8	20
Withdrawal	10	—	—	12–38	17		18
Condom	7	—	22	6–19	=14		14
Diaphragm (with or without jelly)	4	30	9	6–13	14	8.9–9.7	12
Enovid [g]	—	—	—	—	—	—	1.2*

* Over-all pregnancy rate based on 578 woman-years (approximately 7,000 cycles) including cycles in which tablets have been missed.

a. WESTOFF, C. F., HERRERA, L. F. & WHELPTON, P. K.: *Milbank Mem. Fund Quart.* 31: *291*, 1953. b. BELAVAL, J., GOULD, C. & GAMBLE, C.: *J. Contracept.* 3: *224*, 1938. c. MORGAN, L. I. & BEEBE, G. W.: *Hum. Fertil.* 6: *88*, 1941. d. TIETZE, C.: Proc. 3rd Int. Congress on Planned Parenthood, Bombay, 1952, p. *108*. e. WESTOFF, C. F.: Family Growth in Metropolitan America. Princeton University Press, 1957. f. DUBROW, H. & KUDER, K.: *Obstet. Gynec.* 11: *586*, 1958. g. PINCUS, G.: in Modern Trends in Endocrinology. Table V, edited by H. GARDINER-HILL, 1961, Butterworth, London, 2nd Series, p. *238*.

In recent years, several other ovulation-inhibiting steroids have been studied in similar trials. These have been chiefly 19-norsteroids used in combination with an estrogen. The progestins tested as ovulation inhibitors in such contraceptive trials are shown in Fig. 4. Their relationship to the substances tested in rabbits is evident. It is clear that an array of steroids is available for such purposes, and it may be confidently predicted that many more will be found. Among the objectives in further exploration for active compounds are substances effective in even lower doses than those thus far explored in order that a relatively inexpensive medication may be available. However, in order to effect adequate menstrual control, such compounds must also be potent regulators of endometrial function.

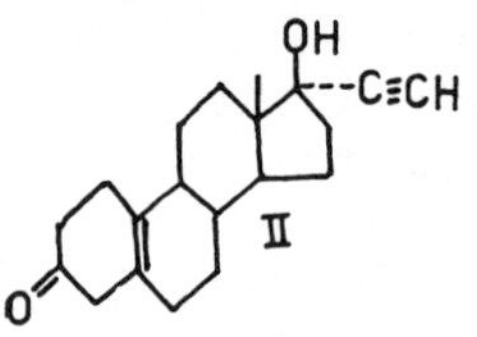

Norethynodrel
(Enovid)

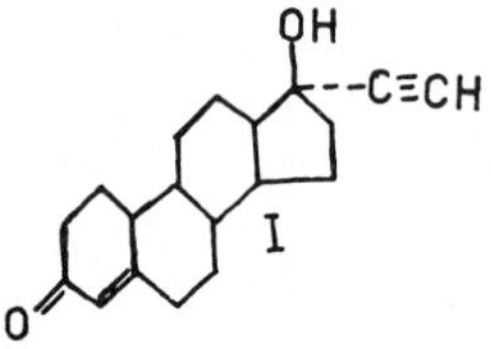

Norethisterone
(Norlutin, Orthonovum)

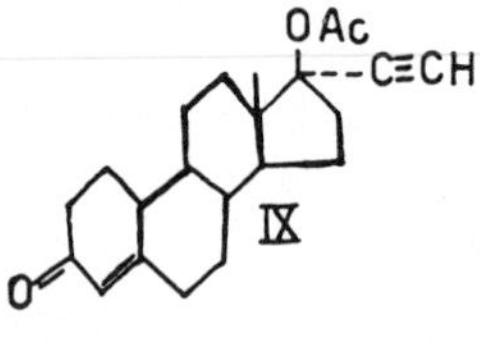

Norethisterone Acetate
(Norlutate)

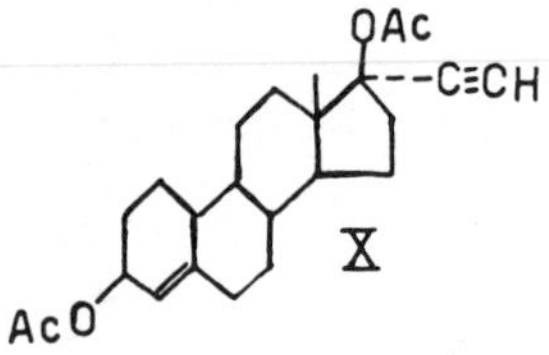

Ethynodiol Diacetate

Fig. 4. Progestins tested as contraceptives in field trials.

We have in progress a study of Compound X (Fig. 4), ethynodiol diacetate (ED). Because of its clear ovulation-inhibiting activity in test animals, we initiated the study with 2 mg tablets of ED plus 0.1 mg of the estrogen we have used with all our progestins, the 3-methyl ether of ethinyl estradiol(11). In Table VIII we present data on over 100 women who have used this medication for periods of up to 16 months. Here we see the same general phenomena that we have observed with Enovid; namely an initial maximal rate of occurrence of "reactions" and breakthrough bleeding which descends to a characteristic minimal level by the fourth cycle of medication. Thus far in nearly 100 exposure years, no conceptions have occurred among these women, probably because of their realization of the need for faithful tablet taking.

The "reactions" reported by these volunteer subjects are the usually occasional episode of headache or dizziness, or nausea, or vomiting. We

TABLE VIII

Patients Taking Ethynodiol Diacetate

Cycle No.	No. of Cycles	% with "Reactions"	% with Breakthrough
1	126	15.9	5.6
2	125	9.6	4.0
3	122	9.0	1.6
4	115	4.3	2.6
5–8	402	3.2	2.7
9–16	246	4.9	1.2

No conceptions in 97.4 years of exposure.

have previously presented data indicating a large psychogenic element in their occurrence (12). Most of the subjects in these ED experiments were questioned prior to their entry into the project concerning the occurrence of such symptoms during their regular menstrual cycles. Of the 122 patients responding to this questioning, 48 reported having had similar symptoms and 74 said that they had no such symptoms. In Table IX we present the data on the pre- and post-medication frequencies of these "reactions." A reporting of any of these symptoms during any single cycle is taken as positive. By ordinary criteria women who had such symptoms before medication but not during medication would be considered as "cured," and on this basis 58% of sufferers were "cured." Similarly, women who allegedly had no such symptoms previous to medication but who had them on any single occasion during medication had them "induced" by the medication, and 39% of the premedication non-reactors became reactors while on medication. Actually these occurrences appear to be random events and exhibit no consistent relationship to medication.

It is clear from the foregoing that effective ovulation inhibition by oral medication has been definitely accomplished in the human. RICE-WRAY & GOLDZIEHER (13) have recently reported on comparative studies with 2,432 women observed in 22,948 treatment cycles. Five progestin-estrogen

TABLE IX

Patients Reporting "Reactions" to Ethynodiol Diacetate

		Number	% of Total
None before or during medication		45	37
None before but some during medication		29	24
"Reactions" before and during medication		20	16
"Reactions" before but none during medication		28	23
% "cured" of reactions	58.4		
% with "induced" reactions	39.2		

preparations were used with complete effectiveness upon proper use of the day 5 to 25 regime. Regularly achieved ovulation control may therefore be taken as a fact. Indeed, contraceptive research projects with steroidal ovulation inhibitors have been conducted throughout the United States, in certain European countries, in Japan, Ceylon, Singapore, Hong Kong and India with remarkably similar data coming from each.

FREE OVUM DEVELOPMENT

Our studies on the control of the development of the fertilized mammalian egg actually originated over 20 years ago when Dr. N. WERTHESSEN and I (14) followed up an original observation of Dr. GEORGE W. CORNER. CORNER found that in rabbits ovariectomized shortly after fertilization the egg enters the uterus at the normal time but fails to grow to normal size or to implant. However, with the administration of an adequate dose of progestin to such ovariectomized animals both normal ovum growth and implantation may be restored. Dr. WERTHESSEN and I developed this ovum response as part of a quantitative progesterone assay. We have found, furthermore, that estrogens administered with the progesterone could inhibit the ovum and/or the uterine response to the progestin. Approximately 20 years later, Dr. MIYAKE, Miss MERRILL, Miss LONGO and I took up again the question of quantitative progestin assay, comparing the Pincus-Werthessen method with a method involving the measurement of pro-

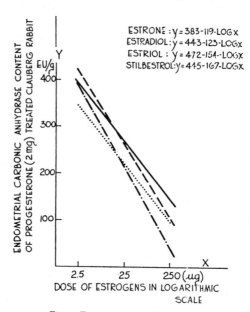

Fig. 5. Estrogens as antiprogestins.

gesterone-induced endometrial carbonic anhydrase concentration increases (15). The enzyme measurement offered advantage in speed and in sensitivity; also the antagonistic, or antiprogestational, effects of the estrogens could be determined quantitatively. This is illustrated in Fig. 5 which demonstrates the relationship between the dosages of four estrogens and the degree of inhibition of the effect of a standard dose of progesterone (16).

Using this carbonic anhydrase assay method, Miss MERRILL and I proceeded to examine a large number of steroids as possible antiprogestins (17). We found a limited number of significantly active compounds. These fell

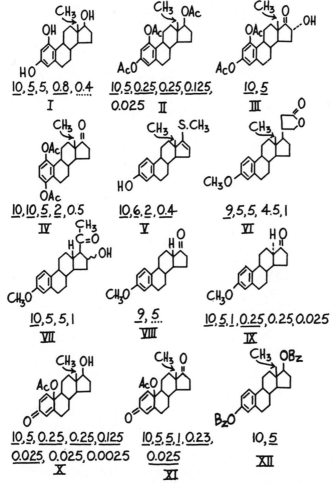

Fig. 6. Estrogen derivatives acting as antiprogestins in the rabbit (underlined doses, in mg, are significantly effective).

into two categories: (a) derivatives or close chemical relatives of the steroidal estrogens and (b) certain non-estrogenic neutral steroids. In Fig. 6 are presented the structural formulae and range of effective doses of the estrogen-like compounds. For the most part, these are active at doses lower than the standard one milligram dose of progesterone against which they act. In other words, like the estrogens of Fig. 5 they act as physiological antagonists. Active, neutral steroid antagonists are depicted in Fig. 7. Their effective doses approximate the standard progesterone dose, and therefore they may be taken to act as competitive antagonists. Among these neutral antiprogestins, several appear to have only this progesterone-inhibiting effect and no other hormonal activity, in contrast to the estrogen derivatives which possess the numerous functions associated with estrogen activity.

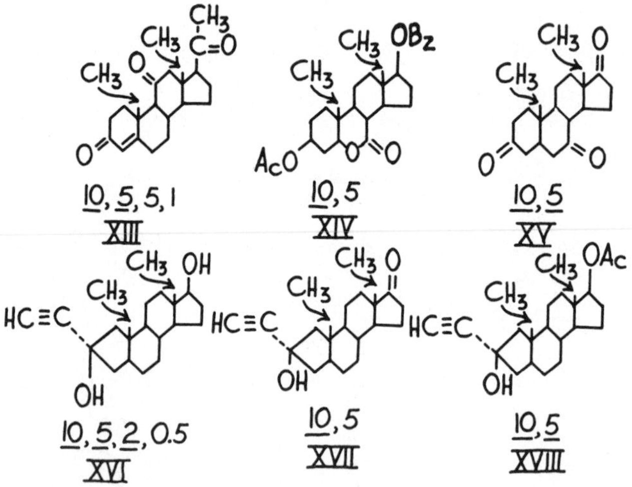

Fig. 7. Neutral steroids acting as antiprogestins in the rabbit (underlined doses, in mg, are significantly effective).

On the assumption that antiprogestins should act to inhibit ovum growth and implantation, Dr. U. BANIK and I have examined the effects of a number of these compounds administered to rats and mice carrying fertilized ova (18). Females were caged with males overnight and examined the next morning for vaginal plugs and sperm. Administration of the antiprogestins was begun 24 hours later (called day 1 of pregnancy) and then on two subsequent days. Among the compounds shown in Fig. 6 and 7 we tested several shown in Fig. 8 and most of them did indeed inhibit implantation in both rats and mice. Some appeared to be effective in one species (e.g., Nos. III and V), whereas others failed to inhibit implantation despite administration at comparable dose levels. This is illustrated in Table X. In addition, it should be noted that antiprogestational activity in

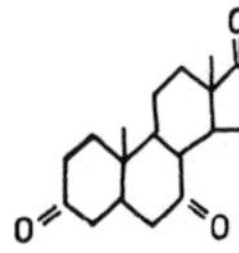

I

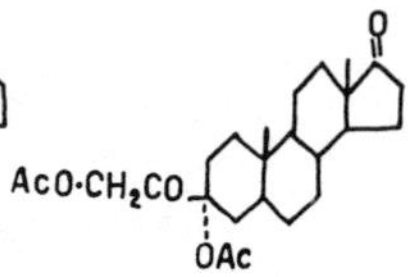

II

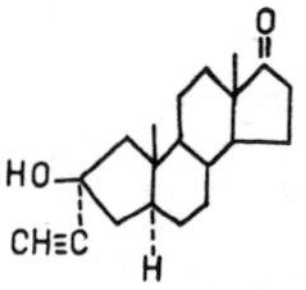

III

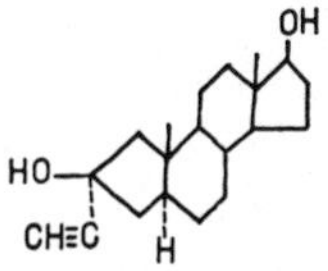

IV

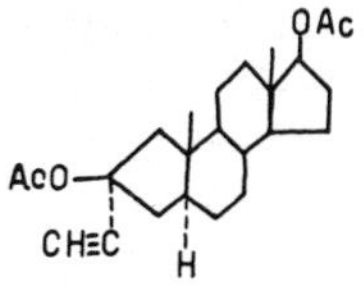

V

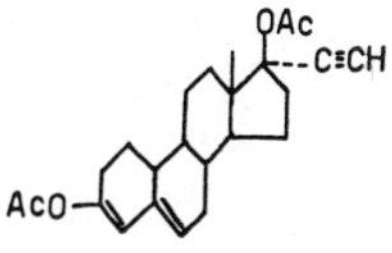

VI

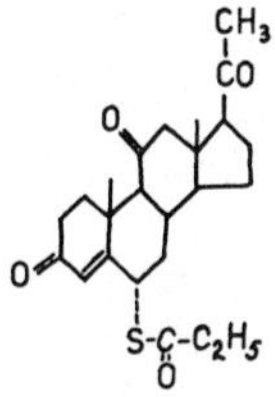

VII

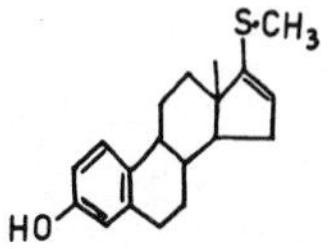

VIII

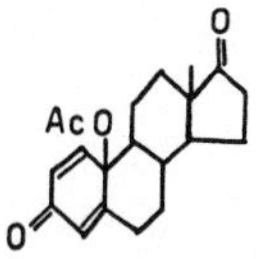

IX

Fig. 8. Steroidal antiprogestins tested as implantation inhibitors in rats and mice.

TABLE X

Steroid effects on the Implantation of Fertilized Eggs in Rats and Mice

Compound Number	Animal	Significant Implantation-Inhibiting Dose, mg per Day
I	Rat	None at 2.5 or less
	Mouse	None at 2.5 or less
II	Rat	None at 2.5 or less
	Mouse	None at 2.5 or less
III	Rat	None at 2.5 or less
	Mouse	2.5 but not 0.5
IV	Rat	0.1 but not 0.02
	Mouse	0.02
V	Rat	None at 2.5 or less
	Mouse	0.5
VI	Rat	0.5 but not 0.1
	Mouse	0.1
VII	Rat	None at 2.5 or less
	Mouse	None at 2.5 or less
VIII	Rat	1.0
	Mouse	0.1
IX	Rat	1.0
	Mouse	0.1

the rabbit is not paralleled by implantation inhibition in rats and mice (compare Fig. 6 and 7 with the data of Table X). We have observed too that among the active compounds doses that are less than 100% effective in preventing implantation may significantly reduce the number of uterine implantations.

Dr. BANIK and I thought that since implantation occurs by the eighth day its inhibition could be more easily accomplished by antiprogestin administration later rather than earlier in the pre-implantation period. To our surprise, administration on day one alone was uniformly effective whereas administration on day three alone was either ineffective or very much less effective. This is shown in Table XI. Indeed, these same antiprogestins administered on day eight and after were practically ineffective in causing embryo death or resorption. We have therefore a group of compounds which will uniformly prevent the free ovum from becoming implanted provided that they are administered on the day following mating.

TABLE XI

Effects of Single Injections on Ovum Implantation in Rats and Mice

Compound Number	Animal	Significant Inhibitory Dose (mg) On Day	
		One	Three
IV	Rat	1.5	None
	Mouse	0.1	None
VI	Rat	1.0	None
	Mouse	0.1	0.1
VIII	Rat	1.5	None
	Mouse	0.1	?
IX	Rat	1.0	None
		0.1	?

This unexpected effect of compounds originally chosen because of their antiprogestational activity on the endometrium raises many questions concerning the factors and processes involved in free ovum development. Thus normally-appearing blastocysts are recovered from the uteri of animals receiving sterilizing doses of antiprogestins. Why do they fail to implant? A large proportion of sterile women apparently ovulate normally but fail to have implantations. Is it possible that certain steroids produced by the ovaries or adrenal glands of these women act the way our implantation-inhibiting steroids do? How will these compounds affect human reproductive processes? It is, I believe, clear that many interesting problems remain before us for fascinating study.

I have attempted to present here the highlights and to dwell briefly on some implications of investigations into aspects of the life history of mammalian eggs. To me it is a most fascinating field for research, perhaps because we are indeed just at the forefront of an era where these and numerous other mysteries of reproduction will no longer be mysteries.

REFERENCES

1. CIPRUT, S., SILVERSTEIN, J. N., SCHWARTZ, H. L., FELDMAN, E. B. & CARTER, A. C. *J. clin. Endocr.* 22, *535*, 1962.
2. MOUDGAL, N. R. & LI, C. H. *Arch. Biochem.* 95, *93*, 1961.
3. LOTTI, G., MONTALE, R. & AZZENA, D. *Boll. Soc. ital. Biol. sper.* 36, *1192*, 1960
4. PURSHOTTAM, N., MASON, M. & PINCUS, G. *Fertil. and Steril.* 12, *346*, 1961.
5. PINCUS, G. & CHANG, M. C. *Acta physiol. latinoamer.* 3, *177*, 1953.
6. PINCUS, G., CHANG, M. C., ZARROW, M. X., HAFEZ, E. S. E. & MERRILL, A. *Endocrinology* 59, *695*, 1956.
7. KINCL, F. A. & DORFMAN, R. I. *Acta endocr. (Kbh.)* (In press) 1962.
8. PINCUS, G. & MERRILL, A. in VILLEE: Control of Ovulation. p. 37. Pergamon Press, New York. 1961.
9. PINCUS, G. in GARDNER-HILL: Modern Trends in Endocrinology. p. 231. Butterworth and Co., London. 1961.
10. VENNING, G. *Brit. med. J.* 2, *899*, 1961.
11. PINCUS, G., GARCIA, C. R., PANIAGUA, M. & SHEPARD, J. *Science* 138, *439*, 1962.
12. PINCUS, G. *Studies on Fertility* 10, *1*, 1959.
13. RICE-WRAY, E. & GOLDZIEHER, J. Prov. 5th Int. Congress on Sterility (in press) 1962.
14. PINCUS, G. & WERTHESSEN, N. T. *Proc. Roy. Soc.* 126, *330*, 1938.
15. PINCUS, G., MIYAKE, T., MERRILL, A. & LONGO, P. *Endocrinology* 61, *528*, 1957.
16. MIYAKE, T. & PINCUS, G. *Proc. Soc. exp. Biol. Med.* 99, *478*, 1958.
17. PINCUS, G. & MERRILL, A. in CORI, FOGLIA, LELOIR & OCHOA: Perspectives in Biology. Elsevier Publishing Co., Amsterdam. pp. 56–61, 1962.
18. BANIK, U. & PINCUS, G. *Proc. Soc. exp. Biol. Med.* 111, *595*, 1962.

GREGORY PINCUS, Sc.D., has been Director of Research at The Worcester Foundation for Experimental Biology, Shrewsbury, Massachusetts, since 1944. Dr. PINCUS was Assistant Professor of Physiology at Harvard University, 1931–1938, Visiting Professor of Experimental Zoology, Clark University, 1938–1945, Professor of Physiology, Tufts Medical School 1944–1951, and has been Research Professor of Biology, Boston University since 1951. He has been a recipient of a Lasker Award, the Oliver Bird Award, and is a Past-President of the Endocrine Society. He is an Honorary Member of the Japan Endocrine Society, The Swedish Endocrine Society, and of the Societé d'Endocrinologie. Dr. PINCUS has received great popular, as well as professional, acclaim as discoverer of "The Pill."

The Place of Sterilization

by

ALAN F. GUTTMACHER

I should first like to address myself to the task of the difference between castration and sterilization. As clear-cut as the difference is to physicians, I find an appalling confusion among the minds of the laity. Castration is utterly different from sterilization. Castration is the removal of the sex glands – in the male, the removal of the testes; in the female, the removal of the ovaries. Sterilization, on the other hand, is not that at all. By modern surgical techniques one simply interrupts the passage of the sex cells, so that the two cells, sperm and egg, cannot meet to accomplish fertilization. In the female, a roadblock is established in the Fallopian tube by tying off and then excising a small portion of each tube. The sperm can progress upward only as far as the roadblock; the egg can only descend downward as far as the roadblock. Thus, there is absolutely no opportunity for the two to meet.

In the male the roadblock is created in the vas deferens, one on each side, the conduit leading from the testicle and thence finally to the penis. This roadblock prevents the sperm cells from making their egress, and therefore they are retained within the male and cannot be ejaculated.

Neither of these techniques in any way affects the sex physiology of the persons operated upon. Menstruation occurs as always; ejaculation in the male occurs without appreciable diminution of the amount of seminal fluid. So that, for all practical purposes, the male or female does not know, as far as their sex lives are concerned, that he or she has been sterilized, except for their inability to impregnate or be impregnated.

The sterilization techniques we use are relatively simple. In the male, in most parts of the world, except this country, the procedure is an ambulatory technique in the physician's office or the out-patient department of a hospital. In this country the male is usually hospitalized, given a general anesthetic, such as sodium pentothal, or a local anesthetic, and kept in the hospital for 24 hours after the operation. In some instances, male sterilization is an office procedure in this country.

Hospitalization is necessary for the female under all conditions; the procedure is performed under anesthesia and a five-day hospital post-operative convalescence is required. Currently most female sterilizations are done immediately following delivery. This has great advantages. Number one, the procedure is simpler since the uterus is high up in the abdomen and the midline, abdominal incision does not have to be as large to operate on the tubes. Number two, no additional hospital stay is imposed, because ordinarily, at least in this country, patients stay in the hospital about five days after childbirth.

Female sterilizations performed shortly after delivery are called puerperal sterilizations. Puerperal comes from the Latin "having borne a child,"and therefore, it deals with that period immediately after childbirth.Ordinarily, the operation is done between one and 24 hours after delivery.

Why do we sterilize? What are the indications? First of all, eugenic; second, therapeutic; third, socio-economic; and fourth, population control.

The oldest indication for sterilization in this country is eugenic. We have twenty-eight states with laws governing such sterilizations in this country. These eugenic laws outline under what conditions we may sterilize within the law of the particular state. Enthusiasm for sterilization on eugenic grounds is constantly diminishing. As we know more and more about eugenics, we feel less confidence in our eugenic decisions. Many feel that one could virtually eliminate the eugenic group and very little loss would accrue.

The second group is, therapeutic. This is largely confined to sterilization at cesarean section, because there is a feeling among women particularly, and with doctors to a lesser extent, that two or three cesarean sections are enough. Actually, there is no mathematical limit for the number of cesarean sections. There is a famous woman who goes to the Woman's Hospital in New York every year and has an annual model by cesarean section. Last year I believe she had her eleventh and I look forward to reading tomorrow's paper for news about the twelfth. By common usage, cesarean sections are usually limited to two or there. There are many therapeutic reasons for female sterilization in addition to repeated cesarean section, such as organic disease of the heart, lungs, kidneys or other organs.

The third indication is socio-economic. This is an ill-defined group, some term it "sterilization for convenience." I do not like the latter appellation. I feel that there is ample reason, in this day of urban living, to limit the size of the family for socio-economic reasons. Such sterilizations are not uncommon in the United States. According to the very excellent study, *The Growth of the American Family*, which FREEDMAN and others published in 1959, based on a survey conducted on 2,713 married white wives between the ages of nineteen and thirty-nine, 9% of American marriages are rendered infertile by sterilization of one or the other of the marital partners.

A new edition of *The Growth of the American Family* is now in preparation, but as yet unpublished. The depth interviews for the 1959 volume were conducted in 1955, those for the current edition five years later, 1960. The 1960 study shows a marital sterilization rate of 10%. Eight per cent of the wives had been rendered sterile through a surgical operation. In half the procedure had been performed only for the purpose of rendering the woman sterile and in half sterilization was not intended, but was simply the natural by-product of other gynecological surgery. Two per cent of the husbands in the 3000 couples had been sterilized by vasectomy in order to make them infertile. This was twice the male incidence of sterilization noted five years earlier.

In Puerto Rico, according to STYCOS' study, of women between fifteen and forty-five, 20% have been sterilized for the sole purpose of ending their fertility. In North Carolina in 1958, according to a study recently published by FLOWERS & DONNELLY, one woman in every forty-three had a puerperal sterilization.

I should like to call to the attention of interested readers a very valuable publication in this field, a selected bibliography of "Surgical Sterilization of Men and Women," which lists 403 articles dealing with the topic. It was written by CHRISTOPHER TIETZE and published by the National Committee on Maternal Health, 2 East 103rd Street, New York City (29) in May, 1962. It is a splendid, unique contribution to this field which can be obtained by writing to the National Committee.

At my own institution, The Mount Sinai Hospital, because of the type of ward patient living in the slums who attends our clinics, we decided some years ago that it was only humane to carry out a socio-economic program of sterilization.

New York City is highly conservative in this matter, and in order not to be considered too radical, we imposed the necessity for the woman to have produced a sixth living child, to allow puerperal sterilization, irrespective of her age or physical condition. This, of course, is wholly voluntary at the signed request of patient and husband. If the woman is thirty to thirty-five, we require the fifth living child; if she is thirty-five or more, the fourth living child. This is called the Law from Mount Sinai.

Be that as it may, I am sure that many of you would quarrel with me and say that we are being ridiculously conservative; others would say that we are being extraordinarily radical. On this basis we sterilize 9% of the patients who have had children on the ward service; and 0.3% of the patients on private service. You see there is some differentiation on the basis of the pocketbook; in this particular instance, the smaller the pocketbook, the larger the family and the better the chance to have one's sterilization request honored.

Actually, the private patient rarely qualifies on the basis of the number of children, because very few of our private patients have sufficient children to justify a parity, socio-economic puerperal sterilization.

Just a word about the legal situation in this country – it is in a tremendous muddle! Most of us do not know whether we are being legal or illegal when we carry out a sterilization without strict medical necessity, such as serious heart disease. There is an aphorism that physicians of this country who perform a sterilization operation simply to terminate fertility operate with good intentions and crossed fingers. Actually, in a state like New York, it would be useful if one of us were bold enough to request the state's attorney to arrest us after a socio-economic sterilization. Then, and only then, would we clarify the legality of socio-economic sterilization in New York State.

An extremely interesting legal development occurred in April, 1962, in the State of Virginia. Because of the legal ambiguity which existed concerning voluntary sterilization, their State legislature passed an unprecedented, liberal statute which was signed into law by the Governor. It provides that any couple may request sterilization of either marital partner and have it performed, provided that a thirty day notification is given, to permit a change of mind, and provided that two physicians recommend the operation. There is no reference to health, socio-economic situation or number of children.

Before leaving the topic of socio-economic sterilization, I should like to make mention of the important work being done by the Human Betterment Association of New York. This organization attempts to interpret human sterilization to both the lay and medical public. Furthermore, they maintain a national roster of physicians who will carry out socio-economic sterilizations. Patients may apply for advice and if unable to pay for the operation, the Association may arrange for it. If a Board of Physicians approve of the application, the Association frequently finances it.

The fourth indication, sterilization for the purposes of population control, is making slow progress throughout the world because today sterilization is a final, irrevocable procedure. We do not have reversible techniques. At Mount Sinai, thanks to the generosity of Mr. HUGH MOORE, we are trying to develop some temporary reversible technique for the male, experimenting with male dogs, not humans. We are attempting to develop a removable clip technique for clamping the vas deferens.

There are similar developments in the female. Drs. NEWMAN and FRICK published in the April 1961 issue of the *American Journal of Obstetrics and Gynecology* some work they did on monkeys at Columbia Medical School on Dr. HOWARD TAYLOR's service. They placed clips on the fallopian tubes of monkeys by the abdominal route, hoping that when removed fertility would be restored. This is an incomplete study, as is our own.

A new development which is really a link between contraception and sterilization appears to be in progress. I am referring to the reintroduction of the intra-uterine ring first popularized by GRÄFENBERG almost thirty-five years ago. He dilated the cervix and inserted a silver ring within the uterine cavity, made in the form of a circular, silver spring, about the size of a quarter. While in position, the ring almost entirely eliminated pregnancy. To remove the ring, the cervix had to be dilated and the ring hooked and drawn forth. Objections to GRÄFENBERG's device were soon documented. The ring, being silver, corroded and often eroded through the uterine wall and was found in the peritoneal cavity, bladder or rectum. Furthermore, irregular bleeding with the ring in position was common and infections were not infrequent. Because of these serious objections, GRÄFENBERG's device fell into disuse.

Almost three years ago, OPPENHEIMER, from Israel, published a report on the use of nonmetallic rings made of twisted silkworm gut. This publication started a whole new era and there are several modifications now being tried all over the world. Some are made of polyethylene plastic, some from silkworm gut and others from nylon. It is too early to give them final assessment but preliminary studies show that they reduce the chances for impregnation tremendously and when withdrawn, pregnancy can be rapidly initiated. They cause cramps in some patients during the first few hours after insertion and occasionally staining during the first cycle. Profuse menses also have been reported. All of these rings are occasionally ejected, particularly during the process of menstruation. Some of the new rings, particularly the one made of nylon plastic, can be inserted through a catheter the size of a 3 Hegar without preliminary dilatation of the cervix and can be removed without cervical dilatation. There is also little evidence of infection to be imputed to these modern rings.

There is no question that if these rings prove as successful as it is now thought they are likely to be, they will remove in large measure the necessity for either male or female sterilization.

Where is sterilization being done for population control? The only two countries from which we have any extensive reports are Japan and India. I understand that in the eight-year period, between 1949 July and 1957 July, 258,235 sterilizations were done in Japan. That averages 33,000 a year. However, the number has increased gradually, so that in 1957, the last year for which I have figures, 44,380 sterilization procedures were performed in Japan.

In India, as reported by Ambassador CHAGLA, they did 41,000 sterilizations in 1960. I understand from Dr. BALFOUR that in the five-year period 1956 to 1960, 125,000 sterilizations in total were done. This is an also gradually increasing number; in 1959 there were 31,000 and in 1960, 41,000.

There are two more things I would like to say. In the first place, I think that the use of sterilization has been greatly impeded by separating it from contraception. I feel that one is permanent contraception, the other temporary contraception. The international Planned Parenthood Federation and the Planned Parenthood Federation of America by concentrating only on birth control methods, have put sterilization into discard; they have virtually pointed an accusatory finger at it. I am sure this is not conscious. It is unfortunate that many have to fragment their energies because many on the PPFA Board are also on the Human Betterment Board, and vice versa. The fact that there is this split weakens the position of sterilization particularly. This is also true on the international scene as well. It seems to me that the two groups should take cognizance of this in their future plans.

On the basis of GREGORY PINCUS' report, sterilization may not be necessary in the distant future; perhaps, after "x" number of years, the improvement in contraceptives may make sterilization unnecessary. To me this appears unlikely because for poorly motivated people sterilization is a much better technique than contraception.

I know this from practical experience at The Mount Sinai Hospital. A Puerto Rican woman living in the slums of New York who has four or five babies will rush as rapidly as possible to have her sixth baby at our Hospital so that sterilization can be done. They refuse to be bothered by birth control techniques. Therefore, I doubt that we can completely write off sterilization. It is likely to have a place, even after the ideal contraceptive is found.

ALAN FRANK GUTTMACHER, M. D., is Lecturer in Obstetrics and Gynecology, at the Medical School of Columbia University, and the Harvard School of Public Health, and was Director of the Department of Obstetrics and Gynecology, Mt. Sinai Hospital from 1952–1962. He has been a recipient of the Lasker Award. Dr. GUTTMACHER was Director of the Margaret Sanger Research Bureau, New York, and is President of the Planned Parenthood Federation of America-World Population.

The Problems of Abortion
The Personal Population Explosion

by

JEROME M. KUMMER

Psychiatrists do well to concern themselves with the impending avalanche of population explosion. The direct bearing that abortion has on population figures is all too apparent. In the United States alone, if we were to take the estimated one million abortions per year and calculate population curves predicated on these abortions *not* having been accomplished, the contrast to present curves would indeed be vivid. Then let us remember what a small part of the total world census we represent.

As psychiatrists we are interested in the significance of abortion on three main levels, as it relates to (1) the abortee, (2) society, and (3) a more specific segment of society, the medical profession.

Induced abortion can be traced back as far as recorded history. It has been found in all societies with almost no exceptions. The reasons for abortion have been legion, ranging from superstition and vanity on the one hand to very real physical and economic pressures on the other. It can be said that varying types and degrees of *relative population explosion* were among the most common reasons for abortion in primitive societies; lack of food and other essentials and the tremendous burden that rearing many children impose on primitive women have been described as primary motives toward abortion.

DEVEREUX (1) is convinced that abortion is an absolutely . universal phenomenon. The wide prevalence of this practice should lead one to consider the possibility that abortion, under certain circumstances, represents an instinctive drive. (Let it be emphasized that "instinct" is not being used in the psychoanalytic but rather the generic sense: "An organized and relatively complex mode of response, characteristic of a given species that has been phylogenetically adapted to a specific type of environmental situation." (2).)

ABORTION IN THE UNITED STATES

In the United States it appears that abortion is part of our social mores with society steadfastly refusing to acknowledge this to be so. The taboo that is discernible surrounding abortion is more concerned with talking about it rather than the actual act itself(3). It is quite obvious that there is a direct derivation of attitudes concerning abortion from the prevailing attitudes toward sex in general. One might readily compare it with society's attitude toward masturbation; no one would deny its prevalence, nor could anyone deny the powerful silence that surrounds it.

The problem of criminal abortion is of enormous magnitude, both in terms of incidence and resultant mortality. Several studies (4, 5, 6, 7) suggest that one out of every five pregnancies in the United States terminates in criminal abortion, or a total of more than one million per year, with a possibility of more than 5,000 deaths resulting therefrom.

The work of GEBHARD et al.(4), of the Kinsey Institute, provided new and illuminating insights into many facets of illegal abortion. Although their sampling was not designed to be representative of our population, nevertheless it is possible to discern meaningful trends, mostly applicable to our urban women with relatively higher education.

Some of the highlights of the KINSEY group's study were: (1) One of every 3 to 4 women having live births had one or more abortions. (2) The higher the educational level, the greater the tendency to seek abortion. Thus white and negro unmarried women with a college education were found to have the highest abortion rate – well over 80% of all pregnancies. (3) Illegal abortion is more a problem of married women having several children, contrary to the popular notion that it mostly involves illegitimate pregnancy. The more pregnancies a women has had, the more likely she is to seek abortion. This agrees with the findings of KOPP (6) in her study which was done 25 years earlier (Fig. 1). (4) A much higher rate of induced abortion in married women occurred at younger ages and in later life (Fig. 2).

To again refer to Figure 1, the curve indicates a very substantial correlation between the number of pregnancies and the tendency to seek abortion. Are these women not seeking to avert a *personal population explosion*; where having another child at a given time represents an excessive strain on the individual's (and her family's) physical, emotional, intellectual, and economic resources?

The curve, midway between a "U" and a "J", seen in Figure 2, demonstrates an unreadiness to bear children early in life and, in later years, a rebellion – a refusal to go through child-rearing again, now that their families are grown. Both curves support my instinct theory – that any woman, with internal and external stresses accruing beyond a given level,

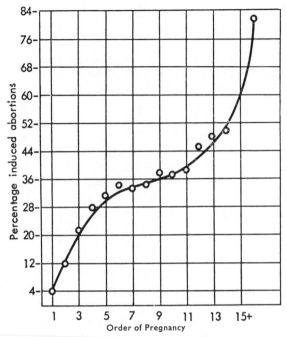

Fig. 1. Percentage of pregnancies terminating in induced abortion according to order of pregnancy (after KOPP (6)).

will seek and secure abortion. Might these not be additional manifestations of the same natural defenses brought out in some of my earlier papers?

The substantial incidence of psychiatric illness precipitated by pregnancy and childbirth, as contrasted with the negligible incidence of postabortion psychiatric illness (discussed in more detail further on), led me to postulate that abortion provides relief and protection for women susceptible to

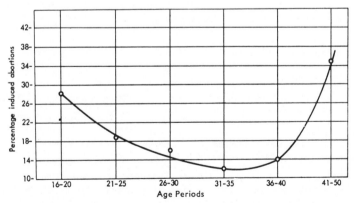

Fig. 2. Percentage of pregnancies terminating in induced abortion for women currently or previously married at age of abortion (from GEBHARD et al. (4)).

disabling psychiatric illness. Far from being the precipitator of psychiatric illness, as was so generally assumed, abortion appears to be a defense against such illness.

Is the markedly lowered fertility rate among schizophrenics and manic-depressives not a manifestation of their natural defenses? (10, 11, 12)

OTHER COUNTRIES

Of the major contemporary nations, only Japan freely permits abortion as a method of birth control, designed to stem the force of their already felt population explosion. The Soviet Union and her satellites, although they now have very relaxed rules concerning abortion, have never acknowledged population control as their purpose.

While we hear more talk these days about population explosion, one might wonder if we do not encounter a resistance similar to that seen against preparing ourselves for the dangers of thermonuclear war or any other disaster. Contemplating such horrible spectres is too threatening to our individual and collective egos, and we defend against this in a variety of ways, mostly through rationalization and denial. Japan, as an isolated example of an industrialized nation in the throes of a population eruption, was forced into concrete action. Legalizing abortion rapidly cut their birth rate in half. One cannot infer that this is a necessary or desirable solution for our country or other western nations. Moral and religious standards in Japan were (and are) such that legalized abortion did not encounter much opposition. Obviously the situation is vastly different in western countries; our social standards cause us to look in other directions for answers to this problem.

It might be helpful at this point to dispel certain popular notions concerning laws on abortion in the Scandinavian countries. Abortion is *not* freely available; they have very strict laws and very methodical procedures for carrying them out. Briefly stated, their laws and procedures are roughly comparable to our practices in this country (but not with our laws!), with one notable exception. They give fuller recognition to socio-medical factors, such as their "worn-out mother" syndrome.

POST-ABORTION PSYCHIATRIC ILLNESS

Although frequent mention of psychiatric illness following abortion is found in American medical literature, up to this time there has been no statistical documentation of such sequelae. As I reported in an earlier paper (9), a preliminary survey among a group of American psychiatrists revealed that post-abortion psychiatric illness occurred either very rarely or, for the most part, not at all. Surveying foreign literature and communications with psychiatrists in other countries, particularly those in

which more liberal attitudes prevailed, tended to confirm the extreme
rarity of post-abortion illness.

GEBHARD and his co-workers (4) were able to show that induced abortion
did not result in the ill effects that had been so generally assumed by others.
Statistically their material gave no evidence of any resultant sterility or damage to capacity for achieving orgasm. Other physical and psychological
after-effects appeared less frequently than had been previously supposed.

If the ill effects of induced abortion have been so grossly exaggerated, we
must ask ourselves why. Might the answer be that this was part of the
means of enforcing the taboo?

MEDICAL ATTITUDES AND PRACTICES

Current medical attitudes and practices, in connection with abortion, add
up to a series of contradictions. While an extremely small percentage of
physicians are believed to be engaged in performing illegal abortions, a
good many refer patients to illegal abortionists indirectly, and some
directly, even in writing(13). While the majority of physicians have a
reasonably tolerant attitude toward this practice, most of them scrupu-
lously avoid even discussing abortion with their patients. This undoubtedly
results in many troubled women having no one but the criminal
abortionist to whom they may turn for advice and relief. "Society," according to one well-known physician-abortionist, "...abandons the
woman in her greatest need." (13)

LEGAL STATUS

This contradiction is further reflected in our society as a whole and more
specifically in our legal institutions. Although criminal abortion is labeled
a felony, the abortees are almost never prosecuted and for professional
abortionists the rate of prosecution is low and the rate of conviction even
lower(3). It is apparent that morals, religion and the criminal law offer
little restraint when it comes to abortion, leading TAUSSIG to remark that
he knew "of no other instance in history in which there has been such
frank and universal disregard for criminal law." (5)

Most therapeutic abortions in this country are in violation of state laws.
GUTTMACHER (14) stated unequivocally "that the abortion laws in the
United States make hypocrites of all of us." More than 90% of the therapeutic abortions done at New York's Mount Sinai Hospital did not fall
strictly within statutory requirements "to preserve the life of the mother."
Hospital authorities and physicians vary widely in their interpretation of
the laws and their willingness to place themselves in jeopardy of prosecution. In a recent survey of California hospitals 18 out of 24 replied that
therapeutic abortions were performed knowingly in violation of the law(15).

RECOMMENDED LEGAL CHANGES

The medical and law-enforcement professions are in need of laws which can provide clear guideposts for therapeutic abortions. Until very recently nothing was done toward modernizing these laws. The American Law Institute, in its 1959 Model Penal Code, proposed a Therapeutic Abortion Statute, which has promise of giving us our long-needed guideposts.

Mr. ZAD LEAVY, Former Deputy Los Angeles County District Attorney, and I have made the following recommendations for a therapeutic abortion act(3, 16). While these are similar to the Model Penal Code, significant differences exist. Therapeutic abortions should be allowed for the following reasons:

Eugenic – mental deficiency in the parents or the likelihood that a congenital disease or malformation will be present in the child.

Medical – where terminating the pregnancy is necessary to preserve the life or the physical or mental health of the mother.

Humanitarian – where pregnancy results from forcible rape, incest or moral irresponsibility of the female (because of youth or mental incompetence).

CONTROLS

Certain controls are recommended which would broaden the base of responsibility and reduce the possibility of abuses. For the medical and eugenic categories it is suggested that the laws permit licensed hospitals to regulate the performance of therapeutic abortions through a qualified committee of staff physicians, composed of at least two obstetricians, one internist, one psychiatrist, and a fifth person. Such committees have been functioning well for some time in most leading hospitals.

Under the humanitarian category, where the decision must be based upon a finding of fact as to the mother's claim of forcible rape or incest, provision should be made for the courts to order an abortion if the facts appear to substantiate the claim. Such a finding of fact is considered to be more within the framework of the courts than within the confines of sound medical judgment.

California has a bill pending, patterned after the Model Penal Code. Although there is excellent support for this bill from the 1960 and 1962 Los Angeles County Grand Juries, organized medicine and other groups, the extremely well-organized opposition, namely the Roman Catholic Church, makes passage in the near future improbable.

It is believed that the harshness of existing laws concerning therapeutic abortion together with the confusion surrounding processing of abortion recommendations help to swell the already large number of illegal abortions. No one is under the illusion that modifying our existing laws will eliminate abortions done illegally. As long as there are any restrictions at all, women with unwanted pregnancies who are determined to abort will find illegal abortionists. This is, however, no reason for abandoning all attempts to prevent widespread termination of pregnancy by unskilled hands.

PREVENTIVE MEASURES

Nor is one under the illusion that modifying these laws is the most important step. Preventive measures are certainly called for; the most significant are:

Consultation Centers – similar to those in Sweden, where women with unwanted pregnancies may go for counseling by competent professionals. With experienced counseling many women find that they can and want to go to term, others may qualify for therapeutic interruptions, and still others can have the possibilities of adoption explored. Those who are still intent on illegal abortion can be educated about the dangers and the necessity for early treatment afterward.

Research toward developing of the "ideal" contraceptive.

Education of the public must include sex instruction for children at levels understandable to them. For adults the sex instruction should be more comprehensive, including information on planned parenthood, birth control and abortion.

PROBLEM AREAS

The problem areas, which must be explored and resolved include:

I. *The drive toward abortion* – among the multiplicity of factors, are we dealing with an instinctive drive?

II. *Psychiatric sequelae of induced abortion* – if these and physical after-effects have been so grossly exaggerated, was it a means of perpetuating the taboo?

III. *Social forces and attitudes*: Is society in fact protecting the mother's welfare by maintaining stringent laws which drive her to illegal abortion?

IV. *Therapeutic abortion laws*: qualified physicians cannot operate honestly within the framework of current abortion laws: the legal threat of prosecution hangs over their heads, when in reality the community has no intention of punishing medical practitioners acting in good faith.

The forces in our society opposing abortion, namely religious and legal institutions, are well-known and quite obvious. What is also obvious is that these social forces have not accomplished their stated goals, maintaining morality and preventing abortion. Instead we are confronted with a sea of heartache and confusion and an estimated 5,000 deaths per year from illegal abortions. Is it not time that we took a long, hard, critical look at these forces in an effort to better understand them and to determine if indeed they are in the best interests of the individual and society?

The problems of abortion are of utmost complexity, requiring study and remedy on many levels from a variety of disciplines. My experience with this enigma has led me to believe that significant strides can be made by utilizing methods borrowed from psychotherapeutic theory and techniques in isolating, identifying, and helping the patient (in this case *society*) deal with the problem.

BIBLIOGRAPHY

1. DEVEREUX, G.: A Typological Study of Abortion in 350 Primitive, Ancient and Pre-Industrial Societies, in Therapeutic Abortion, edited by H. ROSEN. Julian Press, New York, 1954.
2. WARREN, H. C.: Dictionary of Psychology. Houghton Mifflin Co., Boston, 1934.
3. KUMMER, J. M. & LEAVY, Z.: Criminal Abortion: A consideration of ways to reduce incidence. *Calif. Med.*, 95: *170*, Sept. 1961.
4. GEBHARD, P. H., POMEROY, W. B., MARTIN, C. E. & CHRISTENSON, C. V.: Pregnancy, Birth and Abortion. Harper and Bros., New York, 1958.
5. TAUSSIG, F. J.: Abortion, Spontaneous and Induced. C.V. Mosby Co., St. Louis, 1936.
6. KOPP, M. E.: Birth Control in Practice. McBride and Co. New York, 1934.
7. STIX, R. K.: A Study of Pregnancy Wastage. *Milbank mem. Fd. Quart.* 13: *347*, 1935.
.8. KUMMER, J. M.: Psychiatric contraindications to pregnancy with reference to therapeutic abortion and sterilization. *Calif. Med.*, 79: *31*, July, 1953.
9. —: Post-abortion psychiatric illness – a myth? *Amer. J. Psychiat.*, 119: *980*, April 1963.
10. —: Value of routine psychiatric examination in treatment of infertility. *Amer. Practic.* 9: *383*, March, 1958.
11. ESSEN-MÖLLER, quoted by E. E. KRAPF: Foreign Letters, *J.A.M.A.*, 118, *315*, 1942.
12. KALLMAN, F. J.: Heredity in Health and Mental Disorder. W. W. Norton and Co., New York, 1953.
13. TIMANUS, G. L.: Quoted in Abortion in the United States, edited by M. S. CALDERONE. Hoeber-Harper, New York, 1958.
14. GUTTMACHER, A. F.: The law that doctors often break. Redbook Magazine, Aug., 1959, p. 24.
15. PACKER, H. L., & GAMPELL, R. J.: Therapeutic abortion: A problem in law and medicine. *Stanford Law Rev.*, 11: *417*, May 1959.
16. LEAVY, Z. & KUMMER, J. M.: Criminal abortion: Human hardship and unyielding laws. *So. Calif. Law Rev.*, 35: *123*, Winter 1962.

JEROME MELVIN KUMMER, M. D., Associate Clinical Professor of Psychiatry, University of California at Los Angeles; Senior Attending Psychiatrist, Santa Monica Hospital, California; Consultant, Atascadero State Hospital, California and of National Safety Council. Publications include: Psychiatric contraindications to pregnancy, Routine psychiatric examination in treatment of infertility, Criminal abortion: Human hardship and unyielding laws, and A psychiatrist looks at problem drivers.

PROSPECTS FOR THE FUTURE

Public Health in an Overpopulated World

by

JOHN E. GORDON & HAZEL ELKINGTON

The startlingly rapid growth of world populations brings two-fold demands on the public health profession (1). First, the health needs of existing numbers of people have to be met: numbers already are so great, and increasing to such extent, as to exceed facilities and the capacity of available trained health workers. This is a technical and administrative problem, appreciated by the profession, costly in terms of time and money. Secondly public health must assume its share of responsibility for creating public awareness of a population problem that is both world-wide and local; and take action to find a solution.

The two obligations have equal significance. Both warrant attention, but the second is the root of the problem. The potential development of public health is inhibited not so much by lack of progress in enlarging its capacities and improving its methods as in dilution of services by the increased numbers of people requiring them. The central difficulty is of populations constantly outgrowing facilities.

PEOPLE AND RESOURCES

Economic and social progress depends on continuously adapting people to resources and resources to people (2). Much of the benefit from agricultural and industrial expansion is being dissipated in taking care of growing numbers of people. Modern methods of production will result in an increasing supply of goods and services. Given time and relatively stable numbers, economic use of resources and technological inventions yet to come will increase the rate at which living standards rise. Together with education and industrialization these are the broad long-term forces tending toward a solution of the population problem.

Public health has a powerful potential influence on the future turn of events. Anti-malarial measures have already opened up huge fertile areas in India, Ceylon and Java for cultivation of food. On the other hand, some major breakthrough in medical science could well result in a means for prevention or cure of any one of the five leading causes of death, and consequently in many more lives being prolonged. Conversely, a disease occasionally becomes resistant to known therapy: antibiotics are already losing their effectiveness against some infectious agents. Or again, a now benign disease may take a virulent form, as influenza has done repeatedly in the past.

The current situation permits no temporizing. Increases in population continue to exceed expansion of resources: and ultimately, unless means are found to create a satisfactory balance, the result will be a lower standard of living for all and, at the worst, social unrest, disease and famine. With the momentum now under way in population growth, all agencies of society are of necessity involved in the search for a solution.

The factors responsible for increased numbers of people are manifold(3). Man in the beginning was equipped with sexual drives and capacities designed for a primitive and dangerous environment. Those were the days when less than half of children born survived to adult age. Meanwhile the social, biological and even the physical environment has changed. In earlier days modification of the environment came slowly, because the means to change fundamental conditions were poor. Modern technology has played an important part but no more than medical science. The concern of public health with improved environmental sanitation, the provision of pure and adequate water supplies, the prevention and control of communicable diseases through immunization, insecticides and antibiotics, and the mounting attention to nutritional disorders, have been the major factors in achieving dramatically lower death rates.

Advances in life expectancy that took a century to accomplish in Western nations are now being made in a decade or two in some of today's pre-industrial societies. In Ceylon, for example, life expectancy rose from 32 years in 1921 to 60 years by 1954. The death rate dropped from 19.8 per 1000 population in 1946 to 12.3 in 1949 following institution of malaria control (4). In the Bursa province of Turkey at a time when rice cultivation was practiced, malaria was endemic and the death rate about 28. In 1941 mosquito breeding was attacked through prohibiting rice culture and malaria control methods were applied on a wide scale. By 1947 the death rate had fallen to 10.

Death rates tend to decline universally while birth rates generally remain high. In repeated instances the lost balance between births and deaths has resulted in the substitution of one health problem for another, a population problem for a specific disease (5).

The population problem affects most aspects of human welfare. The health professions have no more obligation than any other discipline to search for a solution, yet some of the necessary action and research is peculiarly within the competence of medical practitioners, administrators and investigators.

THE IMMEDIATE PROFESSIONAL RESPONSIBILITY

Health conditions today are far from ideal: it is no unreasonable estimate that half the people in the world are sick or undernourished. The immediate problem public health has to face is how to expand standard services to take care of the increased demand. It is just as urgent to improve existing facilities. For both tasks, research is needed to develop resources, define problems and translate needs into practical objectives. Plans must be made for more hospital beds, clinics, laboratories, provision for rehabilitation, nursing homes and convalescent centers. Urgently required are more doctors, nurses and ancillary workers, but today, with the choice of so many attractive and lucrative careers, the proportion of young people entering the public health service is declining. Even in the United States there is not enough medical staff for hospitals, health centers, teaching institutions and research laboratories.

Populations grow unevenly, according to the variables of age, sex and other characteristics. They have different distributions by time and place, and individual groups have different kinds and incidence of disease. Official and voluntary agencies have to adapt service arrangements to the changing size and character of the community. For instance, the longer life span provides an older population. With more people living beyond age 65 years, there are more chronic illness and more people with physical or mental handicaps. An outstanding feature of public health of the last decade or so is the attention increasingly given to control of such ills as cancer, heart disease and mental disorders.

In the international field, health conditions are complicated by the growth of modern communications, as witness the recent epidemic of smallpox in Great Britain originating in the arrival by air from Pakistan of a person with that disease. In a contracting world, the health concerns of individual countries are no longer isolated problems, but more and more inter-related with those of their neighbors.

The World Health Organization is making strides in control of such afflictions as yaws, trachoma and leprosy. Much remains to be done. WHO and various individual countries participate in provision of supplies and qualified health workers, with the aim to stimulate and train people of the country to take on responsibility for their own concerns. Problems of health have different applications in every individual nation, town and village, and can only be solved by the energetic cooperation of local agencies. A fundamental aim is to educate the public to accept modern public health procedures, which oftentimes run counter to local habits, customs and beliefs. Many instances are on record of a thoroughly sound health measure rendered ineffective through failure or disinclination of a people to accept it: for example, the resistance in the United States to fluoridation of water.

POPULATION CONTROL

The problems of more people, different kinds of people and national interdependence require that public health expand its traditional concern with the control of deaths to include control of births. In Europe, population growth has been halted from time to time by plague, famine and war. During the 18th and 19th centuries, vast numbers of people emigrated to the New Worlds (6). Then came limitation of births by means available and suitable to the particular people concerned. Roman Catholic France evolved a pattern of population control along lines that differ materially from those of Roman Catholic Ireland or Protestant England. Today there are no new world frontiers with emigration a ready solution: therefore a selective reduction in births would appear to be the only answer.

Of known birth control measures, no one procedure is suited to all cultures, but at least one is available for any particular society. Methods include mechanical means such as the condom, diaphragm and douche: chemical jellies, creams and foam tablets: and, taking advantage of physiological processes, the rhythm method or safe period. A variety of steroid compounds have been developed as effective contraceptives in pill form, but to date the cost is prohibitive for people of low-income countries and the compound must be taken every day for 20 days between menstrual periods, a further disadvantage. Much research is in progress toward an improved oral contraceptive of longer action, and economically within the means of needy families. In the meantime, other proved and inexpensive methods are available, perhaps not wholly ideal but within a range of effectiveness sufficient for a practical control of conception.

Population control measures have been known and practiced in varying degree in all cultures throughout recorded history. Primitive methods now largely discounted for moral or ethical reasons have ranged from infanticide to abortion and senilicide. Unhappily, the practice of abortion persists and is currently a serious health problem in many countries in spite of religious, medical and commonly legal sanctions against it. More than one million induced abortions per year are reported in Japan, or roughly one for every live birth. Induced abortion was legalized in Japan in 1948. In European countries the incidence of illegal abortions per thousand live births is estimated to range from 300 in Czechoslovakia to over 1000 in Hungary. In Chile, the estimate is of 500 per 1000 and the practice is seemingly widespread throughout Latin America. In Turkey, the high incidence with resulting detriment to the health of mothers and children is considered almost as urgent a problem as that of tuberculosis. Abortions are frequent in the United States. According to the KINSEY report, 22% of married white females had had at least one induced abortion by the time they were 45 years of age. By 40 years of age, 25% of single white females had become pregnant and between 88 and 95% of these extramarital conceptions were resolved by abortion. The prevalence of abortion suggests a demand by the public for some form of birth control. It is a major method of birth control for millions of people. The alternative is family planning by contraception, or sterilization.

Sterilization is practiced extensively in Puerto Rico and performed at many public hospitals for a minimal fee. HILL, STYCOS & BACK reported that sterilizations in public and private hospitals corresponded to 17.8% of total hospital deliveries for 1949, and as many as one fifth of all wives had had what is locally termed "the operation". Sterilization is practiced increasingly in other countries, including India, Japan and Pakistan. While less objectionable than abortion, no such drastic and irreversible method of birth control is believed universally suited to the common need. As with abortion, a more reasonable substitute is seemingly family planning by contraception.

Birth control by whatever means is a concept foreign to many societies. The cultural obstacles blocking the rapid adoption of contraceptive practices often appear insuperable. Birth control cannot be forced on a people, nor should it be withheld from those who want it. To be widely acceptable, methods must conform to religious and cultural patterns, be simple, cheap, efficient, safe, reversible, and with no side effects. No one method meets all these requirements, but within varying degrees of efficiency and acceptability suitable methods exist and more become available. The main difficulty lies in getting people to use them.

The ultimate responsibility for limiting family size rests with the individual couple. Deaths within a population have declined largely by reason of medical progress implemented in its practical applications by government and society: the individual has had secondary responsibility. The control of births presents the opposite situation and is the harder task. Motivation is a vital consideration. The demonstration that five children are no longer necessary to assure that three live to become adults is a strong incentive. More survivors also provide visual evidence of the difficulties of providing proper education and material advantages.

PUBLIC HEALTH AND POPULATION CONTROL

The approach of the individual and of society to birth control may be said to have been based thus far on principles of curative rather than preventive medicine (7). People commonly resort to birth control when family size exceeds material resources. Their aim is to remedy or ameliorate a situation already developed. The more logical first step would appear to be adoption of the principles of prevention, to encourage spacing of births throughout childbearing age by inculcating in the newly married the advantages in health and welfare to be derived from using logic and reasoning in planning their families. Experimental evidence has shown spacing of births to be beneficial to the health of mothers and children: the optimum interval in a series of observations was three years between births. Evidence accumulates that shorter intervals result in higher morbidity and mortality, both of mothers and infants. Economically, the advantages of spacing are obvious: for example, the strain of putting three children through college at the same time, when one at a time could be financed. There is the basic obligation to provide for the physical and cultural needs of all living children before more are brought into the world. Planned spacing accomplishes a relative limitation of numbers.

The advantages of the preventive approach to family planning become evident when the desired number of children has been achieved. After couples have been accustomed to spacing their children, methods are familiar and experience has been acquired when the need so generally arises for limitation of size of family. While the active interest of individual families is essential for the success of any national program for population control, society also has an obligation.

With the world as it is today, every country would be wise to make a careful survey of its population to determine whether or not a problem of overpopulation exists, and if so to formulate a considered population policy. Some will find the remedy in inducing their people to cooperate, through educational campaigns on population control adequately supported by a defined public policy. In Western countries population control has come from individual conviction, but this is a slow process. In some parts of the world there is need for direct initiation of effort by government, and many have instituted programs for family planning under pressure of population increase. In some countries the government extends moral and financial support to voluntary organizations, in others the government itself has instituted programs.

In Japan a family planning program is administered centrally by the Ministry of Health and Welfare through the Maternal and Child Health Section of the Children's Bureau (8). Magazines, newspapers, radio, movies, lantern slides, all means of publicity are used and have exerted a noticeable effect on popular attitudes. Some large companies in business and industry include family planning services as part of welfare measures for their employees. The birth rate in Japan declined from 34.3 in 1947 to 17.5 in 1959, halved in little over a decade. The decline was achieved mainly through induced abortion, which developed to such extent as to become a matter of concern to the Japanese Government. According to the 6th of the two-year surveys conducted by the Population Problems Research Council of the Mainichi Newspapers in April 1961, 40% of women reported at least one abortion. Currently about 40,000 midwives have been licensed as family planning instructors, to work towards the substitution of conception control for abortion and sterilization: a reported 42.5% of wives in Japan under 50 years of age now use contraception.

In India the highest priority is given to family planning in the 3rd 5-Year Plan which began in April 1961. Operations center in the Ministry of Health, and birth control clinics are a feature of larger urban health departments. In rural districts family planning and public health activities are associated. A variety of contraceptive methods is offered, including rhythm. Sterilization is not generally used, although in Madras City a sterilization program was initiated in 1958. Men are paid 15 rupees ($3) and women 25 rupees ($5) to undergo the operation. The program was extended to the state of Madras 18 months later. The state of Maharashtra started a similar campaign in December, 1959.

A Family Planning Scheme, 1960–65, estimated to cost 6 million dollars was approved by the Pakistani cabinet in October, 1960. By November, 1961, there were 641 family planning centers in the country. A total of 530 doctors, 450 health visitors and nurses, and 5000 village aid workers had had training in the principles and methods of birth control directed towards staffing these centers and incorporating them in the public health work of the country. Male sterilization by vasectomy has been approved and is performed in government hospitals. The use of oral contraceptives is under consideration.

Other countries have organized similar services. In Barbados, government subsidized birth control clinics first opened in May, 1955. Hongkong has a government subsidized program carried out as part of the social welfare and public health activities of the colony. Korea has budgeted about $400,000 for expenditure on family planning in 1962, the emphasis to be on public education. A training program for doctors, nurses, midwives and community leaders began in November, 1961.

THE NEED FOR MORE KNOWLEDGE

Progress in population control is limited among other things by lack of understanding of the processes of fertility. Population research to date has been predominantly demographic, social and economic, with secondary emphasis on biologic aspects. Many basic questions remain unanswered relating to menstruation, ovulation, conception, sterility and the diseases and physiologic states which modify fertility. Preoccupation with contraception should not cloud the opposite problem of helping women who want children but have difficulty in conceiving.

Many clinical trials of contraceptive measures have been made under the controlled conditions of hospital or outpatient clinic. The need is for more field trials in general populations, such as those of KOYA (9) in rural

Japan. The objective there was to determine how many people could be induced to take up contraception, how conscientiously they would follow the program, and finally to assess the effect of the program on population numbers as judged by birth rates. Some 1161 families in three rural villages were observed, beginning in 1950. Originally they were offered 8 different contraceptive methods: the condom proved the most popular, with diaphragm and jelly and the safe period (rhythm method) next in order. After 7 years, 75% of families were using some contraceptive measure. Birth rates were 26.7 per 1000 population before the program started: they dropped to 13.6 after 7 years, exceeding the decline in the country as a whole but achieved in this case mainly through use of contraception instead of abortion. In a coal mining village annual rates for abortions decreased from 16.2 to 8.4 per thousand population, while age adjusted birth rates declined from 27.6 to 13.9 per thousand.

Observations in a rural population of India, at Ramanagaram, Mysore state, and in a suburban population of New Delhi, beginning in 1952 and ending after 18 months, constitute the only field investigation concerned wholly with the rhythm method of contraception (10). Data are available from other sources, but under conditions where rhythm was employed secondarily to some other agent or as one of several methods used. The studies suggest that the method is not the best for use in a general population. Some persons have difficulty because of menstrual irregularities: a high grade intelligence and motivation are required for its success. In this study relatively few took the trouble to learn its proper use and as a field trial the results were negative.

A study in 23 rural villages near Lucknow, India, by BALJIT SINGH has been in force since 1952. Materials and instruction on contraception by foam tablet, oil and sponge, and rhythm techniques were provided to a population of 8000 persons. Acceptance was greatest for foam tablets, but for all methods did not exceed one-third of eligible women. From the results obtained the conclusion is justified that the rhythm method is not suited to the Indian culture. The remaining two methods were rarely used.

The India-Harvard-Ludhiana study of population dynamics began in the autumn of 1953 in the Ludhiana district of the Punjab, northern India, and ended in July, 1960 (11). The aim was to determine whether contraception would be accepted and if so to evaluate its effectiveness. One village of 1087 people was observed in an exploratory study to determine choice of method. Five procedures were offered: rhythm, coitus interruptus, contraceptive paste and pad, salt solution and pad, and foam tablets. Most people chose foam tablets. Subsequently this contraceptive method was the main reliance in the principal study, begun in 1956 and continued for 4 years. Although the initial enthusiasm was commendable, actual use according to directions over an appreciable time was at a low level, such that no measurable impact on birth rates was demonstrated. After 2-½ years, 17% of all couples where the wife was 15 to 44 years old were using foam tablets. Another 8% were using the rhythm method or abstinence. The population of the villages remained close to stable, despite a high birth rate and a relatively low death rate, but the result came about through migration to other localities, primarily cities. With people as they are and with existing knowledge of the social and biological factors influencing birth rates, the fundamental impression was that control of population numbers is not to be had by a crash program centered in a few years of effort. The attempt to alter social habits is most successful when introduced slowly, discreetly and with a sensitive regard for local attitudes. Generalities do not suffice. Control measures must be fitted to the individual situation.

OPERATIONAL ORGANIZATION

An independent agency of government could be developed to organize and implement effective programs for family planning, but seemingly it is more practical and less exhaustive of time and money to take advantage of existing organizations. The official organization for public health is an agency of society well fitted to undertake the practical work of a program for birth control. Trained staffs are accustomed to meeting people in their homes, they have technical methods of inquiry applicable to family planning, and an extensive experience in education of the public. This applies solely to operational procedures: the belief has been stated earlier that the cooperation and effort of all disciplines is needed in the general endeavor. Education of the public to an awareness of the problem, the derivation of facts upon which to work, the cultivation of public opinion must engage the activities of all agencies of society, including public health, each in its particular sphere.

Venereal disease, alcoholism and mental illness are among the accepted responsibilities of official public health agencies, with emphasis on the health aspects. All have an important social component, along with problems of morals, ethics, and religious beliefs. When mental health came to be recognized as a medical problem, an independent department of mental health was created in many places. Now the tendency is to recognize mental and physical disabilities as being closely allied, with much to be gained by unified effort. There would appear much advantage in recognizing that control of births is similarly a health problem, to be integrated with other public health procedures.

The American Public Health Association includes a concern with population dynamics among its established policies, stating forcefully that:

1. Public health organizations at all levels of government should give increased attention to the impact of population change on health.

2. Scientific research should be greatly expanded on (a) all aspects of

human fertility; and (b) the interplay of biological, psychological and socio-economic factors influencing population change.

3. Public and private programs concerned with population growth and family size should be integral parts of the health program and should include medical advice and services which are acceptable to the individuals concerned.

4. Full freedom should be extended to all population groups for the selection and use of such methods for the regulation of family size as are consistent with the creed and mores of the individuals concerned.

Some state and local health departments in North America are fostering increasing numbers of family planning programs. A logical place for these activities is in the division of maternal and child health.

A growing number of schools of medicine and public health, particularly graduate schools, are giving attention to population dynamics, but so far minimally. The health professions are too little aware that the population problem is one of the major health hazards in the world today, and that they have an obligation to contribute within their capabilities to amelioration of the broad social problems involved. Some aspects are entirely within their interests and responsibilities. They have an important function in influencing governmental decisions and the conduct of operations, if the public welfare is to be safeguarded.

Education of the public in so intimate a matter as contraception is a formidable task. There is no universal approach. Interest must be stimulated within the framework of established cultural concepts. The demand so created can then be satisfied by provision of methods, materials and advice. Without direction, information on control of conception tends to spread by hidden routes and not always reliably. Urbanization, education and other social changes favor more rapid spread of ideas because people get together more, read more and talk more. With exposure to mass media, ideas and social customs tend to become more uniform. A public health approach to birth control brings discussion into the open and provides for direct communication between experts and the public on preferences, needs and the practicability of procedures. Ideally, the target should be the adolescent, so that when the time comes for marriage the idea of planned and responsible parenthood is firmly implanted. Practically, and under present conditions, the place to start is with the mother after the birth of the first baby.

SUMMARY

The solution to the population problem is to increase production of material resources and to limit numbers of births. The latter is clearly to be recognized among health problems. Being in large part responsible for population growth through success in lowering death rates, public health has a moral obligation to aid in achieving an ecologic balance between man and his environment. It has the facilities for an active part in research, services and education directed toward lowering birth rates. Public health centers exist. More must be provided and traditional services expanded to include a control of births as well as deaths.

REFERENCES

1. GORDON, J. E.: Population Problems in a Contracting World. *Yale J. Biol. Med.*, 34: *60*, 1961.
2. OSBORN, F.: Population: An International Dilemma. New York, Population Council, 1958.
3. United Nations Dept. of Social Affairs, Population Division: The Determinants and Consequences of Population Trends. New York, United Nations, 1958.
4. COALE, A. J. & HOOVER, E. M.: Population Growth and Economic Development in Low-Income Countries. Princeton, N.J., Princeton University Press, 1958.
5. WOYTINSKY, W. S. & WOYTINSKY, E. S.: World Population and Production: Trends and Outlook. New York, Twentieth Century Fund, 1953.
6. HAUSER, P. M. & DUNCAN, O. D. (Eds.): The Study of Population: An Inventory and Appraisal. Chicago, University of Chicago Press, 1959.
7. GORDON, J. E., WYON, J. B. & INGALLS, T. H.: Public Health as a Demographic Influence. *Amer. J. med. Sci.*, 227: *326*, 1954.
8. Asia Family Planning Association; Family Planning in Japan. Tokyo, Asia Family Planning Association, 1961.
9. KOYA, Y., KUBO, H., YUASA, S. & OGINO, H.: Seven Years of a Family Planning Program in Three Typical Japanese Villages. *Milbank Mem. Fund Quart.*, 34: *363*, 1958.
10. Report on Pilot Studies in Family Planning, Vols. I and II. New Delhi, World Health Organization Regional Office for S.E. Asia, 1954.
11. GORDON, J. E. & WYON, J. B.: Field Studies in Population Dynamics and Population Control. *Amer. J. med. Sci.*, 240, *361*, 1960.

JOHN EVERETT GORDON, Ph.D., M.D., F.R.C.P. (London), is Professor of Preventive Medicine and Epidemiology, Emeritus, Harvard School of Public Health. Dr. GORDON is a Consultant of the United States Public Health Service, of the Department of the Army, of the World Health Organization and of the Institute of Nutrition of Central America and Panama. He was formerly a Field Director of the Rockefeller Foundation. In World War II he served as Chief of the Preventive Medicine Division, European Theater of Operations, U.S. Army, and later as Consultant in Preventive Medicine, Allied Forces in the Pacific. Dr. GORDON has been awarded the Distinguished Service Medal, the Legion of Merit, Bronze Star Medal, Army Commendation Ribbon (U.S.A.), Order de la Santé Publique and Croix de Guerre with Palm (France), Liberty Cross (Norway) and Order of the British Empire; honorary member of various American and foreign scientific societies. He is author of several books and many journal publications on acute communicable disease, chronic disease, traumatic injuries and population dynamics.

HAZEL ELKINGTON is a Research Assistant in the Department of Demography and Human Ecology, Harvard School of Public Health.

The Unwanted Child *

by

ABRAM BLAU

> "Man doth not live by bread only.'.
> – Deuteronomy, VIII, 3'

A serious public health hazard of the population explosion is the growing possibility of psychological injury to infants who are unwanted and consequently suffer maternal privation. Some of the major factors in maternal rejection will be discussed here, together with the psychiatric disorders that may be the outcome.

Mothering, on the other hand, is the indispensible ingredient that serves to nurture the infant's life drives and help him develop individuality and emotional responses, especially social interchange and the capacity to love. Errors in the course of this unfolding process make for varying degrees of personality disorganization, psychiatric disturbance and retardation of development.

At the outset, it may be noted that a complacent faith in nature is not enough. Nature seems little concerned about preventing disease and hardship, and prolonging life. Rather, its principle is preservation of the species by natural selection, survival of the fittest, and trial and error chance. By contrast, medicine lines up with religious and humanistic philosophies concerned with the basic worth and dignity of the human being. It is true that illness, death and hardship are natural events. But these evils are no longer accepted with resignation as being inevitable. Science and culture are toiling endlessly to improve the lot of man, to prolong his life and reduce illness to a minimum. Today, protests against avoidable adversities are voiced in ever-widening circles, especially among less privileged peoples, with resulting new political and international pressures.

Some sample statistics indicate the wide extent of the problem: From

* From the Child Psychiatry Division, the Institute of Psychiatry, (M. RALPH KAUFMAN, M.D., Director), The Mount Sinai Hospital, New York, N.Y. Presented at the American Psychiatric Association Annual Meetings, St. Louis, Missouri, May 10, 1963.

1955 to 1959 there were 59,207 out of wedlock births in New York City (PAKTER et al., 1961). In 1962 in New York City about 3000 children were on referral for adoption and about 20,000 were under institutional and boarding home care, some 2000 of them less than two years old. Each year from 2500 to 3000 babies under age two require long term care (WASSELL, 1963). Recently KEMPE and associates (1962) described the "Battered-Child" syndrome, the extensive physical abuse of young infants and children by adults, frequently with permanent injury or death. In a one-year survey 302 hospitalized cases were found and 447 cases were known to district attorneys. These figures only hint at the widespread danger of injury to children who have the misfortune to be unwanted.

Maternal Rejection

The condition of being unwanted is an emotional catastrophe. To the child it is a vital matter having to do with his immediate survival and with the very foundations for developmental processes serving his whole future life as an individual. Mothering involves actual manoeuvres that feed and foster, or by their absence, stunt physical, psychological and emotional growth. The more we come to know about the behavioral activities and stimuli that are necessary for the proper care of the infant, the better will be our position for prevention and treatment.

Maternal rejection involves a wide spectrum from minor isolated reactions to extreme physical and emotional deprivation. Indeed, some ambivalence probably occurs in all parent-child relationships and the extent varies from time to time. Some parents may orient better to a child in one stage of life and not in another, for example the mother who adores babies but cannot abide older children, or vice versa. Be that as it may, the fact remains that the maternal relation to neonate and infant is critical because at this particular time she continues to be the one most responsible for his life.

More important than the mother's conscious overt attitudes is her unconscious behavior. Indeed, a pregnancy may be unwanted and yet good affectional attitudes may develop after the birth under the influence of the child. Or the reverse may happen – the pregnancy is wanted, and then the baby for one reason or another is rejected. Also, the variety of congenital behavior patterns of newborns may affect the mother's response. Some mothers respond best to a quiet baby, others to an active one, and differences may call forth negative attitudes in the mother (EASTON & BLAU, 1963).

The mother's emotional maturity; her readiness and ability to undertake the responsibility of her child's care, is of utmost significance. It involves her own personality development and whether or not it is easily decompensated by the demands of motherhood. Some women lack the capacity to care for an infant or child. Their emotional poverty and their own need for support make it impossible for them to give care in sufficient quantity. Such a woman tends to exploit the baby in a parasitic fashion, unwittingly neglecting his needs for hers, sometimes by too much care as well as too little.

In humans there is meager evidence for an automatic maternal instinct. The infant-caring pattern seems to develop in each woman in the course of her associations with the baby. Reciprocally, as the mother cares for the baby, each baby also influences the mother in how to care for him. To be sure, a great deal depends on the woman's past experiences with her own mother, her female acculturation in early childhood by care of siblings and doll playing, the development and acceptance of her feminine role, her ability to love in a giving manner, the mastery of her own narcissistic needs, as well as how much she receives in the way of supportive love supplies from her mate and others in her world. Many primiparous women who expect a natural surge of maternal instinct immediately after delivery are quite disappointed. This factor may precipitate a postpartum depression that withdraws the mother from the infant for a critical period at the very start.

Of course, one must avoid placing blame for maternal rejection simply on the mother, as was the fashion in the twenties and thirties. In the practice of child psychiatry, deliberate rejection is not found as commonly as are failures in the face of good conscious intentions. A mother cannot be blamed for her neurosis, an illness that comes from her own background, or from the stresses of her life situation that test the limits of her maternal capacities. Moreover, it takes a special kind of knowledge to care for children. More education is needed for child rearing as well as planned parenthood, especially as society grows more complex. Good child care is a skill and an art. Some acquire it intuitively from their elders, while others do better with training and assistance.

Mother's Role in an Infant's Psychological Development

For long it was thought that the organism is born with inherent patterns of maturation which emerge naturally according to a fixed inner timetable, irrespective of the environment. The neonate was regarded as a physiological automaton with lines of development characteristic of the species, modified only by individual hereditary variations. The young infant was considered incapable of emotional reactions and regarded as insensitive to psychological and other environmental influences, needing only the simplest care of food and warmth. Faulty development was simply attributed to inborn constitutional defects, birth injury or congenital disturbances of the brain. Increasingly, however, human and animal studies disprove this view and underscore the significance of maternal care in the dual framework of maturation and development.

The human infant is born the most immature of all mammals, even missing many capacities that other animal infants already possess, such as the chick's ability to peck, and the calf's to walk. However, his advantage is that inherent maturation potentials can collaborate more with outside environmental and cultural factors for fuller development. But therein also lies the danger of maldevelopment, especially with regard to mental and emotional aspects.

In the womb the fetus is a parasite. When the child is born, a symbiotic relationship with the mother begins with all its implications of reciprocal social interchange. The promise of full development is autonomy, combined with a wider symbiosis which leads to the many partnerships of social living.

In the first three months the baby mostly needs help to establish basic visceral adjustments to the new outside environment in terms of breathing, thermostatic temperature control and gastrointestinal nutritional functions. The cry, that first automatic reflex indicator of failure in his homeostatic visceral balance, signals his needs to the mother. Its associated visceral reactions are also the anlage of anxiety and emotional insecurity for which he must eventually build up his own psychological defenses.

The mother helps him make other very important transitions from intrauterine life. Kinesthetic proprioceptive and tactile senses are stimulated by firm holding, close physical contacts, cuddling and rocking to gradually wean him from intimate uterine movements. Talking, singing and humming acclimatize him to new auditory sensations, and develop his limited perceptive capabilities, paving the way for distant communication by sight and speech.

In this initial phase the infant is undifferentiated psychologically from his mother. He seems to perceive himself fused with her, as if her body, breast, personality and ministrations were one with him. After about three months, when he is viscerally stabilized, voluntary motor and sensory capacities begin to emerge, enabling him to make searching oral-visceral-manual-tactile investigations of his own body and the outside world, particularly his mother and objects around him. Pleasurable emotional reactions appear in the form of the smile, with spontaneous cooing, responsive vocalizations and reactions of relaxation and compliance. Meanwhile, the mother-infant symbiotic interaction continues to afford mutual gratification, and to him it is a fundamental growth experience.

The infant's problem now is to get to know his mother better and differentiate her from himself, so identifying and separating himself and other material and social objects in his environment. Gradually, first part-objects, transitional objects and part-self, then a full self are identified. In the supportive comfortable medium of the mother-infant relationship, his basic ego functions begin to emerge and develop, laying the foundation for cognition and thinking, motor movement, eye-hand coordination, language, and other autonomous ego functions.

Still very sensitive and easily frightened, he needs much protection from disorganizing tension until he has better understanding, finer capacities, and the wherewithal to handle his own anxiety and security feelings. For this reason I have recommended to new mothers that the neonate and young infant can be given much attention without danger of being spoiled. Of course, later on the situation changes and his care requires setting limits, some frustrations and the start of self-discipline concepts.

From about three to twelve months, a higher level of symbiosis continues between mother and child until he becomes able to walk independently, to leave her and explore the world more widely. He begins to see himself as a separate individual, but his mother is still very essential as the need-satisfying and protecting person. Of necessity his psychology is egocentric; reality and his powers are misinterpreted as omnipotence and omniscience in his unity with the mother. Out of these relationships and gratifications comes his sense of self-confidence. To him love is the assurance of his mother's presence and care, which in time becomes incorporated into his psyche as inner assurance and security. At about eight months he reaches a significant crisis in his individuality and appreciation of the mother's separate role, suffering acute special anxiety on being separated from her. However, with gradual forays away from her, together with the confidence that he can return and find her when he needs her, he begins to gain more independence.

Although in the first half year he cannot understand or tolerate much frustration, in the second half the mother starts to teach him one of the most important lessons of life – to postpone gratification and set his sights toward self-discipline. This capacity comes from his growing memory and inner knowledge that his tensions will be relieved in short order and more and more he learns to control and master them by himself.

Of course this schematic outline is an oversimplification of what we know and much that we still have to learn. Nevertheless, it indicates concrete ways that the mother serves the infant's development. The transitions vary from child to child, and the mother must adapt flexibly to each child's unique differences. Certainly his individuality and separation from mother is only a partly formed base in the first year and much of it consolidates later as his ego continues to develop in both functional and security capacities.

Maternal Privation in Human Infants

FREUD discovered retrospectively the etiological significance of early life experiences for personality development, psychoneuroses and psychoses by using regressions and symptomatic behavior as indicators. A quarter of a century ago, more direct scientific evidence began to accumulate. Earlier, a number of feral or wild neglected children were reported and, later, striking examples came from deprivation situations of illegitimate children who were subsequently adopted, and from differences of foundlings growing up in institutions in contrast to those having one-to-one family relationships in foster homes. More recently, lesser maternal privations in apparently normal homes drew clinical attention.

Probably the first scientific record of gross human neglect starts with ITARD's account in 1801 of the "wild boy" of Aveyron, a child found running wild in the forest. Educational attempts to help this boy were the forerunners of modern-day therapeutic attitudes toward mental retardation. Similar cases of feral children have been reported by FEUERBACH (1833), FERRIS (1902), SQUIRES (1927) and GESELL (1940).

In 1940 DAVIS, a sociologist, reported the case of an illegitimate five-year-old girl isolated from birth. Unwanted by the grandfather, she was confined in an attic and just barely looked after by her mother. Undernourished, apathetic and mentally blank when discovered by the authorities, she was taken first to a county home, then to a foster home and finally to a school for defective children. She improved very slowly, but continued to be virtually an unsocialized creature. DAVIS concluded that human personality was determined by a child's communicative social contacts as much as by organic equipment.

Speaking on "Primary Affect Hunger," LEVY (1937) asked: "Assuming for the moment the value of maternal love as an essential component in the development of the emotional life, what happens when this element is left out of the primary social relationship? Is it possible that there results a deficiency disease of the emotional life, comparable to a deficiency of vital nutritional elements within the developing organism?" Further he stated, "As an instrument in modifying behavior, the power of maternal love may be seen most clearly in life histories where it is absent – a kind of ablation experiment in social life. That the difficulty in these cases is due to a primary affect hunger seems a reasonable assumption, even though not proven by any direct experiment or by statistical checks."

LOWREY in 1940 reported a study of 28 children in foster homes who had had three years institutional care as infants. The early isolative experience appeared to cause a deficient personality with unsocial behavior, hostile aggression, lack of patterns for giving and receiving affection, inability to accept limitations, and insecurity in adaptation.

Later, GOLDFARB (1943) compared two groups of older foster home children, 40 who had been in foster homes from infancy and 40 who were previously in institutions to about the age of three. The institutional children showed more psychopathology in terms of speech problems, withdrawal, timidity, emotional responsiveness, and aggressive destructiveness.

Recently, from a comprehensive comparative longitudinal study of 75 institutional and 75 family infants, PROVENCE & LIPTON (1962) presented specific observational data regarding maternal deprivation of institutional children.

From a psychoanalytic viewpoint, RIBBLE emphasized (1943) the disorganizing results of deficient mothering on the infant's development. In 1945, SPITZ reported a comparison of institutional foundlings with infants born in a prison for delinquent girls. For the imprisoned mothers, their babies were a main source of gratification and received considerable attention. However, the foundling babies, with similar good care, received less individual attention by nurses. The prison babies grew well, were active, agile and vocal. The institutional ones, in contrast, developed poorly, were susceptible to illness, and had a high mortality rate; at about two years of age, many could not eat alone, spoke only a few words and were retarded.

Then, in 1946 SPITZ drew attention to "Anaclitic Depression," arising in infants placed for temporary institutional care after about six months at home with their mothers. At first the separated infant acquired a sad expression and clung to adults. After a short while apprehension and crying appeared when an adult approached, quietened after much effort, but with the sad look remaining. Finally, complete withdrawal and dejection developed, with a frozen rigidity of mien. When the mothers returned within three months, many of the babies recovered completely and became friendly and happy again. But if the mother was not restored, the process continued in many to the point of deteriorated stupor or agitated idiocy. Within a year, a high proportion died, while the less depressed infants became susceptible to infections, had insomnia, lost appetite and weight.

Subsequently, BOWLBY (1952, 1960) wrote an extensive review of maternal care and mental health, and drew further attention to depression, withdrawal and inactivity in separated children, especially when hospitalized. The condition can be reversed by prophylactic care and frequent visiting by the mother, or special attention by a mother surrogate (STEIN, RAUSEN & BLAU, 1959). For such situations I introduced a volunteer "Mother Bank" service for pediatric cases to compensate affectional needs therapeutically when the actual mother was not available or could not fulfill the child's needs (BLAU et al., 1959).

In the forties, KANNER (1943, 1949) described "Early Infantile Autism" in certain disturbed children of university parents. This condition was characterized by profound withdrawal, resistance to human contact, an obsessive demand for sameness in the environment, language and speech defects (sometimes to the extreme of muteness and pseudo-deafness) and a preference for relations with inanimate objects. KANNER's view, later elaborated by RANK (1955) and others, was that the mother's cold intellectuality and inability to create a warm emotional climate prevented the child's ego from developing.

Over the years it became apparent that serious ego disorders can arise in infants and young children from maternal deprivation. Various childhood psychoses or schizophrenias were described (BENDER, 1955, MAHLER, 1952). Some investigators linked maternal privation as the etiological factor in childhood affect impoverishment, lack of self-identity, poor social and interpersonal adjustment, retardation of speech and intellectual cognitive functions, as well as other developmental delays. Taking an integrated approach, I proposed (1962) that these were true neuropsychiatric effects, and that such behavioral disorganizations became imbedded as structural maldevelopments in the brain. Similarly, childhood psychosomatic disorders have been related to faults in early mother-infant relationships (WENAR, 1962).

Maternal Privation in Animal Infants

While in humans we wait on such clinical instances of maternal privation, so called accidental experiments in nature, in animals more direct experimentation is possible. A large literature has accumulated of related observations on sheep, dogs, birds, rats, monkeys, chimpanzees and others (SCOTT, 1962). Here I will refer only to some of HARLOW's findings on monkeys (1959, 1962).

Originally, to raise sturdy animals for physiological research, infant monkeys were separated from their mothers after birth and placed in a controlled sterile regime. A higher rate of survival was achieved but later it was noticed that these robust monkeys were emotionally disturbed and different from animals born in the wild or raised with their mothers. The isolated laboratory-bred creatures sat quietly and stared into space, or circled the cage over and over again, or clasped their heads in their arms and rocked. Many peculiar compulsive mannerisms developed, such as pinching the same patch of skin hundreds of times a day, and occasionally even chewing and tearing at its own body. The approach of a human led to self-aggression, lacking any usual defensive patterns.

Strikingly, sex behavior was seriously disturbed. Sex drive was not absent since males and females approached each other and made tentative sexual moves of female presentation or male mounting. However, unable to orient themselves correctly, none succeeded in mating. They were also failures socially, paying scant attention to neighboring animals, and when caged with companions sat in opposite corners with little interaction. No heterosexual behavior occurred between male and female cagemates even after living together for seven years. Efforts to foster matings during the female's estrus led to vicious fighting. Attempts to mate deprived animals with experienced sexually adequate monkeys from the breeding colony also failed.

Prompted by these observations, HARLOW undertook experimental studies of mother-infant relationships. Newborn monkeys were raised with wire adult-sized effigies having a nipple from a feeding bottle protruding from the breast area. Other wire dummies were covered with terry cloth. Emotional attachments developed toward the cloth dummies, and little or none to the wire dummies, regardless of which provided milk. In fright-inducing situations, infants clung to the cloth dummies for protection. Even after two years separation, attachment to cloth effigies persisted, showing the cuddling needs of infants over and above feeding.

In other respects, however, the behavior of these monkeys at the age of from three to five years was indistinguishable from those raised in isolation. Without question, they were aberrant socially and sexually, and in a psychiatric sense, psychotic. When some of those disturbed females were impregnated after much difficulty, they turned out to be extremely poor, neglectful, and even cruel mothers. Clearly, infant monkeys, too, need live mothers for adequate psychological and social development.

DISCUSSION

Why is mothering so important for the infant and child? Most significantly, it seems to affect the life urge and variations in the emotion of love. Hitherto, we thought of life as a wholly instinctive pattern. Now we have to reconsider how much is the product of maturation and development after birth. Certainly, in its simplest basic form life resides in the protoplasmic cell and can be nurtured and grown by special techniques of tissue cultures. Life in higher multicellular organisms is another matter, involving social, psychological, and other intricacies.

In FREUD's formulation of life and death instincts, the Eros-Thannatos conflict, life is the antithesis of death. In the final analysis death is the end of all life, and at best the life of the individual is temporary. Death is inherently absolute, and life a transient phase. And though the life drive, too, has innate roots, this must be continually fed, fostered and protected like a tiny flickering flame.

In the infant, life does not seem to come along wholly spontaneously. From a glowing ember it must be carefully nursed and fanned to full expression. Born singularly helpless, the human infant as a separate entity is always close to death. Alone he is without nurture and open to extinction. His modicum of life must be protected, watched and shielded by others for a long time before he can live independently. To carry on, his physiological life has to be supported psychologically and socially. This is vividly corroborated by the high infant mortality from marasmus and anaclitic depressions due to early emotional deprivation. Partial deaths and distorted lives are displayed by the psychiatric disturbances that many of the survivors develop.

Indeed, good maternal care sets the stage for many essential lifelong attitudes – confidence, hope, faith, selfesteem. In his 1959 academic lecture to the American Psychiatric Association, MENNINGER regarded hope as a basic but elusive ingredient in our daily work of teaching, healing and diagnosis as physicians. He quoted RICHTER who found that even animals, when placed in situations that offered no chance of escape, gave up and rapidly succumbed to death as if suffering from loss of hope. HARLOW's maternally deprived monkeys became fearful, withdrawn, hopeless, and eventually failures as adults.

Apparently, this subsidiary need for replenishment of the life drive does not end with infancy but continues to a greater or lesser extent as long as we live. Just as the newborn needs to be charged by the mother with libidinal life supplies in order to be able to go on living, so it seems that recharging must continue normally throughout life. Even as adults, many common behavior patterns like fantasy, sleep, dreaming, friendship, love relations, approbation, social contacts serve to recharge our libido and life drive. Failures or reversals of libido are found in most psychiatric syndromes, particularly in depersonalization and depression, and call for restorative measures. A significant part of psychiatric therapy consists of helping the individual recharge his libido and neutralize destructive trends.

Centripetal and Centrifugal Love

The love concept as used here is not to be confused with romantic notions. It is not merely a sentimental flowery abstraction, a pleasant emotion, an idealized attitude with delusionary qualities, or a sexual pleasure, although it may have all or some of these features. Basically, love as libido is essential stuff of life, particularly to the infant and child. Without it he can die and even should he survive, deficiencies are apt to distort his life.

The infant is subservient for his vital needs on others. He must be loved to be served and he must sense love to learn about it. Love and the good life as he perceives it are made up of a multitude of small acts that protect him, gratify his needs, allay his fears, control his anger, nurture him, teach him. To the infant, love is not merely a pleasant luxury. It means survival, a life and death matter, a very real and vital necessity.

The nature of his love at first has to be selfish and egocentric, flowing centripetally towards himself and seemingly insatiable. The stream of his infantile childish love is fed and sustained by the mature adult type of love enjoyed by his mother. Her love is giving, centrifugal, unselfish. It represents the reversed type of feeling that he must attain in growing to maturity.

The child seems to seek the original intrauterine state of homeostasis and balance. However, maturity and mental health entail being able to love and work creatively, and to enjoy it as the essential part of life. Before the child can afford to love outwardly, he must have a sense of enough inner love.

In psychoanalytic terms his primary narcissism must be kindled, his secondary narcissism fostered and his object relations developed. It is through love that he finds himself and others, acquires his identity alongside the identity of others, his capacity to emote and to sense emotions in others, and to learn from identifications and socializing with other people.

Love is no more an instinct than is hate. Both are inherent potentialities. One needs to be developed, the other controlled and directed. The problem in living is to fuse the two drives, to develop the creative capabilities of love and to channalize the destructive possibilities of hate toward constructive aggression. Left uncivilized hate can take over the fragile organism and set irreversible patterns of self-destruction, anti-social behavior and the host of reactions that make up psychiatric disorder.

Activation of the life drive by the mother's affective responses and care establishes the infant's gradually increasing line of psychological and social communication. The ensuing sense of security frees his energy to cope with inner and outer challenges. In simple terms, security means a sense of adequacy in the face of anxiety. In the course of growth this conflict between security and insecurity, stability and instability, organization and disorganization continues, with the child's psychological balance depending upon his mother and others. Eventually he builds up his own defensive and inner systems to become a more autonomous organism and in good time develops his identity and individuality.

Sexuality

At the turn of the century FREUD first drew attention to infantile sexuality and the significance of sexual deviations in personality disorders. His findings were confirmed by psychoanalytic observations over the years and now we have experimental evidence in animals that maternal deprivation can seriously distort sexual development.

What does this singular finding mean? It would seem that sex, at least in higher animals, is not a simple biological response, but a complicated psychosocial activity intricately interwoven with factors of communication, emotional interchange, individual security and the capacity to love in a giving object-relation sense. Teleologically, since these deprived animals can become poor mothers, this may be a kind of natural eugenics in operation, – namely, nature's way of disconnecting the line of propagation of faults.

Basically, sex is the most intimate level of social communication, in man only partly serving propagation and more a way of social interaction for libidinal or love supplies. Grossly disordered individuals cannot make this interchange at all, moderately disturbed people can approximate it mostly at a biological level, and only mature persons are fully able to enjoy it with facets of love and friendship, mutually recharging their life and libidinal status.

There is still much to be learned about sexuality. Certainly, it does not appear out of the blue at puberty, but is an evolved capacity that starts early in life. Of course, its original elements are very different from the final product; infantile and childhood libidinal behavior bear little resemblance to adult erotic activities. Yet the common denominator seems to be social and love relations which start as far back as the earliest moments of the mother-infant interaction.

CONCLUSION

Increasingly, it has become clear from clinical and experimental evidence that the maternal care of the infant is critically essential for proper psychological and social development. In addition to physical nurturing, the infant needs intimate tactile contact, kinesthetic, vocal and visual stimulation, as well as full emotional relations with his mother.

Deficiencies in maternal care lead to serious disturbances in mental health and development. Fundamentally, maternal care fosters life drives, love capacities and socialization. The unwanted child is in danger of maternal deprivation. Consequently, that situation must be considered an important public health hazard of the overpopulation problem, calling for more planned parenthood to prevent emotional cripples.

BIBLIOGRAPHY

BENDER, L.: Twenty Years of Clinical Research on Schizophrenic Children, in Emotional Problems of Early Childhood, edit. G. CAPLAN. Basic Books, New York, 1955.

BLAU, A., BARKER, S., KLEINBERGER, E., ENNIS, J., ROWE, A. & HILLARD, B.: The Collaboration of Nursing and Child Psychiatry in a General Hospital. *Amer. J. Orthopsychiat.*, 29: 77, 1959.

BLAU, A.: The Nature of Childhood Schizophrenia: A Dynamic Neuropsychiatric View. *J. Amer. Acad. Child Psychiatry*, 2: 225, 1962.

BLAU, A.: The Theory of the Parent-Infant Relationship, *Int. J. Psycho-Anal.* 43: 249, 1962.

BOWLBY, J.: Maternal Care and Mental Health. World Health Organization, Monograph No. 2, Geneva, 1952.

BOWLBY, J., ROBERTSON, J. & ROSENBLUTH, D.: A 2-Year Old Goes to the Hospital. *Psychoanal. Stud. Child*, 7: 32, 1952.

BOWLBY, J.: The Nature of the Child's Tie to his Mother. *Int. J. Psycho-Anal.* 39: 350,1958.

BOWLBY, J.: Grief and Mourning in Infancy and Early Childhood. *Psychoanal. Stud. Child*, 1960.

DAVIS, K.: Extreme Social Isolation of a Child. *Amer. J. Sociol.*, 45: 554, 1940.

EASTON, K. & BLAU, A.: Neonatal and Mother-Infant Observations in Child Psychiatry Training. *J. Amer. Acad. Child Psychiatry*, in press, 1963.

FERRIS, G. C.: Sonichor, the Wolf-Boy of India, published by the author. New York, 1902.

FEUERBACH, A. VON: Caspar Hauser, Simpkin and Marshall, London, 1834.

GESELL, A.: Wolf Child and Human Child. Harper & Bros., New York, 1941

GOLDFARB, W.: Infant Rearing and Problem Behavior. *Amer. J. Orthopsychiat.*, 13: 249, 1943.

HARLOW, H. F. & ZIMMERMAN, R. R.: Affectional Responses in the Infant Monkey. *Science*, 130: *421*, 1959.

HARLOW, H. F.: The Heterosexual Affectional System in Monkeys. *Amer. Psychologist*, 17: *1*, 1962.

HARLOW, H. F. & HARLOW, M.: Social Deprivation in Monkeys. *Sci. Amer.* 207: *136*, 1962

ITARD, H. M. G.: The Wild Boy of Aveyron, Paris, 1801, trans. by G. and M. HUMPHREY. Century Co., New York, 1932.

KANNER, L.: Autistic Disturbances of Affective Contact. *Nerv. Child*, 2: *217*, 1943.

KANNER, L.: Early Infantile Autism. *Amer. J. Orthopsychiat.*, 19: *416*, 1949.

KEMPE, C. H., SILVERMAN, F. N., STEELE, B. F., DROEGEMUELLER, W. & SILVER, H. K.: The Battered-Child Syndrome. *J.A.M.A.*, 181: *17*, 1962.

LEVY, M. D.: Primary Affect Hunger. *Amer. J. Psychiat.* 94: *643*, 1937.

LOWREY, L. G.: Personality Distortion and Early Institutional Care. *Amer. J. Orthopsychiat.*, 10: *576*, 1940.

MAHLER, M. S.: On Child Psychosis and Schizophrenia: Autistic and Symbiotic Infantile Psychoses. *Psychoanal. Stud. Child*, 7: *286*, 1952.

MENNINGER, K.: Hope. *Amer. J. Psychiat.* 116: *481*, 1959.

PAKTER, J., ROSNER, H. J., JACOBZINER, H. & GREENSTEIN, F.: Out of Wedlock Births in New York City. *Amer. J. Publ. Health*, 51: *846*, 1961.

PROVENCE, S. & LIPTON, R. C.: Infants in Institutions. International Universities Press Inc., New York, 1962.

RANK, B.: Intensive Study and Treatment of Preschool Children Who Show Marked Personality Deviations, or "Atypical Development" and their Parents, in Emotional Problems of Early Childhood, edit. G. CAPLAN. Basic Books, New York, 1955.

RIBBLE, M.: The Rights of Infants. Columbia University Press, New York, 1943.

SCOTT, J. P.: Critical Periods in Behavioral Development. *Science*, 138: *949*, 1962.

SQUIRES, P. C.: Wolf Children of India. *Amer. J. Psychol.*, 38: *313*, 1927.

SPITZ, R. A.: Hospitalism. *Psychoanal. Stud. Child*, 1: *53*, 1945.

SPITZ, R. A.: Anaclitic Depression. *Psychoanal. Stud. Child*, 2: *313*, 1946.

STEIN, M. L., RAUSEN, A. R. & BLAU, A.: Psychotherapy of an Infant with Rumination. *J.A.M.A.*, 171: *2309*, 1959.

Time Magazine: Venezuela, Illegitimate Family, 81: *30*, 1963.

WASSELL, M.: Director of the Division of Allocation and Maternity Shelter Care, Bureau of Child Welfare of New York City, personal communication, 1963.

ABRAM BLAU, M.Sc., M.D., C.M., Associate Clinical Professor of Psychiatry, State University of New York, College of Medicine (Downstate Medical Center); Attending Psychiatrist in Charge, Child Psychiatry Division, The Mount Sinai Hospital, New York City. Publications include: Benign Schizophrenia, Collaboration of the Nurse and Child Psychiatrist in a General Hospital, The Nature of Childhood Schizophrenia.

The Protection and Improvement of Man's Genetic Inheritance

by

FREDERICK OSBORN

This chapter is concerned with problem of genetic inheritance. It will not attempt to cover the problem of social inheritance, although these twin aspects of population quality are not easily separated.

There is convincing evidence from both psychological and medical genetics studies that variations in genetic factors have a part in determining individual variations in intelligence and personality as well as in susceptability to disease and many serious abnormalities. Revealing studies have been made on identical twins reared at home or reared apart, on siblings, on adopted children reared in homes or in institutions, and on random pairs. When the environment is closely similar and the heredity varied, there are large individual differences which can only be explained by differences in the heredity. When the heredity is held constant and the environment varied there are differences which must be accounted for by the differences in the environment. We will not attempt an analysis of these studies in the brief space of this chapter. Their findings are quoted because, if there were no scientific basis for believing that individual differences were influenced by variations in heredity, it would be useless to discuss the "improvement" of our genetic inheritance.

Individual differences range from differences in intelligence and emotional balance to physical differences ranging from vigorous good health to disabling defects. The extreme range of defects are the easiest to study; they are easiest to measure, and if they run in family lines they are most easily located. Further, they are of particular interest to a large professional group, the whole medical profession. For these reasons the first individual differences to be studied from a genetic point of view have been departures from the normal in the form of defective development, extreme susceptability to disease, and mental defects arising from constitutional causes.

Large scale interest in this field developed among doctors after the second world war, and greatly hastened the pace of investigation.

As a result of these studies we have come to realize that genes that cause defects are not limited to those families afflicted, but that many such genes are spread widely through the population. We have learned that the genetic consequences of artificial radiation, of life-saving influences in medicine, and of new migration and marriage patterns are reflected in an accumulation of deleterious genes over and above the subtle equilibrium previously established by natural forces. Methods are being devised to detect the individuals who are carriers of genes that cause defects as well as to treat some of the defects at an early age. Increasing medical knowledge and increasing public interest have led to the establishment of heredity counseling centers, and to a new recognition of the importance of heredity in human affairs.

It is generally accepted that genes that make for defect originate in so-called "mutations" which occasionally take place in one or another of the many thousands of genes which are present in pairs in every human cell. Usually the mutated gene is a recessive, that is, it does not have its harmful effect unless the other gene in the pair has the same character-istics. The chances of two such genes meeting as a pair depend on the number of such genes distributed throughout the inter-marrying popu-lation. Thus if one person in a hundred carries a particular deleterious gene, the chances of his mating with a person with a similar gene are one in ten thousand. This may seem like a small chance, but in a large popu-lation such as that of the United States it may mean a great number of defective persons.

With every increase in the proportion of people who are carriers of a particular defective gene, there is an even greater increase in the likelihood of a mating in which two such genes will be paired in the same fertilized cell. When this happens, there will be a defect. If the defect is lethal, the two deleterious genes will be taken out of circulation. If the defect is minor, but of a sort to make marriage or reproduction less likely, the genes are to that extent less likely to survive. Thus at some point nature establishes a balance in which, for every new deleterious gene brought into circulation, a similar gene is lost from circulation. The human race carries a consider-able load of defect. Geneticists believe that most people carry at least a few deleterious genes, – some geneticists put the average as high as eight, – and at least 2% of the babies born into this world will carry all their lives some major or minor genetic defect. We get along just the same, but if the load became much heavier it might seriously threaten our future.

Most scientists are afraid that the proportion of carriers of deleterious genes may be increasing now quite rapidly – though the results in the form of a great increase in defect will not be apparent for several generations. Exposure to X-rays and to fall-out from atomic explosions is thought to be increasing the mutation rate, while at the other end, where failure to reproduce takes genes out of circulation, medical science is carrying an increasing number of people with some kind of defect through a period of successful childbearing. Diabetics for instance formerly died early, and the genes for diabetes were lost with them. After a cure was found in insulin, they survived and led useful lives, but were not generally able to have children. Now means have been found for enabling them to have children, and the safe delivery of the children of diabetic mothers is a commonplace in all our hospitals. The deleterious genes remain in circulation, and the proportion of diabetics is undoubtedly increasing from generation to generation. Of course we can get along with a lot more diabetics, and with good medical care they can live happily and bear diabetic children of their own. But there is a limit beyond which this process cannot be carried, and if we consider not diabetes alone, but all the other ills to which the human race is genetically heir, that limit is not far away. The fear of the scientists is that the accumulation of deleterious genes may creep up on us unaware, and after a few generations burst out in an uncontrolable explosion of defect.

Evidently the doctors and the public health authorities have a new and heavy responsibility. It cannot be carried out without an increase in public understanding. The current evidence from established heredity clinics indicates that couples will run a considerable chance of defective children rather than remain childless. It is the practice in heredity clinics to give the couples who come to the clinic for advice the whole picture on their heredity so far as it can be determined by a study of their family histories and their own condition, and if possible to give them an estimate of the chances of their having an unsound child. When a husband and wife each carry a recessive deleterious gene similar to one carried by the other, the chances of their having a defective child are one in four, with two children carriers of a single gene, but themselves without defect, and the fourth child being neither a carrier nor defective. Couples in such a position, knowing that they have one chance in four of having a seriously defective child, and that two out of four of their children are likely to be carriers, still frequently take a chance that things will turn out all right. Heredity clinics have been a great help to many anxious couples, but from a eugenic point of view it is hard as yet to assess their value. Perhaps a better education of the public in genetic matters will have the necessary effect. But we cannot rule out the possibility that any serious reduction in deleterious genes will not be possible by voluntary means alone. It would probably take a grave and terrible increase in the proportion of people born with crippling genetic defects to bring about acceptance of compulsory limitation of childbearing by carriers.

There is at least one dreadful form of insanity which comes on in middle age as a result of a mutated dominant gene. Because the gene is dominant, half the children of a couple, one of whom is going to be afflicted will develop the insanity. It is probably possible to detect the carriers. The disease could be wiped out in a generation, and the untold suffering of tens of thousands of people forever avoided. But no serious consideration is being given to such a possibility.

There is one consolation for our present neglect of genetic deterioration. Knowledge in this field is advancing rapidly. Each year an increasing number of defects are being defined, the type of hereditary transmission understood, and in many cases means found for spotting carriers. By the time the public and the public health authorities are ready to attack the dreadful scourge of genetic defects as in the past they have attacked cholera and yellow fever, the science of medical genetics should be ready with knowledge sufficient to make the attack successful.

Arbitrary methods may some day be necessary to control the growing incidence of genetic defect. But there is little chance of the public accepting such an impairment of everyone's "right to have children" unless there is a far better understanding of human genetics than we have at present and a better appreciation of the responsibilities of parenthood.

Quite a different situation exists with respect to intelligence and personality. There is a genetic base to individual variations in these traits as there is in variations in health and defect. But there is no need to consider arbitrary controls for improving the genetic base for intelligence and personality. A great improvement could undoubtedly be made without in any way infringing on anyone's "right" to have children. Very slight changes in our social institutions and in the psychological factors which influence the size of individual families would probably tip the balance of births in a direction favorable to genetic improvement. Most of these changes are already being demanded by people who want to improve the environment in which children are brought up, quite apart from any genetic factors.

The fact is that no one knows whether in the United States today the genetic base is improving or deteriorating. In the early days in this country, when the death rate was particularly high for the people least able to fend for themselves, there was probably a trend towards the survival of the more vigorous and able stocks. A generation ago, when the death rate had gotten to be very low for almost all of our people, there were large differentials in the birth rates of different social and economic classes. The more educated people were having the fewest children. Many scientists took this as an indication that the genetic base for intelligence was on the decline. Others held that there was not much evidence for believing that the more educated people of the country on the whole had any better hereditary qualities than the less educated. Both sides agreed that the differences between couples within each social class were much greater than the average differences between social classes, and that nothing was known about the quality of the individual couples who were having the most children in each of the social classes. Today, over 95% of the children born alive live beyond their 30th year, and with the spread of birth control social class differences in size of family are much diminished. There is little evidence that any great changes are going on in genetic quality.

But there is room for great improvement. On this everyone is agreed. We know that genetic quality affects achievement. If we could raise the genetic quality of the lowest 20% in our population to a level above the present average, we would be making a tremendous contribution to the improvement of American life. There are many present trends which could be exploited to make such an improvement possible. The most important of these trends is the continuing spread of birth control.

Recent studies indicate that most American married women use some form of birth control to prevent or postpone further births after they have had two or three children. Even among Catholics, 85% of fecund Catholic wives age 35-39 use some form of birth control including of course the rythm method approved by the Church. The spread of birth control has been an important factor toward equalizing the birth rates of different socio-economic classes. Its use and effectiveness is constantly increasing. If, as scientists expect, means are soon found for preventing conception by some form of immunization, or by taking an inexpensive and occasional pill, there should be great opportunity for reducing the number of unwanted children born in this country.

There are good grounds for believing that unwanted children are on the average less well endowed genetically than the average for the country as a whole. Such a statement brings a howl of protest from a great number of believers in the American ideal of equality, but it is time they should face the situation with a little sense of reality. To take an extreme example, the number of illegitimate children born in this country is quite high, in some areas or groups as much as 10 or more per cent of total births. It is fair to say that most illegitimate children are unwanted. It must also be recognized that people who have illegitimate children have on the whole somewhat less socially valuable traits of character than do people whose children are born in wedlock. To some extent at least, perhaps to a considerable extent, genetic as well as environmental influences have operated to make these people behave differently from their neighbors. Eliminating illegitimate births would reduce the survival of whatever genetic factors are involved and thus tend to reduce the proportion of people at the lower levels of personal responsibility. (It would at the same time reduce the proportion of children brought up in an inferior environment, as would most other changes which would improve the genetic inheritance.)

Illegitimate births are not the only unwanted births today. Many unwanted children are born to married couples. When they are unwanted because there are already enough children in the family they are not a genetic handicap, though they may pose an environmental problem in their bringing up. But when children are born to couples who do not want them because they are not ready for the responsibility of children, or do not want the responsibility, or can't take care of them, we may suspect that the parents have on the average somewhat less vigor and competence than their neighbors, and that this difference has to some degree a genetic base. Here again we may hope that the increased use of family limitation may be to genetic advantage.

Of course we have no guarantee that better methods of birth control will produce these results. They will only be effective if our people are so informed, and so influenced by a strong public opinion, and so situated in their economic life, that all these forces will operate to reduce illegitimate and other births which are not positively wanted by both members of the couples involved. In this country none of these forces have been so directed. Great numbers of young or ignorant people have only the haziest notion of what methods of birth control are effective and how they should be used; social workers are seldom much motivated to instruct on birth control, indeed many would lose their jobs if they did; under present economic arrangements, mothers with illegitimate children and others with large families of unwanted children are usually paid children's allowances which increase with each child, and the fathers of illegitimate children are seldom found and required to pay for their upbringing. Surely different attitudes and methods could be found without diminishing the care we properly want to give to children who are brought into the world through no fault of their own.

The fear has been expressed that such general access to birth control would on the one hand lower our moral standards, and on the other hand so reduce the number of births that the race would soon die out. Neither fear is justified by recent experience. Access to birth control has undoubtedly shown up a lot of people with low moral standards, but the much larger proportion of responsible people who are now raising children have a birth rate well above that of a generation ago. There is no reason we should encourage people with low moral standards to reproduce, which is just what we are doing in far too many cases. We should save our encouragements to reproduction for those who are most likely not only to bring up their children well, but are also able to give them a good genetic endowment.

Besides the trend to birth control there are many other trends which properly understood could be turned to genetic advantage. There are trends towards an increasing social and job mobility and the elimination of fixed hereditary classes, and a trend towards giving everyone a chance at the best education he is capable of absorbing. These are all trends towards sorting people out according to their genetic qualities and putting each into the kind of life and work for which they are genetically most fitted, whether as artists, business men, ministers, mechanics, lawyers or manual laborers. These changes are important for the effects they may have on the mating of like with like. Many studies have shown that there is a natural tendency for men and women to marry people who are like themselves in physical appearance, coloring, intelligence, tastes, interests and social background. Of course there are many exceptions, and people notice them and find it hard to believe the story told by the statistical studies, that like tends to marry like. There is another notable fact about marriage. People only marry people they have actually met.

Not long ago people moved about much less than they do today; they were forced to marry the people they met on the neighboring farms or in their immediate locality. They did not have much chance to meet and marry people who were like themselves in their genetic qualities, though their social background was likely to be similar. Today the situation is very different. People move about a great deal, not only from place to place, but also from one social group, work group, and educational level group, until they are likely to find themselves among people who are like themselves far more than was the case a generation ago. By this, and by the fact they have a larger circle of acquaintance than in the past, assortative mating is undoubtedly on the increase. We should encourage it and take advantage of it. By changing the distribution of genes assortative mating makes for a greater number of people with particular and special qualities. An increase in assortative mating would increase genetic diversification in the process of adapting to the diverse elements of our society. One could expect a greater variety of specialized talents.

But there is another aspect of assortative mating. In association with selection it can rapidly change gene frequencies. This means that if certain genetic types of people had fewer children than the average, the proportion of such people would diminish from one generation to another. They would be selected against, and the frequency of their type of gene in the population would diminish. On the other had, if certain other types had more children than the average, their type would increase from one generation to another, and the frequency of their type of gene would increase.

Thus while assortative mating should be encouraged because it will make for a greater variety of specialized talents, society should at the same time try to provide conditions which would tend to influence the birth rate of different kinds of people in different ways; means should be found to encourage larger families among couples who are above the average of achievement in their particular activity, and at the same time conditions should be such that those couples who are less successful would tend to have smaller than average families. The influences which could be brought to bear range all the way from the climate of public opinion to the use of economic measures such as larger income tax deductions for children through the whole period of their education.

The search for means of getting such a discriminating selection of births has only just begun. Studies by students of population on the social, psychological and economic factors which affect size of family have provided a number of leads as to the conditions under which people want to have more or less children. Much further research is needed to find out what particular conditions would make for the kind of birth selection which is needed, but the problems are not impossible of solution. The needed changes will be the more easily accepted because they will also tend to improve the environment in which children are brought up, and so can be urged for other than genetic reasons. If they can be made effective, we could reasonably hope for not only a greater variety of talents, but a constantly higher level in those qualities which have a common tendency towards achievement in all environments.

The protection and even the improvement of our genetic inheritance should not prove a difficult task compared to many other social advances man has already made. The obstacles are ignorance and misunderstanding. The education of public opinion is the first necessary step towards a resumption of the slow but rewarding process of evolution by which man made his long upward climb.

REFERENCES

American Eugenics Society. 1959. *Heredity Counseling* (Ed. Helen G. Hammons, Paul B. Hoeber, Inc. New York.

ANASTASI, ANNE, 1958. *Differential Psychology*, Macmillan, New York.

DOBZHANSKY, THEODOSIUS, 1955. *Evolution, Genetics and Man*, Wiley & Sons, New York.

FREEDMAN, RONALD, WHELPTON, PASCAL K., & CAMPBELL, ARTHUR A., 1959. *Family Planning, Sterility and Population Growth*, McGraw-Hill, New York.

NEWMAN, H. H., FREEMAN, F. N., & HOLSINGER, K. J., 1937, *Twins, A Study of Heredity and Environment*, University of Chicago Press.

OSBORN, FREDERICK, 1940, *Preface to Eugenics*, Revised Ed., Harper & Bros., New York.

REED, SHELDON C., 1955. *Counseling in Medical Genetics*, W. B. Saunders, Philadelphia.

SCHWESINGER, GLADYS, 1933. *Heredity and Environment*, Macmillan, New York.

SINNOTT, EDMUND W., DUNN, L. C., & DOBZHANSKY, THEODOSIUS, 1958. *Principles of Genetics*, McGraw-Hill, New York.

TYLER, LEONA E., 1956, 2nd Ed., *Psychology of Human Differences*, Appleton Century Crofts, New York.

YAUKEY, DAVID, 1961, *Fertility Differences in a Modernizing Country: A Survey of Lebanese Couples*, Princeton University Press, Princeton.

FREDERICK OSBORN has had a varied career as a corporation and foundation executive, and as a writer in the field of population studies, in which he has been active since 1930. In World War II he was commissioned Major General, Director of the Information and Education Division of the Army. He has served on many boards of corporations and at various times as a trustee of Princeton University, Carnegie Corporation, The Frick Collection, The Milbank Fund, and The Population Council, of which latter he was the President from 1952 to 1960. He is author of Preface to Eugenics (1940), and Population: An International Dilemma (1958)' and with FRANK LORIMER, of Dynamics of Population (1934), and of numerous papers and articles.

Better Genes for Tomorrow

by

Hermann J. Muller

PERILS OF OUR PROGRESS

Man of today is the "heir of all the ages," both in regard to the marvelous and fearful culture that he has built up for himself, and the incredibly capable genetic organization, conferred by biological evolution, that has made it possible for him to fashion this culture. Yet we know that we have attained no utopia, and that our perils and problems have enormously increased in consequence of the increase in our potentialities. Most of these perils arise from the short-sighted use of our transcendent modern science and techniques for the intended benefit of restricted portions of humanity, but in opposition to the benefit of humanity in general, and for the intended benefit of people of the present-day world, but at the expense of those who will come after us.

This unbalanced situation is of course most glaringly illustrated in the application of modern technology to the development of weapons of mass destruction. It is similarly evident in our present unparalleled successes in the despoliation of our natural resources. Readers of these pages will also have come to recognize, as a third major peril, that twentieth-century medical and industrial techniques, combined with ancient ideologies, are promoting a population growth so widespread and rapid as to be degrading human living over ever greater areas, and to be threatening both the material and mental basis of culture in the world in general.

It is not so widely realized that our triumphs of medical and industrial technology, through the very same practices as those by which they foster overpopulation, are conducting an ever more effective assault upon that inner source of all human potentialities – our genetic constitution. For the forces that are unleashing the population explosion are undiscriminating. They work by defeating the operations of the natural selection that prevailed through ages past. These were the processes whereby those individuals who were especially heavily loaded with defective genes tended to survive in smaller numbers than the rest and to leave fewer offspring while, conversely, those endowed with genes especially helpful for the species tended to survive and multiply more abundantly.

Today, as has been pointed out in the preceding article by OSBORN, the vast majority of persons born, even when subnormal, are enabled to reach maturity. Moreover, under modern conditions, foresight, conscience, and competence seem to express themselves rather by successful restraint in reproduction than by abundance of offspring. In this connection it is to be noted that detrimental mutations continue to arise in each generation anew, at such a rate that something like 20% of persons receive some newly arisen mutant gene, and that such genes, once arisen, tend to be handed on down through an indefinite succession of generations. They tend to continue until the lines of descent that carry them die out as a result of their own incapacity. Thus it is evident that under modern conditions, so long as this dying out is seriously interfered with, human populations must become ever more defective in their genetic constitution, until at long last even the most sophisticated techniques available could no longer suffice to save men from their biological corruptions.

It follows that, if the social system should for centuries manage to withstand the strain caused by the persistence of these practices, people would again find themselves dying before maturity, or failing to reproduce, in consequence of their innate infirmities, at just as high a rate – one or more in five – as that which they had suffered from in primitive times. And these human failures would be but a token of the many more who just managed to drag out their existence. On the other hand, if civilization should then break down, the miserable, decrepit remnants of men, denied its support, would perish under the, to them, intolerable rigors of primitive life.

Yet it is not a foregone conclusion that the epitaph "*Sic transit gloria*"will be applicable to the unprecedented enterprise of mankind. It is becoming increasingly recognized that, in dealing with global politics and ideologies, the tools of dispassionate analysis and creative imagination, working in the service of humanity at large and powered by modern science and technology, can and must find ways to turn our perils to our profit. To succeed in this men must learn to advance in increasing cooperation, and to utilize their newly-won nuclear furies, potent chemicals, and sophisticated computers in conquests over natural difficulties, instead of over each other. So too in matters of reproduction: today's dilemmas, raised by the shortsighted applications of science, can and must be met by the development of more far-seeing science, and of techniques founded upon it, that are used in behalf of mankind everywhere, and with due regard to the future. Moreover these same practices will, as we shall see, redound powerfully to the benefit of the individual participants. However, in this situation just as in international relations, deep-seated changes in attitudes, based on a more scientific and ethical insight into human values and needs, will be necessary to allow the implementation of the required reforms.

The mainspring of these reforms will be found not in fear but in hope. It would be pitiful and shameful if we, the proud "Lords of Creation," were to limit ourselves, in the genetic field, to the task of merely mending our fences, and holding our own in a constant struggle against decay. No, the same means that best enable us to defend ourselves against genetic deterioration can also serve, when applied with greater intensity, to *advance* our genetic position significantly. Moreover, we have no more reached any limit in the possibilities of our genetic advancement than in those of our cultural advancement. Herewith the genetic situation is lifted out of the realm of dire foreboding, and dangers to be gloomily warded off, into that of inspiring opportunities, inviting our zealous efforts.

MISCONCEPTIONS TO BE AVOIDED

In seeking ways of resisting deterioration and effecting actual improvement in the human genetic constitution we must recognize, first of all, that every person, and every group of people, represents an inextricable complex of both heredity and environment. In the development of psychological characteristics the human being is especially plastic, being influenced drastically in personality, mentality, and capabilities by his cultural environment.

Despite the potency of the environmental forces, differences in the genes have also been proved to play an enormous role in the causation of the differences found between individuals with similar cultural and physical backgrounds. But when peoples of radically different circumstances are compared, such as those living under primitive conditions versus those under modern industrialism, or underprivileged or pariah groups, on the one hand, versus first-class citizens of the same country, on the other hand, the environmental disparities are so overriding that whatever differences in the genetic basis of psychological traits may or may not exist between them are entirely obscured. Doubtless differences do exist between peoples, or races, in the frequencies of genes affecting psychological characters, as they certainly do for some physical characters, but we cannot by present means judge what they are. However, the ease with which individuals and groups born and brought up in a culture alien to that of their parents take to and succeed in the adopted ways indicates that these "racial" genetic differences, whatever they may be, must be comparatively unimportant. Certainly they must be much smaller than the genetic differences, in regard to the same characters, that are prevalent among *individuals* of any one comparatively homogeneous population.

As for the more conspicious physical differences between peoples, as in their pigmentation, facial and hair form, and body build, and in some associated physiological traits, such as tolerances to differing temperatures, altitudes and foods, it has become evident that these consistent diversities have evolved in adaptation to the different climates and other natural conditions of life to which the respective peoples had been subjected over thousands of years. However, the modern techniques which are spreading throughout the world are proving so effective in aiding men against the diverse difficulties which had sundered them that these special adaptations are rapidly losing the advantages they afforded in their given domains. Thus, except for extraordinary situations, such as enormous altitudes, groups of practically any ethnic type can today survive successfully in any region habitable by another type. This consideration, and also those discussed in the preceding paragraph, illustrate how hollow are the pretensions of the racists, in claiming a genetic basis for their delusions of superiority.

Similar considerations apply to the arguments of the so-called "social Darwinists," who maintain that classes of lower economic and social status are genetically inferior and should therefore reproduce less than those of higher status. No reasonable person can deny that the modern extension of educational and other opportunities, as well as better living conditions, to economically less favored groups, has served to uncover among them surprising resources of native mental ability, moral fiber, and physical vigor. Moreover, it is notorious that until comparatively recent times the more "cultured" families of any population – those of the nobles, well-to-do burghers, and city-dwellers generally – tended gradually to die out and to become replaced from the ranks of rising rural workers and craftsmen. The celibate priesthood alone contributed a strong influence of this kind. Yet the supply of able persons did not seem to become reduced in the process. Doubtless there was some filtering of better talent, selectively, into the socially higher ranks, but the natural selection occurring within the masses must during most of this long period have been enough to largely compensate for any such drain.

Despite powerful counter-currents, the economic, social, and educational forces of the modern world are, fortunately, moving it in the direction of ever more meaningful human rights, and of the more potent democracy needed to maintain those rights. Under these circumstances, the institution of discriminatory conditions against social or ethnic minorities is increasingly felt to be abhorrent, while their institution against majorities is entirely anachronistic. Similarly, special privileges for favored classes are passing away, along with the other relics of ancient aristocracies. All this is essential for the removal of brakes on progress. This being the case, it is evident that any attempt to intentionally manipulate the social system, so as to make child-bearing or child-rearing harder or easier for one ethnic group, or for one social or occupational class, than for another, would meet with deserved defeat and obloquy.

The really important genetic inequalities of man are those between individuals, and they are commonly much greater than the differences, in the same genetic respects, between the averages of different social or ethnic groups. It is these individual differences, therefore, that must be dealt with in any policy for genetic conservation or advance, and in judging these differences every effort must be made to discount differences referable to social and ethnic groupings and backgrounds. Most important of all in this connection, procedures intended to promote genetic well-being should be thoroughly democratic in their mode of application. That is, they should involve entirely voluntary decisions, arrived at freely by those participating in the undertakings. At the same time, the choices should represent reasonable judgments, actuated by a soundly based set of values. How is this paradoxical seeming combination of conditions to be arrived at?

ADVANTAGES OF THE POSITIVE APPROACH

It is generally recognized that free democratic government, if its operation is to be salutary, requires well-grounded popular education. Similarly, if genetic betterment is to be conducted in a democratic manner toward wholesome objectives it is essential for the public in general to be led to understand and appreciate the principles of evolution and genetics, especially in relation to themselves and to humanity in general. Without such education they cannot gain a due perspective on the past and on the mighty possibilities of the future. The outlook thus engendered will help to imbue people with a sense of responsibility to later generations, along with a feeling of fulfillment in cases in which they themselves are able to be active agents in the great advance of mankind.

Such basic education will make people more receptive to the advice of the specialists of heredity clinics, concerning the likelihood of the children of given parents, in given unions, being genetically well or ill endowed in diverse particulars. Already there are a number of such clinics performing useful functions, and it is to be hoped that this method will become increasingly influential. It should be realized, however, that it suffers from certain limitations. Thus, one of the principal aims of this work must be to influence the choice of partners in such ways as to minimize the production of children who *manifest* a defect, and to maximize the *concatenation* of valuable traits. This work is very valuable in itself, but it has no direct effect on the task of major genetic importance: the influencing of gene frequencies in the population at large in desirable directions.

Such an influence is, to be sure, brought to bear when given persons are warned that they have definite genetic defects and are thus discouraged from having children. However, these cases are usually concerned with rare abnormalities of specific types. Let it not be forgotten that practically everyone really carries a fair number of less noticeable yet significant defects in more or less hidden form, along with some genes of especially favorable kinds. What would be ideally suited for substantial progress in this situation would be a rate of reproduction graded according to an over-all estimation of each person's genetic composition. This is in fact the feat that natural selection did accomplish with man in the long run in ages past, by assessing each individual on the basis of his achievements, even though environmental inequalities caused numberless errors to be committed by this method. However, the day when similar ratings could be made for people in general by geneticists is neither in sight nor around the corner.

In fact, no single science or discipline could competently weigh all these factors, in relation to the present and possible future conditions of life. Moreover, a clinician or a committee who attempted to give advice along these lines would probably be regarded with skepticism and often with resentment by the person or couple in question. Realizing the "subjectivity" of the judgment arrived at, they would tend to substitute their own subjective appraisals of themselves. But, on the whole, there is no appraisal so faulty as self-appraisal. Thus we should have come full circle back to the present reproductive disorder in which wishful and egotistical thinking, hand in hand with lack of thinking, lead the way in the race to procreate, while forethought, conscience, and humility drag behind.

Nevertheless, no real impasse is involved here. For there is in any large population a fair number of persons whose attainments and performance are clearly extraordinary, demonstrating a combination of high abilities, all-round fitness, and, in some of these cases, unusual humanity of disposition. One must of course beware of the biases about people that arise during their heydays. However, at longer range from them in time and space, truer estimates of the merits of their lives emerge among specialists in the same lines of activity as the persons had engaged in, and can thus become available to the interested public. The next question is, how could these comparatively objective means of judgment serve in the implementation of genetic betterment?

There is in any present population a considerable proportion of couples – from 2 to 8%, according to age – who would like to have children but who are unable to because of the sterility of the male partner. An increasing number of these – perhaps more than 10,000 per year at present in the United States, according to GUTTMACHER (1961) – are utilizing the procedure termed "AID," that is, artificially controlled insemination by a physician, with semen from a donor selected by him but unknown to them, and they are thereby enabled to have children. Follow-up studies show that, in general, this method has been highly successful, as judged both by the happiness of the couple's subsequent married life, and by the well-being of the resulting children. How much more, then, would these couples have welcomed the opportunity to have children by controlled insemination, if they had to begin with been well grounded in genetics, evolution, and the problems of society, and if in addition they had been enabled to utilize the procedure in such a way as to make a significant contribution to human progress!

They could have made such a contribution if they themselves had been given an opportunity to participate in the selection of the germinal material, from among banks of it derived from persons judged, in the perspective of time, to have been of outstanding worth. Technically, this procedure would even now be entirely feasible. For the method of preserving the germ cells of a man for an indefinite period without deterioration, in a deeply frozen condition, is already well established, thanks to a long succession of researches (MONTEGAZZA 1866, JAHNEL 1938, SHETTLES 1940, HOAGLAND & PINCUS 1942, HOAGLAND 1943, POLGE et al. 1949, SHERMAN & BUNGE 1953, BUNGE & SHERMAN 1953, BUNGE, KEITTEL & SHERMAN 1954). The culmination of these is represented by recent work by SHERMAN (1963), partly parallelled by that of a Japanese group (IIZUKA & SAWADA 1958, SAWADA 1959, NAKAJIMA et al. 1962), which have put the techniques of processing and preservation on a thoroughly practicable basis.

In fact, banks of frozen human germ cells are at present in existence in a number of places. However, no attempt has yet been made to provide these germinal reserves with material from outstanding sources. This being the case, even the couples resorting to this form of "pre-adoption" (to use JULIAN HUXLEY's term) still have no ground for departing from the accepted pattern of secrecy for such cases. So too, the all-important matter of the choice of the germinal material still rests with the clinician alone, and only he is aware of what choice was made. It is then maneuvered to have the official record of parentage made under the direction of another physician, from whom knowledge of the procedure used was purposely withheld, so that the de facto adopting father – the social father – becomes falsely registered as the genetic father.

In such cases the subterfuges employed, although sordid, were justified because they enabled the participants to practice a new and higher ethics than that of the past, an ethics made possible by the more advanced techniques and knowledge of the present. In another generation, however, considerable sections of society will feel scandalized at the backwardness of the mores and legal attitudes that occasioned such indirections and resulted in such inadequacies, for persons who were putting forth their best efforts in the interests of the whole population. With the building up, in the future, of ever richer stores of valuable germinal material, worthy couples denied by sterility from having children possessing the husband's own genes would feel cheated by man even more than by nature if they were also deterred, by society, from rendering it the supreme service of bringing a part of its precious biological resources to fruition.

Moreover, such couples would consider it a triple humiliation if, while permitted to devote themselves to such an undertaking, they nevertheless had to accept these conditions: (1) that they were to have no voice in the choosing of their child's paternal heritage, (2) that they were to be kept in ignorance concerning this choice, and (3) that they would force themselves, their child, and the public to live a lie concerning its origin. Conversely, the thousands of sterile couples who today practise pre-adoption would be joined by many more when the opportunity was opened to them to participate in the choice of their children's heritage and when, with the spreading of the practice, it became widely recognized as a notable social service, and therewith cast off its blight of secrecy.

But even today, despite the arbitrariness and furtiveness now characterizing pre-adoption, the practice is being taken up increasingly not only by sterile couples but also by some who could have reproduced in the ordinary way. The fertile couples resorting to it are oftenest cases in which the husband would have been likely to transmit to the children a serious hereditary defect. Besides these, there are couples utilizing the method in whom some hereditary incompatibility, as for instance in blood groups, exists between husband and wife, that would threaten the well-being of their child. Finally, some men and women are already to be found among us who, though by no means ill-endowed, are idealistic enough to prefer for a child of theirs a biological heritage of even more promise than their own genes would be likely to provide. As yet, such couples are thwarted by lack of the required facilities for exercising germinal choice. However, this lack is not primarily based in difficulties of a biological kind.

Thus a nucleus is already on hand which might in the course of time develop into a much more considerable enterprise, one that eventually became more than adequate to counteract any tendencies to genetic deterioration and to institute in their stead substantial genetic advancement in varied directions. Requisite for such an undertaking would be not only extensive, long-treasured stores of germinal material, representing natural faculties and predispositions of very varied types, but also ample records concerning the lives and characteristics of the persons from whom the material had been derived, and records concerning their close relatives, including of course their progeny. Couples who thought of assuming the grave responsibility of utilizing such material, and who satisfied requirements of competence to do so, should be assisted, in coming to their decisions, by advice from diverse counsellors. These should include geneticists, physicians, psychologists, and specialists in the activities that had been pursued by the prospective donor, as well as persons with an unusually well-rounded understanding of the general problems of man and society. Preferably, at least twenty years should have elapsed since the death of the donors considered. This is a provision which it would gradually become more practicable to follow as the supplies of germinal material increased, and as research disclosed ways of rendering smaller amounts of it effective.

Among the advantages of this type of positive approach to genetic betterment is the very fact that because of the difficulties raised by the mores prevalent today, it will for a considerable time to come be taken up by a comparatively small minority. For these will consist in unusually large measure of persons of independent mind, imaginative but rational in their thinking, deeply motivated ethically, and strongly oriented socially: in a word, practical idealists. Thus the standards adopted in the choosing of germinal material by these persons will tend to be exceptionally high; they will be inclined to take earnestly into account the records and counsel available to them, and, in general, to give especially serious consideration to the making of their choices. In this way a wholesome precedent will be set, and a new set of attitudes and mores, pertinent to the procedure of germinal choice, will take shape. In consequence, the larger numbers who later take up the practice will find these attitudes already established and, after the fashion of followers everywhere, they will tend to conform to the patterns already marked out for them.

This manner of origination and growth of the practice of germinal choice must result in the generation by it, in its early stages, of a clearly exemplary lot of children. These living object lessons will constitute the most persuasive argument to others, and will thereby lead to ever firmer acceptance and greater prevalence of the practice. At the same time, progress will gradually be made in regard to other matters underlying the making of effective choices. For one thing, the available stores of germinal material will be considerably added to. Secondly, the techniques concerned with re-production, including germ cell processing and cultivation, will be improved, perhaps radically. Thirdly, the methods of forming genetic judgments and of getting data for them will become more advanced. Fourthly, the public will become better educated and motivated with regard to genetics and evolution in general, and with regard to human needs, means and goals in particular. Fifthly, the whole field of evo-lutionary possibilities, values, and directions will be subjected to ever more searching investigation, criticism, and creative thinking. In all these connections, moreover, the fact should not be lost sight of that whatever increment the practice of germinal choice may produce in the number of persons at the uppermost levels of understanding and of social propensities – and some tangible increment of these kinds should appear even in the early stages – this increment will, by a process of positive feedback, exert an influence in better promoting all the advances previously mentioned. Thus the process will be self-increasing.

THE TRANSITION IN MOTIVATIONS

However, so deep-seated a change in human outlook and conduct as that here discussed must inevitably be confronted by powerful psychological obstacles. These will take the form both of habits of mind that are ingrained in the individuals and appear to them as self-evidently right, and of social institutions, including legal and religious forms, that support, sanction, and sanctify the individuals' feelings and convinctions. Nevertheless, we know, from the differences found in the attitudes and practices of different peoples and also from the drastic changes in such respects that have occurred before our eyes within a few decades, under the impact of recent economic, political, scientific and technical revolutions, that even changes of the magnitude here in question lie well within the range of plasticity of the individual and of society.

The central psychological obstacle in the present situation is the attitude of individual genetic proprietorship, or pride of so-called "blood." Its artificiality is evident in the desire of a man, and also of his wife, to have a child who will hand down his name, that is, a son, although in genetic fact his daughters inherit some 5% more of his genes. Of course in primitive societies that did not realize that the father played a role in conception no such feeling of *genetic* proprietorship of the male could exist. In fact, even in some not-so-primitive societies, such as those of Eskimos or Polynesians or Ethiopians to whom the role of the male in conception is known, there is nevertheless no strong feeling of *genetic* proprietorship attached by him to his children. Thus it is often felt an honor, by husband as well as by wife, if she has a child by some distinguished visitor, and the child is as well loved and cared for as the ones whom she has conceived by her husband. The same genuine attachment is seen to spring up, even in our own society, for children who have been adopted early, when they were really wanted by the couple.

It is clear that the natural attachment for one's children results from the experiences of close association with them, of nurturing and sustaining them, and of being loved, trusted, and played with by them in return. Natural selection has provided us with the predisposition of having these feelings aroused in us in these ways, since this arrangement was of survival value for the species. But of course we are also equipped by nature with egotistic emotions, leading to vanity. Consequently, once we know of the existence of biological inheritance or genes we may become inclined to rate our own genes and our own idiosyncracies above those of others. Thus also we tend to see in our genetic descendants an extension of ourselves, such that their progress reflects credit on us, and their survival is our survival.

However, a more realistic consideration of the situation will show our own particular genetic combination to be, in the long view, very ephemeral, usually much more so than the ways of thought and feeling that we transmit culturally in our families. It will usually show, in addition, that we have about as much to be ashamed of in ourselves genetically as to be proud of. It will reveal us as being one small even though potentially significant mote in the whole human assemblage, a mote constitutionally inclined to overestimate itself. This greater realism will lead us to see that we can lead much more meaningful lives if, instead of insisting that just exactly our own genetic peculiarities be handed down, we exert ourselves to leave humanity better and stronger than we found it, either culturally or genetically or both, by whatever means we can most effectively accomplish this. By this course, moreover, we will actually do more to bring about the continuance, with enhancement, of what is best within ourselves, and we will thus partake in greater measure in humanity's continuance.

For we are, potentially at least, beings who can reason and who can create with our minds and hands, and for whom it is natural to use these means to further the well-being and promote the advancement of our species. It is this potentiality which is most characteristically human in us, and most valuable. We can be truest to our own natures and we can achieve the best grounded selfrespect if our efforts in these directions have been significant. In relation to the question here confronting us, this means that – to paraphrase what my friend CALVIN KLINE has said – we should feel prouder of what we have consciously produced by means of our head, hands and heart than of what we have automatically produced by means of our reproductive system. And let us hope that later generations also will judge us rather by the progress that we have thereby implemented for them by means of our conscious strivings, including those of germinal choice, than by the foibles that our own personal genes may happen to give expression to among them in ages to come. That is, our truest genetic contribution to posterity would consist of our brain children, those fathered by our deliberate germinal choices. It is in successors of this kind, therefore, that we could, on genetic grounds, take the most justifiable pride.

Similarly, in regard to the legacy of a cultural sort that we bequeath to posterity, our truest individual projection into the future in cultural respects resides in the persons of those in whom, through the rearing and education they received from us, our spirits have become imbued. If at the same time these persons represented our germinal choices we would achieve a form of survival more genuine than that prevalent today. All these considerations show how essential it is, for the couples undertaking pre-adoption, that the privilege of choosing the germinal material be vested in them. It is mainly this aspect of the matter that raises the process into an act of creation on their part, and this act far transcends in its creativeness that of ordinary reproduction. Herein lies one of the principle inducements and sources of strength for the new morality of reproduction as compared with the old. In this way human freedom and human rights are extended into a new dimension.

The pathway to germinal choice that we have discussed is the most direct one. But, just as has happened in the case of other techniques that raised radically new possibilities, multiple pathways are opened that all lead in essentially the same direction, out of the mores of the past. Thus, the new possibility of readily storing germ cells in a deeply frozen condition offers an obvious means of germinal protection for the increasing number of persons who are subject to exposure to influences damaging to their genetic material or to their capability of reproduction. Among such influences are irradiation, such as might be received in high-altitude or space flights, in work with sources of radiation, or in war. Mutagenic chemicals constitute another considerable group. Even against bodily injuries that resulted in sterilization or in death itself such storage might be desired by some couples as a germinal insurance. In these ways the stores could be considerably augmented, and later generations might find some of this material of exceptional value.

A similar situation is likely to arise through the utilization of germcell storage as a complement to vasectomy, by the increasing numbers of men who would use such sterilization as the most effective and convenient means of birth control, provided only that they could be sure it was not irrevocable. Thereby the stores of germinal material might become vastly increased, by the contributions of persons who had also paid the costs of this service. And except in special cases, in which the donors had disapproved, some of this material also might later be made use of by others.

All this, by making a far wider range of choice available in the future, would be conducive to greater utilization of the stores by the population in general. Ideally, everyone for whom it was possible would come to adopt the insurance of having some of his germinal material subjected to long-term storage. Among the reserves thus accumulated there would inevitably be not a few, the value of which had not been recognized in their own time, but which became more adequately appreciated and utilized subsequently. Ultimately, then, the choices would not be limited by the decisions of a few individuals or groups who had controlled the acquisition of the stores. In this way the procedure would develop a broad and thoroughly democratic basis, and proceeding from this basis, with the aid of relevant records and counsel, each couple would strive for what in their considered judgment was the best.

Quo vadimus?

Although such judgments must strive to be rational they must certainly be value judgments at the same time, as our intentional use of the word "best" in the preceding sentence implied. But there is no real contradiction here. For it is the function of all rationality to work out ways of gaining our ends, that is, of more effectively pursuing and promoting our values. Moreover, since different values of ours sometimes run counter to one another, it must be a part of this operation to try by rational means to coordinate values, sometimes reconciling them, sometimes subordinating one to another, sometimes working out more basic values, the pursuit of which is more inclusive and results in greater all-round, long-term fulfillment.

Of course human nature is intrinsically many-sided, in that for a wholesome personality diverse psychological needs must all be met, as for instance love of a number of kinds, including a feeling of oneness with one's fellows and even with nature, esthetic excitement of varied types, joy in work and accomplishment, curiosity, hope, and zest in diverse bodily feelings. All these, and much more, must have an opportunity for fulfillment if the spirit is not to suffer, in some direction, from a deprivation that, becoming ever more gnawing, tends to eat out the heart of the whole. We have been shaped to have all these needs, and therefore these values, because our efforts to meet them result, on the whole, in the enhancement of our strength in ways that serve the survival and advancement of the species. Moreover, the values are in the main so balanced and adjusted that in conflicts between them those take precedence the pursuit of which result in longer-range fulfillment for us or at least for our fellows. In static societies folk mores and codes, themselves worked out through long experience, often aid in charting the course through such situations. But individual reasoning is also indispensible in gauging the possible effects of different choices. And in societies that are undergoing change, as a result of the introduction of techniques, knowledge, or points of view new to them, the old codes may fail and individual reasoning must assume more responsibility.

At any rate, if reason shows that the individual's actions in pursuit of certain more immediate desires are such as to be conducive to his earlier death, or to his misery in the future, the reasonable individual will if at all possible sacrifice the present for the future, although on rare occasions his fortitude or self-control may be insufficient and intense pain or some unbearable deprivation or overriding emotion may cause him to act against his own interests. Similarly, he will, if he has a socially oriented upbringing, tend to identify his interests with those of his fellows, or of the species, in consequence both of his native fellow-feeling and of his realization that this constitutes his greater self. He will therefore make similar sacrifices for his community, his group, or his species, subject to the limitation that when personal deprivations are carried too far the returns become too greatly diminished, both for him in a personal, psychological sense and in regard to his effectiveness in serving others.

All this, then, shows that the multiple values of humanity, while real, are subordinate to the value represented by service to the community in general. They occupy this subordinate position not only as a result of biological natural selection but also, in a more decided way, in the codes of almost any community, and, finally, in the judgment of the rational individual who is at the same time socially minded.

It is not surprising, in view of all this, that despite the enormous differences in the traditions, religions, and social customs of different human groups, the more prevalent groups have developed very much the same set of basic ethical values, and that, on the whole, these serve the more general aim of promoting the welfare of the group. Moreover, any such set of values, concerned with the pursuit of psychological and material objectives, also has implications regarding the relative esteem in which different traits of character, mentality and disposition are held. For the more approved traits will be those more conducive to the pursuit of the recognized ethical values; hence they too must be such as to promote the well-being of the family and group to which the individual belongs. It follows that thoughout most of the world, and in cultures of varied kinds, especially high approval has been given to the types of character that are strong in genuine fellow-feeling, love, sympathy, benevolence, and integrity, and that accordingly find expression in what we call the Golden Rule. Likewise highly approved in most societies are wisdom and mental capability in general, including competence in expression and in workmanship. Occupying high places also are fortitude, stability, joy of life, and perceptivity.

This whole combination of faculties, working together, which we may epitomize by the term "cooperatively acting intelligence" or "intelligent cooperation," is the combination, unique in man, which has enabled him alone to engage in social evolution, thereby developing civilization and finally science, and giving him unprecedented ascendancy among all living things. It would have been strange if man had not realized that these were the faculties of supreme importance for him and had not exalted them accordingly in his cultural codes and institutions. Yet during the historic period the emphasis on these traits has often been so vehement, even so desperate, as to disclose that men in general still fall pretty far short in these respects, as compared with the models held before them in parable, precept, and fable. This is only to be expected, for these qualities are needed even more, under conditions of modern civilization, than we usually have them, yet the processes of natural selection that developed their genetic basis have been slackening. Unquestionably the human race would be better off if men in general had the native endowments, in regard to these faculties, possessed by those individuals already among them who have them in highest degree.

That people have a basic realization of these shortcomings is shown by their repeated and often pathetic strivings to do better in these regards and also by the prevalence of feelings of guilt regarding their own nature. Surely the great majority of them would jump at the chance if they could somehow come closer to their own ideals of the good, the wise, and the capable. Similarly, they would eagerly seize such an opportunity for their children, unless they were held back by the grip of ancient tradition.

We should not deny that, barring world catastrophe, social reforms and improvements in upbringing will enable people in the future to attain much higher levels of feeling, understanding, and performance than those of today, even without changes in their genetic endowment. Perhaps too, some day (and some of my biologist friends think it will be soon), advances in the control of physiological and developmental processes will be of powerful aid for the same purposes. However, the higher the native capacities are, the more potent will the influence of an improved environment be in enabling the individual to attain to greater heights. Let us, then, do the best we can for later generations by the means that we have already gained.

It is nevertheless true that different existing cultures, despite their basic agreements, place somewhat different emphases upon the different faculties mentioned. However, this tendency toward diversity is rather to be welcomed than deplored, especially in a time like ours, in which we are aware of only the general direction of the light. Likewise, the special preferences that different groups, families, and individuals have for particular abilities and predispositions (e.g. volubility versus reserve), like their preferences for different bodily characteristics, will be serviceable in enriching the factual basis for later judgments, the future range of choice, and the potential versatility, available to people of coming generations, provided only that the clearly basic values noted above, those common to mankind in general, have also been striven for.

Beyond this, however, it should also be recognized that large groups in all present societies are still relatively undeveloped ethically. Some follow ancient patterns of thought that included no idea of progress and allowed little or no opportunity for decision-making regarding matters of principle. One of the traits of character they would value most is rigorous conformity and adherence to archaic modes of thought and behavior. Others, such as some teenage delinquents, acknowledge practically no standards or ideals except for the fads they avidly follow, the appeal of which is superficial and escapist. Again, there are great numbers uncritical enough to allow themselves to be duped and stampeded by paranoid demagogues and dictators. How can these powerful trends be reconciled with any salutary democratic form of germinal choice?

Our previous discussion has stressed the essential role of sound education in the principles of evolution and genetics, especially as they apply to man, in lifting people to a higher sense of their responsibility toward future generations, and in making them more conscious of the unique combination of faculties that lies at the root of mankind's greatness, but that is still in sore need of enhancement for meeting the ever more difficult problems of modern civilization. It is of course the people who have been deeply reached by this education, who will tend to feel stirred at the prospect of participating in the promotion of human progress. Just this group will also have an especially well crystallized awareness of the basic human values to be striven for, and their main objective will in fact be the furtherance of these values themselves, Moreover, being a vanguard group, one courageously challenging traditional mores, they will be unusually predisposed to recognize the major importance, for sustained progress, of those components of character and intellect that make for creativity, honesty in thinking, moral courage, and venturesomeness – attributes that tended to be inadequately appreciated throughout the long periods when the culture of mankind was nearly static. In this way the ground will be laid for genetic progress in the direction most needed by a democratic society.

The precedent thus set will be reinforced as the children thus engendered, reaching maturity, are seen to enjoy, on the whole, unusually favorable endowments. Moreover, during the same period, a very much larger section of the public is likely to have acquired a point of view much like that which had actuated the pioneers in germinal choice. For it is to be anticipated that in progressive countries – again, barring global catastrophe – there will have been a further extension, deepening, and integration of education, bringing to nearly everyone a realization of the evolutionary basis of the world and man, together with an awareness of both the grave dangers and the stirring possibilities ahead of us. At the same time, the social advances are likely to have been such as to lead to an increasing conviction that democratic methods must be used, and developed further, for meeting the great challenges confronting mankind. Thus the time will have come when the example that had been provided by the pioneers of germinal choice will be far better appreciated, and will be followed, in its selection of aims as well as in its methods, by a considerable and growing portion of the population.

Any powerful tool can be misused, but that is all the more reason why, if it falls into good hands, it should be used, and used well, for otherwise it will be left only for those who would misuse it. Certainly a Hitler or a Mussolini might be able to establish among his people a vicious form of controlled reproduction – controlled by him, and perhaps producing a few mimics of himself and many docile slaves. Most likely this attempt would after a while defeat itself, but it could in the meantime do untold harm. However, such an undertaking would bear no more relation to that of germinal choice than the use of an ax in killing a man bears to its use in building a house. In both cases, it would be equally senseless to prohibit all use of the instrument in order to prevent its misuse. On the contrary, a people who had engaged in actual germinal choice would be especially likely to resent the interference of a dictator, to be appalled at his aims, and to join in overthrowing him.

Signs of paranoid tendencies are among the expressions of unsound mentality that persons engaged in germinal choice for the purpose of enhancing basic human values would be especially alerted to, and likely to recognize and detest. Obviously, paranoids, as well as exhibitionists and "four flushers" generally, would try to put themselves forward for multiple propagation. But that is a main reason why records, counsel, and a period of serious deliberation are advisable, before any choice is decided upon. Similarly, both members of the couple should have passed the age (at least 21) before which flippancy and irresponsibility are too prevalent.

However, the feature of the method that would do the most to prevent the making of mistakes of the kind in question lies in the requirement that, after enough time has passed to make such a rule possible, only germinal material that has been preserved for at least twenty years after the decease of the donor be put to use. During this period any natural children of a prospective donor, having grown up, may have added a little to the data available for genetic judgments concerning him. But the main function of such a "cooling-off" interval is that it will provide time for the specious pretensions of the megalomaniac, the charlatan, the empty charmer, the unscrupulous schemer, the "big brass," and the eminent "stuffed shirt" to have become recognizable for the shams they really were. Conversely, solid worth will be likely to have withstood much better the attritions of storm and tide, and to have become more clearly manifest.

The above discussion has concerned itself almost entirely with psychological traits, because these are the ones in which progress is most important for our species. However, as will be almost universally agreed, a worthy mind and a wholesome character can develop and function more effectively, and can attain deeper, more all-around fulfillment, if harbored in a sound body. To be sure, concessions can be condoned in regard to some less essential attributes when these are far overshadowed by outstanding worth in more important respects. Yet on the whole the salient bodily benefits will also be sought for. Among the more significant of these are a high degree of physical command over one's person, general health and vigor, and delayed senescense.

On the other hand, the conspicuous differences in physical characteristics of form and coloration which engage so much popular attention at present represent in large degree matters of "taste." Disputation concerning these would be not merely foolish but even dangerous. Any given people, within the course of only a few centuries, is likely to change its own ideal of figures and features. This is readily seen on comparison of the portraits made in the same country in two different periods, for in these portraits the eminent personages of the day are shown with their features subtly warped, into closer conformity than they really were with the then popular ideal type. Thus the American heroes of 1776 tended to be shown with prominent or aquiline noses, whereas the "arrow-collar 100%" Americans of 150 years later were represented with short straight noses. Meanwhile, cosmetics can engage in almost as much remodelling as the artists. So we may, in a neutralist spirit, leave such fads to run their courses, if they must, and may remember that the counter currents in different places and times will tend to balance one another, and to maintain a kaleidoscopic variety of superficial multiformity that will continue to lend spice to personal associations.

WHY PROGRESS?

Whenever a new way of life, challenging to the old mores, presents itself, all sorts of arguments, often mutually contradictory, are thought up, in the attempt to prove that the old ways are better. Thus in the ancient Roman world, in the period when its own malpractices were leading toward its disintegration, most priests and rulers found the doctrines of Christian charity, of the brotherhood of man, and of the non-divinity of the emperor, most reprehensible and subversive, and put up what they thought a strong case against such heresies. Not long afterwards, however, these alleged aberrations became generally accepted throughout the same region, albeit usually in a rather perverted form that allowed major concessions to the predatory practices of those in positions for perpetrating them. But as time has gone on increasing numbers have realized that ours would be a much happier world if these professed principles were to be further incorporated into the structure of society and more wholeheartedly followed in individual living.

The advances in democracy and in the acceptance of human rights, continued over a dozen centuries but with much greater momentum recently, have shown that it is in fact possible for life to be lived much more humanely than was commonly the case in imperial Rome, especially when the technical and economic reforms associated both as cause and effect with these changes in outlook are included in the picture. The enormous benefits, both material and psychological, have been obvious. Unquestionably humanity can travel much further along this road, especially if more attention is paid to making the upbringing of children and also the conditions of life and work of adults more wholesome, freer from unnecessary repressions, and provided with greater scope for work that is appreciated and companionship that is reciprocated.

However, even this is only part of the story. For although those cynics may be decadent who see the element of tragedy as necessarily the most significant thread in all human life, and who maintain that under almost every human mask there lurks a demon of ingrowing desperation, nevertheless it must in common honesty be admitted that the tragic conflicts that take place within most normal individuals are not all caused by faulty upbringing and avoidable evils in the social system. They are in no small measure also the result of the fact that some of our urges, natural to primitive man, such as those which express themselves in combat, must be curbed to a degree uncomfortable to us, to allow the functioning of civilized society, while, conversely, some of our other impulses, such as those expressed in civilized amenities toward persons in competition with us, may be so inadequate as to be replaced by a guilt-ridden and frustrating hypocrisy.

Thus, men grievously need the Golden Rule, but the Golden Rule grievously needs men in whose very nature it is more deeply rooted than in ours. These men would not require the wills of saints, for their way of life would be normal to them. They would take it for granted, and could live full wholesome lives, joyously carrying out the ever greater enterprises made possible for their strengthened individual initiative, working hand in hand in free alliance with their enhanced cooperative functionings. At the same time their personal relations would be warmer and more genuine, so that they could enjoy more of the love that gives itself away. Along with this, less forcing would be required of them in extending their feelings of kinship to those more remote from their contacts.

We do not argue that any personality can be free from inner conflicts. For almost all acts of life in a complex world call for the organization of one's urges and the consequent subordination of some to others. However, a nature in which there was a stronger genetic basis for the positive affections, led by love, and a lesser basis for the negative ones, which reach their acme in hate, would find itself much less wracked and strained in bending its efforts so as best to serve society than would a nature having the genetic basis of the man of today, which is surely the same as that of the man of the stone age. Moreover, in a society in which more individuals were similarly endowed in this respect, an individual more nearly in accord with this ideal would find ampler and deeper reciprocation. Thus the sacrifices involved in the pursuit of "the good" would be minimized both from without and from within the individual.

At this point a digression may be made in order to clear up possible misconceptions regarding the degree of certainty involved in genetic selection for traits of the kind in question. Few persons acquainted with genetic principles would any longer dispute the important role played by differences in genes in causing persons to differ markedly in respect to the strength of the affective traits here under discussion, as well as in regard to emotional propensities in general. Such genetically based differences are of course more readily demonstrated in studies of psychologically less advanced animals, as in comparisons between different breeds of dogs, since here the relevant environmental factors can be better equalized, and the genetic differences are more uniform. These studies have shown the existence of very marked differences in such respects, while of course these differences are even greater between different species, some being far more socially disposed than others. There is no reason to question the existence of similar differences in man.

Nevertheless, as we have previously pointed out, ethnic and social groups cannot be compared genetically in regard to these traits, because of the large and more or less consistent differences in their cultural backgrounds. Moreover, since these backgrounds also differ markedly from one individual to another within the same group, the genetic differences even between the individuals of the group are commonly obscured and overlaid by the environmental ones. Yet, as in the case of all traits that are strongly influenced in their development by both hereditary and environmental factors, we can be reasonably sure that individuals who are clearly outstanding in some such respect do have a marked genetic basis for it, as well as an environmental basis. Consequently, intentionally practised selection that is based on the character as it is actually expressed will exert considerable genetic influence in the given direction, just as natural selection does.

In this connection it should be distinctly understood that one can hardly ever be sure, in advance, of the result of any given conception. This is not only because we cannot know the degree of influence of the environment on the parents and the offspring in the given case, but also because the random play of genetic segregation and recombination prevents the prediction of just what will be inherited. But, for all that, there will be a trend, and the trend will be strong enough to allow highly significant genetic results to be obtained in just one generation of selection. That this must be the case is evident from the fact that, genetically, the child stands *on the average* half way between his two parents. To couples engaging in germinal choice the individual uncertainties involved will be made clear. Those who decide for it will be the ones who accept these uncertainties and hold them to be, for them, outweighed by the propitious individual possibilities, and by the promise inherent in the over-all trend.

The same kind of considerations apply to selection for psychological traits concerned with any aspects of intelligence. This is because the intelligence of an individual, like his emotional make-up, is the resultant of a highly organized biological system, the development of which depends on many different genes and also on many features of the individual's environment, especially his cultural environment and his experiences generally. In fact, since intelligence actually consists in the ability to adjust and readjust, according to previous as well as present experiences, it is in a sense the most subject to modification by the environment of all the individual's functions. Accordingly, we may readily be led to wrong conclusions regarding the relative mental capabilities of groups, as well as of individuals, as a result of their having had very different cultural opportunities to develop in one or another mental direction.

And yet, it is also clear that, between individuals of any one human group, enormous genetic differences in mental capability also exist, ranging them all the way from hopeless idiots to persons who, given only an average chance, will be likely to make a highly meritorious contribution of some kind, that involves really creative thinking. Persons of the latter type, moreover, are far more aided in their mental development by a given amount of improvement in their environmentally based conditions and opportunities than are those of average native ability. Here again, then, those who have become genuinely outstanding are sure to represent not only a favorable environment but also a very fortunate genetic endowment. Moreover, evidence exists that some relatively rare individual genes have decided effects of this kind, giving relatively sharp segregation within families. Among these there are some concerned with rather specialized types of mental ability and others very generalized in their effects.

The same kind of case exists for the conclusion that man under modern civilization would be much better off if the genetic basis of his mentality were to be raised, so as to be comparable with that of the most intelligent persons now living, as for our previous conclusion that he would greatly benefit by the raising of the genetic basis of his affective social proclivities. One of the greatest bugbears of our present-day youth consists of the painful efforts they expend in trying to glimpse – or to *evade* glimpsing – a pitiful few of the highlights of the modern view of the world they live in, of human relations, and of the activities of mankind. This is the view that natural and social scientists, along with engineers and other specialists in techniques, have succeeded in winning for them. By no means all of this inadequacy of our youth arises from faulty methods in bringing up and educating them. Yet it is of practical importance for the people in general to have a sound grasp of many of these matters that have thus far eluded them, if their country and their world is to be run democratically, in their own (and therefore in mankind's) true interests. For the knowledge does exist, in bits, and it is being used – or abused – by persons of partial vision, and of insular allegiances, in ways that could lead to disaster, rather than to the increasing triumphs of humanity that all-around understanding, coupled with social motivation, would achieve. Thus, it is imperative that the people's voice in matters of general policy, and also in more special matters, be an intelligent voice, and today this has as one of its major requirements a scientific understanding.

Aside from these more directly practical considerations, we should not overlook the enormous enrichment of life that a more adequate view of the world and man, as disclosed by modern science, can bring to those participating heartily in this breath-taking experience. For those to whom it comes readily, and even for those who find it laborious but possible and worth-while, there is an enormous exhilaration in mastering the principles underlying the workings and structure of the natural world, and also of the uses to which they may be put by man, in following the paths by which these principles were discovered, and in contemplating the grand pano-ramas as well as the vignettes of existence as already perceived. There is additional stimulation for those who press the quest further, for the greater extension of our vision.

All this is in a sense a human birthright, and those who would confine it to a tiny aristocracy of intellect, as it is confined today, are guilty of the same kind of snobbery as were those who believed in hiding "higher studies" from the masses by expressing them only in Latin. Yet today, for most of humanity, much of this knowledge, most of the thought processes involved, are inescapably locked up in what to them must remain an unreadable Latin. It is the right of the man of the future to gain the transcendent view to which his eyes of today cannot penetrate. It is the duty of the people of our own times to help in making this possible for our successors, by taking the steps that would endow men with the invaluable gift of ready understanding.

But still we meet objectors who complain that man should not be too intelligent for his circumstances. A nation of intellectuals, they say, is unhappy in a world where the majority must be hewers of wood and drawers of water. This is truly a short-sighted view, the view of the slave-owner. It ignores the fact, attested to by history, that the more men's eyes are opened and the greater the social and technical freedoms they win, the more do they themselves find ways to reduce their routine labor. The more do they devise means of operating on a higher level, utilizing calculations, machines, psychology, medicine, social science, so as to allow them ever greater scope for more engrossing enterprises, deeper quests, nobler constructions, farther ranging adventures. Man not merely discovers world beyond world, he also creates them. But to do so he must advance within himself. And it would be shameful to deny these opportunities to men in general.

Finally, let us consider the objection that man in any given period cannot foretell what his situation and requirements will be in later generations and that therefore by trying to remold himself according to his present lights and values he may be actually unfitting himself for the future (see for instance DUBOS, 1962). For with changes in culture and unforeseeable improvements in knowledge and techniques, it is said, present needs are likely no longer to apply, and some present evils, as we now regard them, may even turn out to be advantages or virtues. So, for example (if we may put words into the mouths of our critics), an earlier generation, using such methods, might have tried to make us parsimonious rather than generous in our ways, dogged rather than flexible, submissive rather than independent of mind, content to get along with little rather than eager to create much. It should be admitted that there are plenty among us who hold such an attitude still, although they are surely not the ones who will lead the way in germinal choice.

In brief, these objectors are defendants of a biological *status quo* or *laisser faire* policy, on the ground (or is it an excuse?) that we are *not progressive enough*, being too short-sighted to know what will be good for us. Can these critics really believe that the persons of unusual moral courage, progressive spirit, and eagerness to serve mankind, who will pioneer in germinal choice, and likewise those who in a more enlightened age will follow in the path thus laid down, will fail to recognize the fundamental human values stressed in our earlier discussion? Or do they really believe that people in general already have in sufficient degree the faculties which make for willing cooperation, that they have quite enough native keenness of intellect, and a bountiful supply of those subsidiary attributes, such as perceptivity, curiosity, expressivity, that render these primary faculties more effective? Do they think that it would be dangerous to have most men as socially motivated, or as able intellectually, as they themselves are? Or would they regard it as a pity and a danger if most men actually excelled them in these respects?

Surely the fundamental values here sought do not represent the short-sighted choices of today or yesterday alone. An enhancement of the faculties by which they are pursued would never make men less suited for "the good life," or for further progressive evolution – quite the contrary. It is these faculties, primarily, which render man so adaptable, and it is because we already have them in some measure that we can recognize their worth and contrive to gain them in greater measure. If in any future culture the possession of these faculties would become a hindrance, or if a lesser development of them would tend to make men more comfortable or more numerous, then that culture would be a decadent one. In that case it would become the first job of man's cooperatively acting intelligence to alter his culture, in such wise as again to promote the forward march of his understanding and of his community of feeling.

Aside from these primary objectives in germinal choice, there would, as we have said previously, be room for manifold divergencies in details. Thus, there might even be minor groups striving in such different directions as boisterousness versus reticence, intense drive versus meditative calm, or versatility versus single-mindedness. There would also be those who strove to emphasize some special gift or proclivity, such as a musical bent, love of bodily effort, unusual kinesthetic sensibility, high retentiveness, etc., etc. But all this kind of division of aim in regard to these lesser propensities would only be salutary. It would represent no fixed policy but would serve to increase the wealth of faculties of the future population. And that population would then be better alerted for considering such problems, and provided with a better basis for assessing the consequences of the varied choices.

There is of course no such thing as the "ideal man," or the ideal organism, and persons (e.g. DOBZHANSKY, 1962, DUBOS, 1962) who charge the advocates of germinal choice with fostering such a goal have either failed to read or failed to grasp the ideas involved. This by no means signifies that "ideals" in a more general sense form no part of the picture, for ideals in the sense of values, and directions in which to strive, are of course of the essence of the matter. But there can, for the person aware of the courses and principles of evolution, be no final, perfect end, certainly not man as he is today, either biologically or culturally. Neither could we regard as near "the end" a population patterned after the persons of greatest mind, heart, and spirit who have ever lived. However, a population possessed of such qualities, if also balanced by a good infusion of the hardihood, humility, and common sense of the "common man," would nevertheless represent a considerable step in a progressive direction.

Where we would proceed from there is a matter we need not worry about now. It would be arrogant and absurd to think that we could at present do better in seeing ahead of such a stage than could the people who had already arrived at it. Let us be glad that the way does indeed seem to be open ended, but let us not take that idea as an excuse for not moving forward where we can in fact see the direction of advance. The greatest contribution that we, as paltry individuals, can make is to aid in getting us to the next step. And as the advance continues, it can become surer, more purposeful, and more effective, and the making of it will constitute the highest expression of human freedom.

BIBLIOGRAPHY

BREWER, H. (1935). *Eugenics Rev.* 27, 121.

BREWER, H. (1939). *Lancet* 1, 265.

BREWER, H. (1961). *Balanced Living* 17, 69.

BUNGE, R. G. & SHERMAN, J. K. (1953). *Nature, Lond.* 172, 767.

BUNGE, R. G., KEITTEL, W. C. & SHERMAN, J. K. (1954). *Fertil. and Steril.* 5, 520.

DOBZHANSKY, TH. (1962). *Mankind Evolving: The Evolution of the Human Species.* New Haven and London: Yale University Press.

DUBOS, R. (1962). *The Torch of Life.* New York: Simon and Schuster.

GUTTMACHER, A. F. (1961). *Babies by Choice or by Chance.* New York: Avon Books.

HOAGLAND, H. (1943). *Scient. Monthly* 56, 56.

HOAGLAND, H. & PINCUS, G. (1942). *J. gen. Physiol.* 25, 337.

HUXLEY, J. S. (1962). *Eugenics Rev.*

HUXLEY, J. S. (1962). *Current* No. 29 (Sept.), 58.

HUXLEY, J. S. (1963). In: Man and his Future, p. 1, ed. G. WOLSTENHOLM. London: J. and A. Churchill; New York: Macmillan.

IIZUKA, R. & SAWADA, Y. (1958). *Jap. J. Fertil. and Steril.* 3, 1.

JAHNEL, F. (1938). *Klin. Wschr.* 17, 1273.

KLINE, C. W. (1961). *Balanced Living* 17, 75.

LEDERBERG, J. (1963). In: Man and his Future, p. 1, ed. G. WOLSTENHOLM. London: J. and A. Churchill; New York: Macmillan.

MACKINNON, J. G. (1960). *The Humanist* 20, No. 2, 89.

MEDAWAR, P. B. (1960). The Future of Man. New York: Basic Books.

MONTEGAZZA, P. (1866). *Rend. reale Istit. Lomb.* 3, 183.

MULLER, H. J. (1935). Out of the Night: A Biologist's View of the Future. New York: Vanguard Press; (1936) London: Gollancz; (1938 in Fr. trans. by J. ROSTAND) Paris: Guillemard.

MULLER, H. J. (1958). *Science* 127, *625*.

MULLER, H. J. (1960a). In Evolution after Darwin 2, Evolution of Man, 423, ed. TAX, S. Chicago: University of Chicago Press.

MULLER, H. J. (1960b). In Evolution after Darwin 3, Issues in Evolution, 214, 237, ed. TAX, S. Chicago: University of Chicago Press.

MULLER, H. J. (1961a). *Science* 134, *643*.

MULLER, H. J. (1961b). *Perspectives in Biology and Medicine* 4, *377*.

MULLER, H. J. (1962). In: Evolution and Man's Progress, p. 22, ed. HOAGLAND, H. & BURHOE, R. W. New York and London: Columbia University Press.

MULLER, H. J. (1963). In: Man and his Future, p. 274, ed. G. WOLSTENHOLM. London: J. and A. Churchill; New York: Macmillan.

NAKAJIMA, K., IIZUKA, R., SAWADA, Y., YOSHIDA, Y., OOKUBO, F. & ISONO, M. (1962). Paper read at 4th World Cong. Internat. Fert. Assoc. in Brazil.

POLGE, C., SMITH, A. V. & PARKES, A. S. (1949). *Nature, Lond.* 164, *666*.

ROSTAND, J. (1959). Can Man Be Modified? New York: Basic Books, Inc.

SAWADA, Y. (1959). *Jap. J. Fertil. Steril.*, 4, *1*.

SHERMAN, J. K. (1954). *Fertil. and Steril.*, 5, *357*.

SHERMAN, J. K. (1963). *Fertil. and Steril.*, 49, No. 1, *14*.

SHERMAN, J. K. & BUNGE, R. G. (1953). *Proc. Soc. exp. Biol. Med.* 82, *686*.

SHETTLES, L. B. (1940). *Amer. J. Physiol.* 128, *408*.

STOKES, WALTER R. (1962). *Marriage and Family Living* 24, *269*.

HERMANN JOSEPH MULLER, Ph.D., D.Sc., was Professor of Zoology, The University of Texas, from 1925 to 1936 and has been Professor of Zoology, Indiana University, since 1945, Distinguished Service Professor since 1953. In recognition of his discovery of transmutation of the gene by X-rays, he was awarded the Nobel Prize in Physiology and Medicine in 1946. He was President of the 8th International Congress of Genetics, held in Stockholm in 1948. Professor MULLER was a recipient in 1955 of the Kimber Genetics Award and in 1959 of the Darwin Medals of the Linnaean Society and the Akademie Leopoldina. He is a Foreign Member of the Royal Swedish Academy of Science, the Royal Danish Academy of Science, the Royal Society of London, the Japan Academy, the National Institute of Sciences of India, and the Accademia Nazionale dei Lincei, and a Member of the National Academy of Sciences of the United States. He was President, from 1956 to 1959, of the American Humanist Association, which designated him as "Humanist of the Year" in 1963. He was co-author of "The Mechanism of Mendelian Heredity," and of "Genetics, Medicine and Man." Professor MULLER is a Vice-President of the World Academy of Art and Science.

Action Programs

The Problem of New Problems

by

Brock Chisholm

In the new era of human social development which began roughly sixteen years ago, after the Second World War, many new problems have appeared. Most of the very important ones stem from man's, or some men's, tremendously increased ability to kill and destroy, or his also greatly increased ability to save and prolong life. The scientific and engineering development of the ability to split and to fuse atoms and the great advances in public health and medical fields have been the chief initiators of these changes.

Since long before the dawn of history man's survival has been by groups in competition to the death with other groups. During some thousands of years certain feeling, thinking and behaviour patterns, associated with survival, have become firmly established. Exclusive loyalty to the survival group, whether family, clan, tribe, city, state, principality, kingdom, empire or nation, has been a demand of the highest priority affecting almost all human beings. As a crime, treason has ranked above even murder in most cultures; murder is often legalized, as in war or execution, while treason never is. The ancient system of survival depended on the ability of the survival group to defend itself against attack and/or to attack other groups successfully, that is, to win wars. To win wars required the largest possible number of fighting men, exclusive loyalty, the best weapons, unquestioning obedience to authority even at the cost of life, adequate supplies of food and materiel, and high morale. The obligation to provide all these has been taught each generation, very forcefully, by the development of strong moral attitudes through myths, systems of heroes, biased history, medals and awards, and public acclaim. In almost all cultures any questioning of these values or of the methods by which they were supported was, and is, strongly discouraged by governmental and private action.

Summary of address before Twenty-third American Assembly. Arden House, Harriman, New York, May 2, 1963.

Under these circumstances of built-in conservatism in the fields of inter-human and inter-societal relationships, adequate adjustment to new circumstances faces strong barriers. When tension arises between survival groups – in recent centuries usually either nations or groups of nations – a highly emotional state of anxiety is produced. In such a state there is a tendency for emotion to take precedence over intellectual function. Conscience, the early-learned system of values to which every person has been exposed in childhood, is mobilised and strong feelings about what is "right" or "good" are felt and expressed. Almost all of us have learned in childhood that when we feel threatened the right and good and effective thing to do is to increase our ability to kill to the greatest possible degree and then to threaten any potential enemy into submission. This has been our standard, admirable and effective pattern throughout history; it is sometimes called "negotiation from strength." Unfortunately for the continued use of this old pattern, the conditions have changed. As soon as the potentiality for destruction became absolute, or nearly so, any increase in power became meaningless. With the weapons now available in the world, nuclear, biological, chemical and conventional, we are capable of killing everyone, including ourselves, at least three or four times over, yet many people earnestly believe that if we can just arrange to be able to kill everyone, including ourselves, say ten times over instead of only three or four times, in some way we would be more secure and less frightened. This is obviously insane thinking, based on emotional reaction and not on intellectual process.

The same situation obtains in relation to our present rapid increase in population. To our ancestors, growth of the survival group was "good;" it increased power and security at every stage of social development. It is now a threat to the whole human species, but we have no tradition of concern about threats to the species; the occasion had not arisen until just recently, long after the systems of values into which we were born were incorporated into our personalities as "conscience values." To have plenty of children has been admirable in practically all cultures and at all times, both for national defence and to provide social security for parents. Only intellectual conviction, which commonly has been subjected to censorship and control by conscience, tells us that large families have become a threat to all of us, so, by all sorts of distortions of reasoning, most of us still avoid the painful implications of our present population situation.

Associated with the population problem is the world's present food situation. The problem is not only that a large proportion of the world's people suffer from lack of adequate food; that has always been true. The important change is in the fact that, while resignation to hunger or starvation was normal wherever there were frequent shortages of food, that resignation has disappeared or is rapidly disappearing from the world. No longer will any people peacefully die of starvation, or even suffer severely from malnutrition. They all know now that it is not necessary, that the human race is quite capable of feeding adequately all its people. We are not doing it because we don't care enough; we have no tradition of concern for such distant threats. Our consciences do not make us uncomfortable enough to drive us to the trouble and expense of organizing food production and distribution on a world basis. The hungry people are not within our concept of our survival group.

It seems that the common factors in these three great world problems, security, population and food, are that they are all threats to the whole human race and that they are associated with new situations not amenable to control by the methods learned from our parents or ancestors. They demand new solutions which require feeling and thinking independently of the accident of our birth into this or that community or group. We do not have social or political institutions which were designed for the solution of world problems, except for a few developed recently such as the United Nations and its specialized agencies, and these are so beset with controls exercised for the benefit of individual nations or groups of nations that it is very difficult for them to deal with world threats. Each nation tends to break down all problems into what is good for "us," at whatever cost to anyone else, the traditional survival group attitude, ignoring the fact that the survival group has now become the human race itself.

Recently a few people in some countries have begun to try to think as members of the human race and beyond the limitations of exclusive national loyalties, but they still meet strong criticism from their own "loyal" compatriots. Still no government has set up a department or institution to recognize and advise on dealing with new threats to the human species, while many governments try to use the United Nations to enhance their own prestige and power or to gain economic or political advantage. In the presence of universal threat we are fumbling badly because few people have developed emotionally and socially to a level of maturity appropriate to a world where security and welfare have become indivisible and where we shall survive as members of the human race or not at all. Out-breeding, out-gunning or out-producing other groups can no longer be counted on to provide security, prosperity or peace, or even survival.

BROCK CHISHOLM, M.D., Sc.D., F.W.A., was Executive Secretary of the Interim Commission of the World Health Organization, from 1946 to 1948, and Director-General of the World Health Organization from 1948 to 1953. Dr. CHISHOLM has received honorary degrees, decorations, awards and honorary memberships from many countries. He is a Vice-President of the World Association of World Federalists and Honorary President of the World Federalists of Canada. Dr. CHISHOLM is also a member of the Advisory Council of the Peace Research Institute of Washington, and a member of the Board of Directors of the Canadian Peace Research Institute. His publications include, "Prescription for Survival," Columbia Univ. Press, 1957, and "Can People Learn to Learn," Harper and Bros., 1958.

General Assembly Resolution on
Population Growth and Economic Development

NOTE BY

THE SECRETARY-GENERAL

1. At the sixteenth session of the General Assembly (1961), a draft resolution on "Population Growth and Economic Development" was introduced, and allocated to the Second Committee. The Second Committee was not able to consider it for lack of time, and the Assembly decided that the item should be placed on the agenda of the next session.

2. A draft resolution relevant to this item was introduced at the seventeenth session with the following sponsors: Ceylon, Denmark, Ghana, Greece, Nepal, Norway, Pakistan, Sweden, Tunisia, Turkey, Uganda and the United Arab Republic. It was considered by the Second Committee at its 866th–869th and 874th–875th meetings. After some amendments, the draft resolution was approved by a roll-call vote of 43 to 14, with 42 abstentions. The draft resolution as approved by the Committee was presented to the General Assembly at its 1197th plenary meeting on 18 December 1962.[1] The Assembly decided by a roll-call vote that it should be considered as an important item requiring a two-thirds majority vote. A vote was first taken on the latter part of operative paragraph 6 in the draft, stating: "and that the United Nations give technical assistance, as requested by Governments, for national projects and programmes dealing with the problems of population;". This part was rejected by a roll-call vote of 34 to 34, with 32 abstentions. The remainder of the draft resolution was then adopted by 69 votes to none, with 27 abstentions. The resolution in its final form [2] is attached as an annex.

---

[1] Presented in a report of the Second Committee (A/5354) with a report of the Fifth Committee (A/5375).
[2] General Assembly resolution 1838 (XVII).

General Assembly Resolution adopted 18 December 1962 *

POPULATION GROWTH AND ECONOMIC DEVELOPMENT

The General Assembly,

Considering that rapid economic and social progress in the developing countries is dependent not least upon the ability of these countries to provide their peoples with education, a fair standard of living and the possibility for productive work,

Considering further that economic development and population growth are closely interrelated,

Recognizing that the health and welfare of the family is of paramount importance, not only for obvious humanitarian reasons, but also with regard to economic development and social progress, and that the health and welfare of the family require special attention in areas with a relatively high rate of population growth,

Recognizing further that it is the responsibility of each Government to decide its own policies and devise its own programmes of action for dealing with the problems of population and economic and social progress,

Reminding States Members of the United Nations and of the specialized agencies that according to recent census results the effective population increase during the last decade has been particularly high in many low-income less developed countries,

Reminding Member States that in formulating their economic and social policies it is useful to take into account the latest relevant facts on the interrelationship of population growth and economic and social development and that the forthcoming World Population Conference and the Asian Population Conference might throw new light on the importance of this problem, especially for the developing countries,

Recalling its resolution 1217 (XII) of 14 December 1957, in which the General Assembly, *inter alia,* invites Member States, particularly the developing countries, to follow as closely as possible the interrelationships existing between economic and population changes, and requests the Secretary-General to ensure the co-ordination of the activities of the United Nations in the demographic and economic fields,

Recalling Economic and Social Council resolution 820 (XXXI) which contains provisions aiming at intensified efforts to ensure international co-operation in the evaluation, analysis and utilization of population census results and related data, particularly in the less developed countries, and which requests the Secretary-General to explore the possibilities of increasing the amount of technical assistance funds for assistance to Governments requesting it in preparing permanent programmes of demographic research,

* General Assembly resolution 1838 (XVII).

Recognizing that further studies and research are necessary to fill the gaps in our knowledge about the causes and consequences of demographic trends, particularly in the less developed countries,

Recognizing that removals of large national groups to other countries may give rise to ethnical, political, emotional and economic difficulties,

1. *Notes with appreciation* the report of the Secretary-General, entitled "The United Nations Development Decade. proposals for action" which, *inter alia*, refers to the interrelationship between population growth and economic and social development;

2. *Expresses its appreciation* of the work on population problems which has up to now been carried out under the guidance of the Population Commission of the Economic and Social Council;

3. *Requests* the Secretary-General to conduct an inquiry among the Governments of States Members of the United Nations and of the specialized agencies concerning the particular problems confronting them as a result of the reciprocal action of economic development and population changes;

4. *Recommends* that the Economic and Social Council in co-operation with the specialized agencies, the regional economic commissions and the Population Commission, and taking into account the results of the inquiry referred to in paragraph 3 above, intensify its studies and research on the interrelationship of population growth and economic and social development, with particular reference to the needs of the developing countries for investment in health and educational facilities within the framework of their general development programmes;

5. *Further recommends* that the Economic and Social Council report on its findings to the General Assembly not later than at its nineteenth session:

6. *Endorses* the view of the Population Commission [1] that the United Nations should encourage and assist Governments, especially those of the less developed countries, in obtaining basic data and carrying out essential studies of the demographic aspects, as well as other aspects, of their economic and social development problems;

7. *Recommends* that the second World Population Conference pay special attention to the interrelationships of population growth with economic and social development, particularly in countries that are less developed, and that efforts be made to obtain the fullest possible participation in the Conference by experts from such countries.

The Politics of Population:
A Blueprint for International Cooperation

by

RICHARD N. GARDNER

December 18, 1962 marked a turning point in the recognition by the international community of the world population problem.

On that day the United Nations General Assembly concluded the first debate in its history devoted entirely to the subject of population. It adopted, with 69 affirmative votes (including that of the United States), 27 abstentions, and not a single negative vote, a major resolution calling for an intensified program of international cooperation in the population field.

Except for the members of the Soviet bloc, all of whom abstained, countries of every major political, economic, cultural, religious, and geographic identification were among those voting in the affirmative. In the presence of an issue of such incalculable importance to the future of mankind, the many divisions which are so characteristic of debates on most international problems dissolved, giving way to a broad consensus on the importance of the population problem.

It may be useful to consider in some detail the significance of these recent developments in the United Nations. Specifically, there are at least four questions that come to mind:

Why was the population problem on the agenda of the United Nations?

What exactly did the United Nations decide to do about it?

What did the United Nations debate reveal about international attitudes to this question?

What program of international cooperation in population should we be seeking in the future?

I.

The short answer to why population was on the agenda of the United Nations at the 17th General Assembly was that the Government of Sweden,

Address before the Twenty-Third American Assembly on "The Population Dilemma" at Arden House, Harriman, New York, Saturday, May 4, 1963 at 8 p.m. D.S.T.

supported by a number of other countries, decided to put it there. But obviously this is not a satisfactory answer. Ten years earlier, a full scale debate in the United Nations devoted entirely to the population question would have been unthinkable. The wide support that developed in the interim for the inscription of an item on the population question and for a Resolution calling for action to deal with it reflected a growing international appreciation of the significance of the population question for the future of mankind.

Until very recently, at least, Western thought has been characterized by an optimistic faith in the inevitability of progress. Despite two terrible wars, a great depression, and the revolutionary ferment which is currently shaking our civilization, many of us still cling to the assumption that the fate of man on earth is destined to improve as time goes on.

This confident assumption is somewhat undermined by the realization that despite all the progress of science and technology in recent years there are more people living in misery and deprivation today than there were at the turn of the century. Of course, there are also more people enjoying adequate living standards. But the increase of the underprivileged has probably exceeded the increase of everyone else. Whether such a development can be considered progress is, to say the least, an open question.

To be sure, some people cite as evidence of progress the upward trend of aggregate statistics. But progress cannot be measured merely by increases in gross national product.

The object of economic development is the welfare and dignity of the individual human being. We must concern ourselves, not with aggregate statistics, but with the progress made in assuring each person a full and satisfactory life – adequate levels of personal consumption, including food and housing, health and education, and also satisfaction of those political, cultural, and spiritual needs that are fundamental to all men.

If the condition of the individual, and not gross statistics, is to be the measure of our progress, then it is absolutely essential that we be concerned with population trends. So long as we are concerned with the quality of life we have no choice but to be concerned with the quantity of life.

There are today some three billion people in the world. It required hundreds of thousands of years, from the beginning of life on earth to the beginning of this century, to reach one and a half billion. Within the last 60 years we have doubled that number. according to United Nations estimates we will double that number again to six billion by the end of this century.

It is obvious from these statistics that the world's population is not merely growing in *absolute numbers*. The *rate* of population growth has increased at an extraordinary pace. The annual growth rate has doubled from 1% in 1945 – itself an unprecedented high in world history – to 2% today. It is expected to go even higher. But even if the present rate of growth of world population is maintained at its present level, the numbers we have to contemplate are staggering.

Whether the growth of world population continues at its present rate, whether a reduction in that rate is brought about by increases in the death rate or decreases in the birth rate, and whether, to reduce the birth rate, measures are found which are consistent with the economic, cultural, ethical, and religious circumstances of individual countries – these are all questions of paramount importance.

It was considerations such as these which led to the inscription of the population item at the 17th General Assembly. But the inscription of this item did not reflect just a generalized concern with the population problem; it reflected a particular concern for the dilemma facing the less developed countries.

The nature of this dilemma can be succinctly stated. For reasons which are well known, the rate of population growth tends to be higher in the less developed countries than in the developed countries – about 70% higher on the average. In many less developed countries the rate of population growth exceeds 3% a year.

About 80% of the one-half billion growth in the world population in the last decade took place in the less developed areas. In the years ahead the highest rates of growth are likely to continue to be in these areas. It is estimated, for example, that, if present rates of growth were to continue, between now and the year 2000 the population of North America would grow from 200 to 300 million, while the population of South and Middle America would grow from some 200 to 600 million.

It is bad enough that less developed countries tend to have a faster rate of population growth than developed countries. But the problem is compounded further by the fact that the less developed countries are less able to cope with the consequences of rapid population growth.

The problem for developed countries is to increase already high per capita income levels and to devote increasing portions of already large national savings to services such as medical care, health, and housing. But less developed countries whose economy is at the subsistence level may be able to save little or nothing at existing income levels for improvement in social infrastructure.

It is all many of the developing countries can do to enlarge the total economic product as fast as the added people. Yet they have not merely to provide additional facilities for increased population but to create new and adequate facilities for the existing population as well.

For newly developing countries the problem of population growth is not, as some people think, the problem of avoiding starvation or finding standing room. It is the problem of finding sufficient savings after current consumption needs are met to assure a tolerable rate of progress toward modernization and higher standards of living based on self-subtaining economic growth.

In some of the world's poorest areas population increase is outpacing the increase in gross national product. As a result there are no resources available for capital formation and no increases in living standards. The prospect is for more and more people to have less and less income.

Just a year and a half ago the United Nations General Assembly set as its goal for the United Nations Development Decade the achievement by 1970 of an annual growth rate of 5% a year in aggregate national income in each of the developing countries. The achievement of this goal will require enormous efforts.

It has been estimated that in the decade of the 1950's the developing countries over-all had a growth rate of 3% a year and a population growth of 2% a year, with annual per capita increases of income of 1% a year. Making the generally accepted assumption of a capital-output ratio of 3 : 1, these countries will have to increase their savings and investment from 9 to 15% of gross national product in order to achieve the goals of the Development Decade. This is obviously a formidable task at present levels of population growth.

Assuming that the goals of the Development Decade are achieved, prospective increases in population will greatly dilute the impact of over-all increases in income on individual levels of welfare. For example, gradual progress toward the 5% annual growth goal during the Development Decade would by the end of this decade increase a $100 per capita income to $123 in a country with a 2% rate of population growth and $111 in a country with a 3% rate of population growth.

Obviously there is much that we do not know about the relationship of population growth to economic and social development. But from an examination of these and other facts one conclusion seems inescapable – that in certain less developed countries it may be virtually impossible at the present time, even with maximum external assistance and maximum self-help, to bring about a rate of economic growth which will provide the rate of improvement in individual living standards which the country seeks to attain and which, more fundamentally, is essential to the proper exercise of the individual's human faculties.

In the light of these hard realities it was scarcely surprising that a large part of the impetus to discuss the population problem in the United Nations came from the less developed countries themselves. In recent years, a growing number of these countries have adopted population policies of one sort or another – policies in accord with their particular economic, social, cultural and religious circumstances.

In July 1962, shortly before the opening of the 17th General Assembly, the Cairo Conference of Developing Countries, including countries from Asia,

Africa and Latin America, unanimously adopted a Declaration which contained the following significant statement:

"Countries that suffer from the pressure of population on resources available should accelerate their rate of economic development, and in the meantime take appropriate legitimate measures to deal with their population problems."

It was against this background of a growing concern that the United Nations General Assembly began its historic debate on the population problem.

II

While the Resolution on "Population Growth and Economic Development" was the first of its kind ever passed by the General Assembly, the United Nations has not previously been inactive in the population field. In the 17 years of its existence the United Nations has

– Established a population unit in the Secretariat (now the Population Branch of the Bureau of Social Affairs),

– Created the Population Commission, a group of government representatives meeting once every two years,

– Held a World Population Conference under U.N. auspices in 1954.

– Encouraged Regional Economic Commissions located in the less developed areas – the Economic Commission for Asia and the Far East, the Economic Commission for Latin America, and the Economic Commission for Africa – to become increasingly active in the population field.

– And organized Regional Demographic Research and Training Centers in Bombay, Santiago and Cairo, to provide advisory services to countries of these regions.

Through activities such as these, the United Nations has been making a major contribution to an understanding of the population problem:

In the field of *information*, it has encouraged and assisted member governments to obtain factual information on the size, composition, and trends of their populations and the interrelation between population growth and economic and social development.

In the field of *training*, it has helped develop a whole range of skills in the demographic field – in census taking, population projections, and economic analysis.

In the field of *discussion*, it has promoted a full and responsible exchange of ideas on all aspects of the population problem.

These contributions of the United Nations should not be underestimated. When the Population Commission met for the first time in 1947, demographic statistics, including census and vital statistics were so incomplete that it would scarcely have been possible to speak knowledgeably of *world* population trends or *world* population problems. It is easy to overlook the fact that if it were not for the devoted labors of the population and statistical sections of the U.N. Secretariat, both operating under the guidance of the Population and Statistical Commissions, we would even now not be able to discern the outlines of the *world* population problem or the problems of most major regions.

Sixteen years of slow, careful accumulation of basic factual information helped lay the groundwork for enlightened consideration of the economic and social implications of population trends.

Building on this solid record of achievement, the General Assembly resolution on "Population Growth and Economic Development" was designed to increase the level of U.N. involvement in the population field. The resolution called for action under five main heads:

First, the Secretary General was requested to conduct an "inquiry" among member states "concerning the particular problems confronting them as a result of the reciprocal action of economic development and population changes."

This inquiry will help focus the attention of responsible officials in all countries on the implications of population trends for economic and social planning, open up channels of communication between policy makers and local demographic experts, and encourage governments without competent experts of their own to seek outside assistance. Such assistance will be available not only from the United Nations but from various foreign governments and private institutions – in the case of the United States, from such agencies as AID, the U.S. Census Bureau, the Ford Foundation, and the Population Council.

Second, the Economic and Social Council of the United Nations was asked, in cooperation with the Specialized Agencies, Regional Economic Commissions and the Population Commission, to "intensify its studies and research on the interrelationship of population growth and economic and social development with particular reference to the needs of the developing countries for investment in health and educational facilities..."

The intensification of studies and research called for under this section will involve not only a substantial increase in the program of work of the population section at U.N. Headquarters, the demographic staffs of the Regional Economic Commissions, and the Regional Demographic Research and Training Centers, but also correlative studies in the educational and health fields conducted in cooperation with UNESCO and the World Health Organization.

Third, the Economic and Social Council was directed to report its findings with respect to all of the foregoing to the General Assembly not later than at the Assembly's 19th session in 1964.

Fourth, United Nations agencies were asked to encourage and assist governments, especially of the less developed countries. "In obtaining basic data and carrying out essential studies of the demographic aspects as well as other aspects of their economic and social development problems."

Fifth, the World Population Conference scheduled for 1965 was requested to "pay special attention to the inter-relationships of population growth with economic and social development particularly in countries that are less developed..."

As noted earlier, the Resolution containing these five action paragraphs was approved overwhelmingly with no negative votes. A good deal of controversy developed, however, over another section not included in the Resolution as finally adopted which read:

"... and that the United Nations give technical assistance as requested by governments for national projects and programs dealing with the problems of population."

This section was widely interpreted as calling for United Nations technical assistance in the actual implementation of family planning programs. It was approved by a narrow margin in Committee but in the Plenary, where a two-thirds majority is required on important questions, it failed of adoption by a vote of 34 in favor, 34 against, with 32 abstentions.

As a practical matter, the defeat of this paragraph did not alter the authority already possessed by the United Nations as a result of previous resolutions of the General Assembly and of the Economic and Social Council to grant technical assistance upon request to member nations.

The momentum generated by the General Assembly resolution was maintained at subsequent meetings of the United Nations which have taken place in the last few months.

A resolution on Intensification of Demographic Studies, Research and Training introduced by the United States in association with Japan and the United Arab Republic was unanimously adopted by the Population Commission in February and the Economic and Social Council in April. This resolution spelled out some of the practical implications of the General Assembly resolution and contained other important provisions as well.

Among other things, the resolution
– Invited the Regional Economic Commissions to intensify their demographic work;
– Requested the U.N. to accelerate preparation of technical manuals for use in demographic work, hasten revision of certain basic demographic publications, and study the use of electronic computers in the analysis of demographic data;
– Requested adequate budgetary provision for this and other work,
– And urged the developed countries to "consider the value to the developing countries" of initiating or expanding research on the inter-relationship between population trends and economic and social development, research related to population such as on health and education, training of experts in the less developed countries in demography and statistics, and providing technical assistance to the developing countries

in census taking, vital statistics and utilizing demographic data in social and economic planning.

Since the passage of the General Assembly resolution the U.N. Secretariat has also begun work on the inquiry to member governments.

This inquiry will take the form of a questionnaire which will be sent to each member of the United Nations or of the Specialized Agencies.

When the answers to this questionnaire are compiled and analyzed and laid before the General Assembly in 1964, the United Nations will have before it the most comprehensive information yet assembled on the attitudes and policies of government on the population problem.

III.

The debate in the General Assembly which preceded the passage of the resolution on "Population Growth and Economic Development" provided a striking illustration of the unique value of the United Nations as an international forum. It was an enlightening experience for all of us who had the privilege to participate on behalf of our respective Governments. It is tempting to describe this fascinating debate in detail, but time will permit only a brief (and inevitably oversimplified) summary of the principal viewpoints which emerged.

The *first* viewpoint was represented by the Government of Sweden and the other sponsors of the resolution – Ceylon, Denmark, Ghana, Greece, Nepal, Norway, Pakistan, Tunisia, Turkey, Uganda and United Arab Republic. These supporters of the resolution argued that population growth posed grave problems for economic and social development and that urgent action was required to deal with it. They advocated a major increase in United Nations activity in the population field – including technical assistance in the field of family planning. Beyond the cosponsors of the resolution support for this viewpoint was expressed by most Moslem countries (e.g., United Arab Republic, Tunisia, Turkey and Pakistan), some countries of Asia (e.g., India, Nepal, Thailand, Malaya and Japan) and some countries of Africa (e.g., Ghana, Guinea and Uganda). This viewpoint found only scattered support in Latin America.

A *second* viewpoint was put forward by Argentina and Ireland, with support from a few other countries, principally in Latin America. These countries questioned the existence of a population problem, challenged the right of the United Nations to discuss it, and were particularly outspoken in opposing a U.N. program in family planning financed from technical assistance funds to which they were contributing.

A *third* viewpoint was expressed by a substantial number of countries including France and other countries of continental Europe, some French African countries and some Latin American countries. These countries conceded the existence of population problems in some areas but argued that action by the United Nations should be deferred pending further study. This group opposed the controversial technical assistance section and took the initiative in introducing the proposal for an inquiry on member countries' population problems.

A *fourth* viewpoint was that expressed by the members of the Soviet bloc. During the General Assembly debate, the Soviet Union and some of its satellites expounded the traditional Communist position that Western discussions of the population problem were based on "neo-Malthusian fallacies" and that population problems ceased to exist under Communism.

This Communist line was poorly received by the Assembly. At least one representative of a less developed country chided the Soviets for favoring planning in all sectors of economic life except the human sector – the one most important in its implications for economic and social growth.

The negative Soviet statement in the population debate was followed by a significant shift in the Communist line. When it came time to vote, the Soviet bloc did not oppose, but merely abstained, on the General Assembly resolution.

What is even more surprising, the Soviet representative at the recent meeting of the Economic and Social Council commended the United Nations for its work in the population field, agreed that population growth is an urgent problem for less developed countries, and announced the willingness of the Soviet Union to provide technical assistance in the demographic field.

This change in the Soviet position on population in the United Nations follows reports of increasing resort in recent years to birth control and abortion within the Soviet Union and some other bloc countries and of KHRUSCHEV's personal interest in a recent publication stressing the economic dangers of over-population.

The recent discussions at the United Nations may signal a new era of Soviet propaganda on the subject of population. Whether because of internal problems, or a desire to cultivate the favor of less developed countries, or both, the Soviet Union now appears ready to exercise leadership in action programs in the population field.

As for the United States, our position in the United Nations debate is already known. We made a strong statement underlining the importance of the population problem, the need for more knowledge about it, and the necessity for each country to determine its own population policy in accordance with its economic, social, cultural and religious circumstances.

More specifically, we expressed support for the resolution on "Population Growth and Economic Development" in its original form, which included the controversial section on technical assistance. We abstained, however, in the separate vote on this paragraph for two reasons:

– First, because it was superfluous, neither adding nor subtracting from the authority already possessed by the United Nations to grand technical assistance upon request to member nations;

– Second, because of our belief that, in the light of the views expressed in the General Assembly debate, United Nations activity should emphasize those three areas in which there was broad agreement among the members, namely, information, training and discussion in population problems.

I shall have more to say about this second consideration in a moment.

IV.

What conclusions can we draw from the United Nations debates on the population problem? What forms of international cooperation should we be seeking on this subject in the years ahead?

I believe we can identify an emerging consensus on the subject of population. My review of the recent United Nations debate has emphasized the differences between the member countries. Yet this debate – just as recent discussions within our own country – also revealed a large measure of common ground.

To begin with, the desire for increased knowledge about population trends, particularly in relation to economic and social development, is now nearly universal. We have passed, almost without noticing it, from a period in which the major uncertainty concerned the existence of the world population problem, to a period in which the major uncertainty is what can and should be done about it.

Moreover, even in the matter of what should be done about the population problem, it is possible to see:

– That there is no significant body of responsible opinion among people of any major religious, ethical or ideological persuasion which advocates totally unplanned or unregulated fertility, although there are sincere differences of opinion about the means which are morally permissible and the effectiveness of the means which are available

– That there is virtually universal agreement on both ethical and practical grounds, that decisions about responsible parenthood can be made only by individual parents themselves in the light of their responsibilities to their children and their society, and to the moral values which govern alike parents, children and societies.

The time has come to develop out of this consensus a blueprint for international cooperation which takes account of the politics as well as the economics of the population problem.

The fundamental concept in such a blueprint should be the principle of free choice.

Despite the growing concensus on the matters already mentioned, differences continue to exist between religious groups on specific methods of family planning. When it comes to implementation of population policy, the views of all groups should be respected. Participation in programs of family planning should be contingent upon the agreement of the country concerned.

As we noted in the Assembly, the United Nations already has authority to grant technical assistance in the population field upon request to member governments. From a practical point of view, however, it is unnecessary to earmark United Nations funds for those particular activities in the population field on which members are seriously divided. The potential resources of the United Nations both in terms of funds and personnel for the implementation of family planning programs are minuscule compared to the resources in member countries. In the pluralistic society of the free world there is a wide variety of sources of assistance from governments, foundations, universities, and even private business firms as well as international organizations.

All of these have something to contribute in the field of population. All can make more substantial contributions in the future than has been done in the past. What we need is an international division of labor, taking account of the comparative advantage, from the political as well as the economic and technical point of view, of the different sources of potential assistance.

The following is a rough blueprint of a program of international cooperation which the United States will be supporting in the months ahead with respect to the key elements of the population problem:

1. Information and Analysis

There is, as noted earlier, a need for more demographic information and analysis, particularly on the interrelation between population growth and economic and social development. Since there is universal agreement on this need, all governments and international organizations, as well as private institutions, can play a significant role.

The United States will continue to support the expansion of United Nations activities in the demographic field. Moreover, the Agency for International Development will respond to requests for assistance from developing countries in preparing, executing and analyzing population censuses, and in utilizing demographic data and analyses in social and economic planning. It will do this both by making United States advisers available and by training experts from the developing countries themselves.

2. Medical Research

There seems to be widespread agreement on the need for more knowledge about the basic life processes which govern child bearing. As President KENNEDY pointed out in a recent press conference, we need to know more about the whole reproduction cycle, and this information should be made more available to the world so that everyone can make his own judgment.

Paradoxical as it may seem, we need more knowledge on how to overcome both involuntary childlessness and involuntary parenthood through measures which are consistent with different religious, cultural, and economic circumstances. We need particularly a great deal more study of human fertility and reproduction.

We support studies to this end through our own National Institutes of Health. Moreover, we favor the conduct of such studies through the United Nations, specifically through the medical research program of the World Health Organization.

3. Health and Social Services

The major obstacle to the implementation of family planning policies in the less developed countries is the lack of a network of health and social services to implement policy at the village level. The development of such an institutional infrastructure is desirable for its own sake as well as for the implementation of family planning policies. It commands wide spread endorsement and should be the object of intensified efforts by governments and private institutions as well as by United Nations agencies.

4. The Implementation of Family Planning Programs

This is the only area in which major disagreements exist and may continue to exist for the foreseeable future. Countries seeking help in the implementation of family planning programs should have access to the wide variety of sources of assistance available throughout the world.

While the United States will not advocate any specific family planning policy to any other country, we can help other countries, upon request, to find potential sources of information and assistance on ways and means of dealing with population problems. The provision of materials for this purpose can best be done by those governments whose citizens are not divided on this question, by private foundations, and by business firms.

The implementation of this blueprint in the years ahead will require flexibility and imagination. The further challenge is to devise programs of action founded on the principle of free choice which make sense in political as well as in technical and economic terms.

RICHARD NEWTON GARDNER, Ll.B., Ph.D., Deputy Assistant Secretary of State for International Organization Affairs, was admitted to the New York Bar in 1952. He was Teaching Fellow in International Legal Studies at Harvard Law School 1953–54, Associate Professor of Law at Columbia 1957–60 and Professor 1960–61. He was Visiting Professor at the University of Istanbul in 1958. Dr. GARDNER has held his present position in the State Department since 1961. He is author of Sterling-Dollar Diplomacy (1956), and New Directions in U.S. Foreign Economic Policy (1959).

Birth Control: Swedish Help to Underdeveloped Nations

by

D. S. GREENBERG

Sweden plans to make birth control assistance a major part of its rapidly expanding foreign aid program. The program has grown from $10 million to $25 million over the past year, and the Swedes are committed ultimately to channel 1% of their gross national product – about $17 billion at present – into various types of foreign aid.

Officials of the recently formed Swedish Agency for International Assistance are not overly optimistic about what can be done to decelerate population growth in the underdeveloped nations, but they realize that Sweden is the only aid-giving country that dares touch the subject. The Swedes, in determining where their relatively limited resources could be most effective in the underdeveloped countries have decided to emphasize birth control. It will by no means be the Swedes' only or principal contribution to foreign aid; their excellent work in vocational training, among other things, is also being made available to these countries, but the prospects are that Sweden, alone of all governments, will be willing to devote relatively substantial sums to promote birth control in any country that wants its help.

It is already conducting small programs, totaling $350,000 a year, in Ceylon and Pakistan and, on the basis of the results achieved there, has been asked for similar assistance by the Tunisian Government. A number of other governments have also made detailed inquiries, leading Swedish aid officials to predict that within 3 or 4 years family planning assistance will comprise the largest single item in Sweden's country-to-country foreign aid effort. Two-thirds of Swedish aid funds are channeled through the U.N. technical assistance program, but plans call for an across-the-board expansion of all activities.

The Swedish interest in promoting birth control, or family planning, is not accompanied by any comforting illusions about the enormous problems involved in decelerating population growth among illiterate,

Reprinted from Science, Vol. 137, pp. 1038–1039, Sept. 28, 1962, by kind permission.

impoverished people. But the Swedes consider it close to futile to attempt to promote economic development without an accompanying effort to reduce births. And from their experiences in Ceylon and Pakistan they are cautiously hopeful that Western family planning techniques can be taught to the underdeveloped nations.

"There is no assurance that we will succeed," CARL WAHREN, secretary of the Swedish aid agency, said in an interview, "but the problem is so urgent that it is utterly irrational to do nothing about it."

THE CEYLON PROJECT

The Ceylon project, which was Sweden's first effort to assist family planning in the underdeveloped countries, was started in 1958 by the quasi-official organization that ran Swedish foreign aid until the Agency for International Assistance was formed last January. The Swedes report that the Ceylonese showed no timidity in requesting assistance. One gets the impression, however, that Swedish planned parenthood groups had something to do with stimulating the Ceylonese request. The Swedish response was tiny by American foreign aid standards. One physician was sent to Ceylon to determine whether it would be possible to develop a program that would rely on existing Ceylonese public health personnel. Two districts, each with a population of about 7000 persons, were selected for the project: one, a village area about 25 miles south of Colombo, with an agricultural population that was about 20% illiterate, had a 1959 recorded birthrate of 31.2 per thousand; the other, a tea-estate area in a mountainous region, inhabited by Indian Tamils, a migratory people who are virtually at the bottom of the Ceylonese social scale, was 75% illiterate and had a recorded birthrate of 39.5 per thousand.

By 1960 the birthrate in the village area had dropped to 27.1, and last year it was down to 23.9 per thousand. The Swedes say that because of the second area's transitory population they have been unable to gather reliable statistics, but the results there appear to have a great deal to do with the tempering of optimism. Swedish aid officials also concede that the apparently favorable results in the village area may be deceptive. They note that many of the inhabitants commute to Colombo, where it is not unlikely they have picked up some birth control information; the village population had a relatively high literacy rate, and, perhaps most significant of all, no figures are reportedly available on the population trends prior to the start of the program.

In the absence of contrary evidence, however, the Swedes are acting on the assumption that the program played a decisive role in pushing the area's population growth sharply downward, and they feel they have picked up some important lessons that may be applicable elsewhere. The

Ceylonese Government was sufficiently satisfied to request extension of the program to still another district.

WAHREN, whose duties include administration of the family planning program, said that one of the principal conclusions drawn from the Ceylon project is that more stress must be placed on using and improving educational techniques and devices such as audiovisual aids. "We found that we first had to get across the fact that it is not an inexorable law of nature for women to bear children every ten or eleven months," he said. "The women in both districts were astonished by this information, and found it rather difficult to accept. But once they grasped this fact, they wanted to know more and we found that they were hungry for information."

"The whole basis of our approach," WAHREN explained "was to make it perfectly clear that our desire was to promote family planning and not merely to suppress births. We have helped infertile couples to have children. We are in this program to help the people have a better life for themselves and their children, any other goal will not succeed."

The Ceylon project, which may well be the pattern for future Swedish family assistance planning, stuck very carefully to the original aim of training local public health personnel. "This is absolutely necessary for us," said PER-ERIK RöNQUIST, who is chief of the aid agency's planning and budget division. "Sweden does not have manpower to export, our principal asset is technical know how and it we are to succeed, we must find ways to use our limited manpower to transmit that know how to local personnel as quickly and as efficiently as possible." Under the guidance of the lone Swedish physician assigned to the project, Ceylonese personnel quickly became integrally involved in the program. The initial approach in the inhabitants of the district was usually made in a fairly casual manner, often during a pre- or postnatal checkup at a public health clinic. This first contact was followed up by a visit to the home, RöNQUIST and WAHREN explained, where additional information was offered but in doses no larger than the couple seemed willing to accept. Finally, contraceptive devices, principally condoms provided by the Swedish Government, were made available without charge.

"The project has cost only $50,000 a year and has employed only one physician. We feel there are a lot of questions that remain to be answered, but we are encouraged," WAHREN said.

While the Ceylon project has been entirely under Swedish direction, the Swedish work in Pakistan has been integrated into that country's large scale family planning program. With an initial annual budget of $300,000, the Swedes have sent three medical teams to Pakistan, each consisting of a physician and a nurse. They also have provided a mobile clinic and have brought three Pakistanis to Sweden for training in the production of educational films and other visual aids. "The educational aspects are critical,"

WAHREN explained, "since we keep running into such superstitions as that contraception will make you impotent or will produce sickly children."

WIDE POLITICAL SUPPORT

While the American foreign aid program annually produces a major battle between Congress and the Administration, Sweden's expanded foreign aid program appears to have the nation's blessing. Swedish aid officials point out that there has been some opposition to the plan to commit 1% of the gross national product to foreign aid but it has come from those who feel the contribution should be greater.

DANIEL S. GREENBERG was graduated from Columbia College in 1953, served as a naval officer for two years, was a reporter for the Washington Post, then spent a year in Congress as a Congressional Fellow of the American Political Science Association. He has been a staff writer for Science for the past two years.

The Initiation of Contraceptive Services

by

Clarence J. Gamble

After the discovery of each new means of promoting health there is a long slow process of public education required before its benefits are generally available. JENNER's discovery of vaccination with cowpox made deaths from smallpox unnecessary, yet thousands continued to die of it. Needless deaths from diphtheria occurred long after the antitoxin was known, and they still happen. So, too, it has been with the health benefits of contraception.

For the spread of new health measures the fundamental requirement is public education. The discoverer and his early followers must tell the world of what is available, and for the greatest effectiveness this should be done as rapidly and extensively as possible. With birth control this was not easy. It was so inextricably connected with sex that the repression of public discussion in this field closed many customary educational channels. MARGARET SANGER's public meetings to tell families that babies could be spaced were raided by police, and her publications were denied the use of the mails on the grounds that they were obscene. Nonetheless she continued her educational program for decades and is still continuing it.

In addition she provided birth control services for the families of the poor. Her Brownsville, N. Y. clinic was closed by the police in 1916, but in 1923 she, with the help of Dr. HANNAH STONE, opened the permanent clinic in New York now known as the Margaret Sanger Research Bureau.

In 1929, the National Committee on Maternal Health under Dr. ROBERT L. DICKINSON, which had been carrying on laboratory researches in the field of contraception, decided to test methods of making pregnancy spacing available in other cities. Miss LOUISE BRYANT, a social worker, was engaged, and Cincinnati, Ohio, was chosen as the first city in which she should work. Because of its newness and the sexual taboo progress was slow. She found, however, that leading citizens were interested in providing this health service for their fellow citizens. With her encouragement they formed the Maternal Health Committee of Cincinnati, and helped leading physicians to open a clinic in the Cincinnati City Hospital.

To assist those in other cities to do likewise, a medical social worker was added to the Committee's staff. Following the pattern of Mrs. SANGER in New York and of others in Chicago, Cincinnati, Cleveland and Philadelphia, she found health-minded leaders to form committees and open contraceptive clinics under the supervision of physicians in cities in Michigan, Ohio, Indiana, Iowa, Missouri, Kansas and Nebraska. The larger cities were chosen, with the hope that they would subsequently encourage similar activity in their smaller neighbors.

The Third International Conference on Planned Parenthood at Bombay in 1952 brought out the fact that while the United States, the United Kingdom, and India had national Planned Parenthood or Family Planning Associations to spread contraceptive services, local centers of clinical instruction were few in other countries. The National Committee on Maternal Health, therefore, using the experience gained in cities in the United States, undertook to accelerate the formation of such groups by local leaders. In 1958 this work of the Committee and the staff which had been engaged in it were taken over by the Pathfinder Fund.

Beginning in 1952 the author and his son, RICHARD GAMBLE, made two trips to Asia; Mrs. MARGARET ROOTS, a social worker from Canada, worked in Asia; Miss EDITH GATES, health educator, travelled in the Near East, Africa, and South America; Mrs. EDNA McKINNON, former field worker in planned parenthood organizations in the United States, assisted in the Malay States, Indonesia, and Nepal; and Miss RUTH MARTIN, a registered nurse, visited Africa and South America. Help has been given with the formation of Associations and clinical services in 43 cities in Africa, Asia, Europe, the Near East and South America. In 19 countries the staff has helped in the formation of national organizations, 9 of which have become (by 1963) members of the International Planned Parenthood Federation.

From the experience in these countries the following conclusions have been drawn.

1. The best progress in providing contraceptive services is made if a group of local leaders can be found with the interest and energy to form an association for the purpose. Even when such services are provided through governmental or other channels, an association has value in continuing education regarding the value and availability of family planning.

2. Though it was helpful to have preliminary contacts and correspondence, when available, these were found not to be necessary. Talks were readily arranged with leading physicians and nurses, and through them community leaders could be discovered and interested in helping their fellow citizens.

3. A field worker in travelling continually learns what methods of organization and of clinical services are proving to be most successful in the

various countries visited. She* can, therefore, offer newly forming associations a wide choice of procedures, enabling them to choose those most suitable to the habits and conditions of their country.

Local leaders, visiting cities in which elaborate clinical equipment and procedures have been developed have sometimes been given the feeling that only these can be effective, and are discouraged and the progress of their groups retarded by the fact that these cannot be duplicated at home.

4. Educational procedures, lectures, discussions, newspaper articles and radio talks, should be planned and local persons guided and encouraged in arranging them. The worker's arrival can be used as a basis for a news item which can often carry the theme that family planning does not require the sacrifice of married life. If clinical services are available they can be mentioned with the street address and the hours when they are open.

5. Printed leaflets telling of the advantages of pregnancy spacing and giving clinic address and hours can be printed in local languages by the local group with the worker's guidance, and using suggestions from samples of leaflets found successful elsewhere. Posters adapted to the customs of the country are also valuable.

6. The greatest element in arousing and continuing local interest was found to be the desire of those working with the association to provide health and happiness for their own neighbors. The form in which this is done varies greatly. In some places, in the early stages, it may be reference to the office of an experienced physician. In others it may be the provision by the Association of services in a government clinic, or the persuasion of government physicians to give the needed instructions. Or it may be by visits to houses by social workers, health workers, or volunteers to give supplies and instructions as directed by the Association's supervising physicians. Each family served becomes an educational center through neighborly discussion. Each is an addition to the force of public opinion, with its bearing on future governmental or familial decisions.

7. Because of the newness of family planning, and the fact that its sexual roots still make it a controversial subject in some communities, the raising of money in the early stages of a family planning committee is extremely difficult. For this reason the provision of the costs of initial activity for lecture halls, printing, room-rent, supplies, and part time or full time workers, has been found in many places to give valuable returns. It may in some places require several years for a newly formed Association to secure adequate local financial support.

8. While much help can be secured from a citizen of the country where

---

* There are situations in which, and persons with whom men are needed to present the values of contraception; for others, women are appropriate. In most cases, however, the personality, interest and ability of the representative are more important than the sex. In the experience of the Committee and the Pathfinder Fund the field representatives, most of them women, have shown these qualities to a high degree.

the work is being done, the field worker does not need to be a native of the country where the establishment of new family planning services is being attempted. In the early stages of the introduction of such services no local person will have had the necessary experience, and much time and expense would be required to train one. To expand the work from the largest city to others it is valuable to discover and train a suitable local person, but local customs often make this difficult. In some multi-racial countries such a person may be able to work only with those of her own race.

9. The most successful family planning associations have been those in which all sections of the community have been included. In some countries in Asia different races or languages have met in this way, and in many African countries the Africans, Asians, and Europeans have worked together. Clinics open to all races were encouraged wherever they were acceptable to local custom.

10. While it might seem that a person from an adjacent country would know local customs better than one from the other side of the globe, this often is not the case. Local jealousies between countries, some of them war-engendered, often make a person from a neighbor-country unacceptable. The very fact that the worker comes from a distance may assure her a better hearing. Fortunately English is so widely understood, especially in medical circles, that the Pathfinder Fund representatives have met with little language difficulty in talking with community leaders.

11. A physician has advantages in some aspects of the work. It is difficult, however, to find a satisfactory physician who is free to travel continuously. With a worker who is not a doctor local physicians do not have the feeling that someone is coming to teach them what they believe they already know. She can quote physicians in other countries and show reprints of their articles. Pathfinder's non-physician workers have been asked to address Medical Associations in many countries, and their talks have been well received. (Talks have also been given in a mosque and a cathedral.)

12. Associations are apt to become less active with the lapse of time after a worker's visit. Members of the Committee may move away, or go on long-leave, or lose their initial interest. It has been found that a visit at least once a year has been welcomed by the Associations and has proven effective in encouraging them to further steps and to expansion into nearby communities.

13. Periodic reminders of the Associations' objectives have been found helpful in maintaining the interest of those already adherents of the movement and in expanding interest among others. Subscriptions to the Family Planning News and to Round the World News of Population and Birth Control have been used for this purpose. Lists have been prepared, usually of 30 or more in each community, of Association members, leading physicians, city officials and other community leaders to whom these bulletins have been sent. The frequent reminder that the new public

health measure is being used in many countries is valuable, and the educational techniques described are often found helpful by the local group. The total value of the mailing to the unconvinced is, perhaps, greater than that to those already Association members.

Some active Associations ask for copies of each issue in bulk to mail from their office, a procedure which makes easier the keeping up-to-date of the mailing list.

14. The argument that family planning is needed to protect a nation from the dangers of constantly growing population was found to appeal to the more intelligent and educated citizens, but except in India and Japan did not seem to be understood by most people. Far more effective than the population explosion was the argument based on the health and economic condition of the family, that children born at spaced and chosen intervals could be given healthier surroundings and a better upbringing.

15. While interest in and provision of contraceptive instruction will eventually spread to all countries, experience showed that the process was greatly accelerated by the ability of the field workers to tell community leaders what other nations had done, and to explain the methods by which the new health service had been provided.

16. The numerous centers for the expansion of family planning services which have followed visits of the field representatives of the National Committee on Maternal Health and the Pathfinder Fund have made the program seem an effective procedure. While the numbers of families instructed have not yet been large they have been increasing.

Moreover the Family Planning Associations are reaching beyond their own cities and aiding in the establishment of new associations and new services. The program is helping to bring nearer the day when the ability to space their children will be available to every family.

CLARENCE JAMES GAMBLE, M.A., M.D., has been a Research Associate at Harvard since 1952. Dr. GAMBLE was Chairman of the Committee on Contraceptives of the Council on Pharmacy and Chemistry of the American Medical Association. Since 1957 he has been President of the Pathfinder Fund, the primary interest of which is the expansion of contraceptive services in many countries. Dr. GAMBLE is the author and coauthor of numerous technical articles on the laboratory and clinical evaluation of contraceptives.

The Role of the International Planned Parenthood Federation

by

GEORGE W. CADBURY

In fifty years we have moved out of the era when control of birth was a dark secret and its discussion could lead to jail. Now we are in a world where, with the exception of a small minority, we can discuss birth control and the planning of our families freely and sensibly as we discuss the dangers of sickness and the fear of death. The minority, of course, have their rights. They need not join in such discussions or take advantage of this phase of modern health technique if they do not want to do so. But they are an even smaller minority than is generally realized, much smaller than the Roman Catholic Church that is the only organized opposition in the world today, since the laity in this matter largely disagree with and ignore the teaching of their priests. They are so small in fact that their attempts to impose their views on the rest of the world are not only improper, but also impertinent. We respect their rights, they must respect ours. The great majority of the peoples of the world are behind us.

In the winter of 1960–1961 my wife and I spent four months in Asia, the continent where half the people of the world live, and we met practically no opposition to family planning. Our only real enemy was ignorance, and lack of information and supplies. In Korea, for instance, the latest books on the subject were published before World War I. In Indonesia, the sixth largest country in the world, hardly anyone had heard of family planning at all.

What we have to discuss then, is how and where we can do something to overcome this ignorance and get the knowledge and the supplies to a world that is desperately waiting. One means of doing so is to use the International Planned Parenthood Federation – the I.P.P.F. – to which I now belong. I came to it after nearly ten years as a Director in the Technical Assistance Administration of the United Nations, because it was so obvious to me that this was the neglected factor in our economic and social planning. I selected the I.P.P.F. because it was a vigorous organization that believed in action, and had the basis of a world wide system to enable the well-to-do countries to help the poorer ones. For the same reason the World Population Emergency Campaign has selected the I.P.P.F. as the best mechanism through which to distribute the help it can raise in North America to the world. The Simon Population Trust and the Oliver Bird Fund in the United Kingdom, the Brush Foundation of Cleveland, Ohio, and many others have done likewise.

The I.P.P.F. started at a conference in Stockholm in Sweden in 1946 as a Committee composed of representatives of societies in the U.S.A., the U.K., Holland and Sweden; it has grown in 1961 to be an international of 32 members. In 1961 to date, Malaya, Korea, Burma and Trinidad have become new members and there are several more on the way. Headquarters are in London, but strong regional organizations are encouraged and there are now four centers – London for Europe and Africa, New York for North and South America, Colombo for the Indian Ocean, and Singapore for South East Asia. Soon there will be others, probably in Tokyo for the Western Pacific and Cairo for the Near East. What then are these Regions to do?

Their first responsibility is to foster national activity and in doing so to recognize that each country and each culture will have their own particular approach. Nowhere in the world has interest, let alone action, in family planning originated in a government. It has always needed a devoted band of pioneers to introduce the idea, to brave uninformed opposition, and to establish the first services. Timidity is too often the most prominent quality of politicians and civil servants, and the courage of volunteers has had to show them that they had no need to fear. The demand is latently present in every country from the ordinary people, but is often obscured by short-sighted military thinking or the inertia of authority. Once the possibility of regulating births becomes known, then the demand comes in overwhelming force. The typical response will come from a group of doctors, who have seen how much family planning techniques can achieve, and at first the service offered will probably be a clinic where doctors will be available to give advice. It is not long, though, before the impossibility of meeting the demand on the basis of individual interviews by doctors becomes apparent, and while the clinics become more popular, at the same time midwives and social workers are enlisted, and soon afterward the supplies and advices are being carried from door to door. In Japan, with a population of 90 million, they have leap-frogged the clinic stage, and the forty thousand Government midwives have been their front line troops from the beginning. In this case there was of course the special and urgent necessity of substituting contraception for abortion. In Puerto Rico, with a population of 2,500,000 there are 1,400 volunteers drawn from every walk of life who have made family planning a normal and acceptable matter for discussion in every village, and who hand out supplies from 1,400 local points of distribution. It is a short step from these widespread attempts to reach the millions who want service, to the use of the regular health service of the country. Full integration of family planning advice with the government health services is the ideal. Antenatal and postnatal clinics and services should give family planning advice as a matter of course. For most people in rapidly developing countries the Government doctor is their usual doctor, and he is in the key position to advise on family planning, as on everything else.

When this stage is reached the role of the voluntary society now changes. It remains the pioneer body in the country; always in touch with new developments through its international contacts, and assuming more and more the role of watchdog on government activity or lack of it. The voluntary society will also have a continuous educational role to fulfill and when governments or officials change it will be able to be on the qui vive to see to it that the emphasis on voluntary population control in government policy is not decreased.

Another major interest of the Regions will be to ensure adequate supplies of contraceptives, and of the right quality. There are many ways of doing this. The most obvious is to encourage commercial firms to come into each country to distribute, or even to manufacture, though this is not always as simple as it ought to be, and much help can be given by those who know the local situation well. There are tariffs and import regulations to be examined and sometimes to be amended or overcome. Contraceptives are sometimes described as medical supplies and at other times as 'rubber goods' and the rates of tariffs and control vary accordingly. In Indonesia contraceptives are not available because of an old pre-independence Dutch law that it is convenient to the uninformed opposition in high places to maintain. In Korea the new Government is favourable, but no one has yet had time to undertake the comparatively minor matter of rewriting the customs regulation. Then there are national policies designed to exclude luxuries which also exclude contraceptives, or plans for national industrialization which prohibit imports in order to force local manufacture. Some of these policies have to be accepted, but they in turn lead to new problems and opportunities, as for instance when local manufacture may be inadequate in quality. Technical assistance to ensure a sound supply of contraceptives is clearly an international opportunity. There are four countries in Asia right now who want such assistance with their manufacturing programme, Korea, Taiwan, Indonesia and Ceylon, and the I.P.P.F. plans to hire an expert who will travel from one to the other at an estimated annual cost of $20,000.

Perhaps the major contribution of a Regional Office will be the fact of its existence as a point of reference and as the repository of a fund of knowledge and experience. It is ignorance that we are fighting, and a well-organized service of information with trained officers available to visit and to demonstrate proven methods will enable enthusiastic doctors and lay workers to speed up the establishment of effective services in their own country. The I.P.P.F. would like to see seven or eight such Regional Centres established immediately, but funds are not yet available, and first priority will have to be given to three or four. Plans are well advanced in South East Asia, centered on Singapore. $30,000 a year would put a Director in the field and finance headquarters for more than a dozen countries. Another group in the Western Pacific, centered on Japan, can quickly be organized for $20,000 a year. The Muslim countries that stretch from Morocco to Pakistan are one of the most eager new groups for assistance and there is a project to establish a Regional Director and an office in Cairo or Karachi for another $30,000. Finally, and facing the most explosive population group in the world, there is a proposal to tackle the Spanish speaking half of this Western Hemisphere at a similar estimated cost to those for South East Asia and the Middle East. Africa, as one will notice, is not yet included in the priorities, and for a number of reasons, the chief of which is the lack so far of local demand, since Africans in their new found nationalism and with their many high death rates, have not yet recognized the dangers of population pressure. There is however a steady minor effort flowing from Europe to Africa and a more extensive organization cannot be long delayed.

Having established Regional Centres for advice and direction the next step is to create training facilities and the first proposal under this head has been made for the Singapore Region where $10,000 to $12,000 would give us a school capable of training 10 or 12 midwives or public health workers at a time in a series of short courses throughout the year. This would be largely done with the practical assistance of the local Family Planning Association and is of course additional to the seminars and courses proposed for the medical profession.

If we can get these Regional Centres into operation then each of them in turn should be able to stimulate the national organizations in dozens of countries in their areas. We can also help these countries directly. At first it will be by way of contraceptive supplies, training for doctors, midwives and public health workers, and then later with equipment, like vehicles and laboratory items, that takes scarce foreign exchange. Nor must help with educational materials be forgotten. A good pamphlet in one language needs translation and printing before it is of use in another. The Philippines want Tagalog, the Africans want over 50 languages, the Latin Americans 2. The Egyptians want Arabic, and the Indonesians Malay. We have much good material in English, but except for the educated classes it is often unreadable. In addition to printed material there have been extremely successful exhibitions but the material has to be duplicated and rearranged before it can even be used in the country next door. For $15,000 the 1960 Singapore Exhibition which drew 100,000 enthusiastic visitors in a week, could be duplicated in a permanent form and shown in all Malay, Chinese and Tamil speaking countries of South East Asia. Our monthly

Bulletin is one of our most important activities, but it only reaches a fraction of those who would read it if it were translated into many languages. It costs us $10,000 to $15,000 a year to publish it in its present form. Double that amount would far more than double its circulation and usefulness.

Finally, I should mention the co-ordination of world-wide biological research and medical information in our Research and Medical Committees. The former is headed by Dr. PARKES, F.R.S., the first holder of the newly founded Chair of the Physiology of Human Reproduction at Cambridge University, and both Committees are composed of the leading international authorities in their field. The search for simpler and better methods of contraception is making great progress. Nor must we neglect the extremely important work that is being done in places like the Margaret Sanger Bureau in New York on sub-fertility, because we are as anxious to help those who cannot have children as to provide the ways and means of limiting family size. What we need now is the recognition of family planning as a normal part of the maternal and child health services of the world, and that recognition can best be given by its acceptance in the World Health Organization. Here the minority still stand in our way. Next year the majority must make their weight felt. In Asia, for instance, the seal of W.H.O. approval is important because W.H.O. is the standard bearer for good health practices, and the exclusion of family planning makes it seem that it is not a normal part of a regular health service.

May I conclude by saying how profoundly moved are all those, who have been working for nearly fifty years in the cause of Planned Parenthood, at the extent of the support they are getting today. Pioneers like MARGARET SANGER must find the aura of respectability particularly hard to bear. Fighters once are fighters always. Then we who have followed the pioneers and have the relatively easy task of consolidating their achievements, are very grateful when new initiatives, such as the World Population Emergency Campaign, emerge, to re-invigorate us and help us to keep our eyes on the main targets. As the Special Representative of the President and Governing Body of the I.P.P.F. I know that all the help they can give us will be welcomed.

GEORGE WOODALL CADBURY, M.A., is Vice Chairman and Special Representative of the Governing Body of the International Planned Parenthood Federation. Mr. CADBURY was Director of the Technical Assistance Administration, the United Nations, from 1951 to 1954. He was United Nations Advisor to the Governments of Ceylon, Burma, Indonesia, Jamaica and Barbados between 1954 and 1960. Between 1929 and 1941 Managing Director of British Canners, Ltd. and Alfred Bird and Sons, Ltd.; 1941 to 1945 Deputy Director of Material Production, Ministry of Aircraft Production (London) and British Air Commission (Washington); 1945 to 1951 Chairman Economic Advisory and Planning Board, Province of Saskatchewan, Canada.

FINAL REPORT ON "THE POPULATION DILEMMA" *

Never before in history have the security and welfare of mankind been so indivisible. Never before has man acquired the capability of achieving his own extinction. These circumstances require him to marshall his intelligence, control his emotions, and rise above his traditional thought and action in an unprecedented way. Failure to do so may threaten not only his prosperity, security and peace, but also his survival.

Among the serious threats to welfare and security, and therefore to peace, is the accelerating rate of world population growth. The less tangible but very real injury to personal development and the maintenance of family life must also be of concern. Rapid population increase and its accompaniments are obstructing economic development, and thereby contributing to frustration, social unrest and political instability in many areas of the globe.

Rapid population growth contributes to difficult and complex problems in the United States.

The Twenty-third American Assembly believes that:

A. Present and prospective world rates of population growth cannot be maintained indefinitely. Such growth contributes substantially to the perpetuation of low levels of living for two-thirds of mankind, and creates difficult problems of adjustment in the economically advanced nations.

B. World birth rates must be reduced in view of the reductions in death rates already achieved.

C. Reduction of family size would produce important gains for many families as well as for entire nations. Unrestricted fertility tends to damage

* At the close of their discussions the participants in the Twenty-third American Assembly of Arden House, Harriman, New York, May 2–5, 1963, on The Population Dilemma, reviewed as a group the following statement. Although there was general agreement on the final report, it is not the practice of The American Assembly for participants to affix their signatures, and it should not be assumed that every participant necessarily subscribes to every recommendation included in the statement.

the health of the mother, impairs family life and restricts opportunity for adequately rearing and educating children.

The time has come for vigorous and coordinated action to alert mankind to the need for a reduced rate of population growth and to develop multilateral and bilateral programs to assist nations which desire to reduce their fertility.

I. WORLD PROBLEMS

A high birth rate obstructs the economic development of low income countries in a number of ways. It diverts resources and hampers economic growth in the less developed economies and makes it necessary to provide for a larger population rather than for a higher level of living. It contributes to imbalance in rural-urban and regional population distribution. It generates an age structure with large numbers of young dependents in relation to workers. It impairs efforts to improve the quality of a population by restricting per capita expenditures for improving health, raising educational levels, and teaching new occupational skills. It reduces natural resources per capita.

Reducing the birth rate and thereby lowering the rate of population increase is of course not the complete solution to the improvement of economic conditions in the less developed areas. It is a major element but other factors – social and economic – are also involved. These include capital investment, technology, diversification of the economy, distribution of income, occupational skills, entrepreneurship, and attitudes and institutions favorable to innovation and social reform. The expansion of international trade and investment would also contribute to economic advance. More effective utilization of natural resources is required; in the short run world resources are sufficient to permit rising levels of living.

International migration can help many persons and temporarily ease some population pressures. It cannot, however, solve the world's major population problems.

Recommendations

The United Nations and the Specialized Agencies should:

1. Expand activities in the field of population.

They have significantly improved population data and research. They should now undertake more comprehensive and intensive population research, particularly on the interrelationships of population, economics and social change, and develop more effective programs for the dissemination of its findings.

2. Expand and strengthen the population staff and the regional population training and research centers.

This would enable the agencies better to assist nations to comprehend their own problems and formulate appropriate solutions.

3. Provide direct aid to countries wishing assistance in family planning programs.

The World Health Organization and other international agencies should recognize the consequences of their great achievements in reducing death rates; they should assist nations in dealing with the resultant population growth.

4. Encourage and support, especially through the WHO, biological and medical research in human reproduction.

5. Strive to contribute to the growing world consciousness of the implications of population growth through appropriate revisions of and additions to youth and adult educational materials prepared for world distribution by UNESCO.

II. THE POSITION OF THE UNITED STATES ON WORLD POPULATION PROBLEMS

The "Statement of United States Policy" to the 17th General Assembly of the United Nations represents an important step forward. It offers the assistance of the United States to nations, upon request, "to find potential sources of information and assistance on ways and means of dealing with population problems."

This policy should explicitly recognize that:

(1) Population growth in all countries affects the destinies of the world's people. It is an international problem of concern to all. (2) Parents everywhere should be free to decide how many children they should have. (3) Sustained progress in economic well-being requires the reduction of population increase.

Recommendations

In view of the relation of population to economic and social development, and the need for bilateral as well as multilateral programs of technical assistance, it is recommended that:

1. Since the ultimate objective of foreign aid is to improve living conditions, the United States give consideration to the way in which developmental plans are affected by population trends.

2. The United States extend assistance to developing nations, at their request, for the investigation of population problems and in support of programs to promote the voluntary regulation of fertility.

3. Administrative means be established by the federal government for disseminating knowledge about population problems and methods of regulating family size.

Such action is needed to implement the statement by President KENNEDY of April 24, 1963, that the government could support increased research in fertility and human reproduction, and make the results more available to the world so that everyone could make his own judgment.

III. DOMESTIC POPULATION POLICY

There must be a greater concern by our national, state and local governments with our own population problems.

The postwar resurgence in population growth coupled with the growth of metropolitan areas has created complex problems not only at the state and local levels but also on a regional and national basis.

Rapid population growth has undoubtedly contributed to additional effective demand and thus to increased economic growth. Although there are no insuperable economic difficulties in the short run, we see increasing dangers in the continuation of the present rate of growth that would double the population every forty years with the prospect of constricted social opportunities and progressive crowding.

Accelerated population growth has already intensified problems of urban congestion, education and transportation, and contributed to pollution of air and water and crowding of outdoor recreational facilities. It has required federal, state and local governments to provide new and expanded public facilities and services with consequent increased taxation. Furthermore, the wave in young workers now entering the labor force constitutes a serious challenge to our economy which is already confronted by readjustment to the advent of automation. These challenges will require special attention.

Recommendations

The American Assembly therefore recommends:

1. Intensified investigation of our population trends and problems—including their long-range as well as their short-term implications.

2. Accelerated research through the United States Public Health Service and private agencies, on the biological and medical aspects of human reproduction so that a variety of improved methods of fertility control are developed.

3. Assumption of responsibility by the federal, state and local governments for making available information concerning the regulation of fertility and providing services to needy mothers compatible with the religious and ethical beliefs of the individual recipient.

Freedom of decision regarding family size is a basic human right which in practice is now effectively withheld from a portion of the American people. This discrimination would be eliminated by making fully available to all adults through public and private agencies information and service regarding the various methods of family planning which accord with the ethical and religious convictions of those involved.

4. The cultivation with the assistance of schools, religious organizations and other cultural media, of a sense of responsibility concerning marriage and parenthood, including the responsibility of bringing into the world only those children whom parents are prepared adequately to care for and educate.

5. Recognition that the United States is an economic and social unit, to the end that all of our citizens, no matter what their area of origin or race, are adequately prepared for full participation in the life of any part of the nation.

Since the end of the war, millions of persons have moved to urban parts of the United States. Many are ill-prepared for life in the areas to which they moved. In consequence, problems of accommodation are severe for the migrants and for the communities to which they come.

6. Our immigration policy should be in accord with the following principles:

a. selection among applicants without discrimination by race or country or origin

b. total immigration should not exceed the present level except in emergencies

c. exclusion of persons who do not meet established personal standards such as those relating to literacy and health save under extraordinary circumstances

d. consideration of (1) special skills, abilities and employment opportunities, and (2) kinship to persons already present in this country

7. The acceleration of economic growth and increased employment opportunities in view of the current levels of unemployment and the impending increase in the labor force.

8. More research on the resources of the United States and other parts of the world with attention to the lessening of waste and protection of the claims of oncoming generations. (In this connection attention is called to the recent report of the National Academy of Sciences-National Research Council on *Natural Resources.*)

9. Appointment by The President of the United States of a Commission to inform, after investigation, the government and the American people of the nature of population problems at home and abroad with respect to: implications for all aspects of American life, and relevance to our efforts, in cooperation with international agencies, to promote economic and social progress throughout the world.

* *
*

The vast majority of the people of the world, including a large proportion of the people of the United States, do not yet recognize the full implications of present population trends. The Twenty-third American Assembly cannot emphasize too strongly that time is running out for the formulation and implementation of world and national population policy.

To continue to ignore world and United States population problems is to ignore the welfare and security of all peoples. We must not remain complacent in the face of a major threat to world peace and survival.

PART II. THE USE OF WORLD RESOURCES

Introductory Note to P. Auger's Proposal

by

HUGO BOYKO

This second volume of the World Academy of Art and Science' publications * deals with the two foremost problems confronting our generation: The first, the accelerated population growth, which is closely linked with the second, the exhaustible natural resources of our planet.

Each of the authors in this volume is searching for an answer to the urgent question of how to achieve a sound balance in the situation caused by these two weighty problems, before one of them should aggravate the other to a point endangering the well-being of mankind.

While the articles dealing with the population problem culminate in a program for planned parenthood, those concerned with out natural resources culminate in AUGER's proposal of a world research institute to investigate this huge problem from a transnational and global point of view.

The author, who is one of the Charter Members of WAAS, has held a leading position in UNESCO for many years and is one of the best authorities in this field.

The Plenary Meeting of the World Academy held in Stockholm in 1963 discussed the ways in which this plan might be implemented at the earliest possible date. It is to be hoped that the necessary financial means will be found and that WAAS, in close cooperation with UNESCO and the other specialized Agencies of UNO, will soon be working together with an organized, worldwide team of scientists and scientific institutions in the direction outlined in this proposal. The policy statement adopted at the Stockholm meeting is printed in the Appendix to this volume, p. 539.

---

* Volume I appeared in the latter part of 1961 under the title "Science and the Future of Mankind" and dealt with the general application of science to the problems facing mankind today.

Plan of an Institute of Studies for the Better Utilization of the Globe

by

PIERRE AUGER

GENERAL IDEA

The most rational utilization of the natural resources of the world, be they renewable or otherwise, has been the object of many treaties and international conferences. This goal constitutes a permanent program in certain international organizations such as the FAO, as well as among the national institutions of various States. The World Academy of Art and Science, a transnational organisation, has also selected the global problem of natural resources as one of the principal and permanent fields of its activities.

In view of world-wide development, the need for such planning becomes more and more pressing, particularly on two principal points. First of all, the constant rise in the level of living standards among the various populations of the world leads to a permanent increase in the demands for materials, water and energy. Secondly, the continuous expansion of the global population arouses concern for the distant and even for the near future of humanity, which must accordingly lead to the taking of great precautions in the utilization of resources that can be exhausted, or at least significantly altered, by uncontrolled exploitation in a way which could result in an irreversible situation.

However, while certain conferences on a grand scale, such as for instance, the one held by the United Nations in 1956, have attempted to establish a complete panorama of the most important questions, and while certain books like 'Our Plundered Planet' have presented such global studies, no permanent organized body exists with a program for planning on a scientific basis with regard to the development, the use, the economy and the rational maintaining of the natural resources, be they mineral or biological, of our globe. Such an organization would, of necessity, require the collaboration of the nations in the principal regions of the globe, as every exception would involve a serious risk of making the conclusions inacceptable or inoperable.

MODE OF FUNCTIONING

No one of the existing institutions, however significant it may be, could seriously take upon itself the execution of all parts of such a program. It could, therefore, only be expected of an institute with a mixed structure, possessing its own laboratories, with local branches and also with study missions at various locations. On the other hand, the institute would have to coordinate a large number of works executed by associated institutions, either national or international. This coordination should include the establishment of concerted plans for research and their application to pilot plants, as well as the proffering of assistance in various forms – financially, materially, and through personnel – for the execution of particular parts of this general plan.

One of the most essential functions, and possibly also the first to be executed and implemented, would consist of the organization of conferences, symposia and colloquia, operating in various directions, and diverse in scope, in program and as to the number of participants. True, as we have already mentioned, such activities currently exist, but they are dispersed among non-governmental institutions like, for instance, the Union for the Conservation of Natural Resources, or inter-governmental organizations with a very varied composition and statute. The result is that these efforts have only a reduced efficacy. Their recommendations and votes have little, if any, effect, as there is no possibility of following up their applications and reporting on the results, with the exception of very limited instances where the conferences take place within a framework of inter-governmental organizations with a very definite action program. In these cases, there is a risk of losing the perspective of the whole, which could lead to incoherence.

The functioning of the projected institute is therefore connected with the constitution of a network of correspondents, whose problems are known so that they can be taken into consideration in the program of cooperation. This association could, of course, only be voluntary, and the authority of the projected institute would function according to the procedures decided upon by the different governments, as well as the national and international establishments. The institute could serve as a guide in their scientific efforts and work towards solving the problems with which its members are faced, after which the syntheses could be published for the information of a large public.

STATUTES

It would be difficult not to give such an organization inter-governmental status – that is, it should be founded by a regular diplomatic convention.

It is of prime importance that the member-states be numerous and include the nations scientifically most developed as well as those which still need important assistance in specific scientific fields. The entire structure must remain, however, independent of any political, economic or linguistic grouping.

A central budget would be necessary to support the functioning of laboratories owned by the organization and the various forms of assistance cited above. In certain cases, the organization would have to act through temporary mission envoys, whose duty it would be to elucidate local problems. But the main task would always remain the preparation of a synthesis of these special efforts to help establish a general policy for the best utilization of world resources, for the benefit of mankind.

PROGRAM

In the first years of its functioning, the organization should devote itself principally to such works of synthesis as are based on results already achieved, after a careful critique of their value. However, for obvious reasons, it will be necessary to approach the scientific study of certain urgent problems as soon as possible, such as for instance, the possible inadequacy of fresh water resources – a problem which has already presented itself in various regions of the globe. Another question, the natural importance of which is apt to grow in the decades, is the problem of the ecological balance and its disruption by human intervention, i.e. the use of insecticides or toxic substances for certain plants, or, either the introduction or suppression of certain species originally absent or present in a specific region. Although research work of this type is being done at various places in the world, no clear doctrine has emerged as yet, such as a synthesis accompanied by an appropriate evaluation of the conditions in the near future.

PERSONNEL

Apart from the personnel of investigators and administrators belonging to each of the associated institutions of the organization, scientists or groups of scientists should also be called upon to deal with certain problems in their own sphere. As the essence of the organization should be of inter-disciplinary character, this would mean involving representatives of the most varied disciplines, such as mathematicists, physicists, chemists, biologists or geologists, who would collaborate closely in working towards solutions of problems and in order to present a common and comprehensive plan. It does not seem likely that a very large permanent personnel would be necessary, at least in a scientific capacity. However, with regard to administration and to the application of certain techniques, such as for instance, the mathematical robot, the existance of a permanent staff is indispensable.

One of the most efficient working methods will, without doubt, be the grouping of a number of highly advanced specialists around a well-defined problem for a period of several months or years. This method, which is akin to the "taskforce" system, is only applicable if these groups find the best available conditions of work, particularly the means of computation, a quick way of documentation, and appropriate equipment.

CONTACTS WITH MEMBER STATES

The organization would be placed at the service of humanity, but could only act through the governments of its member states, as the application of the institute's plans, as well as the realization of its projects depends on them and their acceptance of the institute's definition of the problems. Therefore, their mutual relation will be of crucial importance. Let us repeat, there can be no question of constituting a supra-national authority, because the implementation of the proposed solutions must remain voluntary. However, since in many cases, it will be a matter of concerted action by various nations, grouped regionally or according to other criteria, the concrete application of the organization's completed plans would necessitate a convention or a treaty between the interested countries, thereby imparting to the accepted plans a very definite diplomatic value.

However, even if the countries would not commit themselves to carry out the proposal of the organization, the member states should, in any case, authorize their scientists to cooperate in the drafting of these proposals and then agree to cooperate by examining, from a positive point of view, the possibility of conforming to the conclusions.

CONTACT WITH INTERNATIONAL ORGANIZATIONS

Here, also, great difficulties could arise either due to attributive conflicts or for reasons of divergent conclusions. However, the prospect of such difficulties decreases if the organization confines its activities to scientific research and the proposals remain of a broad nature, without entering the specific fields of immediate application.

Frequent contacts and preliminary liaisons should, of course, be established as early as possible.

PIERRE VICTOR AUGER, D.es-S., has been Professor on the Faculty of Sciences, University of Paris, since 1937. He was Director of Higher Education, Ministry of Education, Paris, 1945–48, and Director of the Department of Natural Sciences of UNESCO from 1948 to 1959. He has been Chairman of the French Committee for Space Research since 1959, and is presently Executive Secretary of the European Preparatory Commission for Space Research (C.O.P.E.R.S.). He is author of Les Rayons Cosmiques (1941), What are Cosmic Rays (1944) and L'Homme Microscopique (1952).

The Use and Abuse of Land and Water

by

C. S. Christian

Most biological species are subject to enforced population adjustments as food supplies and competition for them vary from place to place and time to time, but man is no longer prepared to accept this passive role. Ultimately some self-imposed control of his population increase will be essential, but the Freedom from Hunger Campaign is concerned with the practical means of feeding the human populations that already exist and those that will inevitably exist in the coming decades.

This World Food Congress is being held in the knowledge that at this very moment a large proportion of the world's population has an inadequate food supply and that the present rate of increase of the world population will surely aggravate this deficiency in many areas. This situation cannot be tolerated in the light of the emerging conscience of the modern world. Direct and positive steps are required to reduce this hunger that now exists and to limit the greater hunger that could face the next generations.

This Congress demonstrates man's confidence in his growing powers to influence his own environment and his own destiny and, furthermore, it demonstrates the increasing willingness of the peoples of the world to assist one another in circumstances of consequence to all the human race.

Man is dependent for his food supply almost entirely on the products of land and water and the plant and animal species of the earth. It is in the practical exploitation, development, conservation and improvement of these natural resources that man must seek the answer to hunger and rural poverty. Although many of the facets of modern civilization – in particular the complexities of finance, trade, and economics, transport and international relationships, will influence the time and speed with which different communities can achieve their aims, it is in the actual field practice

Paper read during the World Food Congress of the Food and Agriculture Organization of the United Nations, Washington, D.C., 4–18 June 1963.

of producing food from land and water by plants and animals that the ultimate solution lies. We must seek more efficient and more complete use of these resources and the elimination of practices that reduce their productivity or cause wastage.

Historical events have led to a concentration of communities of people in certain defined areas where they are now committed to support themselves irrespective of the world distribution of natural resources. The size and location of these historically determined areas bear no logical relationship to the present population density, or needs. Any readjustment of these national boundaries on a grand scale is unlikely; so each community is faced with the necessity to use the resources it now possesses to its best advantage.

It would be unrealistic to believe that all people on this earth will be equally well nourished but we must go as far towards this objective as is humanly possible, and must be less than satisfied with anything less than the impossible.

Each country presents a unique problem, with its own degree of population pressure and needs, its own kind and magnitude and deficiencies of natural resources, its own stage of economic and social development. The world problem of hunger, and the use of land and water to alleviate it, is not one problem. It is a multitude of problems as numerous as the number of countries and the distinctive regions that comprise them.

The industrially well-developed countries can afford a high standard of land and water use through high inputs such as irrigation developments, fertilizers and machinery, and, because of advanced education systems, by a high degree of practical application of advanced technical knowledge. For example, the amount of fertilizer used on arable land in Europe is twelve times that used in Asia and Africa and, in 1960, the number of tractors in Europe and North America was four times that of the rest of the world. Favourable price arrangements for agricultural products are made possible in industrial countries by the high average income. The trend in such countries is to use land even more efficiently and to raise yield per unit area still higher. As income derived from industrial exports permits importations from food surplus producing areas, industrial countries, even those with dense populations, are not likely to face any critical food problem in the near future even though the reserves of land awaiting new development may be small.

Where industrially developed countries also possess substantial areas still available for increasing cultivation, there are situations conducive to the production of further surpluses of agricultural products for export. To what extent these actual and potential surpluses can help solve the world food problem, or to what extent they may inhibit the development of less developed countries through market interactions and so actually aggravate the problem, are major items requiring study. What major breakthrough can be made in this field in the light of all the political ramifications within and between countries remains to be seen.

Another group of countries includes those which are less developed industrially and have only moderate to low density populations, such as some countries in South America, Oceania and Africa. In the main, these have substantial areas available for further expansion of production and considerable scope for increasing yield per unit area. The application of known scientific methods could alleviate food deficiencies in most of these countries and provide surplus food for export. However, in this category there is a wide range of national earnings from the export of primary products, such as minerals, surplus food and industrial crop products, and also very different levels of production, standards of living, and technical application. Sociological, economic and technical problems involved in achieving expanded production will vary accordingly. Those countries which are economically poor and have low educational standards will find it particularly difficult to gain momentum without very substantial technical and material aid from outside. The rate of development of an expanded and more efficient agriculture in many of these countries will be acutely affected by world prices of food and industrial crop products and by their rate of accumulation of economic strength through industrialization.

In a separate category are the countries which also have limited industrial development but already have dense and rapidly increasing rural and urban populations with a low income per head, and limited areas for new cultivation. It is in this group of countries, which include many Asian countries, that the food problem is most acute and where it is likely to develop most seriously and be most difficult to overtake. Low input and less widely practised technical knowledge at present suppress the general level of food production per unit area. Human diets need to be supplemented in both calories and animal proteins. Vast importations would be necessary to offset total deficiencies and the finance and transport which would be required for this would seem to make this an impracticable solution. In these countries, the productivity of much of the land has declined as the result of long cultivation. The need to use land for the production of rural products for export because of the low level of other export earnings and the growing demand on land for industry, and for housing rapidly increasing new generations, imposes further limitations on food production potentials. In these countries, there is the threefold problem of arresting the processes of land deterioration, of raising yields per unit area, and of bringing the remaining land, often poor land, into production. To provide the necessary capital, fertilizers, machinery and other inputs necessary to achieve these aims, a parallel economic development on a broad front is essential.

My point, before discussing land itself in more detail, is to emphasize first that, no matter what we know about advanced methods of land and water use, many economic and social factors have, and will continue to have, the major controlling influence on what can be applied. A knowledge of the advanced technologies is essential, but economic resources, as well as intellectual strength, are also essential if this knowledge is to be put to work.

LAND

Land is commonly spoken of as though it were a single variable, with good land at one end of the scale and poor land at the other. In reality, land is a complex of many interacting factors, all of which affect its production potential. It can be described as the combination of all features at and near the land surface which influence the welfare of mankind. Land must be considered as the whole vertical profile at a site on the land surface from the aerial environment down to the underlying geological horizons, and including the plant and animal populations, and past and present human activity associated with it. There are many features in this total profile, some easily observable like the soil and the vegetation, some measurable such as the rainfall and surface slope, but many not so readily observed or measured, such as the internal drainage and aeration features of the soil, the rate of chemical weathering and chemical migration in the soil, the level of microbiological activity, the variations in the microclimates, and the precise impact of former land use by man. The many features of this total profile vary from site to site and their many combinations and interactions result in a vast array of land types, each with its own potential and limitations for agriculture or forestry, each presenting its own specific barriers to the achievement of maximum plant or animal production. Rarely does one feature alone determine productivity. It is the combination of all that is important, and if we are to understand land we must think of it in terms of this complex rather than only of the individual components of it.

Primitive man was just another species adjusting himself to the world in which he lived, competing with other species for what it provided and making the best use of it. Man's intelligence gave him certain advantages and he had the initiative to choose other species of value to him and to reproduce them in greater quantities and in locations where he most needed them. In doing so, he pushed many of them far beyond their natural habitats and, in order to favour their growth he learns to modify the natural environment and also to select certain varieties of the species better adapted to new conditions and better able to serve his particular purpose. Thus arose the practices of forest cutting and of cultivation of land to remove competition, of planting crops, of conserving water and irrigating land where water supply was inadequate, of clearing trees and shrubs to allow grass to grow, of domesticating animals and of improving plant production by adding manures and residues to the soil.

There emerged the many traditional practices of land use characteristic of different regions. Many of these were admirably suited to the conditions of the past when populations were so much smaller. Nomadic grazing made good use of pasture by following seasonal growth in different areas, shifting agriculture allowed encroaching weed species to be eliminated by regenerating forests and permitted land to slowly re-establish its fertility before it was cultivated again, irrigation and the addition of manure to soil increased yields and made crop growth possible in areas where crops would otherwise have failed.

Some of these practices are still essential parts of the socio-economic patterns of certain communities but, as populations have increased their pressure, the long continuation of some practices has disturbed many of the equilibria which were established in the land profile under more or less stable natural conditions. Man did not understand these complex changes, and, because their effects were slow to develop, they were not easily recognized. Time has shown that the inherent productivity of land may decline although the practices may have given temporary increased returns. Today the world is faced with large areas of land where the natural process of wind and water erosion has been accelerated and surface soil has been lost; where continued cultivation and the removal of nutrients in crop and animal products, particularly under monoculture, has led to a substantial reduction in soil fertility and deterioration of soil structure; where excessive or unwise irrigation, without adequate drainage, or irrigation of unsuitable types of land, has led to rising water tables, water-logging and salting, to the point where crop production is no longer possible; where forests have been over-exploited and valuable species eliminated, and where the removal of forests has changed the hydrological regime of an area, affecting stream flow and underground water; where over-grazing or bad grassland management has caused the loss of better pasture species with their replacement by bare ground or by inedible or less nutritious competitors.

In the last few centuries, and particularly in the last few decades, science has learnt a great deal about land and the causes of land deterioration. It is now possible to correct many of the faults of past practices and to design land use projects so that these need not recur. Unfortunately, this in-formation is far from being universally applied and land is still deteriorating over vast areas. The challenge to rehabilitate despoiled lands and to prevent their extension is still as great a challenge as is the development of new lands, and the gains to be achieved in many countries where increased food production is most needed may be even greater than that to be obtained from new lands. Before disturbing traditional practices, however, planners should be sure that what they have to offer is, in fact, better and that communities are economically and sociologically capable of making the replacement.

Science has also learnt a great deal about the individual factors and processes affecting plant and animal growth. Our knowledge is far from complete, but, by applying the approaches that are known and by experiment, many types of land which have low natural productivity can now be modified and their productivity raised far beyond the hopes of a century ago.

There are five groups of principles related to increasing crop yields. They are:

1. To correct deficiencies of the factors which directly influence the nutrition of the plant and to provide an optimum balance between them. The two main practical measures involved are (a) to provide irrigation or drainage in order to produce better water relationships, and (b) to apply, as fertilizers, the deficient plant nutrients, and to raise the total level of nutrients, in balance, to a point that the plant can make full use of the water available to it.

2. To control competing weed species and pests and diseases.

3. To develop varieties of crop species which are adapted to the climatic regime of the areas and which can make optimum use of both water and nutrient supplies.

4. To adopt land cultural practices which maintain land in a suitable physical condition, and land management practices which encourage an accumulation rather than a depletion of soil fertility – for example, by crop rotation, or mixed crop and animal husbandry or mixed grass-legume pastures.

5. To adopt modifications of mechanical procedures which permit more productive and economic operations, including such things as speed of cultivation in areas with a short growing season, precision of planting, better irrigation, fertilizer and pesticide application, efficiency and proper timing of harvesting, and better processing, storage and transport of the harvested product.

The kind of practices that are most beneficial will vary with the type of land and its history. With full application of the principles that have been established in the sciences of land, plant and animal production and forestry, the opportunities for increasing productivity are already available. The word "principles" is used deliberately because, although there usually are established practices available to accompany these principles, they relate mostly to the areas where the principles have been studied. There is a danger in transferring practices too freely from one area to another; broad principles can be expected to apply, but their application and limitations in new areas must be determined locally by field trial and investigation. This applies to the economic and social aspects of land use just as much as it does to the technical aspects. A good deal of very well-intentioned technical aid has been made less effective than it could have been because the complications of local conditions of climate, soil, and society were not recognized. To have technical information is necessary; to know where and when it applies is what makes it useful.

One overall principle must be stressed, with equal application to crop, pasture, animal, and forestry production. It is that maximum production is attainable only when all factors are satisfied. Irrigation without fertilization, or vice versa, or either without using a suitable crop variety, will not give maximum yields, nor is it likely to give the most economic returns. Often the combined effect of satisfying two or more factors is far greater than the sum of the separate effects, and economically very much sounder. The four ways in which increased crop yields are most universally obtained are the application of fertilizer, the use of irrigation or soil moisture conserving practices, the use of improved adapted plant varieties, and the control of pests and diseases. Even to adapt one of these principles to a new location requires a certain amount of experimentation and technical skill. To combine a number, possibly including other practices from the five groups of principles previously enunciated, requires a well organized experimental approach, and, in difficult circumstances, good research work. If developing nations are to raise the level of food production over wide areas and varying land types, it is important that they should build up their resources of technical personnel, and research and investigation facilities as rapidly as possible. Even with the most favourable rate of expansion, there would be an appreciable time lag before real effects on production were felt.

The World Land Picture

On the average there are about 5 hectares, or 12.5 acres of land surface fo-each member of the world's human population at the present time.

Broadly speaking, 35–40% of the land surface is said to be virtually unavailable for agricultural use, because it is arid or cold, salty, or too mountainous, or because it has already been occupied by cities or roads, or is covered by inland waters. Of the remaining useful area, about 20 thousand million acres, one-sixth is cultivated for crop production, one-third is described as meadow land or pasture of value for grazing domestic animals, and one-half is covered by forests and woodlands. The figures represent world proportions and they vary considerably from region to region. For example, in the three land regions with the densest population – Europe, Asia and Mainland China – the proportion of cultivated land exceeds 30%, but in all other major regions it is much lower and ranges from as low as 0.5% to only 17%.

The importance of irrigation is indicated by the fact that the densely populated countries – Mainland China, Taiwan and Japan – have approximately half of their total arable areas irrigated. The comparable figure for Asia is about 30%, and for the whole world about 15%.

In general, cultivated land produces more calories of human food per unit area than grazing or forest land, and irrigated land more than rainfed land. Both produce a wider variety of produce of value to industry.

To meet the food and other agricultural requirements of increasing populations in the relatively near future, there will certainly be pressure to increase the areas of land which are cultivated and irrigated, and particularly those which are used for cereals, in order to produce the basic calorie requirements of human diets. To provide better-balanced diets, however, increased emphasis must be placed on other food products, especially those richer in proteins, such as the pulses, milk, meat and egg products.

As the regions which are now most deficient in food, and the ones where future populations are likely to be the greatest, are mostly areas where rice is the main staple food, particular attention needs to be given to the increased production of this cereal, or to its replacement by some other acceptable food. For this reason, the activities of the International Rice Commission of F.A.O., and the International Rice Institute recently established in collaboration by the Government of the Philippines and the Ford and Rockefeller Foundations, have a particularly significant role to play in world food production developments.

The world's areas of cultivable land are gradually being encroached upon by urbanization and industrialization and in many areas this has already reached the point where deliberate control of the future use of land by planning authorities is essential to safeguard valuable arable lands.

F.A.O. statistics indicate that, for each unit of land currently cultivated, jhere are about $2\frac{1}{2}$ additional units suitable for cultivation. It is not clear tust what categories of land are involved and a proportion certainly exists in difficult environments. However, the future expansions of cultivated areas must be largely at the expense of pasture and forest land, although there is also some scope in the reclamation of flooded and degraded areas and in the development of delta lands. At the present time, forest and pasture lands are not everywhere well used and some encroachment by cultivation will be permissible; but these assets are valuable in themselves and cannot be lightly destroyed.

For instance, where low protein diets occur, it would seem desirable that future food production programmes should include an increase rather than decrease in animal production and, where socially acceptable, meat production as well as milk products. The low efficiency with which animals convert plants into human food is an argument against feeding to animals food that could be used directly for human consumption, but grass eating animals have the advantage of being able to forage for their own food from crop residues and areas which are not used for cultivation. Although mechanization and modern agricultural science may eventually push the boundary of cultivated areas far beyond present limits, there will still remain areas of grasslands and woodlands, which would be unproductive unless used for animal production. Moreover, cattle and buffalo are important for draught purposes, especially in cultivated land areas, and are likely to be part of the agricultural scene for a long time to come. Through the return of dung, animals contribute to the maintenance of soil fertility and, in many areas, mixed animal, pasture and crop production has been found to be the most economical way to maintain productivity. Where dung is used for fuel, much of this soil fertility building is lost and it would be desirable, where feasible, to provide wood or other fuels or sources of heat to replace it.

Another aspect of animal production, of significance to soil fertility, is the trend to transport animal foodstuffs, rather than the animal product itself, and to produce the animal products nearer their urban markets. This is influenced by the part that plant products play in industrial processes and the usefulness of the by-products for animal production. Involved in this is the transfer of soil nutrients from one part of a country, or the world, to another and the need to ensure their replacement before exhaustion reduces the level of productivity.

The inevitable reduction of pasture areas by the extension of cultivation emphasizes the need to achieve higher levels of efficiency in the use and management of the remaining grazing lands which, apart from food, also produce the animal fibres so important for man's clothing and protection. Our knowledge of pasture improvement and utilization is less advanced in the tropical regions but the lag in application of knowledge is widespread in most regions. Grazing lands are often treated carelessly, as though they were inexhaustible, or expendable.

Forests are equally important for the welfare of man and wood products must continue to play an ever increasing part for building and construction purposes and for fuel, and as a source of new products and export incomes. Of comparable importance is the place that wood pulp must play. For instance, in the period 1956–58, the average consumption of pulp per head for newsprint in the Pacific area was over 25 times greater than that for Asia, and there were nearly as large disparities in other uses of pulp products. As educational and industrialization programmes proceed, this gap must gradually be narrowed. The demands for forest products are likely to increase at rates even greater than populations. The welfare of the developing nations requires that their potentialities for forest products and plantations should be developed and safeguarded. As with pastures, this will involve the intensification of improvement and management practices. At present, less than 20% of the world's accessible forests are subjected to any form of planned management and a very small proportion to advanced management practices.

It has been necessary to refer several times to the need for adequate fertilizer to obtain optimum crop production on both irrigated and unirrigated land. Australian and New Zealand experience shows that this can apply equally well to pasture lands.

Fertilizer is one of the costly inputs that low income rural producers without credit or finance facilities cannot afford. Yet it has been estimated that the use of moderate amounts of fertilizers on existing cultivations in the food deficient regions could increase food production by at least 50%, and, combined with other practices, by 100%. In 1959/60, the world consumed 27 million tons of commercial fertilizer. F.A.O. has estimated that, if half the food increase required by the end of the century is to be obtained as a result of fertilizer applications, the world consumption will need to rise to at least 100 million tons. Much of this increase will be required in the low income, densely populated regions. Unless this fertiliser is produced, and its purchase by farmers in these food deficient countries made possible, there is little hope of those countries achieving their production targets. Planners may very well have to judge whether fertilizer factories, or fertilizer finance schemes, should not come before costly irrigation, or new land settlement, schemes.

WATER

So far we have referred to water mainly in its place in the land complex affecting plant production, but water has many roles to play, in domestic and urban uses, industry, power production, for livestock and irrigation, recreation, and as a source of food. Some of these roles are competitive and, where water is limited in quantity, decisions must be made about how it can be best used.

Were it possible to desalinate water at an acceptable cost, the oceans and seas could supply man's water needs for all times, but, in spite of progress in this field, it seems that present costs still restrict the available methods to special circumstances. Most predictions concerning the more extensive use of desalinated water for agriculture involve assumptions about technological improvements in the future which have yet to be substantiated. The scope for industrial or urban use is probably much greater, but it is likely, for a long time to come, that the source of fresh water for agriculture and food production will be the rain that falls on the land surfaces. We should be careful not to be carried away too readily by the visionaries who talk of irrigating inland deserts far removed from coastal areas, with desalinated sea water. The costs and difficulties of transporting water to such distant areas are likely to be equally as important as the problems of desalination itself.

The practical value of the great salt ocean and seas, apart from their place in the general recirculation of water vapour to the atmosphere, is mainly for transport, recreation, and in the food resources they provide.

The food harvested from the world's oceans and fresh-water sources constitutes only about 1.5% by value of the world's annual food production, although it is really more valuable than this because it is a source of animal protein. Certainly the potential resource is much greater and many countries have made rapid increases in their harvests in recent years. Some people consider the salt and fresh-water oceans and seas have a potential for fish and plant production even exceeding that of the land itself, and even as a source of fertilizer for crop production. This is a fascinating subject but too speculative to pursue here. Practical conclusions must await much more research. It is encouraging, however, to note the development of international co-operation in studying the oceans of the world, for marine resources can be over-exploited in specific areas just as easily as plant and animal populations on land. A knowledge of marine environments and the ecology of species is essential for sound harvesting controls as much as for harvest expansion.

The ultimate source of the world's fresh water required for agriculture, livestock, domestic, urban and industrial activities is rain. The average annual precipitation over all land surfaces is equivalent to about 26 inches of rainfall. Although this would be sufficient for a high standard of agriculture everywhere on suitable soils were it evenly distributed, there are in fact many deficient areas, and so the prospect of reliably increasing precipitation by artificial stimulation of raindrop formation is enticing. Unfortunately this is still a subject for argument and must be left as something for future assessment rather than as a practicability of the moment.

The world's fresh-water resources appear in three forms –

1. Fresh-water streams and lakes, replenished by run-off from the land surface.

2. Underground waters, not all of which are fresh, replenished by percolation from the land profile and from streams.

3. That part of rainfall which does not reach the first two, but which evaporates from the land surface or is transpired by plants.

The first two are transportable, in the sense that the water can be manipulated by engineering procedures such as pumping, damming, diversion, and distributed for use elsewhere. The last resource must be used where it falls.

The proportion of water in these two categories, transportable and non-transportable, varies considerably from place to place. In Australia, with an annual rainfall averaging about 18 inches, run-off has been estimated to average only 10% and water entering underground reservoirs considerably less. In this dry continent, only 15% to 20% of the water received as rain can be stored, or pumped, and redistributed.

In contrast, in the U.S.A., the average annual rainfall is nearly 30 inches. Run-off alone amounts to about 30% of this. In a continent of about the same size, about ten times more water is directly controllable by engineering procedures.

In smaller regions of high rainfall with land surface features conducive to high run-off, the figure may be of the order of 70% or 80% or more. Over much of the world surface, however, the greater part of the rain received is used or wasted where it falls and a relatively small proportion is available as transportable water.

It is this transportable water, however, that looms largest in the public eye. This is because it is controllable water, and there is growing competition for it from industry, domestic users, and farmers. Some of these uses are alternatives, some are conflicting, but there is also scope for complementary and multiple uses. Water used for power is usually available for re-use in other ways. In industrially advanced countries like France and the U.S.A., industry demands between 40% and 50% of the water at present consumed and domestic and urban users only 10%. In many rural countries a high proportion of the water conserved is used for irrigation.

The surface stream systems and the underground aquifers within individual river basins are usually closely interconnected and their uses need to be considered in conjunction. Any major interference in one part of the system can have a serious impact on the hydrological or land use features in other parts. Misuse of catchment lands and forests, excessive irrigation of upstream lands, the restriction of stream flow and of flooding by storage or diversion, the over-exploitation of underground water in some areas, and the pollution of water by industry will all have impacts on land and water use, and on the rights of land and water users elsewhere in the basin. For these reasons, and because of the needs to plan the various competitive and multiple uses of water in relation to developing national needs, there is now general acceptance of the importance of planning the use of land, water and industrial resources of a river basin together. It is not always practicable to do this with the degree of precision that is desirable, because the essential hydrological, engineering and other data required are varied and extensive, and it is difficult to predict the extent of industrial and population growth and changes, and hence the nature of water demand many years ahead. Furthermore, developing nations do not always have the capital resources to proceed with the development of the water resources of a whole river basin at one time, nor will they always have the time to wait for a comprehensive plan to be completed. In order to have a more immediate effect on agricultural production and to keep within their capital resources, it may be necessary for countries to proceed with smaller schemes controlling only part of a drainage basin or even small local storages to serve a few or even single farms, especially in semi-arid areas.

Flexibility in planning must be maintained because new technologies and new needs emerging at each stage of development will introduce essential changes. Wise planning will more often follow a step by step approach, with an attempt to view each new water use project as part of the best overall plan that can be produced at the time. It should, however, include the continued accumulation of data to permit more precise planning at each stage.

As many river systems traverse several countries, the necessity for international negotiations and agreements may hold up major developments for a long time. Delays are caused by the difficulty of allocating benefits equitably in the future, and because the basic data for assessment and design are usually inadequate. That agreement can be achieved has already been demonstrated by the Indus River Agreement between India and Pakistan, the Rio Colorado Agreement between U.S.A. and Mexico, and by others.

The planning of water use in a whole river basin is a complex piece of work calling for the combined efforts of people in many technical fields. It is important that it should not be dominated by any special profession, whether this be engineering, forestry, agriculture, industry, economics, law, legislation, or administration.

In the context of this Conference, we are more directly interested in the use of transportable water resources for food production in the food deficient areas of the world.

The world's irrigation areas cover more than 300 million acres and it will probably be necessary to double this at least by the end of the century. There are not good data on the land and water resources available for increasing irrigation, but it would seem that this objective could certainly be achieved if required. In the past, many schemes have been less productive than they might have been because insufficient attention was given to the kind of land to be irrigated, the hydrological problems that could emerge, or the type of agriculture to be practised.

The greatest abuses of valuable irrigation water are its use in excessive quantities leading to wastage and waterlogging, or in inadequate quantities giving less than optimum production and often leading to land salting, its use on unsuitable land, and its use by farmers who, though well practised in other forms of land use, do not have sufficient knowledge or resources to make full and efficient use of their new environment.

In new projects, there should be equally thorough pre-planning investigation of land as of the engineering features, and drainage should be regarded as an essential part of the irrigation plan. To ensure that farmers can make efficient use of irrigation water, there should be a farm demonstration or extension programme to teach new landholders irrigation farm practices, a credit or finance scheme to enable them to purchase fertilizers, agricultural chemicals and equipment, a plant breeding and seed production programme to ensure that plant varieties suitable to the high production conditions produced by irrigation are available, and an organized marketing scheme to dispose of the product. Many irrigation areas still suffer from deficiencies in these requirements, and it has already been stressed that the rehabilitation of misused land may frequently give more immediate and greater economic returns than the development of new areas.

Irrigation in arid regions produces dramatic results, but it has been found that supplementary irrigation in moderate rainfall conditions may make better use of water. Apart from selecting the type of land, careful consideration must also be given to the conditions under which irrigation water is used.

The development of further irrigation schemes will make important contributions to food production, but we should not lose sight of the fact that the greater proportion of the existing world's agriculture is practised with rainfall alone as the source of water, that is, water which must be used where and when it falls.

The amount of rainfall necessary for a satisfactory level of agricultural production varies widely between different environments and forms of production but over large areas where irrigation is not possible rainfall is insufficient for maximum growth, and water is the factor that sets the ultimate limit to production. It is important that this water be used well.

Taking an average annual rainfall of 20 inches (or 500 mm) as a rough basis for comparing regions, we find that about 15% of South America and Europe receive less than this, but in Africa and North America the proportion is about 50%, in Australia 60%, and Asia 70%. Irrigation water can be supplied to only a very small fraction of these areas.

Water deficient areas face three kinds of problems. The first is to impound, for controlled use, as much as possible of the intermittent, and, in lower rainfall areas, relatively small quantities of run-off. This will often mean many small storages and good designs are essential to avoid wastage. The second is to ensure that the crop varieties and methods used on cultivated land lead to the efficient use of water. Agricultural research programmes in semi-arid and arid areas should include more specific reference to the efficiency of water use by plants as a measure of their success. The third is to modify and manage the extensive plant communities on the extensive uncultivated areas, so that as much as possible of the rain which falls is channelled back to the atmosphere through plants useful to man or his animals, rather than through useless plants or by wasteful evaporation from inert surfaces. This can be achieved in part by pasture and forest improvement and management. Unfortunately, as rainfall decreases, the economic return per unit area also decreases, and with it the level of expenditure which is justifiable per unit area of land. In areas of very low rainfall, the emphasis swings from the development of a vegetation resource to the safe utilization of the natural resource in a way which is compatible with its conservation. Unfortunately, the vegetation of many of the drier regions of the world has been over-exploited to the extent that the level of production from the small amounts of rainfall received is now much lower than from the original vegetation communities, and in many arid areas, uncontrolled exploitation is still aggravating the problem.

Conclusions and Proposals

A review of land and water resources of the world leads to the conclusion that the total physical resources are ample to supply the food and other agricultural needs of the growing world population for the remainder of this century at least, and probably much longer. The challenge is to use these resources effectively in face of their unequal distribution in relation to population density and economic wealth. The available scientific knowledge is capable of meeting this challenge, but economic and political factors may continue to retard the full use of world resources and the free flow of products from one part of the world to another. The regions which are now most deficient in food are the ones where future populations are likely to be the greatest, and it would be unrealistic not to urge that each food deficient country should endeavour to solve its own food problems as far as possible from its own resources.

The application of science to increase production is not only the application of knowledge. It usually costs money and involves the use of greater quantities of material resources than those used for present levels of production. If standards of land and water use are to be raised quickly enough to match the increase in food requirements by the application of modern agricultural technology, it will be necessary somehow to concentrate greater economic resources than those which have ever been available in the countries largely dependent upon a rural economy.

Each country has its own variety of land and water resources, suited to different forms of land use, its own range of plant and animal habitats with their specific problems. Each country is in a different stage of development and presents different economic, scientific, and sociological barriers to the increase in food production. Each has its own sociological, economic and cultural hopes and ambitions and these will, and should, influence the pathways by which it approaches national development.

A developing country will face the need to make decisions on the various possibilities for land and water development, and to make choices between the development of new areas, rehabilitation of old areas, and the establishment of supporting industries and services for agriculture and forestry.

We come to the question: how can the food deficient countries best be assisted in making these decisions and developing their own programmes of land and water use?

We believe that the general principles of good land and water use are sufficiently well established to provide the appropriate scientific approach to most new situations but that the actual technological practices, based on these general principles must be selected and adapted to each new situation by trial, experiment, or research. We have recognized dangers that lie in assuming that scientific and technological practices can be transferred directly from one region to another and therefore see the need for each country to augment its scientific and technical resources so that it can make these adaptations.

Of the wide scope for direct technical assistance that this presents to helping nations, I believe that the form of aid with the likelihood of most permanent and continuing effects lies in helping countries to know themselves, to understand their own resources, problems, and possibilities, so that they themselves know what scientific, technical, and economic developments they need most urgently. If this can be achieved, developing countries will be in a position to establish their own order of priority of action, and to draw upon the mass of world scientific information and aid, selectively, according to the approaches that are most appropriate to meet their own particular array of problems.

International agencies and individual countries have already made considerable efforts in this general field, and countries have established various organizations for this purpose. In spite of this, it is doubtful if many countries, even advanced countries, have a sufficiently penetrating, comprehensive and co-ordinated understanding of their resources and what is involved in improving and developing them, to permit adequate overall resource planning; and in overall planning we must include socio-economic changes such as agrarian reforms, as well as project planning, and the advancement of science and education programmes.

Unfortunately, the departmentalization of government structures, and of sciences too, is not always conducive to the presentation of a balanced or complete picture. Often the difference in status or competence between departments or their officers leads to too much emphasis on one area, or on one field of science, at the expense of other possibilities which may be more worthy.

A knowledge of one type of resource indicates where its potentialities lie but it does not indicate whether that resource should be developed in one area in preference to others, or whether several resources or services might not best be developed conjointly.

Most countries could benefit from a more balanced and more co-ordinated approach to the assessment of their natural resources, even where development has already proceeded a long way. But food hungry nations cannot wait for long term, detailed programmes to be put into effect and completed.

Any attempt to survey all the characteristics of the resources of a country would be a colossal and time-consuming task and would produce a mass of detail which would be impossible to collate and interpret. What is required is a quicker, selective and progressive approach examining all resources objectively, sufficient at each stage for decision making, followed by more selective and intensive effort where and when it is most useful.

An approach which would appear to be ideal for adaptation to this purpose is what is referred to as the integrated approach to land survey and assessment, the term "land" being used in its comprehensive sense. Over the last fifteen years in Australia we have had considerable experience of this method in very extensive areas of underdeveloped and partially developed country ranging from arid to wet, tropical climates. We have learnt a good deal about its possibilities. These land resource surveys have been described elsewhere, and I will content myself with a few generalizations on how they could operate.

The surveys combine the use of aerial photographs with selected field studies. A relatively small group of scientists, each a specialist in a different field of resource study, works as a team in the field and laboratory, to understand, classify, and map areas of land, and to assess their broad development possibilities and problems. The approach is based on the concept of Land Systems (natural landscape patterns) and Land Units (the several distinctive land types which comprise and characterize these patterns), and aims at identifying those areas that can be considered together from the point of view of further research, or development, and those areas which must receive separate and different attention. The concepts can be applied at different scales and a preliminary reconnaissance survey can be made to select the more promising areas in which more intensive studies can be concentrated. The particular aspects of these areas deserving immediate examination are indicated and also the type of technical personnel and facilities needed to develop the work. Decisions on appropriate action can be made at each successive stage, leading to the progressive concentration of appropriate activity in each selected area, according to what the previous stage has shown to be most urgent. Science and technology of the right kind are brought to bear on the most urgent problems of each area as they are defined by survey, field trial, observation, experimentation, or pilot project. On the other hand, if circumstances require that immediate development of a certain kind proceeds, the broad framework of information provided by this approach will permit the development to be put into perspective and compared with other possibilities.

To assist countries to establish resource assessment programmes, or to further develop those already in progress, help will be required in training the necessary personnel, and here I would like to make a suggestion. It seems to me that there is a place for an international centre to train individuals, but more particularly to train teams of people, in the concepts, methods and techniques and operation of surveys, assessments, and preliminary use-planning of land and water resources and related services. In the first instance, such a training centre might concentrate on primary survey and field assessment techniques for the newly emerging countries, but I visualize that the institute would itself evolve and would introduce more comprehensive training in the application of socio-economic and other special studies related to general resource use. It could hardly fail to develop as a centre for information and objective advice to which countries could refer for help on the continually emerging technical problems related to resource planning, and it could become a channel through which the interchange of personnel might be arranged. As teams were trained, it would be helpful if arrangements could be made for the provision of material aid to enable them to operate in their own countries.

If such a scheme were adopted by F.A.O., or perhaps some of the great Foundations, it would assist countries to establish a sound basis for resource development, for unless outside economic aid is of a prodigious nature, the natural resources of a country must set the pattern for economic development and, in turn, define the paths along which science and technology should grow within the country in order to serve its essential practical requirements.

The Training Centre could help fill a gap so often referred to by representatives of developing countries in terms of "wanting advice to know what they need". It could be complementary to, rather than conflict with, other international organizations concerned with the broader aspects of economic planning, or those providing economic or technical aid to approved projects, for it would help countries to be better prepared before making submissions to these other organizations. Development projects could be expected to emerge as obvious and logical consequences of thorough resource assessment.

The Centre would provide postgraduate and specialized training, and would not attempt to duplicate the formal training of existing educational institutions. Expansion in these facilities will certainly be needed to provide the increasing number of trained personnel required at various levels. Where such formal training is concerned with field practices of land and water use, which are so much influenced by local environmental and sociological conditions, it is extremely important that this training should be given in the atmosphere of these local environments. Too frequently, students who are trained overseas return to their countries with a need to completely readjust themselves to ecological conditions, and it is not surprising that many take a long time, or even fail, to do this.

To apply known science to the variety of agricultural production conditions in each country, there will be required increasing numbers of technically trained people who may not always be able to produce original ideas but who certainly must be thoroughly familiar with the circumstances to which the scientific principles and practices are to be adapted. It is important that, in the agricultural and animal production fields at least, more and more effort should be directed towards establishing basic training facilities within the developing countries themselves, or at least within regions, but this should in no way interfere with the overseas training of selected personnel for specialist activities which will always remain important.

There will be increasing need, too, for top level supervision or guidance of research and development projects. Until countries can themselves provide adequately trained and experienced senior personnel, they will need to continue to call on advisers from other sources. There are several observations that should be made about advisers. First, the expert advisers should be truly expert. This means that they must be not only capable people in their own fields but also knowledgeable in the application of their field in the particular region where they are advising. They must also be good advisers. These requirements are difficult to meet, but it is a responsibility of international agencies and contributing countries to ensure that their experts meet these qualifications as far as possible. A second generalization concerning expert advisers is that an endeavour should be made, wherever feasible, for them to operate with a trainee from the country they are aiding, so that when they leave there is an experienced individual left behind to continue the work. A measure of an adviser's success might well be how soon he can vacate the task, knowing that the country will be able to carry on without him. A third requirement is that advice should be continuous and consistent. Nothing is more disturbing to a project, and to the people of the country directly concerned, than to have discontinuity of expert advice; but what is even more disturbing is when successive experts on the same project approach it with different concepts. All may be equally good, but when local trainees are not experienced adherence to one method consistently is extremely important. For this reason, the practice of the adoption of individual projects in developing countries, by particular institutions in other countries, is to be commended and encouraged, for this procedure does offer scope for both continuous and consistent assistance.

Finally we might ask, from where will the incentive come for developing nations and their governments to do the most important things? I have often heard advisers who are attempting to give aid to a country comment that they doubt whether the recipient country is as genuinely enthusiastic about the activity as the adviser himself. One would expect that the growing nationalism of new countries and the vital need for production increases would provide this; but their needs, starting with the individual who is hungry or needy, must filter through the nation and finally be crystallized into action. There are many barriers in the way and many opportunities for good or bad decisions. I suggest that many of these barriers arise from uncertainties, from inadequate precise knowledge. I suggest that the greatest incentive to developing nations can arise from a confidence in their own knowledge of their potentialities, and how they themselves can achieve them. If the world gives them the means to know themselves, their resources, and how to use and preserve them, they will accept the challenge to ensure that these resources are developed soundly.

C. S. CHRISTIAN, M.S., University of Minnesota (1932), studied at Rothamsted Research Station in England 1932–33. As a member of the Genetics Section, the Commonwealth Scientific and Industrial Research Organization, he did research in the genetics of wheat and later on pasture plant breeding and pasture ecology. In 1946 he was asked to establish a unit to make scientific surveys of undeveloped areas of Northern Australia with the objective of determining its potential for primary production and development. This work has since been extended to Central Australia and to New Guinea and some developed areas of Southern Australia. On a mission to India in 1959 he planned the Indian Central Arid Zone Research Institute at Jodhpur. He has been the Australian representative on the International Rice Commission and President of the Australian Institute of Agricultural Science.

Natural Resources, Policies and Planning for Developing Countries

by

JOSEPH L. FISHER & ROGER REVELLE

Developing countries need to know a great deal about their natural resources of land, energy, water, and minerals, and about the industries, products, and services closely associated with them. They also need to make headway in translating that knowledge into programs of development. These two closely associated goals are important to developing countries because resource industries are dominant in their economic life, because improvement in the resource sectors usually is a prerequisite of escape from situations in which rapid population increase is accompanied by low productivity and income, and because raw material exports frequently have to be depended on for foreign exchange with which to purchase needed capital equipment. Furthermore, subsequent growth will be conditioned by the pattern of location of population and industry and by the development experiences established during the earlier phases of economic development when natural resource occurrences and characteristics are more influential.

The central purpose of this paper will be to characterize the role of resource policies and plans in the advancement of less developed countries. Resource policies, which are the more general principles and guidelines for development, and resource planning, which translates policies into concrete terms for land, water, energy and minerals, may be thought of as the connecting links between science and technology on the one side and higher economic and cultural attainments on the other. Of course, natural resources do not tell the full story of economic development; a skilled and capable labor force, capital plant and equipment, an enterprising and well trained cadre of industrial managers, and impartial and decisive government administration are also vital. However, in a real sense, the whole economic pyramid rests upon raw materials and environmental

Reprinted from the United Nations Conference on the Application of Science and Technology for the Benefit of the Less Developed Countries, November 1962, by kind permission.

resources and realization of their potentialities through the application of science and technology.

These considerations and others to be examined later have already been found to be of great importance in the developing countries, many of which have been making notable headway in analyzing their resource potentialities and translating them into effective policies and plans. In this paper we shall try to summarize the broad objectives of resource policy, to consider the conditions favorable for rapid and sustained progress in resources development, to indicate some principal elements of resource policy making and planning, and to discuss these elements in terms of specific situations in a selected less developed country. Finally, we shall point out several significant problems or obstacles to resource development that are common to many less developed countries.

CHARACTERISTICS OF RESOURCES
AND BROAD OBJECTIVES FOR THEIR DEVELOPMENT

Natural resources differ from capital and other kinds of resources primarily in their relatively fixed geographic location and extent. Many raw materials can be extracted from the ground or harvested from the land and waters and shipped to distant points for consumption or further processing, but they all begin in a more or less fixed place and exist in finite amounts although neither the precise physical nor the economic extent may be known. There is the further characteristic that most resources are depletable in some sense. Mineral reserves in any particular location are depletable in an absolute sense; that is, they may be used up economically if not physically. The renewable resources of agricultural land, forests, grass lands, and fish populations may be exploited to the point where they can be reestablished only at prohibitively high cost, if at all. Another characteristic is that resources are the first links in the economic chain: resource materials enter technological processes early and then have applied to them varying degrees of fabrication and transportation on their way to becoming final consumer goods and services.

Every country needs to learn what resources it has, what their economic potentialities are, and how to translate mere existence into useable products and services. It must also determine where its comparative advantages lie and how these may change, since it will have insufficient capital, skilled manpower, or other means to develop all its resources in any given time period. This will mean for many countries a continuing concentration on food and fiber production for domestic consumption with less attention to production of mineral or agricultural raw materials for exports. For other countries the reverse will be true.

Each country will want to fit its resource development plans in with broader economic development plans. This frequently will call for investments and other activities to increase per-man and per-acre yields in agriculture along chosen lines, diminish over-all the number of agricultural workers, expand rapidly certain industries which at relatively low levels of capital intensity will make use of easily obtainable raw materials, and expand and diversify the energy base.

Economic activity in most of the less developed countries is heavily concentrated in the resource industries compared to more developed countries. In Brazil, for example, about 60% of the labor force recently has been engaged in agriculture, forestry, fishing, mining, and quarrying; in India about 70%; and in other less developed countries the percentage is even higher. In Italy, Japan, Mexico, and Spain the per cent of the labor force in resource industries has ranged in recent years from 40 to 60, while in the United States it is about 13. National income arising in the resource industries has also made up the larger part of total national income in nearly all the less developed countries, although the percentages are somewhat lower than those cited for the labor force, principally because of the lower level of labor productivity in agriculture than in industry.

Improvements in agriculture and the other basic resource industries in nearly every instance will be necessary, if early stages of economic development, are to be followed by diversified industrial development. All economic policies and plans therefore will be heavily oriented to resources. Resources, plus their transport and basic processing, become the core of development planning to provide food, water, building materials, heat, electric power, and many other items. First attention will usually be given to domestic sources for most of these, although a number of less developed countries have been able to export one or two particular raw materials in which they are especially well endowed as a means of obtaining yet other raw materials from other countries.

With these characteristics in mind the primary objective of resource policy may be stated. It is to promote the achievement of national objectives through development of land, water, energy, and minerals:
– at least cost;
– on a sustaining basis having in mind the conservation of existing supplies, the discovery of new sources, and the development of cheaper or more plentiful substitutes;
– with a high multiplying effect on further economic development;
– with significant contributions to better relations among nations for the advancement of all;
– so as to encourage a wide and equitable sharing of costs;
– so as to minimize or offset the difficulties of adjustment in particular regions and among particular groups.

Particular resource policies and plans may be tested against these objectives. Obviously these objectives overlap one another, are complex and difficult to determine in precise situations, and involve numerous contradictions. Policies and plans must be compromises among them. For example, least cost production in agriculture, if pursued relentlessly, might force large numbers of farmers out of agriculture and out of their particular farming regions before they could be retrained for other economic activities or before programs could be set in motion to aid them in adjusting to living in other communities. The requirements of national defense may also conflict with the least cost principle. Equitable sharing of costs is most difficult to define since it must be relative to individual values and broad social objectives which themselves are changing.

CONDITIONS FOR PROGRESS IN RESOURCES DEVELOPMENT

A number of conditions may be laid down for rapid and sustained progress in resource development. These will vary in relative importance from country to country, but will obtain to a significant degree in virtually all places. They include:

a. Increasing scientific and technical knowledge about resources, especially those on the more immediate horizon of development.

b. An improving ·professional education system for increasing the number of scientists, engineers, economists, industrial managers, administrators, planners, and others; and an improving general educational system in support of citizens' understanding of the part resources can play in economic advance.

c. Access to world sources of raw and processed materials and to world markets since self-sufficiency is either impossible or at least very costly for all countries.

d. Some containment, if possible, of the pressure of population at least in many of the less developed countries.

e. Reasonably stable government and competent administration.

f. Willingness to work hard and to save in the interest of more rapid development, to the extent of capacity.

g. Appropriate help from other more developed nations in finance, real capital, education, and technical aid on a carefully selected and fitted basis.

In many ways these conditions set out for progress in resource development are simply the specific application of the more general conditions of economic growth. Resource policies and plans must not only take them into account, but should aim at improvements leading to more effective utilization of new technology through increasing the skill of the labor force, fostering more efficient industrial management, providing lower cost electric power and heat, a better transportation system, and an increase of social capital in many forms.

ELEMENTS IN THE RESOURCE PLANNING PROCESS

Given the broad objectives for resource development and some knowledge as to the general conditions which will favor such development, how can the more specific and practical work of resource policy formulation and planning be improved? Two interrelated elements or aspects require consideration: *framework* and *decision*.

The *framework* element includes the relevant basic data (geologic, hydrologic, geographic, economic); social patterns and institutions within which resource development has to be worked out; systematic long-range estimates of demand and supply of resource materials as these are related to population estimates and foreseeable technologic changes; and the general goals of national and regional plans. The framework consists essentially of a layout of data, technologic possibilities, alternative supply sources, economic trends, institutional situations, and the like within which policy and planning decisions are made.

The *decision* element focuses on ways in which policy and planning decisions are actually made in public and private sectors of an economy. Decisions regarding broad policies for resources development, long-range development plans and budgets, particular resource projects, and administrative implementation are not clearly separated in practice; there is a continuum of decisions across a band from the more general to the more specific. Attention here will be given to the improvement of resource decisions by such means as benefit-cost, linear programming, and input-output analysis. These techniques can aid in appraising the merits of alternative resource development projects and systems of projects such as river basin development schemes and industrial complexes. Case studies of existing projects can also lead to improvements in future decisions. This element is concerned with the whole process by which decisions are reached; with the political, social, and aesthetic factors as well as the technologic and economic, and therefore with the points of view of various groups and with the conditions that have to be satisfied if their support, or at least acquiescence, in the decision is to be assured. It is not too much to say that the primary objective in resource planning is to establish an efficient decision-making process, important though particular investment and other decisions may be.

Framework

Resource policies and plans have to be visualized in various contexts: one of the most useful of these contexts is the long-range interrelated projection of demand and supply for resource products and services. Such a set of estimates may be made: *first*, by projecting the larger economic and demographic aggregates such as population, labor force, gross national product and its major components, and the like; *second*, deriving from these chiefly on the basis of historical relationships the demand for such resource products as meat, cotton, steel, construction lumber, fertilizer, and the like; and *third*, calculating the requirements for the basic resources of crop land, forest land, water, energy commodities, and metals from which products in the second stage may be produced. In this manner a bill of requirements for resource products and the basic resources themselves may be worked out within the constraints of anticipated increases in population, work force, productivity, and national production. It will be helpful to work with ranges, probably quite wide ranges for years farther into the future, which will embrace a high, a low, and one or more intermediate estimates. Precisely where actual demand falls within the range will depend on how new technology is applied in industry, how consumer wants shift, the extent to which new sources at home or abroad open up, and the directions and effectiveness of policies designed to change the course of events which otherwise would follow.

On the supply side, the estimated requirements would have to be met within the overall constraints imposed by quantity and quality of known and potential natural resources as well as by the technical and economic capacity of the country or area in question to discover, extract, process, transport, and utilize these resources or those it can obtain from other countries. Technology and economics will form the bridge between estimates of demand and the manner in which they are satisfied. With skillful balancing of the variety of supply possibilities with estimated demands, with careful attention to the estimating of net returns of alternative courses of action and to economies of scale, development of the economy can proceed along efficient lines. One of the greatest difficulties in building this kind of framework will be the uncertainties which surround new technology and the rate of application of existing technology, and this is especially true for less developed countries.

Such a framework of projections is well suited for exposing incipient gaps between projected demand and likely supplies and for making estimates of possible changes in the relative prices of resource products.

This kind of exercise has been done for resources in the United States.[1] The resource demand estimates, which are derived from projections of basic demographic and economic aggregates such as labor force and production, have been used as reference points in the analysis of supply possibilities and difficulties. For example, in the energy resources field consumption of all fuel and power, measured in a common unit, is estimated to increase about threefold by the year 2000 compared to 1960, while population is estimated to increase about 85% and gross national product

1. LANDSBERG, FISHMAN & FISHER, *Resources in America's Future*, published by The Johns Hopkins Press for Resources for the Future, Inc., Baltimore, 1963.

by more than four times. Within the total estimated increase in all energy, the shares of the several energy commodities and sources are expected to change. The most dramatic prospective shift will be in atomic energy; relative shifts among the conventional sources of coal, oil, and natural gas will be less marked than during the past century. Demand estimates (perhaps they should be called speculations) show atomic power to increase from virtually nothing in 1960 to 480 billion kilowatt hours in 1980 and 2,500 billion kwh in 2000, by which time well over half of the new electric power installations may be nuclear reactors. These are medium level estimates; a wide range of possibilities exists. The conventional fuel sources of coal, oil, and natural gas are expected to increase also but at much slower rates; by 2000 the demand for oil may increase by three times, natural gas by nearly that much, and coal by about 75%.

Built into these projections of atomic power and other energy sources are numerous assumed changes in technology, some of them major. Failure to achieve considerable cost reductions in the production of atomic power will mean that conventional energy sources will have to be relied upon much more heavily, or other new sources such as oil shale, tar sands, low grade coal, and possibly unconventional sources will have to be drawn upon, if the energy sector is to grow in total as projected.

Estimates of investment requirements for enlarged raw material production may be related to projections of demand for the materials themselves. Foreign trade enters into the picture in several ways: foreign demand has to be added to domestic demand for domestic raw materials, foreign supplies have to be subtracted from total supplies needed in order to get what will be required from domestic sources. A long range, interrelated, demand-supply framework such as has been described can help to set the stage of more realistic resource policies and plans, although it will not specify what the policies and plans have to be. The projections bring major problems into focus and narrow the range of useful courses of action. The working through of these projections requires at least a minimum knowledge of aggregative demographic and economic trends, of technical relationships between resource inputs and outputs of resource products and services, as well as scientific and technical knowledge about the basic resources themselves. The greater the amount and the higher the quality of such information, the more realistic and useful will be the framework of projections. Wide ranges in the demand estimates will be the better part of wisdom; policies based upon such projections should also be flexible so that they may be altered in the light of unfolding events.

Another useful instrument for framework planning is comprehended by the term systems analysis, by means of which a resource complex is stripped of non-essential elements and placed within a model that expresses the significant interrelationships. The principal variables may then be manipulated in such ways that the output or performance of the system can be described quantitatively and tested against performance criteria. Typically, high speed computers will be necessary to do this. Systems analysis in this sense has been experimented with, both in theory and in simulated practical applications in a number of resource situations including river basin development schemes.[2] This kind of engineering-economic analysis can throw much light on the efficiency of alternative development programs and, placed in relevant political and administrative formats, can aid greatly in reaching wise decisions. Still other kinds of framework exist or can be constructed, – for example, legal, administrative, and institutional, which can aid in placing resource planning in better perspective, but these are not elaborated here.

Decision

The processes of policy-making and planning are carried on within whatever frameworks (demand-supply system, legal, institutional, and others) may be constructed. How may these processes be made more effective so that one project or phase of the actual plan that is undertaken may lead easily and logically into the next? Here we are concerned with the strategy and sequence, with the smooth meshing of the several parts, in such a way that initial impulses toward development can exert a multiple effect on the economy and the whole plan can move toward fulfillment with a minimum of delays and detours. Especially we are concerned with the way in which policy and planning decisions are made and with their quality and effectiveness. The improvement of decisions is to be achieved partly by better facts and analysis, and partly by improving the way in which facts and analysis are used. On issues of major significance decisions are governmental decisions in the public sector and top management decisions in the private sector. Over all are the broad political decisions as to national goals and policies; underlying all are the preferences, motivations, and actions of individuals.

Several kinds of analysis may be useful in guiding those who make decisions about policies and plans. One kind which has been used in the United States, especially in the water resources field, is called benefit-cost analysis. Essentially this comprises the identification of alternative projects for achieving roughly the same purposes, an estimate of the costs which will be incurred over the life of the project, and a comparison of the estimated benefits and costs for each of the alternative projects. Many difficulties arise in this kind of analysis, some of which have to be settled arbitrarily. What shall be the assumed length of life of the project? What would be the appropriate rate for discounting the flow of future benefits and future costs? Should the rate be related to some private market rate of

2. MAASS, HUFSCHMIDT, FORMAN, THOMAS, MARGLIN, & FAIR, *Design of Water-Systems*. Harvard University Press, Cambridge, 1962.

interest or should it be a public or social rate? What course of prices and costs should be assumed for the future? Perhaps most vexing of all is the question of what range of particular benefits and costs should be included in the analysis at all; especially, should those of a more intangible, remote and social nature be included – and if so in what way?

Much attention has been given to benefit cost analysis in the United States and indeed for most water development projects federal law requires that such analysis be undertaken and the result presented to the Congress along with other information about the proposed project. Uniform procedures have been established and form the basis for field investigation of benefits and costs. Questions like those raised here have been given a good deal of critical attention in recent years, and as a result benefit-cost estimating techniques have been refined, somewhat more sharply delimited, and in general made more understandable and useful. Benefit-cost estimating for alternative resource development projects may also be helpful in less developed countries although lack of a competitive price system including a money market, the large size of many projects in relation to the resources available for accomplishing them, and the necessary emphasis on social purposes make the technique clumsy and ineffective in many instances unless it is severely limited to appraising the merits of specific alternative projects, for example, dams of different heights or in nearby locations.

Also of use in less developed countries may be the input-output kind of analysis in which the sectors of the economy are viewed in terms of the relationship between the input of resources and other items on the one side and the output of final products and services on the other side. Data can be gathered and organized in such a way that the coefficients expressing these relationships may be calculated and a matrix established. It then becomes possible to assume a mix of final outputs and calculate the inputs that will be required to give the desired results. Such a schema can be used to estimate the effects of alternative paths of national development; regional input-output matrixes would permit the testing of larger scale resource projects.

Several difficulties arise at once: a considerable amount of technical and economic data are needed, although to some extent the input-output technique can be used with a minimum of data; the technical coefficients relating inputs and outputs may change especially in countries growing rapidly and shifting toward more industry and more mechanized farming. This technique, however, does enable broad appraisals and comparisons of different sets of resource development projects to be made.

A more narrow and focused variant of this approach is the linear programming model in which outputs of particular items, for example, are regarded as a function of a number of independent and variable factors. With the relevant data inserted, such systems of equations may be manipulated in various ways and made to yield solutions which are optimal in terms of selected criteria. Other analytical methods useful in improving decisions include game and queueing theories, simulation, minimax and related techniques.

In addition to these more technical means for improving policy and planning decisions, we must call attention to the importance of the way in which data and analysis are handled at the points of decision. Essentially this is a matter of organizing and bringing forward various kinds of evidence bearing on the policy or the plan in such a way that a comprehensive and balanced picture is made available to the decision makers at the time the decision has to be made. The evidence obviously will include engineering and economic analysis, and it should also include broad social, political, and aesthetic argument. The broader the policy or plan under consideration, the more general will be the evidence and argument. The more narrow and focused the policy or plan, the more specific and perhaps quantitative it can be. Finally there can be no substitute for well trained, politically and socially sensitive persons in the decision making positions – persons who will be able to bring together the various plans and analyses with a keen appreciation of the conditions which will have to be met if necessary support is to be obtained. Policy making and plan making at the higher and more general levels tend to be political acts concerned with the public sector or the regulation of the private sector. In national planning as carried out in most of the less developed countries, the scope and general role of the private sectors are also marked out in the plan so that the larger private resource decisions are embraced by and consistent with the public decisions.

RESOURCES PLANNING AND NATIONAL DEVELOPMENT: AN EXAMPLE FROM PAKISTAN

Resource policy and planning have to be viewed in the full context of national development if they are to serve that cause effectively. A development strategy must pull together the natural resource potentialities with the available manpower and capital resources in a dynamic program for resource and national development. Particular attention should be given to shortages and obstacles of a general economic nature (e.g. insufficient savings, foreign exchange, or trained manpower) and to those related more closely to natural resources (e.g. low agricultural productivity, high-cost energy materials for heat and power, or undeveloped mineral resources). Insufficient or poor quality data for better resource planning frequently will be the first obstacle.

The interrelationships involved in resource planning for national development and the need for a development strategy may be illustrated in the case of agriculture in many of the less developed countries where yields are depressingly low and have not risen very much in recent years. Usually more than one factor of productivity limits yields: lack of water at the right place and time, sometimes too much water, not enough fertilizer, farms too small in size, and others. An integrated and concentrated attack on these factors is needed and will involve communication with farm operators, social and economic analysis as well as much applied agricultural research, and better administration of agricultural programs. Achievement of initial momentum is essential but not at the cost of foreclosing future possibilities. Above all, a strong economic motivation on the part of farm operators and workers must be created. Program and expenditure choices usually exist – for example, development of surface versus underground water, or new agricultural land versus more intensive cultivation of land presently farmed. In laying the basis for wise choices, interrelated social, economic, and engineering analysis, frequently using modern techniques such as those mentioned earlier, can be highly effective.

Many of the principles of resource development and the kinds of analysis useful in resource planning are revealingly illustrated by the problem of agriculture in West Pakistan.[3] The flat, fertile Indus Plain, most of which lies in West Pakistan, contains the largest single irrigated area on earth. With its sandy and silty soils, year-round growing season, large surface flow of water, highly developed system of irrigation canals, huge underground reservoir of fresh water, underground pools of natural gas, and a wide range of crops that can be grown, the Plain is one of the chief physical assets of the world's fifth most populous country. Yet, despite potentialities, incomes from agriculture remain very low, and there is a deficit of both calories and animal proteins in the diet of the people. Population is increasing more rapidly than food production.

One of the problems of agriculture in West Pakistan is waterlogging and salt accumulation in the soil, caused by poor drainage in the vast, nearly flat Plain. Agricultural production is also held down by a shortage of irrigation water. Because of canal seepage and other losses, only about half the water diverted from the rivers is available to crops. Much of the planted area receives too little water to prevent salt accumulation. Chemical fertilizers, protective measures against plant diseases and pests, and high-yielding plant varieties are very little used. Other handicaps are the system of land holding and primitive methods of cultivation.

In establishing the framework for agricultural development, the need to raise present per capita food production by 30 to 40% and the range of probable population growth in West Pakistan of between 50 and 100% over the next 25 years must be considered. Increases in sugar and cotton production will be required to meet the demand of both East and West Pakistan.

3. The following discussion is based on the work of the U.S. White House – Interior Panel on Waterlogging and Salinity in West Pakistan, undertaken in 1962.

As living standards rise, the relative demand for fruits, vegetables, and livestock products will grow. Additional increases in agricultural production will have to be based on export markets or industrial use of farm products.

Maps of the mechanical composition, salt content, and cation-exchange characteristics of the soils are needed, not only as a basis for determining cropping patterns, but also for planning capital expenditures for development. For example, the high salt and sodium contents of the soils in much of the Indus Delta region raise serious question concerning the economic potentials of these lands. Considerable further investigation is needed to determine the areas of fresh and saline underground water, and the chemical composition of the salt water. Much of the latter has a sufficiently low salt content so that it can be used for irrigation when diluted with fresh canal waters.

A plan for greatly increasing agricultural production is being devised by means of which technological possibilities can be brought into effective relationship with economic feasibilities and human capabilities. In the northern two-thirds of the Plain, the supply of irrigation water for actual consumptive use by plants can be doubled, in part by river regulation through surface storage, but chiefly by constructing a network of carefully-spaced tubewells to recover canal seepage and allow controlled mining of the underground water. The tubewells will also make it possible to leach the accumulated salts out of the soil and ultimately to eliminate water-logging.

Yields per acre can be increased by providing more irrigation water, and water the right time, by the use of fertilizer, by controlling plant diseases and pests, by the development and use of improved seed and crop varieties, and by the introduction of better cultivation practices. Each of these five production factors may increase yields 20% when applied singly, but in combination they could give increases of 200 to 300%. In order to integrate all the factors of production, it is necessary to concentrate their application in project areas of manageable size. Analysis of the hydrologic processes involved, and of the economics of fertilizer production, indicate that the project areas should contain about a million acres. If adequate capital and technical manpower can be made available, it should be possible to initiate development of a new million-acre project each year.

Linear programming analysis shows that the principal benefit from the tubewell water will come from the maximum possible expansion of the planted areas during the summer season in the most profitable crops.

Electric power for pumping water can be obtained either by hydroelectric development in the mountains and foothills of the north, or by thermal plants using natural gas. West Pakistan is fortunate in having fairly large reserves of natural gas, which can be used also as a source of nitrogenous fertilizer. With electricity, phosphate fertilizers can be made from imported raw material.

To attain momentum in increasing production, an optimal sequence of capital investment is essential. First expenditures should be for development of underground water and drainage, fertilizer plants, pest control facilities, training and organization of technicians, administrators, and field workers to assist the farmers, development of better plant varieties, and needed investigations. Later, roads and transportation facilities must be provided to haul a greatly increased volume of agricultural products to the cities and towns. Processing mills and textile factories will have to be built to utilize these products profitably. Still later, a farm machinery industry will be needed, and factories to produce consumer goods for the farmers will ultimately be required. Only a few conveyance channels to carry off salty waters in order to maintain a salt balance will be needed at first, but many of these relatively expensive structures must be built within about 20 years of the initial development.

In the northern two-thirds of the Plain, an initial capital investment of about Rs 260 to 285 an acre is needed in order to allow integrated use of the primary factors of production. Ultimate expenditure may be several times this amount. After full development, the maximum net increase of crop value in the northern area from additional water, fertilizer, plant protection, and presently existing better plant varieties, could be Rs 3.6 billion, equal to twice the average gross production during the last decade, excluding livestock.

All aspects of the program rest on vigorous education and agricultural extension efforts to guide the farmers in carrying out their part of the task, ample credit to make the farmers' participation possible, and efficient marketing and distribution facilities. Massive and determined effort, and continuing experimentation will be necessary to transmit new technical skills to very large numbers of desperately poor and illiterate farmers, and to create economic conditions in which they will be motivated to help themselves.

SOME COMMON PROBLEMS OF RESOURCE DEVELOPMENT

A few common problems of resource development in less developed countries may be listed here. Some are theoretical; some are practical. Research and experimentation offer the best avenues for dealing with them. The kinds of analysis suggested in this paper seem promising. These problems include:

– Improving the amount and quality of resource data, both scientific and economic, and further testing of analytical methods so as to make the data more useful in planning.

– Determining a strategy of resource development in national economic growth. What are the main elements of such a strategy? What variables are critical for forward motion and how may they be manipulated? What sequence and combinations of industrial investment, workers, training, agricultural improvement, and occupational and regional shifts are called for in each country for the resource sectors?

– Interrelating more closely the food and raw material shortages in some countries with surpluses of production or capacity in others.

– Devising workable international arrangements for financing resource development, for market and price stabilization, and for technical aid in resource planning.

– Finding an effective division between public and private sectors with appropriate interrelating of the two. The line of division will, of course, vary from country to country according to its particular history and present situation.

– Appropriate safeguarding of the productiveness of basic resources, such as soil and water, and of the quality of the natural environment.

– Adjusting to the declining relative importance of agriculture and some other resource industries in national economies. This will involve a balancing of programs for raising agricultural efficiency (better farming practices, improved processing and marketing of crops, more machinery and power, better health and education, more credit) with programs of industrialization, principally in urban areas.

– Adopting cost-reducing technology in resource activities as rapidly as possible.

Within each country, and perhaps within each sub-national development region, an organizational means for resource development planning, at least for the coordination of such planning, will be beneficial. Some countries have such arrangements; others do not. Typically this will mean drawing together representatives from a number of departments or agencies of the government spanning the various natural resources of land and agriculture, forestry, fisheries, water and power, energy, minerals, and the like so that comprehensive and multiple purpose policies and plans may be worked out. In many countries, this may be done within or in conjunction with national and regional planning bodies. To begin with, data gathering and research in the resources field should be coordinated and given central attention.

Since common problems of resource policy-making, planning, and development are to be found in one form or another in virtually all less developed countries, and since the more developed countries will also have to take some part in solving them, frequently through the use of analytical techniques as described in this paper, there would appear to be much to be gained from a more concerted attack on them than has thus far been made. We suggest, therefore, that consideration be given to the establishment of a World Resources Development Institute with the following purposes:

a. To undertake, and stimulate others to undertake, scientific, technologic, statistical, and economic research on natural resources, especially as such research bears on policy and planning.

b. To foster exchange of information, and perhaps to establish a central library of knowledge.

c. To encourage the education and training of resource specialists through seminars, fellowships, exchanges of personnel, and the like, working in relation with existing universities and public and private institutes.

d. To build an international panel of resource specialists for technical aid in water, land, energy, and minerals, with emphasis on the planning of developments in these fields.

e. To cooperate with various groups concerned with resources, including other international agencies, national and sub-national organizations, and appropriate private groups.

Direction of such an institute could be by an international board of world leaders in the resources field, of scientists, engineers, planners, economists, administrators, and educators. Possibly the national academies of science or some similarly respected bodies could act as sponsors. Financing might come from participating countries or organizations, foundation grants, or from the United Nations or its specialized agencies concerned with resources. The institute could be a part of United Nations, or it could be outside UN but cooperating with UN and certain of its specialized agencies.

JOSEPH LYMAN FISHER, Ph. D., is President of Resources for the Future, Inc. He has been Planning Technician, National Resources Planning Board; Associate Divisional Director, U.S. Department of State; Economist and Administrative Officer, the Council of Economic Advisors. His publications include "Natural Resources and Technological Change"; "The Role of Natural Resources" in "Economic Development, Principles and Patterns," and "Research in Regional Economic Growth" in "Problems in the Study of Econom icGrowth," and "Resources in America's Future" (with LANDSBERG and FISCHMAN, Johns Hopkins Press, Baltimore, 1963).

ROGER REVELLE, D.Sc., Ph.D., is Professor of Oceanography at the Scripps Institute and Dean of Research, the University of California. Dr. REVELLE is Chairman of the Special Committee on Oceanic Research of the International Council of Scientific Unions, a member of the Commission on Oceanography of the U.S. National Academy of Sciences and of the Commission on Mathematical, Physical and Engineering Sciences of the National Science Foundation.

Design for a Planet

by

ROBERT C. COOK

The science of ecology has been solely the concern of intellectuals too long. If modern, urban-industrial man does not learn what ecology is and place himself in balance with his environment and his fellow living creatures, ecological forces may destroy him.

Complicated though it may be in detail, the concept of ecology seems simple enough to win universal acceptance. The word was derived from the Greek word for house, oikos. Ecology undertakes to unravel and understand the total interactions of all organisms – plants, animals and man – with each other and with their environment. One of the great pioneers of ecological research, the late ALDO LEOPOLD, put it this way:

A harmonious relation to land is more intricate, and of more consequence to civilization, than the historians of its progress seem to realize. Civilization is not, as they often assume, the enslavement of a stable and constant earth. It is a state of *mutual and independant cooperation* between human animals, other animals, plants, and soils, which may be disrupted at any moment by the failure of any of them. Land-despoliation has evicted nations, and can on occasion, do it again. As long as six virgin continents awaited the plow, this was perhaps no tragic matter, – eviction from one piece of soil could be recouped by despoiling another. But there are now wars and rumors of wars which forestall the impending saturation of the earth's best soils and climates. It thus becomes a matter of some importance, at least to ourselves, that our dominion, once gained, be self-perpetuating rather than self-destructive.

When CHARLES DARWIN wrote his Origin of Species, the word "ecology" had not yet been coined. Yet its essence is to be found in his concluding paragraph:

It is interesting to contemplate a tangled bank, clothed with many plants of many kinds, with birds singing on the bushes, with various insects flitting

Reprinted from *Population Bulletin*, Vol. XVII, 3, May 1961, pp. 41–42, by kind permission.

about, and with worms crawling through the damp earth, and to reflect that these elaborately constructed forms, so different from each other, and dependent upon each other in so complex a manner, have all been produced by laws acting around us.... There is a grandeur in this view of life [whereby from simple beginnings] endless forms most beautiful and most wonderful have been, and are being evolved.

DARWIN's principle of evolution is universally accepted today, but his message of the interdependency of life has gone unheeded. Urban-oriented, 20th-century man of the asphalt jungles and penthouse gardens might seem to be far removed from the "tangled bank" DARWIN described. But despite the enormous advances in scientific and technical knowledge which have given man wings, a longer life span and the ability to bounce his words off the moon, he is still dependent on the ecological balance of his environment.

Consider four basic factors in the ecological complex: space, air, water and people. Air and water have always been considered "free" and the great open spaces inviolable. The multiplication of people is already changing this, and for the worse. Space, air and water will become priceless should the population of this country double to 360 million, as expected, in only 40 years.

About 75% of this population increase is expected to be in the large cities and their environs. Space, that finite factor in the ecological complex, will have prime importance as today's high urban population densities spread over larger areas.

The air is becoming increasingly polluted with waste which, in smog-infested areas, eats holes in nylon stockings, makes the eyes smart, increases respiratory illnesses and may even cause cancer.

Man has shown the most reckless disregard for ecology in his misuse of water resources. He has desecrated the beautiful rivers of this continent and many of their tributaries.

Violation of the ecological balance evokes even heavier penalties than physical inconveniences and health hazards. It strikes at the very basis of human culture and civilization.

In the two chapters following are reproduced two challenging statements by men who have given years of thought to the broader cultural and spiritual consequences of ignoring the ecological imperative. They see the matter from very different points of view, but the warning is clear and simple: new powers involve responsibilities as well as privileges. Man is profoundly and massively violating the ecological balance. The penalty could be no less than the destruction of modern civilization.

Man has now touched the edge of space. Can he focus his vision and imagination nearer home, repair the damage which has been done and keep this planet a fit place on which to live?

Population, Space, and Human Culture

by

Henry B. van Loon

We, like all other forms of life, must maintain a working relationship with our environment. But while this relationship is still fairly simple and direct for all other organisms, ours is now maintained through each other, as a group, and through the patterns of behavior and the values of that group. This has given us a freedom of movement and expression that no other creature has, but, at the same time, it has also made us responsible for our own well-being. We must, therefore, seek to know ourselves and the world around us as best we can if we would insure the brightest possible future for mankind.

Space is both a measure and a function of our environment, and a resource in itself. For the lower forms of life, its values are quite tangible and easily measured; for us, on the other hand, because our relationship with our environment is no longer direct, but through our culture, it has come to have intangible ones as well. It is our appreciation of these intangible values and how they may best be implemented that determines whether and at what rate we, as a civilization, advance.

The direct and tangible relationships between ourselves and our environment have been well studied; the intangible ones have not. We can approximate how much food we shall probably have, how much coal, how much iron, by the year 2000. We can figure how much room each one of us shall have, depending on our numbers. We know very little, however, of the effect of space or lack of it on our cultural development. We do not know whether or not there is a point in the decline of per capita space and resources beyond which the cultural growth of a nation is arrested, and whether or not we are anywhere near such a point.

About a hundred years ago, von Liebig wrote(1),

"A nation arises and develops in proportion to the fertility of its land.

Reprinted from a symposium, Population Control, Vol. 25, No. 3 (Summer 1960), by permission from "Law and Contemporary Problems," published by the Duke University, 1960.

With the exhaustion of the land, culture and morals disappear. However, the intellectual properties of the nation do not vanish; it is our consolation that they merely change their dwelling places."

This statement not only poses a fundamental question, but also hints broadly at the answer. The question, of course, is: Why does disruption of the landscape bring about a cultural decline? The hinted answer is: The development by man of a cultural relationship with his environment has brought about a physico-psychological relationship between environment and culture within his civilization that may not be too different from the psycho-somatic interrelationships that exist within the individual. The human being whose continued existence is no longer dependent on his ability to maintain rapport with his environment through change in his individual characteristics – form and function – has simply passed these requirements on to his state, nation, or civilization.

We would be deluding ourselves, furthermore, were we to think that VON LIEBIG's thesis is rendered obsolete because of our industrial development. Industry is simply an extension of the process that began with agriculture – a capacity to exploit resources. Fertility of land has the same significance for an agricultural society, to all intents and purposes, as have total resources for an industrial one. If we substitute environment for fertility of land, VON LIEBIG's statement immediately is brought up to date. The plain facts are that culture and environment are so intimately linked that the quality of an environment has as direct an effect on the quality of a culture as a culture, through its values, has on the space and resources of a civilization.

The relationship between primitive man and his environment could very simple be expressed: A region could support as many people as its resources times its space could feed. The relationship between us and our environment is somewhat more complicated, however, and has been expressed formulaically by Dr. PAUL B. SEARS, Chairman of the Yale University Conservation Program, as $\dfrac{(R_s)}{(P)} f(C) = 0$, in which R is resources, s is space, P is people, and C is their culture. All of these factors are variable, of course, but space, the subscript of resources, is variable not only in tangible, but in intangible ways as well. It can have endless values to us because of the cultural approach to environment that we have developed; and conversely, the continuation of our culture depends on the fullest exploitation of our space's aesthetic as well as material potential. It behooves us to study the implications of this in some detail.

SPECIFICS OF THE CASE

It is not yet 200 years since the Constitution of the United States was written and adopted. This new departure in governmental philosophy and form brought about an unprecedented degree of freedom in human-environmental relations. What is more, this occurred in a brand new land and just as man was getting hold of a new source of power – namely, steam. The consequent outburst of energy, both physical and mental, that took place was phenomenal. Free minds and strong bodies sustained by a new and fertile soil moved without hindrance in all directions, using whatever was needed of space and resources, and there was spawned such a collection of "tinkers and geniuses," as EDMUND FULLER called them,(2) as had never before been seen. Few countries since Greece in its heyday have boasted as many men of genius of all kinds – in relation to its population, of course – as did ours in the early 1800's.

In a scant 150 years, however, we have converted our country from a storehouse of raw wealth and space to what may well become a slumridden, have-not nation; from a land of men to one of members. The signs of the conditions for social stratification and decline are everywhere evident – the disease is already well advanced in our culture. But to be more specific as to what we may do to save ourselves from going the way of other civilizations, let us review the actual state of our space and resources and see, if we can, where we now stand. It is, of course, impossible to make direct comparisons with the past or with other present-day countries with anything approaching scientific accuracy, but some valid analogies and comparisons can certainly be drawn.

On a world-wide basis, population rose 30% from 1900 to 1940, while the production of food increased only 10 to 12%. Since 1940, world population has risen at an even faster rate than before; world food production, however, actually declined during the war and did not regain its prewar level until 1952, since which time, it has continued to increase, but not by any means at the same rate as has population(3). Meanwhile, we have been proceeding on the assumption that because we have a "food surplus," our larder has no limits. Actually, of course, it has. Our present surplus is largely the result of a politically useful schema by which we pay "farmers" to take the capital out of our soil, which our grandchildren should have, and deposit it to their personal accounts. This cannot go on indefinitely, and it will not.

In the late 1930's, when we were seriously worried about our future, our Government made a most exhaustive study to determine the total number of acres that might be profitable used for farming and came up with just under 500,000,000 acres. At that time, we were already using some 300,000,000 acres (we had been using almost 360,000,000 in 1930)(4). Since then, by concentrating on the best land only, using much more fertilizer, cutting down on our exports and what we feed to horses and mules, we have managed to take care of our much larger population (177,399,000 in 1959 as compared with 122,755,046 in 1930) with only about 420,000,000 acres. It has been estimated that by 1975, our population may be 225,000,000 and that to feed those people would require about 550,000,000 acres, under present productive levels. By increasing the annual amount of fertilizer from 5,500,000 tons used in the 1953–55 period to 10,600,000 tons and by applying this fertilizer to 48% of the acreage used instead of 30%, however, we could reduce the acreage to about 430,000,000(5).

All of this looks quite promising; but this kind of performance cannot go on indefinitely. After certain levels of production are reached, the response of the land to more fertilizer appears to be negligible. Production thereafter depends more and more on intensive cultivation. Thus, although Japan uses twice as much fertilizer as Europe and five times as much as we do, it has not been able appreciably to increase production per acre since 1935(6).

Meanwhile, we are steadily increasing not only our total, but our per capita needs for other resources of all kinds: for sources of energy, for metals, and for other materials that are all very finite in amount. While the demand for food increases more or less arithmetically with population, the demand for all other resources appears to increase geometrically. In short, however we regard our resources, all indications are that somewhere within the next twenty or thirty years, and in some respects possibly sooner, our larder, which has seemed so inexhaustible, will turn out to be like any other barrel. Yet, ours has only recently been tapped.

In any practical sense, living space on the planet Earth is finite in amount, too. True, the thrifty Dutch continue to reclaim land from the shallow margins of the North Sea, but only fast enough to make up for fertile land lost to roads and urban use. True, also, tall apartments continue to multiply and grow taller on an expensive piece of rock called Manhattan Island, but even this ingenious scheme has its limits. By and large, therefore, we shall have to make do with the existing land surface for the foreseeable future.

For the wisest and most effective use of that surface, we shall require help from many sources, not least from science. Yet, ironically, it is the applications of science that threaten us with a crisis in our relation to the space on which we live. For science has, through lowering our death rate while our birth rate remains high, brought about an unprecedented increase in human numbers. Moreover, in raising our material level of living, science has vastly increased our demands upon raw materials. And while it has probably lessened the amount of space required to provide each of us with food, it has made necessary great new highways, factories, and other greedy consumers of space. Finally, at the same time that pressure upon space has thus been steadily growing, the utilities, conveniences, and diversions made possible by science are monopolizing our time and attention; the elaborate rituals of modern civilized life are divorcing us more and more from contact with the world of nature of which we are – inescapably – a part.

Even the word space itself begins to connote to us only outer, astronomical space. The result is a kind of mass hypnosis, a fascination with celestial form-sheets and planetary scoreboards. This may be, as we are assured by some specialists, essential to our physical survival as a nation, or it may not be. There are some cogent reasons, however, aside from expense, for thinking that the dangers may outweigh the insurance. Be this as it may, this new emphasis upon the promises of outer space deflects our concern from the more immediate kind of space problem that involves our daily lives. When we become more concerned over Soviet priority in reaching the moon than in guiding the design and location of highways and suburbs, one wonders what will be left to arouse our patriotism. As a distinguished American once said, "A man may die in defence of his home, but not his boarding-house"(7).

The present land area of the fifty states of this country is 3,552,226 square miles (land area only); its population, 177,319,000. This same area in 1900 contained 75,994,575 people. The number of acres per capita, accordingly, has fallen during this period of time from 22.4 to 12.2. This is still a generous allowance compared with Japan, where the corresponding figure is just under one. But at our present rate of population increase, it is estimated that we shall have only about seven acres per capita in the year 2000, while in less than a lifetime of seventy years, we shall be little better off than the Japanese are today – and unless we match their skill and energy in exploiting our resources, we shall be a great deal worse off.

How much is too many people? This depends upon way of life and the values that are considered most important. Bands of hunters and fishermen may require several square miles per capita, besides wide buffer zones to protect them against outside interference. A simple farming people can get along with a few acres per capita, provided they are not dependent upon the rain that falls elsewhere and do not need anything from outside. A highly industrialized state, such as Ohio, can accommodate 9,000,000 persons in a space that was once crowded by fewer than 20,000 Indians.

But these instances are deceptive. The hunters and simple farmers may require wide buffer zones, such as "the dark and bloody ground" or the Egyptian desert, to give them sure protection against constant raids. And it is seldom that any economy above the primitive level is self-contained – it must have access to acres beyond that of its immediate occupation. Thus, of the scant million who work in Manhattan Island, 370,000 do not even live there, but commute, while the 14,049,000 who live in the Metropolitan New York area survive by virtue of the production and activity of our whole continent and lands beyond the seas(8). To regard familiar urban densities as the universal norm for the entire habitable earth is not simply an error, therefore; it is a cruel injustice.

Several circumstances make the issue more than academic. One is a prevalent mood induced by the industrial revolution and noted long ago by ORTEGA Y GASSETT. This is a feeling never before entertained by sane mankind – that effortless abundance is the normal order of nature. As the efficiency of mass production increases, it becomes steadily more difficult to counter this idea, although unlimited mass production hastens the depletion of essential capital in the form of raw materials.

This suggests a further difficulty in the logical planning of space and numbers. The sheer and steady increase of population in a finite space offers superb opportunities for gain to those in a position of advantage. Slum properties are notoriously profitable in relation to investment and maintenance. WILLIAM H. WHYTE, Jr. has shown how much of the wealth of the United States has come from increased value attributable not to effort, but to the sheer momentum of increasing numbers in a space that remains unchanged(9). This, of course, was the basis of HENRY GEORGE's "single tax." This notion, that society, not the individual, should benefit by increased values not attributable to individual enterprise, has been laughed away repeatedly, only to bob up with remarkable persistence in serious discussions.

Beyond the mood of optimism and the temptation for profit is a profound biological fact. Man has become the dominant organism on earth not only because of his manipulative skill and highly developed central nervous system, but equally because of his powerful reproductive instinct. In this field of experience, powerful subconscious drive is reinforced and intensified by many aspects of consciousness. The slightest knowledge of cultural history, or even its current documentation in magazine advertising, shows this to be true. We conveniently forget that the strength of this impulse results in the advent of countless human beings whose arrival was by no means consciously invoked and whose welcome, to say the least, is dubious. Meanwhile, we have gone all out to insure the survival of as many for as long a time as possible – thus reducing the death rate, while dealing furtively and ineffectively, if at all, with the birth rate.

Again, our very attitude towards space is confused and ambivalent. Nor is this attitude unique, for the same is true as regards other resources – say, the forest and water. The forest is a source of materials and intangible values – and at the same time, our rival for space. Water is necessary for survival – yet, a convenient dumping ground for toxic wastes. Similarly, we require space for living, work, and recreation – but have gone to extraordinary lengths to annihilate it by rapid transit and communication. Thus, we both love and hate space – an inconceivably bad formula for any rational approach to intelligent planning.

PLANNING FOR THE FUTURE

Keeping in mind that both our continually growing pressure upon space and our relative disregard of its importance are ascribable to deep-seated aspects of human nature, what, in a technological sense, is involved in space-planning?

Any planning we may want to do for the future must, of course, be predicated on a thorough understanding of the conditions to be met and the objectives to be attained. It is obvious that we face an inexorable decline in our total resources, no matter what new ones we may find. It is obvious, too, that we shall increase the rate at which we use them for some time at least, especially those that are most available. There will also be a continuing shortage of food on a world-wide basis until the rate of population increase is brought under some kind of control. Lastly, our space, that 10% or so of the surface of the globe that is fit for human habitation, has been most badly used and has deteriorated. Thus, in our formula, both resources as a whole and space in its tangible form have been reduced so markedly that any chance of maintaining a balance in the future will depend on how soundly we plot our course, how fully we take advantage of those values that are intangible.

Now, for our objectives. Obviously, we want to survive. But are we willing to settle for physical survival alone – or, rather, can we? Can we take it for granted that so long as we can keep ourselves, as a species, alive, we shall automatically continue to evolve and be able to cope with life's demands for improvement and change as they come along? Shall we not be taking a truly great chance if we decide to take no responsibility for our continued cultural growth but rather leave it up to nature? Is it not possible that having once taken on the responsibility for our own evolution to a fair extent, we may already be beyond what might be called a point of no return; that we may already be so far along that road that any failure to take the responsibility for our continued growth, to develop the right cultural values, to use the space we have left correctly, physically as well as aesthetically, may bring to an end our freedom from the control of physical, adaptive evolution?

Our cultural evolution has enabled us to increase in numbers. Thus, it has greatly increased our chances of bringing forth the minds that could move our culture onward. But – and this is the key to the whole problem – cultural gains have always been made in those countries that have had the resources; and always when the ratio of men to resources has become too high the intellectual properties of the country have vanished, as VON LIEBIG wrote, to reappear somewhere else. Now there are no new lands to which our intellectual properties can go if we spoil the ones we have. Our continued cultural evolution, our lives as men, thus depends on how we exploit our environment.

Specifically, we should begin now on the following two-part program: planning for the immediate future, and planning for the years beyond. Part one should be a continuation of the investigation into the tangible values of our environment, or space. Part two should be an investigation of the intangible values and an attempt to integrate them with the tangible values, so that we can learn how to make the most of our environment's aesthetic potential, in order to compensate for the loss of space and resources that we must inevitably face.

From the point of view of its use to us, the value of our space – our land – is declining rather rapidly, although increasing in cost, for two very definite reasons: the one, because we are not yet taking the trouble to find out the ultimate best use or uses of each piece of land before doing something with it; the other, because we must use more and more machinery and can thus use only those lands or resources that can be handled by it. This is true whether we are speaking of farms, coal mines, or land for subdivision. In almost every case, the machine now largely determines what we do and where; and this is becoming the rule in almost every country as it, too, is forced to use more and more machinery.

There is a definite need, then, to extend the principle of multiple-use planning, as understood by foresters and conservationists, to land-use management as a whole, and to then integrate with this work a thorough understanding of the conditions that have been introduced in resource development and land-use by our increasing reliance on machinery and the growing interdependence of our economy. This does not mean that we should try to set out in detail how each piece of property is to be used; that would lead precisely to the kind of regimentation we must avoid. But it does mean that we should begin to develop means by which to arrive at fairly good estimates of the various possible values to us of any particular lands or regions, and an order of priority for those values.* With these, we can then set up the guidelines within which free enterprise can operate without the risk that one man's work will spoil another's. This is now being done, of course, in a small way through zoning in our communities; it is being done in a larger way by our valley authorities. The principle must, however, be extended and combined with the conditions set by our technology to bring about an understanding of how our land – our space – should be managed best to meet our present-day needs.

*   *
*

At the same time, we know almost nothing of the intangible values of our environment – of space – or their effects on us as individuals and as a group. The effects of space, of form and color, on man have been known for centuries by our master builders or architects: the lines of columns in the Egyptian temple to overawe the populace, the peace and sanctuary of a Gothic chapel, and so on. But we know very little of why these things are so; and because we have not been able to give these effects a statistical

* Editor's note: This is now being realised by the "International Biological Programme" of the International Union of Biological Sciences.

measure, the public, which is apt to think that statistics and truth are synonymous, is very reluctant to admit their existence or validity.

Yet, this subject must be mastered, just as we had to develop and bring together the body of knowledge that is now known as the science of psychology. The presently intangible values of our environment can have as profound effects on us and on our culture as do the physical, tangible ones. We must know them, have some measure of them, and be able to use them in order to keep the "R_s" (resource-space) factor in our formula as high as possible, and for as long as we can.

This brings us to the last and most important point: the place of the legislator and the lawyer in the whole scheme of our cultural life process. Our laws are, in some ways, much older than our present culture. They are an extension, in part, of the controls and rights we felt instinctively when our relationship to the world around us was still physical; the conventionalization, for the rest, of those concepts as to how we should live together that we have worked out for ourselves. The speed and security with which our culture can move ahead will depend largely on how well we are able to judge the moral rightness and cultural worth of the course that our scientists say we should follow. It is in this that our lawyers must help us, for our culture can be no better than the concepts on which it is based; and those concepts can do no good until they are translated into workable arrangements for our daily use. The scientist and the lawyer must work together closely in the interest of mankind; the scientist to give us facts, the lawyer to help us make them useful.

There is a need now to establish some organization, or group, of scientists and lawyers to begin to draw together all that we know on the whole subject of our cultural relationship to our environment. This group should not be large; it might well be patterned on the one brought together by President HOOVER some years ago to study the social trends of the nation(10). It should not try to carry out research itself; it should rather act as a steering committee and clearing house for information, working through regional organizations to gather information on our resources, space, and needs, advising on research, and bringing together and making useful all work now being done by others that could increase our knowledge of our interrelationship with our environment. In this way, we may be able to learn how to establish a successful working arrangement with our environment within the time we can afford. After all, another 2500 human beings moved in to share our living space while you were reading this.

BIBLIOGRAPHY

1. JUSTUS VON LIEBIG, Familiar Letters on Chemistry (1844).
2. See EDMUND FULLER, Tinkers and Genius (1955).
3. HARRISON SCOTT BROWN, JAMES BONNER & JOHN WIER, The Next Hundred Years, passim (1957).

4. *U.S. Department of Agriculture Yearbook*, 84–110 (1938).
5. BROWN, BONNER & WIER, *op. cit. supra* note 3, *passim.*
6. *Ibid.*
7. This remark has been ascribed to HENRY A. WALLACE.
8. *World Almanac*, 303 (1960).
9. WHYTE, *Urban Sprawl*, Fortune, Jan. 1958, p. 103.
10. See President's Commission on Social Trends, Report (1933).

HENRY B. VAN LOON, an architect and planner with the firm of Perkins and Will, is a member of the American Institute of Architects. He is co-author of Urban Development Guidebook, (1955), and formerly Executive Director of the Pennsylvania State Planning Board.

Better Living through Conservation Planning

by

SANFORD S. FARNESS

The topic I have been asked to discuss refers to the obvious need for general environmental planning, placing emphasis upon our natural and cultural environment as a "dwelling place" – our habitation on earth.

I assume that you are all aware of the need for such environmental planning and that we do not have such planning in process anywhere today. We have only various kinds of disconnected, partial efforts at environmental design – metropolitan and urban planning, rural programs of various kinds and water programs mainly at the Federal level. Also, I am not going to identify the numerous and growing catalogue of defects and complaints regarding our external environment which range from metropolitan air pollution at one pole of our society, to continuing soil erosion at the other. Neither am I going to resume that perennial practise of trying to "adequately define conservation." Perhaps we can agree that neat, precise definitions of the broad-ranging attitudes comprising conservation thought must always be partial and to that extent misleading.

I would like briefly to characterize some needed human capacities which we will have to painfully acquire as individuals before we can really achieve "conservation planning for better living," and realize vitally important conservation values in our society. If enough of us choose to personally fulfill these needs of our time we will then automatically open up possibilities for transforming our environment, which after all, is only a direct reflection of ourselves at any time.

FIRST NEED – REALIZE OUR POSITION IN HISTORY

Where do we stand today – what are some main limitations which, if overcome, can open transforming possibilities? Every age is an age of transition, but each age has certain unique characteristics. Our age and its problems properly began with the Renaissance. Man's individual

Reprinted with permission from the "North American Wildlife and Natural Resources Conference, Washington, D.C., March 1961.

awareness of himself – of his ego – then took place on a broad front for the first time. This was part of a mysterious new capacity for perception and thought. Directed inwardly it produced individualism.   Directed outwardly it produced scientific behavior and knowledge. Political democracy, awareness of freedom, Western scientific knowledge, our present view of nature, and technology, with all of their positive and negative qualities, are quite recent gifts of the last four hundred years – gifts which suddenly are now diffusing over and transforming the entire non-Western world.

Man's present sense of himself and nature is therefore really quite new. Western culture has in fact just passed its graceful childhood period – a childhood which began in ancient pre-Christian times and now has reached a dubious adolescence. Our present landscapes and settlement patterns are expressions of all the disharmonies, conflicts, strengths, and awkwardnesses of cultural adolescence. Much of the unconscious beauty and harmony of childhood has flowered in the settlement patterns of historical times. We travel with longing to historical examples of early landscapes, cities, towns and countrysides still present in Europe like ghosts of our forgotten past, expressing all of the profundity and completeness of uncorrupted children.

At home we confront in despair our adolescent vitality running away with us in a violent urge to produce and consume. We confront our lack of balance and sudden giantism in metropolitan growth with our embarrassing acne of urban and rural slums, our infected rivers and our eroded and scarred landscapes. We confront in dismayed surprise our recent ignorance and disregard of fundamental biological and ecological principles which earlier peoples often intuitively recognized and expressed in their settlement patterns.

SECOND NEED – TO CLEARLY DISTINGUISH CAUSES FROM EFFECTS

We are also confused yet and do not speak clearly about cause and effect relationships. Our fathers have advised us in years past that adolescence is a difficult time, full of crises, and some of our elders still living among us have forewarned us that life is difficult, that the vine is known by its fruits, that a little knowledge is a dangerous thing, and that "know thyself" is a venerable rule of wisdom. But like true adolescents, we have refused to listen. Our inner and outer conflicts are growing however and the work of our hands, our cities and landscapes, are beginning to pall on us.

We are also prone to conveniently identify the causal factors behind our problems as external causes – technological change, economic forces, lack of proper legislation, the structure of governmental agencies, and a host of others. In small ways though we have been forced to confront ourselves and already secretly know that we will sooner or later be forced to turn our fascinated eyes away from our settlement patterns and learn who we are and what part we had in creating them. Our secret knowledge tells us that if we do this it will clarify much. We can then turn our gaze back to our environment and clearly recognize ourselves in what we see.

We will then realize afresh an old principle – that man creates and is responsible for his world – that every man is an artist because everything he creates is expressive of his purposes – including the forms of his knowledge.

If our countrysides and cities are ugly, it is because we lack a personal will for beauty. If our community structure has dissolved into chaos it is because we have lost our personal capacity for community life. If our central business districts look like slick, giant supermarkets and our farms and rural landscapes look like vast factories for resource conversion it is because we have no higher purposes than producing and exchanging commodities. If we have dishonest and shallow architecture it is because we express these qualities.

Need we go on? These points are truisms, but they are so fundamental they are easy to overlook. They bring clear a fundamental limitation facing environmental planning today – the continuing refusal to accept personal human decisions as the basic causal factors creating our settlement patterns and their problems. Most of the problems we identify and research are symptoms. This state of affairs raises to fundamental importance questions having to do with how we create our knowledge, our research methods, our conceptual systems and, in brief, the theory of knowledge underlying present environmental research.

THIRD NEED – MORE REALISTIC AND PENETRATING RESEARCH PROCEDURES

We annunciate pious, elaborate statements about our lack of understanding of our settlement patterns and state that vast quantities of objective and theoretical research are needed. Serious evasions of reality are becoming more and more apparent as our national establishment for settlement pattern research grows in size and annual outlay.

Cultures and settlement patterns are *materializations* of man's thought forms. Man is given the world of natural forms and principles. Within it man creates his own forms and principles.

If we don't understand how our settlement patterns came to be, then we need to study the creator of these forms – man. Every cultural artifact is an effect of human thought and purpose as cause. We can read and understand these causal factors in the forms around us if we have the will to do it. Our cities, villages, countrysides and technology are a clear, legible alphabet of forms. There is no mystery about them or need for abstract theories of settlement forms after the analogy of mechanics, physics, or organics.

Let us take our settlement patterns as our alphabet of physical forms and read them directly for what they say. Man is man because he can't help being an artist – everything he does is expressive – it has form (pattern) and meaningful content. Form is man's alphabet as well as nature's. Let us, in short, have some environmental research in terms of human purposes and meanings. Let us correlate environmental problems and forms with human thought content. We will then be able to separate effects from causes in our research and open doors to future settlement patterns truly expressive of ecological principles and of man's unfolding inner nature. It is inconceivable that man's outer world should not mirror his inner nature. The two are one.

FOURTH NEED – DEEPER PERCEPTIONS
AND CONCEPTIONS OF NATURE AND MAN

If we are to create humane possibilities for environmental design – for a healthy equilibrium between man and nature in our metropolitan areas, regions, watersheds and localities – we need fresh and deeper perceptions and conceptions of both man and nature. Otherwise in our present mood we will completely ravage nature and turn ourselves into automatons.

One of the breath-taking aspects of American history is the very brief span of years required for only a handful of people to exhaust and deplete vast amounts of forests, soils and wildlife. It is apparent that formidable human purposes were inwardly acceded to and at work in the 19th century.

Let us note here that "People Pose the Problems" of conservation not only or primarily because of sheer quantitative population pressures, but through the purposes and knowledge inwardly selected for realization in life.

*   *
*

Prior to the 16th century and the "Age of Science," there existed an intimate, concrete and personal contact between man and nature. In a sense man and nature were one. Now this oneness between man and nature is largely lost.

In our subsequent one-sided emphasis upon producing and consuming in our commercial culture we have acceded to viewing nature and ourselves almost entirely in terms of exchange value – as commodities. A commodity has no "being," no self-determination, no inner formative principle. A commodity has a "price." Commodities can be manipulated and organized as means toward monetary ends – as pure "resources." So we commonly speak in our researches and conservation work today of "natural resources" and "human resources."

The term "resources" is a narrow utilitarian concept and its widespread adoption indicates that this is the way we now prefer to view nature – as a set of commodities completely subverted to the price system and human consumption. But to view the earth as primarily a set of resources for conversion into our happiness is surely a dream of our adolescent years – now, perhaps, turning into a bad dream and possible into a future nightmare. And we persist in speaking about ourselves as "human resources" as if man could be other than his own end.

How can we awaken to truer thoughts and perceptions of man and nature? Surely not by simply extending quantitative methods and inorganic science. In the near future we can look forward to absorbing whole sets of regional surveys and resource inventories into exquisitely complex computers and running elaborate tests of alternative resource development schemes. This will bring us no further along the path toward enlightened development of our environment if our present concepts are still at work. Quantitative methods are of course necessary and are a great human achievement. What is now necessary is to go beyond them.

Western culture was the first to manipulate nature through the primary "scientific" concepts of motion and number and we have been taken in by them. We have learned to apprehend nature as matter made up of atoms, electrons, and, as of late, mysterious energy. Our perceptions of the formative living principles inherent in organic nature are almost completely repressed. Urban man under the spell of abstract monetary and physical concepts and locked up in cities, is now progressively estranged from a living experience and awareness of biological principles. The ancient bonds between man and nature are getting very weak. We cannot effectively relate our sense of responsibility, our weakened feeling or principles of ethics to nature if it is conceived as systems of electrons, energy or atoms.

It is time for our concept makers – our researchers – to make some clearer distinctions between the inorganic, the organic and human realms. In this way we may again recover a sense of the realities in nature and man beyond the quantitative that will open new possibilities for designing our environments.

Organic nature also presents itself to us not as just abstract matter or energy, but as something actively forming and expressing itself in the world. To understand it at this level we need to develop concepts adequate to these formative principles. We can then humanly relate ourselves to nature because we inwardly experience and express our own formative principles.

The kind of thought that we attach to our sensory impressions actually creates our facts, our conclusions and our meanings. In this sense when we perform research and create knowledge, we choose and determine our consciousness of the world. Up to now we have preferred to obscure our role in this regard.

The future possibilities for beautiful and balanced environments are bright if we choose to first understand and then bring into living ecological harmony the creative, formative principles evolving in both nature and ourselves. This will require, however, that we reject and then push beyond our reductive, quantitative notion of "natural resources" which is determining much of our conservation approach today. Whether we do this or not is an ethical choice.

FIFTH NEED – UNIFIED ENVIRONMENTAL DESIGN

This need involves healing the split between urban-oriented planning and watershed planning.

Regional planning has evolved only recently and its scope and methods are still in an experimental, formative stage. City planning, on the other hand, with roots that reach back into ancient civilization, has emerged in the United States since World War II as a widespread field of activity with relatively standardized theory, procedures and scope. It is focused upon improving the physical environment and guiding the future growth of individual cities.

The beginning of *regional metropolitan planning* in America dates only from the 1920's when metropolitan problems began to receive serious attention. Los Angeles County created the first Regional Planning Commission in 1922. The first completed regional plan, "A Regional Plan for New York and Its Environs' 'was privately sponsored by the New York Regional Planning Association in the 1920's.

The beginning of *regional watershed planning* is also quite recent, dating from the 1920's. Three basic and related ideas and their application have been progressively evolving since that time. These are: (1) the multiple use concept, (2) the watershed unit approach, and (3) unified environmental development.

The historically separate origins of metropolitan and watershed regional programs have resulted in separate and distinct education, theory, methods and institutionalization. These factors are now creating unfortunate limitations in solving environmental problems and needs when urban and watershed problems are interdependent. Unrealistic distinctions between urban and watershed concepts are being perpetuated in existing planning agencies, in university planning curricula and in the inherited structure and functions of local, state and federal resource-connected agencies.

As mentioned earlier, the first environmental planning programs in America had their origins in the city. This resulted in a deep pre-occupation with urban land use problems. The postwar metropolitan regional programs of today have not overcome this limitation. They do not commonly use concepts and procedures adequate to modern environmental problems. Natural elements – land, water, space and the sustaining larger environment – have not come into full focus as important basic elements in a healthful and desirable human environment. Consequently, factors such as regional stream pollution, agricultural problems, water allocation, open space, flood plain protection, recreation facilities, waste disposal and conservation needs receive inadequate consideration in most metropolitan programs.

On the other hand, this urban one-sidedness has been paralleled by specialized water, flood control and agricultural programs of the many federal, state and local agencies ranging from the Corps of Engineers to County Soil Conservation Districts. Many of their activities are fine examples of land-water studies. However, most of their programs unfortunately ignore the growing urban character and interrelationships of the problems and needs of our society. In many of their studies and programs it appears as if urban populations and cities hardly exist. This constitutes another one-sided approach to current environmental problems.

Present trends point to a vast increase in the regional diffusion of urban settlement with a resultant intermixture and blending of rural and urban environments. It is becoming apparent that present urban-oriented regional programs and present water-land oriented programs will not be adequate to deal with the new problems. Integrative adaptations are needed in professional educational curricula, in government agency functions and in the concepts and procedures of planning agencies. Our physical environment has been excessively divided and fragmented among specialists in urban areas, agriculture, land, water, public health, recreation and so forth in both education and government practices. A great many subject specialists, agencies and citizens are without coordinative concepts and factual data that permit awareness of present environmental interdependencies.

Important innovations in our times are the diffusion of urban population and activities across farming areas, the urbanization of farm populations, limited access highways, mass automotive transportation, vastly increased agricultural and industrial production, intensive use and consumption of natural resources, urban metropolitan aggregations, large and complex sewage treatment and water supply systems, mass recreation needs and pursuits and increasing incomes and leisure time. Most of these social and technological changes are only at their beginning. The problems created and the characteristics and needs of the future are in many respects already apparent. They require unified environmental study and design, integrating the heretofore one-sided procedures and concepts of metropolitan and water-land planning, for solution. Balanced attention needs to be given to all aspects of the environment – to water, land, agricultural, urban, industrial, residential and recreational needs.

In this context, land and water emerge as closely related resources. All human activities involve the use of both elements with varying effects. Water and land can no longer be meaningfully analyzed, developed or allocated in isolation from each other. Because water resources are more critical than land resources, watershed factors and water-use decisions will play a leading role in determining future environmental health conditions and economic development possibilities.

Conservation and nature management objectives in an urban age must now consider the total environmental complex as a problem in applied ecology. Conservation objectives need to be extended to urbanism in all its forms, including urban planning as one mode of land-water use and management.

And correspondingly, urban planning must extend its concepts to include all conservation principles and techniques. An urban plan for a city or metropolitan area is at the same time a general plan for land-water development, use and management, although this fact is not kept in awareness or made explicit under present urban planning practices.

An urban age, with 90% of our future population expected to live in cities and metropolitan complexes, clearly demands some form of unified environmental design. This will also be necessary for the creative reshaping of present metropolitan environments. It is a sobering commentary and rude shock to our scientific and technological pride to realize that we have not even mastered the elementary need for providing our urban populations with pure water and air. Such an attempt would require a fundamental transformation of our urban patterns.

Because of the absence of operative ecological principles in our perceptions and thought habits we find the following contradictions.

The whole history of American urbanism has been based upon the notion of growth as indefinitely extended. A state of relative equilibrium or balance, which is central to ecological insights, is defined as something abnormal or degenerative.

Quantitative concepts convert the earth successively into resources – commodities – dollars. Nature ends up obscured and obliterated in the statistical and monetary tables of economic base studies. We no longer see the elements of nature represented or symbolized, and any sense of limits is lost.

Conservation planning holds out great promise but it is apparent there is great work to be done.

Mr. FARNESS is Professor of Planning, School of Urban Planning and Landscape Architecture, Michigan State University, and was formerly Director of the Tri-County Regional Planning Commission, Lansing, Michigan.

The Unit of Survival is the Human Race

by

Hudson Hoagland

Throughout at least five hundred million years of biological evolution, there has been a paradox in that both social togetherness and aggressive combat have had survival value for the species. Individual animals, especially males, and rival groups and colonies of animals – invertebrates, fishes, birds and mammals – fight over territory. Man's wars have also been over territory – not only geographical and economic, but ideological too. Konrad Lorenz has called man an unusually quarrelsome ape. He has facetiously remarked that man appears to be the missing link between anthropoid apes and human beings. Man has evolved beyond individual combat but not yet beyond combat between groups and nations.

In only 18 years, since Hiroshima, this situation has changed profoundly in that fights between sovereign states can in the foreseeable future send man down to extinction. An environment of nuclear and biological weapons has, in our lifetime, made nationalistic aggressions a terrible liability. Adaptation to this new weapon-environment is hard to attain in view of both our biological and social history.

It has been said, probably incorrectly, that the dinosaurs became extinct because their brains were too small. We may become extinct because our recently evolved cerebral cortex may be too large – a sort of phylogenetic tumor that can produce absolute weapons but is unable to control our 100-million-year old hypothalamic and limbic centers to mediate hates and aggressions. While aggressive behavior is with us to stay, a major question is whether we can find alternative ways of expressing it in the resolution of international conflicts. Can lawless sovereignty be controlled or abolished before it abolishes us?

I suggest that there are some rays of hope.

Republished with permission from "The Humanist," 22, No. 2–3, 1962, published by the American Humanist Association, Yellow Springs, Ohio.

In the past we have fought our fellows over all sorts of issues but ideologies have been the major causes. It has been said that prior to this century more blood may have been shed over religious issues than over any other. One recalls the bloody religious and territorial Crusades of the 12th and 13th centuries and the terrible wars of the 16th century between Catholics and Protestants. Think how our own North and South hated each other over a century ago and of the two territorial and ideological world wars of this century. Twenty years ago we hated the Japanese and West Germans. Yet today they are our friends. Fortunately, there is an ephemeral quality about our xenophobias and other group hates. In contrast to this, men in increasing numbers are coming slowly to realize that there will be nothing ephemeral about a major nuclear war.

Communism is a mystique, a religion to which vast numbers of people adhere. But history teaches us, as with all religious intolerances, that its virus will ultimately become attenuated. Catholics and Protestants no longer want to kill each other. Nobody cares enough about the theological issues to fight over them. Given time, if we can get enough of it, we may expect, in the light of history, a similar resolution between the ideologies of the East and West.

Already over the last few decades there has been evidence of significant decreases in ideological differences between the West and the Soviet Union. Since STALIN's death, concentration camps have been abolished and political arrests have been greatly reduced. There is more freedom of speech, freedom in selection of place or residence and of work, and freedom to travel. Western tourists are encouraged to visit. Class distinctions and differences in earnings in the Soviet Union have increased. Thus, scientists, engineers and plant managers are members of elite groups and are highly paid compared to others.

SCIENCE AS MELIORATOR

The vastly extended program of science education in the Soviet Union and the high esteem in which science is held there is not compatible with fanatical faith in an authoritarian ideology. ANATOL RAPOPORT (1) has pointed out that the ethical principles inherent in scientific practice are based on the conviction that there exists objective truth and there are rules for discovering it. Moreover, on the basis of objective truth, unanimity is possible. But this unanimity must be achieved by independent arrivals at convictions, never through coercion, personal argument, or appeal to authority.

The concept of the dignity and brotherhood of man which is common to many ethical systems is a condition necessary to the pursuit of truth. Science leaves no room for the rationalization of quasi-ethical totalitarian ideologies and racial hatreds. These are maintained by coercion, by the exclusion of experience, and supported by sacrosanct fictions that are shattered once scientific inquiry is turned upon them. Repeatedly authoritarian myths and dogmas have succumbed to scientific inquiry.

Scientists are charged with special ethical concerns for the discovery of truth. But truth is never found in a final or ultimate sense. As J. BRONOWSKI (2) has said, a society that believes it has found ultimate truth simply imposes it by force and is an authoritarian society. Such a society is monolithic and resists all change. This is in contrast to a society that seeks the truth and must change and evolve progressively with new discoveries.

The fraternity of scientists transcends geographical and racial boundaries. Scientists can function only if they have mutual respect for each other as individuals. BRONOWSKI has pointed out that a scientist may be quite wrong in his conclusions without being wicked in the eyes of his fellows. This is in contrast to the thinking in static authoritarian societies where to dissent is heresy or treason. All scientists must be heretics and respected for their heresy in dealing with the status of current scientific concepts if science is not to remain static. Freedom of inquiry and of dissent is necessary for the advancement of science. Dogmatic ideologies are as much out of place in the behavioral and social sciences as they are in chemistry and physics. These ethical aspects of science are inevitably eroding to the dogmas of communism.

Whether we approve or not, the United States during the past 40 years has moved increasingly in the direction of practices that are regarded by many as socialistic. This further narrows the gap between East and West. The dominance of our central government is evidenced by our graduated federal income and inheritance taxes, by federal subsidies and contracts to private industry for defense purposes. It has been said that the third largest socialist economy in the world is our Department of Defense, ranking in size after the government of the Peoples Republic of China. Federal support of science, subsidies for farmers, and our social security and other welfare programs are also illustrations of this trend. In contrast to the increase in class distinctions in the Soviet Union, class distinctions in the United States have decreased over the last 40 years.

Today's Russian communism compared to that of a generation ago seems in some aspects of its practice closer to western democracy than it does to the fanatical communism of China, despite the continuing tensions of the cold war. Peiping holds that under KHRUSHCHEV's anti-Stalin line the Soviet Union has grown fat and bourgeois and lacks revolutionary zeal in dealing with the West. Thus social evolution on both sides reduces the conflict of ideologies and slowly prepares for a new era.

TRIBAL LOYALTIES ARE NOT ENOUGH

But the challenge of that new era faces us now. War can no longer serve as an instrument for continuing national diplomacies. The dedication of our foreign policy to the disarmament of nations and to a world order of law enforcible by a supranational agency could, I believe, galvanize world opinion if pressed with vigor and imaginative leadership. If we are to survive, man must develop loyalties to mankind to replace his parochial tribal loyalties and the hates they engender. The historian ARNOLD TOYNBEE (3) has said:

"Ye foolish teen-age-minded tribes and sects, have you not yet grasped the truth that all of you are inseparable fractions of the human race, and that, if you send mankind down the drain, you are bound to go down with it? We have to be human beings before we can be either Russians or Americans, either Communists or capitalists. If man commits genocide on mankind, not even a memory will survive of our precious nationalisms and ideologies."

Six months after Hiroshima, ALBERT EINSTEIN called upon his fellow scientists to make the world understand in these words:

"We can only sound the alarm again and again. We must never relax. We must never relax our efforts to arouse in the peoples of the world, and especially in their governments, an awareness of the unprecedented disaster which they are absolutely certain to bring on themselves unless there is a fundamental change in their attitudes toward one another as well as in their concept of the future. The unleashed power of the atom has changed everything except our way of thinking."

What is our way of thinking? In another context a century ago, LINCOLN put the problem in his second inaugural message. "The dogmas of the quiet past," he said, "are inadequate to the stormy present... as our case is new, so we must think anew and act anew. We must disenthrall ourselves, and then we shall save our country." He thus expressed the change from the individualist, pioneer society, to that of a unified nation. It was a turn from survival by individual combat to survival by group co-operation. It was the logic of history: "In union there is strength."

Our habits of thinking in relation to aggressive nationalism are deeply ingrained. A man's particular ingroup, be it family, clan, city, religion, political ideology, class or nation, is concerned with status, position and property. He regards the group into which he has accidentally been born as superior to other groups and calls on his gods for assurance and support. Like some other animals, e.g., ants, baboons and yaks, he is prepared to fight and die for his group. Foreigners, i.e., members of other groups of the same species and minority groups low in the pecking order, have always been objects of suspicion and antagonism. The socially accepted attitude is typified by "my country right or wrong" and "I'd rather be dead than red." One fights and dies for one's territory, whether one is a Siamese fighting fish, bird, rat, lion, elephant, seal, Athenian-Spartan, Roman-Carthaginian, Frenchman-Algerian, or an American or Russian in the nuclear age. These aggressive group aspects of human nature are a direct product of millions of years of biological evolution.

NEW PATTERNS OF THOUGHT ARE NEEDED

The beliefs we hold so strongly are mostly established by accident of birth and what we learn, hit or miss, before we are 7 years old. Emotionally charged prejudices are propagated from generation to generation by parental and adult prestige and by the use of myths and symbols. The strongest beliefs one holds may bear little relation to the facts and realities of life as related to the common good. Surely every group – every nationality – cannot be superior to every other group in the world at the same time, but such is parochial ethical belief and its products, chauvinistic nationalism and religious, class and racial intolerance. It is time now to extend the concept of unity from the nation to mankind – if only as a means of survival.

BROCK CHISHOLM(4), former Director-General of the World Health Organization, has expressed our dilemma. I quote him:

"Man must now learn to live with himself and to get along with all others in the world. He must reshape his entire pattern of thinking and behavior in order to build up a completely new system of human relationships adjusted to a changed world. We must realize that some of our ways of doing things are obsolete – one of them being the traditional method of group survival by ruthless competition with other groups. At this stage of world scientific and technical development, ruthless competition has to be replaced by cooperation based on mutual understanding, compromise and agreement.

Equal concern for the welfare of all people, for the whole human race, is not within the tradition into which any of us was born, so it has no conscience value. It has to be learned intellectually against the pressures of many and limiting loyalties which have strong emotional support. One of our most widely accepted faiths has been that the welfare, prestige, security and power of the group into which we happened to be born or adopted early in life are more important than all the rest of the people of the world. This is absurd, but difficult to grow out of. Most of us have been entirely the creatures of accident; the accident of time, place, and family of our birth – all of which are very poor and unreliable reasons for believing anything. Example: the press picture of a gaggle of Southern mothers with children in arms screaming imprecations at a clergyman and his child at a desegregated school.

Yet most children in the world are still being taught that utterly false doctrine which makes the welfare of part of the human race more important than that of the whole. The development of children has become a highly complicated matter because of the new kind of adjustment to the reality that is needed in this world as it is now. Every prejudice, every orthodoxy which limits freedom of thought, each prescribed and unchangeable attitude, is an obstacle in the way of developing better human relations and peace in the world. We need to stop giving children final answers, rights and wrongs, local or any other kind of certainties; and to allow them to look at everything, encouraging them to prepare to do their own independent thinking.

The most pressing problem of our generation seems to be the necessity to liberate our children from our own limiting loyalties. If we can do that, then they will be able to cope with the population explosion, food distribution on a world basis, security – which means a world police force – and all the other problems and threats to humanity with which we are showing ourselves unable to deal.

For the first time in the history of the world we must recognize that the unit of survival is the human race. We will survive to prosper as the human race or not at all."

In short, survival depends on a grueling race between education and disaster.

TO OPPOSE WORLD DOMINATION
– NOT COMMUNIST IDEOLOGY AS SUCH

In connection with our ways of thinking and how our thinking might be changed, HENRY A. MURRAY (5) has made valuable suggestions. He proposes that our government should announce clearly and unequivocally that the objective of our foreign policy is to abolish war and institute enforcible world law and world government as the only alternative to domination of the world by one state. Even if communism is abolished everywhere, there is no guarantee of peace because of man's group aggressions and lack of enforcible international law to control them.

We should stress the ideal of world fellowship through the use of "art, heart and intellect." From this an imaginative symbolism and mythology could yield new art forms and depth dimensions. MURRAY holds that it is basically true that people prefer harmony to discord, affection to disaffection, peace to war, life to death – and that they can be educated from birth to moderate their aspirations for profit, property, power and prestige.

MURRAY insists we should stop defining our opposition to communism as a religious and ideological war. Indeed, we should stop using the word communism and stop proclaiming that our policy is to "fight communism," because that word carries a religious potency to redress ancient wrongs among underprivileged and formerly exploited peoples. Our expression of hatred for communism merely increases its fanaticisms and drive, and hence the achievements of its supporters. He argues that the productivity of the Soviet Union and China mount if we retain our dragon role. In a socialist economy the problem is how to maintain the motivation of workers. It can't be for money and private property as with us, but we are giving them the challenge, the incentive, and their forward thrust by our very menace. We reinforce bonds between communistic countries by our irrevocable opposition.

But if we state that we are opposed to any single state that proposes to dominate the world, our position will accord with those of other countries, including the Soviet satellites, conceivably in accord with the Soviet Union itself vis-a-vis the inflated ambitions of China. In any case, we shall be weakening the links that bind the communist bloc.

MURRAY maintains that if we hold that it is communism we're fighting, we will automatically become the enemy of every country converted to communism, which now means about one third of the population of the earth. Through their propaganda fanned by mutual hates, we become the presupposed cause of all the grievances of the masses and the target of their vindictiveness. We should stress that while we are utterly opposed to communism at home we do not dictate to other states their religion or internal politics.

Finally, MURRAY points out that we should break up the ideology of communism and anti-communism into their component parts. They are:

a. state capitalism vs. private capitalism.

b. autocracy and total control of people vs. democracy and partial control.

c. hypertrophy of ambition for world power vs. moderation or suppression of such ambition.

d. the importunate conversion of peoples by covert penetration, deceit, and violence vs. gradual conversion, if any is attempted, by forthright persuasion and demonstration.

By this separation the word communism is stripped of its unholy power to arouse bellicose emotions. The real enemy is exorbitant ambition for world power and the devilish means that the communists have devised to attain it.

MURRAY says we should congratulate the USSR on its truly astonishing achievements and on the extension of internal freedom since STALIN. The Russians are hungry for praise as we were 130 years ago for praise from the British. Thus, we should welcome and aid the development of their consumer goods industries – thus soften their ardor and share their desire for the good life.

The Greek poet HESIOD, writing in the 8th Century B.C., said: "Zeus has ordained this law for men, that fishes and beasts and winged fowls should devour one another, for right is not in them; but to mankind he gave right which proves far best." Unfortunately during the intervening 2700 years mankind has never been able to agree upon what is right, and nations have devoured each other, each in the name of its own righteousness. Different versions of what is right held by conflicting groups have been the source of our wars and major calamities. The threat of nuclear extinction is now holding these differences in check, but this balance of terror is too precarious to endure.

It is imperative that nations disarm and negotiate their differences and come to accept a world of enforcible law. Our choice is between ultimate destruction by accident or design on the present course and a chance not only of survival but of a rich future for mankind. There are risks in breaking out of the temporary security of the arms deadlock, but they are far less than the continuation of nationalism uncontrolled by law.

There have been a number of plans proposed for disarmament and for the control of national aggressions. One of the most promising of these is described in "World Peace Through World Law" by GRENVILLE CLARK & LOUIS B. SOHN(6). The authors have presented detailed plans for modifications of the United Nations Charter and the operations of a progressively strengthened United Nations as an instrument for the controlled disarmament of nations and maintenance of peace.

World ethical thinking is hard to change, but it does change. There are a number of human institutions and practices that were supported in the past by the thought and ethics of the best men of their times. These include slavery, infanticide, burning of witches, gladiatorial circuses, and religious human sacrifices. The abolition of these practices was thought to be contrary to human nature, but they have been abolished. War also is a human institution, and we know that it must be abolished or, President KENNEDY has said, it will abolish us. This is the great challenge to our species, and the decision of our generation can be final.

BIBLIOGRAPHY

1 ANATOL RAPOPORT, "The Scientific Approach to Ethics." *Science*, 125: 796 (1957).
2 JACOB BRONOWSKI, "The Values of Science." New Knowledge in Human Values. ABRAHAM H. MASLOW, Editor, Harper & Brothers, New York (1959).
3 ARNOLD TOYNBEE in *Globe Magazine*, Toronto Globe and Mail, Nov. 18. 1961.
4 "BROCK CHISHOLM: What interests me most in the world today." Julie Medlock. *World Union* 1, 22 (1961).
5 HENRY A. MURRAY, "Unprecedented Evolutions." Evolution and Man's Progress. Edited by HUDSON HOAGLAND and RALPH BURHOE. Columbia University Press (1962). (Also in summer, 1961, issue of *Daedalus*, p. 547.)
6 GRENVILLE CLARK & LOUIS B. SOHN. World Peace through World Law. Second Edition. Harvard University Press, Cambridge (1960).

HUDSON HOAGLAND, Ph. D., Sc. D., has been Executive Director of the Worcester Foundation for Experimental Biology since 1944. He was Visiting Lecturer in Physiological Psychology at Harvard University in 1945–46 and Research Professor of Physiology, Tufts Medical School from 1946 to 1950, and at Boston University since 1950. Professor HOAGLAND is President of the American Academy of Arts and Sciences. He is a Fellow of the World Academy of Art and Science. The present article was presented as the closing address given under the title "Prospects for Survival" at the first national Conference of the Congress of Scientists on Survival in New York, June 17, 1962. It was published in The Humanist, 22, No. 2–3 (1962) and is republished with permission.

Population and Food Supply

by

ROBERT C. COOK

FOOD NEEDS IN RELATION TO POPULATION GROWTH IN VARIOUS REGIONS

Although it is unfortunately true that gluts of food arise periodically in those areas in which there is least need for more food, it is equally true that a majority of the people now living on the earth do not have enough to eat, and unless the present rate of expansion in food production is greatly accelerated, their hunger will not be appreciably assuaged within the next decades. Thus, in the light of present population trends, the efforts now being made to solve the world's problem of hunger are not realistic.

In the world picture of food needs and population growth, these four features deserve to be highlighted:

(i) Demographic changes take place slowly. There is no prospect that there will be a sudden decline in the world birth rate. Barring catastrophes, there is a good prospect that the world death rate will decline still further. Hence, during the immediate future extending over the next few decades, there is every prospect that population growth will continue at a rapid rate.

(ii) A vast increase in the production of food to meet the inevitable population increases over the next decades is imperative if appalling disasters are to be averted and the possibility of an orderly and constructive transition to a satisfactory, stable balance between food and population is to be assured.

(iii) If such a transition is to be achieved, the magnitude of the operation must be recognized. It is all very well to say that "much more food can be produced." To create the technology and the education and the storage and transportation facilities and everything else required to bring this transition to pass is an operation on a scale far vaster than anything contemplated in the plans either of individual governments or of the co-operative undertakings now contemplated by United Nations agencies.

Reprinted in part from United Nations "Freedom from Hunger Campaign" Basic Study no. 7, August 1962 by kind permission.

(iv) Indefinite multiplication of people on a finite planet is impossible. If the rate of population growth which is occurring in some areas of the world today were to be applied to the total human population of the planet, within only two or three centuries the entire land surface of the earth would be covered with human beings.

There is a definite limit to the number of human beings that the earth can accommodate. It would not be realistic, at the present stage of scientific development, to take into account space travel and other technological advances as factors offering a possible solution to the problem. If there is ever to be enough and to spare for all – if the promises of security, and freedom from hunger and fear are to be realized – stabilization of population will eventually be unavoidable. How long it can be postponed without the gravest consequences is one of the most important questions facing humanity today.

Population predictions

The question of the amount of food necessary to feed future populations hinges on the balance of births and deaths around the world. The critical area is represented by the 2,000 million people living in the high-birth-rate, technologically under-developed countries.

The rates of population growth which now exist offer scant prospect of improved economic conditions for the people of the under-developed countries; in fact, the reverse is the case. During the next decade, if present trends are maintained the world will tend to become divided even more markedly into two distinct groups, as follows:

(i) The demographically stable, industrialized nations enjoying relatively high levels of living, where effective fertility regulation exists or is developing. This includes the whole of Europe, the Soviet Union, North America, the temperate-zone countries of Latin America, Oceania and Japan.

(ii) The demographically unstable, largely subsistence-level countries that are now struggling toward economic development; almost two-thirds of the world's people live in these countries. In none of them does there seem to have been any effective effort to reduce fertility, except on the part of numerically insignificant minorities of the population. This group of countries includes all non-Soviet Asia (except Japan and Israel), tropical Latin America, and most of Africa. The "rising expectations" that swept the world of the early 1950's are in danger of being extinguished by the new multitudes born into very marginal conditions of living, and needing to be fed, clothed and housed.

The persistence of poverty and hunger in the face of the very real potential for food production and economic development in Brazil demonstrates a tragic truth: little advantage is gained from such a potential if the ability and capacity to exploit the natural resources and to build up social and economic capital do not proceed hand in hand with population growth.

The large proportion of children in Brazil constitutes an unproductive segment of the population that requires not only food but also expensive investments in schools and health services. These requirements for social capital grow rapidly and divert capital resources from development of the means of production. The interplay of economic and demographic factors in this area as elsewhere, is extremely complex and can only be stated in general terms. Developmental economic theory is still in the exploratory stages and enjoys nothing like the elegance of classical economics.

CITIES AND FOOD

The agricultural revolution, the increasing power to control epidemic diseases, and improved transportation have all combined to usher in a new era in the growth of cities. The city, in turn, has had far-reaching influences on the quantities and qualities of both mouths and calories – and its influences have greater and greater force today, in the economically "developed" as well as the economically under-developed countries.

As has been pointed out above, world population is growing at an unprecedented rate today; and the rate of growth of urban population is even greater. Today, over 20% of the world's people, or more than 500 million live in urban areas of 20,000 or more inhabitants, compared with only about 2% in 1800. Over three-fifths of today's city dwellers (13% of total world population) live in cities of 100,000 or more.

The United Nations Report on the World Social Situation, 1957,[1] referring to the sudden spurt of urban growth in under-developed countries in recent years, points out that by 1950 Asia had one-third of the world's total large-city (100,000 or more) population. Comparing the trends of urban and rural population growth in various parts of the world, the Report points out that whereas in the majority of the less-developed countries the rural population has also increased, though at a slower rate, the absolute size of the rural population in many of the more developed countries has remained stationary or even declined.

In 1950, the world's major regions of industrial urban settlement were Australasia, northwestern Europe, northern America, northeast Asia, and southern South America. These areas included about 25% of total world population but 52% of the total living in cities of 100,000 or more. Australasia was the most heavily urbanized, with 47% in cities of that size.

During the past twenty years, the USSR has been undergoing extensive urbanization. In 1959, 48% of the USSR population was living in cities, compared with only 32% in 1939. In twenty years, the urban population grew by almost 40 million, an increase of two-thirds. In 1949, 23% of the total population and almost 50% of the urban population lived in cities of 100,000 or more.

1. United Nations, Bureau of Social Affairs, Report on the World Social Situation, Sales No. 1957 IV.3. E/CN.5/324/Rev. 1 ST/SOA/33.

It has been estimated that 20 million mainland Chinese migrated from rural to urban areas between 1949 and 1956. Mainland China's inland cities have experienced a remarkable rate of growth. Estimates indicate that in the western provinces alone, Lanchow grew from 200,000 in 1950 to 680,000 in 1956; Paotow from 90,000 in 1949 to 430,000 in 1957, and Kalgan from 270,000 in 1949 to 1,050,000 in 1957. Furthermore, there is a heavy concentration of mainland China's urban population in the larger cities.

In some regions of the world, a single large city – usually the capital city – contains a high proportion both of a nation's total population and of its urban population. In many countries, well over 50% of all the urban population is concentrated in the capital city. This is especially true of several Latin American countries. More than one-fourth of all Latin Americans live in cities of 20,000 or more and about one-fifth live in cities of 100,000 or more.

The concensus of competent opinion appears to be that in the world as a whole, the trend toward the city is by no means at an end. Even in the highly urbanized industrial nations of the Western world, it appears that the proportion of the population residing in major metropolitan agglomerations will continue to grow. The rural population, which is by no means entirely devoted to agricultural pursuits at the present time, constitutes less than 20% of the total; the farming population is less than 10%.

In the agrarian countries, an overwhelming majority still lives on the land. There, employment is to a large extent inadequate and unproductive, so the present large drift to the city can be expected to continue. The effect of this migration will largely depend on the speed with which industry will be able to create jobs.

How urbanization affects food supplies

The persistent and accelerating movement of population towards the cities increases the already complicated problem of hunger in the economically less-developed regions of the world. This fact is significant for the following reasons:

In the first place, an increase in the supply of *marketable* food is needed. A greater output of food does not necessarily result in a greater surplus for the urban population, and in countries where farming is still at subsistence level the farm population, itself increasing, may consume much of its increased output rather than selling it. Therefore, the production of food must rise considerably faster than the growth of the farm population if there is to be enough food for urban markets.

Secondly, more food must be taken to the cities, and for this, better transportation facilities are needed. In many cases these are practically nonexistent or are totally inadequate to meet the new demands made on them.

Thirdly, facilities for storing and preserving food must be set up, particularly where large year-to-year fluctuations in crops make it difficult to secure a steady supply of food. At present there is a high proportion of waste in the under-developed regions and stored food is often spoiled by rats, mice and insects.

Lastly, food supply is not the only problem connected with urbanization, housing, health and civic services are needed, and capital is often diverted from the production and distribution of food to social development programmes.

The United Nations Report on the World Social Situation [2] sums up the problem as follows:

"Ideally, productivity in agriculture would rise at a rate meeting the cities' growing demands for food as well as the demands of export markets while permitting the release of agricultural workers at a rate meeting the rising demand for labour in industry and services. In practice the transition does not proceed so smoothly, and in many countries today something quite different is happening: productivity is hardly increasing at all, while masses of rural workers come to the cities looking for jobs that either do not exist or from which they are barred by illiteracy and lack of skills."

PRESENT FOOD SUPPLIES
AND ESTIMATED FUTURE REQUIREMENTS

Present food deficits

There are vast differences in diets throughout the world. These reflect such factors as types of crops and livestock produced, food preferences, level of living, and amount of trade.

The common pattern in most countries is a basic reliance on staple cereals and starchy foods. These are supplemented, when consumers can afford them, with the more expensive, nutritionally protective foods. As incomes rise above subsistence level, the more expensive foods are first added to diets and then begin to replace the staple foods.

Some idea of the imbalance in the relation between the population and the food production of various regions can be gathered from Table I, which shows the relative shares of the world's agricultural production (nearly 90% of which consists of food and food crops) and of the world's population in the various regions for the year 1958.

Most information on national diets consists of estimates of average food supplies available per person. In considering the information, two things must be kept in mind. First, the data that they are based on are often scanty or inadequate, so that the results are, at best, an approximation.Second, extensive studies have shown that even in the best fed countries of the world, there are large groups of people with low incomes whose diet is

2. Op. cit (1957).

deficient in protective food. Therefore, when a country's average per capita food supply is barely adequate, a large proportion of the population is subsisting on a sub-marginal diet. Despite these limitations, existing figures do provide a useful measure of the pattern of food consumption throughout the world.

By any standard, diets are poorest in the Far East, the region which contains over half the world's population. Throughout most of this region, the people have a daily average *per capita* calorie intake considerably below the standard estimated by FAO as adequate, taking into account the climate and physical size of the inhabitants. It is estimated that between 300–500 million of the population in this region is under-nourished and an additional 500 million do not get enough food of the right kind. The percentage of calories obtained from grains, starchy roots and sugar is an inverse indicator of quality of diet, and this figure is extremely high, in the Far East (about 80%). Consumption of meats, vegetables, fruits, pulses, and other quality foods is correspondingly low. In terms of minimal adequate diet, therefore, the situation in this area is far from satisfactory.

TABLE I

Regional Shares of the World's Agricultural Production and Population for the Year 1958

Region	Agricultural production (per cent)	Population (per cent)	Index of Per Capita production (World average = 100)
Western Europe	15	11	133
Eastern Europe (incl. USSR)	17	10	162
Northern America	21	7	316
Latin America	8	7	121
Far East	28	53	53
Near East	4	4	90
Africa	4	7	60
Oceania	3	1	583
World Total	100	100	100

Source: Estimates supplied by FAO.

While the energy content of the diet in Africa is higher than in the Far East, the quality of the diet is poorer due to the heavy dependence on starchy foods. Diets in the Near East and Latin America are generally better than those in the Far East and in Africa. Many of these countries have an average *per capita* intake of over 3000 calories; but in other countries the diet is below this level. The greatest need of these regions is for proteins of high nutritive value. In the rest of the world, particularly the industrialized countries, the situation is much better. Intake of calories averaged about

3000 *per capita* and the proportion derived from grain, starchy roots and sugar ranges from 40% in North America to about 63% in Europe.

A comparison of estimated levels of *per capita* consumption of food for immediate pre-war, early post-war, and recent periods is shown in Table II.

Two points are readily apparent from that table. The diets in the developed and under-developed countries are widely different in all three respects. While the developed countries have surpassed pre-war levels of calories and proteins, the under-developed countries are still below pre-war levels of proteins, and only just above pre-war levels of calories. This is in spite of the great efforts that have been made to increase the world's food supplies.

How far are existing levels below desirable levels? Exact measurement is difficult because while there is general agreement on what characterizes good and poor diets, there is no widespread agreement on nutritional requirements or standards except for calories.

TABLE II

Levels of Daily per Capita Consumption of Food by Regions and Groups of Countries

Regions	Calories			Total protein (grams)			Animal protein (grams)		
	Immediate Prewar	Postwar	Recent	Immediate Prewar	Postwar	Recent	Immediate Prewar	Postwar	Recent
Far East	2120	1910	2070	63	54	56	8	6	8
Near East	2320	2190	2470	76	70	76	15	14	14
Africa	2180	2100	2360	61	61	61	15	15	11
Latin America	2140	2380	2470	66	67	67	30	29	25
Europe	2850	2870	3040	85	91	88	27	31	36
Northern America	3140	3120	3120	89	90	93	50	60	66
Oceania	3270	3180	3250	97	95	94	65	65	62
Group I*	2130	1960	2150	63	56	58	10	8	9
Group II*	2910	2850	3060	86	91	90	33	40	44
World	2410	2260	2420	72	66	68	18	18	20

Source: SUKHATME, P. V. (1961), "The World's Hunger and Future Needs in Food Supplies," *J. Roy. Statist. Soc.*, Series A (General); 124, 477.
* The Group I countries include the Far East, Near East, Africa and Latin America (except River Plate countries). The Group II countries include Europe, northern America, River Plate countries and Oceania. These groups correspond fairly closely to the under-developed and developed countries of the world.

However, in recent studies conducted in FAO certain targets have been set for daily *per capita* consumption of calories and animal proteins and the comparison of these targets with estimated actual levels of consumption affords at least an approximate indication of the extent of present deficiencies. For calories, these targets are based on the widely accepted FAO calorie requirement scale. Those for animal proteins are based on the consideration to bring the quality of the diets in the under-developed countries some-what closer to the levels enjoyed by the developed countries in so far as this is feasible and advisable under the conditions of the under-developed countries. Such a comparison is shown in Table III for the four "under-nourished" regions: Far East, Near East, Africa, and Latin America except the River Plate countries.

While the present averages of consumption of calories in the Near East, Africa and Latin America are at or near the target figures, there is a deficien-cy of some 10% in the Far Eastern region. Deficiencies of animal protein consumption are however more serious, and this is so not only in the Far East, but in the Near East and Africa as well.

TABLE III

Present Levels and Minimum Targets for Daily
Per Capita Consumption of Types of Foods in Under-Nourished Areas of the World

	Far East		Near East		Africa		Latin America*		Total Under-Nourished areas	
	Present	Target	Present	Target	Present	Target	Present	Target	Present	Target
Calories	2070	2300	2470	2470	2360	2460	2370	2410	2150	2340
Animal Protein (grammes)	8	15	14	20	11	20	19	20	9	16
Index	100	141	100	117	100	128	100	105	100	133

Source: SUKHATME P. V. (*op. cit.*), pp. *498* and *504*.
* Excluding River Plate countries.

The "index" shown in this table represents the proportionate increase in *per capita* consumption required to achieve a minimum level of adequate diet at the least cost, within realistic possibilities of change. The data indi-cate that the level of diet in the under-developed countries of the world would have to be raised by a third, on the average, to achieve these targets.

Trends in demand for foodstuffs

A number of factors have an important bearing on the trends in demand for foodstuffs. Probably the most important factor influencing the total world demand is that of population growth. The average growth of world population from 1950–59 has been estimated at 1.7% per year, but this rate varies by regions from less than 1% in Europe to nearly 3% in Middle America (Central America, Mexico, and the Caribbean region).

The age and sex composition of population also influence food requirements since the needs of children, women, and men vary. The large proportion of children in rapidly growing populations may reduce average calorie requirements to some extent. But this is probably outweighed by the fact that children and young adults both need large amounts of proteins.

A third factor, as we have seen, is urbanization, and a fourth is the effect of rising incomes on food consumption.

Post-war experience has demonstrated the accuracy of the 1943 Hot Springs Conference declaration that "The first cause of hunger and malnutrition is poverty." The demand for food at existing levels of income in the under-developed countries often does not produce diet which is sufficiently nutritious.

TABLE IV

Estimated Percentage of Calories Derived from Cereals,
Starchy Roots, and Sugars for Areas and Selected Countries

Area	Per cent	Area	Per cent
Far East	80	Europe and USSR	63
China (mainland)	83	Federal Republic of Germany	50
India	76	United Kingdom	48
		USSR	72
Near East	72		
Egypt	77	Northern America	40
Turkey	75	Canada	43
		USA	40
Africa	74		
Morocco	75	Oceania	48
Nigeria	74	Australia	49
		New Zealand	43
Latin America	64		
Argentina	51	Under-nourished areas	78
Mexico	72	Well-nourished areas	57
		World	70

Source: SUKHATME (*op. cit.*), page *493*.

Studies by FAO [3] indicate a remarkable uniformity in the relation between income and expenditure on food over a wide range of countries at different levels of income and economic development, despite wide variation in cultures and food habits. In economies where most of the population is at the margin of subsistence, the main effect of an increase in income will be an increased demand for food. In such countries, an increase of 1% in income leads to an increase of between 0.7 and 0.8% in demand for food. This ratio may be referred to as the "income elasticity of food." But as average income increases, the demand for food does not

3. FAO, *State of Food and Agriculture*, 1957, pp. 70–110; 1960, p. 113.

increase in the same proportion. Therefore, if the programmes for economic
development in the under-developed countries should succeed in raising
per capita income for any length of time, the induced demand for food
would eventually abate at a higher level of consumption. None the less,
this immediate increased demand is an important consideration in the development of countries with low incomes.

In the more developed countries, the "income elasticity of food" described in the preceding paragraph, is about 0.4; for grains and starchy
foodstuffs, it is lower still, and even assumes a negative value. Thus, an
increase in *per capita* incomes in these countries leads to a relative decline in
demand for basic foods, and contributes to the food surpluses that have
appeared in some relatively advanced countries.

The difficulty of obtaining satisfactory nutrition under low-income conditions is indicated by the figures in Table V which shows the number of
hours a worker receiving the average manufacturing wage rate in specified
countries must work to earn the cost of one day's food for one person at
three dietary levels. The first dietary level is representative of economically
under-developed countries; the second, of countries at an early stage of
industrialization, the third, of economically advanced countries. Each diet
is composed and priced in terms of food customarily eaten in the specified
country.

Clearly, the more nutritious and expensive diets are beyond the means of
the average factory worker with a family in the economically under-
developed countries. Moreover, since the incomes of factory wage-earners
are usually higher than the incomes of farmers and farm workers, and the
latter make up the bulk of the labour force in under-developed countries,

TABLE V

*Number of Hours of Work Required for an Average Factory Worker to Earn the Cost (at 1953 Retail Prices)
of Three Representative Diets for One Person for One Day, in Selected Countries*

	Diet 1	Diet 2	Diet 3
Calories	2100	2500	3000
Grammes animal protein	10-12	15-20	40-45
Hours of work required:			
India	2.1	2.9	4.5
Japan	1.8	2.3	3.8
Italy	1.1	1.5	3.2
Mexico	0.6	0.8	1.4
Sweden	0.4	0.6	0.9
Denmark	0.3	0.4	0.7
Canada	0.2	0.3	0.5
United States	0.2	0.2	0.4

Source: FAO, *State of Food and Agriculture,* 1957, p. 108.

the calculations of hours of work shown in the table may well be optimistic.

The importance of income in determining both the level and pattern of food consumption indicates the essential connexion between economic development and progress in nutrition. As the 1957 FAO report on the State of Food and Agriculture points out, no substantial improvement in nutrition is likely until productivity is raised and the general run of people in a country earn higher incomes, although there may be some improvement for the population as a whole and major improvements for special groups such as expectant and nursing mothers, and children of school and pre-school age. Such improvements may be brought about, in the absence of income changes, by such means as nutritional education and special welfare schemes.

Population growth and food requirements

In considering how population growth affects the need for food, it should be made clear that the statement on page 458, that "the level of diet in the under-developed countries of the world would have to be raised by a third" if minimum dietary targets are to be achieved, applies only to existing population levels and does not take into account the additional food which will be needed for growing populations. When FAO's *First World Food Survey* was published in 1946, the growth of world population was estimated at about 1% per year. The current estimates quoted above show an average rate of 1.7% in the world as a whole during the 1950's, and the future projections indicate even more rapid growth. In the developed countries, which are already enjoying adequate average levels of nutrition, population is expected to increase 28% over the 1958 level by 1980. On the other hand, the population of the under-developed countries as a group is expected to increase by 56%.

The estimates shown in Table VI indicate that food supplies in the under-developed countries must more than double between 1958 and 1980 if the increasing population is to be fed at a minimum adequate nutritional standard. This means an annual average rate of increase of nearly $3\frac{1}{2}$% in food supplies. This is a higher rate than the average annual increase in food production over the past seven years in these countries.

Although annual increases of food production for the world as a whole have been greater than this over the past few years, much of the increase has taken place in the economically developed countries. Moreover, although in under-developed countries, agricultural production has increased only somewhat faster than population growth, the situation is entirely different in the economically developed countries. Food supplies in countries which were already adequately fed have increased, and, particularly in North America, surplus food stocks have developed despite sustained efforts to control production.

Thus, both in quality and quantity, the nutritional gap between the

TABLE VI

Percentage Increases of Food Supply Needed During 1958–1980
to meet Anticipated Requirements in Various Regions of the World

	Projected population growth 1958–1980[a]	Per capita increase of food supply presently required to meet target	Total increase of food supply, 1958–1980 required to meet target and population growth	Rate of annual increase needed 1958–1980	Recent annual rate of increase in food supply [b]
Regions					
Under-developed Countries	56	33	107	3.4	2.7
Latin America	85 [c]	5 [c]	94 [c]	3.1 [c]	2.5 [d]
Far East	55	41	86	2.9	3.0 [e]
Near East	62	17	90	3.0	3.1
Africa	36	28	55	2.0	1.3
Developed Countries	28	—	28	1.2	3.6
World	48	14	69	2.4	2.9

[a] Based on United Nations "Medium" projections as shown in "The Future Growth of World Population" (United Nations Publications, Sales No. 58 XIII 2).
[b] Computed from averages of food production in 1952/53 and 1959/60, FAO, *State of Food and Agriculture*, 1960, and FAO, *Yearbook*, 1959.
[c] Excluding River Plate countries.
[d] Including River Plate countries.
[e] Excluding mainland China.

economically less advanced regions and the economically advanced countries has tended to widen.

These trends have been the result of the paradoxical supply and demand situation in developed and under-developed countries. In the economically advanced countries, agricultural output can be expanded easily because of the high level of technology and relatively abundant capital available to farmers. With food consumption already at a high level, increases in *per capita* income go mainly into non-agricultural goods. This, coupled with a moderate population growth, results in slow growth in markets for agricultural commodities, so surplus stocks have tended to accumulate.

In the less-developed countries, agricultural output is increased only with difficulty. With a rapidly growing population, demand is rising rapidly and, while a good deal of any increased income is spent on food, the low level of income precludes purchase at commercial prices of agricultural commodities produced by the advanced countries. Free or "cut-rate" distribution of food from the food-surplus areas could disrupt the agricultural economies of the under-developed areas, setting off a chain of reactions which would not be useful to discuss here.

Agricultural policies of the developed and under-developed countries

TABLE VII

Grain Area, Production and Yields 1948–52 and 1956–58, for Regions of the World

(Area-million hectares; production-million tons; yield-tons per hectare.)

		1948–52	1956–58	Percentage increase
World	Area	609	665	9
	Production	699	911	31
	Yield	1.15	1.37	9
Europe (exc. USSR)	Area	72	74	3
	Production	108	132	22
	Yield	1.50	1.79	19
Northern America	Area	104	94	−9
	Production	169	189	12
	Yield	1.63	2.01	23
Latin America	Area	28	35	25
	Production	31	41	32
	Yield	1.11	1.17	5
Near East	Area	22	28	27
	Production	24	31	29
	Yield	1.09	1.11	2
Far East	Area	231	257	11
	Production	252	352	40
	Yield	1.09	1.37	26
Africa	Area	41	44	7
	Production	27	30	10
	Yield	1.52	1.47	−3
Oceania	Area	6.3	6.2	−2
	Production	6.8	6.6	−3
	Yield	1.08	1.07	−1
USSR *	Area	105	126	20
	Production	81	128	58
	Yield	0.77	1.02	32

* Includes pulses.

Source: FAO *Production Yearbook*, Volume 13.

reflect the situation just outlined. In the more advanced countries, these policies have been aimed largely towards adjusting agricultural production to the level of domestic demand and commercial exports and towards bringing the incomes of farmers more into line with those of other occupations. These policies, however, have not been completely successful in achieving either aim. The result has been a trend towards lower relative farm incomes and unused production.

In the less-developed countries, agricultural policies have, in contrast, been aimed largely at increasing agricultural output through capital investment and increasing productivity. Price policies have been established largely to protect consumers and avoid inflation, although the use of producer incentive prices is now beginning to encourage increased output.

Prospects for increasing food production

The levels of food production *per capita* in various regions of the world since before the war are shown in Table VIII.

A quick inspection of this table might suggest optimistic conclusions regarding the trend of *per capita* food production in recent years, since world *per capita* production is now well above the pre-war average. However, of the under-developed regions (Latin America, the Far East, the Near East and Africa), only in the Near East has *per capita* food production exceeded pre-war levels in the last three years.

What are the prospects for the under-developed areas? Region by region, the prospects over the next decade appear to be as follows:

Near East

This area as a whole now produces most of the food it consumes. Except in the case of the United Arab Republic and Libya, there are no substantial imports of food. Consumption *per capita* in terms of calories per day ranges from a little over 2000 in Iran to over 2700 in Israel, the latter being the only country with a fairly high quality of diet. In other countries, grain products – mainly wheat – are the mainstay of the diet. However, consumption of fruits and vegetables is relatively high in nearly all the countries.

It is probable that over the next decade agricultural production in the Near East will increase slightly faster than population growth.

The United Arab Republic faces a problem of limited land and water resources with which to grow food for a large and rapidly growing population. Food deficits will probably increase in the future.

Latin America

This region promises to remain a problem as regards food. With present population growth, it is doubtful whether agricultural output can keep pace with population growth. Consumption of food *per capita* varies widely among the countries – ranging from less than 1900 calories per day in Haiti* to nearly 3.000 calories per day in Uruguay. Argentina and Uruguay produce nearly all the food they consume and export substantial quantities. Most of the countries are trying to achieve greater self-sufficiency and had had considerable success, but unless more effort is devoted to agriculture, net food imports will probably increase over the next decade.

In common with other under-developed areas, Latin America is going through a period of rapid social change. The existing systems of land tenure may change in the years ahead, possibly causing a temporary disruption in food and agricultural production.

---

* This estimate was made before the hurricane disaster in October 1963, Ed.

Africa

If the political problems of emerging statehood can be mastered quickly, the outlook for increased agricultural output *per capita* over the next decade is good. Consumption of calories per day ranges from over 2100 *per capita* in several countries to over 2600 *per capita* in others. No country has to rely on substantial imports of food, and a number produce food commodities for export.

The substantial land and water resources available for development will be a great asset if capital and technical assistance are extended.

Far East

This is the world's chief problem area as regards food. Once a net exporter of grain, it has become a large net importer since the second World War. It still produces large export surpluses of fats and oils, rubber, tin, and jute which earn a large proportion of its foreign exchange.

Although food production has increased since the immediate post-war period, output *per capita* is still below pre-war levels, strikingly so in several countries. Food consumption is considerably below the estimated requirements as indicated earlier.

All the countries in the region have begun long-range development plans for agriculture. A number of problems threaten the successful accomplishment of these plans: lack of sufficient capital for investment, high illiteracy rates, particularly among farmers, soils badly depleted in some areas by centuries of cultivation, and a constantly declining amount of arable land *per capita*.

The agricultural potential of the more sparsely populated rice bowl countries (Burma, Thailand, Laos, Cambodia, and South Viet-Nam) will probably languish for lack of demand for export. In Japan and Taiwan, where agriculture is very intensively practised, it seems doubtful whether yields will continue to increase as they have over the past decade. Other countries, such as the Philippines, Indonesia, Pakistan, Ceylon and India will be hard pressed to increase farm output faster than population.

More foreign financial and technical assistance will be necessary to achieve even modest increases in agricultural output *per capita*. Otherwise, foreign exchange earnings will be largely absorbed in payments for food imports.

MEANS OF INCREASING OUTPUT OF FOOD

There is no doubt that the potential definitely exists to increase substantially the world's food output. The possible means include bringing new land into production so that there can be a higher and better quality production on present agricultural lands; and massively supplementing agricultural production through synthesis of the basic food elements or by culture of lower plant forms such as yeast and algae.

TABLE VIII

Indices of per Capita Agricultural Production, 1948/49 to 1959/60, by Regions

	Prewar average	Average 1948/49– 1952/53	1953/54	1954/55	1955/56	1956/57	1957/58	1958/59	1959/60 (Prelimi- nary)
Indices, average 1952/53–1956/57 = 100									
All Agricultural products									
Western Europe	93	89	101	101	102	102	105	105	109
Eastern Europe and USSR	84	91	97	95	103	111	113	122	122
North America	89	100	101	97	99	100	93	99	99
Oceania	104	99	100	98	101	100	95	106	104
Latin America	108	98	98	100	100	101	104	105	104
Far East (excluding mainland China)	110	92	99	100	102	104	101	103	105
Near East	95	92	102	97	98	104	105	106	104
Africa	93	95	100	100	100	102	97	98	95
All above regions	96	94	99	98	101	103	102	106	106
Food products only									
Western Europe	93	89	101	101	102	102	105	106	109
Eastern Europe and USSR	85	91	97	95	103	112	114	123	122
North America	87	99	100	97	99	101	96	102	101
Oceania	110	102	103	99	101	95	92	105	99
Latin America	103	97	99	101	99	103	103	103	100
Far East (excluding mainland China)	108	92	100	100	102	104	100	103	105
Near East	95	91	103	97	98	105	105	105	103
Africa	96	96	101	100	99	101	96	96	92
All above regions	95	94	100	98	101	104	103	107	107

Note: These indices have been calculated by applying regional weights, based on 1952–56 farm price relationships, to the production figures, which are adjusted to allow for quantities used for feed and seed. For mainland China no estimates are included, until more complete data are available. The indices for food products exclude coffee, tea, tobacco, inedible oilseeds, animal and vegetable fibers, and rubber.

Source: FAO, *Survey of Food and Agriculture*, 1960, page 13.

Additional lands

Hardly more than a tenth of the total land area in the earth is now classed as arable. According to rough FAO estimates, about 1,400 million hectares, out of a total of 13,531 million, can be considered to be arable land, fallow land, or orchards according to existing definitions (Table IX). About two-

TABLE IX

Areas of Crop or Grazing Land in the World, by Regions

Region	Total area (Million hectares)	Arable land and land under tree crops (Million hectares)	Per cent	Permanent meadows and pastures (Million hectares)	Per cent
Europe (excluding USSR)	493	153	31	77	16
USSR	2240	221	10	370	16
Northern America	2151	229	5	279	13
Latin America	2049	102	5	369	18
Near East	1151	76	7	193	17
Far East	2091	366	18	275	13
Africa	2502	222	9	554	22
Oceania	854	26	3	452	53
World	13,531	1395	10	2569	19

Source: FAO *Production Yearbook*, 1959, page 7.

TABLE X

Increase of Area in Major Crops, 1948–52 to 1958 for the World and Regions

Region	Millions of hectares 1948–52	1958	Per cent change
Europe (excluding USSR)	90	91	+ 1
USSR	119	141	+ 19
Northern America	133	120	— 10
Latin America	44	56	+ 27
Near East	27	33	+ 22
Far East	313	361	+ 15
Africa	61	67	+ 10
Oceania	6	7	+ 16
World	793	876	+ 11

Source: FAO *Production Yearbook*, 1959.

thirds of this total – somewhat less than 900 million hectares – are actually devoted to major crops; the rest being in temporary pasture, fallow, or minor crops. Another 2,600 million hectares (19%) are in permanent meadows and pastures. The remainder of the land, amounting to about 70% of the total, now produces little or no food.

The cultivated area of the world has increased significantly since the end of the second World War, as indicated in Table X, which shows an increase of more than 80 million hectares in land under major crops between 1948–52 and 1958. How much more land could be brought under cultivation? Estimates vary widely, according to the assumptions made. These range from the position that only minor increases are possible to the far more optimistic position that almost three times the present area could be effectively utilized. Unfortunately, no comprehensive, detailed survey of the possibilities throughout the world has ever been attempted.

The largest areas of potentially cultivable land not now being cultivated are located in the tropics, especially in South and Central America and Africa and to a lesser extent in south-eastern Asia. Vast areas of land in the equatorial forest zones are either not used for agriculture or very sparsely cultivated by systems of temporary, shifting agriculture which support exceedingly small populations. In addition, there are huge areas of tropical savannahs now being used, at the most, as grazing ranges for cattle which supply very little food. In general, the fertility of these unused or little used lands in the tropics is low and they tend to deteriorate quickly by erosion and leaching when they are cleared for cultivation. Largely for these reasons, mankind has had little success in developing stable, high-yielding systems of agriculture in the tropics, except in some relatively small areas where natural conditions are unusually favourable, as in Java and the Caribbean

TABLE XI

Increase of Total Catch of Fish, Crustaceans and Mollusks, 1938–1959, for the World and Regions

Region	1938	Average 1948–1952	1959 Preliminary figures
Europe	5.6	6.4	7.9
USSR	1.5	1.8	2.8
North America	3.2	3.6	4.0
Oceania	0.1	0.1	0.1
Latin America	0.2	0.5	3.0
Far East	9.1	7.4	15.5
Near East	0.3	0.4	0.4
Africa	0.9	1.0	1.9
World Total	20.5	21.2	35.6

Source: FAO, *State of Food and Agriculture*, 1960, page 20.

Islands. While the difficulties are not insuperable, to make possible a very large addition to the cultivated areas in the tropics with satisfactory yields would require radical changes in the prevailing methods of agriculture – in fact, a thoroughgoing revolution in the economies and cultures of these parts of the world.

According to one estimate,[4] 20% of the unexploited red soils of Africa and South America might be brought under cultivation, thus adding about 360 million hectares to the world's area of food-producing land, and another 40 million hectares might be added in Sumatra, Borneo, New Guinea, Madagascar, and other tropical areas. The interpretation of this estimate depends on assessments of the extent of cultural and economic transformation that could be brought about, as well as of technical possibilities.

The arid deserts and semi-arid highlands, both in the tropics and the temperate zones, account for another large fraction of the world's uncultivated land. With irrigation, some of these lands could be made highly productive. The practicability of utilizing them for agriculture depends primarily on the availability of water supplies and of capital for the irrigation works. Within the present limits of technical possibilities, some hundreds of millions of hectares of irrigated land might be added. The possibilities are more extensive in Africa, the Near East, and central Asia, but there is also scope for important additions, through irrigation, to the land resources of some of the more densely populated countries of southern and eastern Asia, including India and Pakistan, Ceylon, and China.

Although the execution of all irrigation projects now considered technically possible in various parts of the world would not increase the world's cultivable land area by a very large percentage, the contribution to food-producing capacity would be proportionately greater, as high yields can generally be obtained from irrigated lands. Studies and experiments now under way may lead to a considerable extension of the technical possibilities in the future. However, "the limiting factor is not knowledge, as in the equatorial lands and the savannahs of the 'new' continents, but finance."[5]

In the well-watered areas of the temperate zones, the two principal areas with large amounts of land not used for crops, although climate and other conditions are favourable, are southern Australia and the plains of southern Brazil and Uruguay. These lands are used mainly for grazing livestocks; the main obstacles to this conversion to crop land are land tenure conditions and cultural traditions. Similar possibilities for extending cultivation in the

4. SALTER, "World Soil and Fertilizer Resources in Relation to Food Needs," *Science*, 23 May 1947.
5. "Possibilities of Increasing the Supply of Food and Agricultural Products by Exploitation of New Areas and Increasing Yields," by W. H. PAWLEY and other experts of the FAO staff, in Proceedings of the World Population Conference, 1954, Volume V (United Nations Publication, Sales No. 1955. XIII.8). A revised version of this paper is being prepared for publication by the FAO in the near future as one of the basic studies for the Freedom-from-Hunger Campaign.

temperate zones of the Northern Hemisphere are much more narrowly
limited. There the main reserves of potentially arable land are in the pod-
zolsoil zones of the Northern USSR and Canada. It has been estimated that
about 10% of these lands, or 300 million acres, might ultimately be brought
under cultivation.[6]

Increased production per hectare

While expanding the area under cultivation will be important, it is evident
that for many regions, particularly the densely settled ones, greater output
per hectare of land will be necessary. There are great potentialities for increasing food production by application of improved practices to land
already under cultivation.

A number of possibilities for increasing yields may be mentioned.[7]

Improved crop varieties

Through the application of modern genetics, within limits crop varieties
can be bred to meet specific requirements, such as climatic adaptation, high
yields, improved quality, and resistance to disease. While much plant breeding work is being done, some of it in under-developed areas, the wide diversity of soil and climatic conditions means that a multitude of varieties
must be developed. Lack of trained personnel and facilities has hampered
progress in this field. Nevertheless, very substantial gains in production
could be achieved in under-developed countries by wider use of the
improved varieties that are now known, in areas for which they are suited.
Ignorance and the bonds of tradition are major hindrances, as well as the
difficulties of obtaining the improved seeds and achieving other changes in
agricultural techniques, on which satisfactory results from the cultivation
of new varieties often depends.

Building up soil fertility

Tremendous increases in food production per hectare could be achieved
by better soil management and more use of fertilizers in under-developed
areas where the natural fertility of the soil is low or where it has been
depleted by destructive methods of cultivation. Efficient crop rotation
schemes involving the use of legumes and grasses to add humus and
nitrogen to the soil are of great importance in this connection, as well as the
use of compost and animal manure in mixed-farming systems. There has
been little or no development of such agricultural methods in enormous
areas of the under-developed world. Chemical fertilizers also could play an
extremely important part in increasing production per hectare. In India, for

6. SALTER, *op. cit.*,
7. LEONARD, "World Population in Relation to Potential Food Supply," *Scientific Monthly*,
Sept. 1957; PAWLEY, and others, *op. cit.*

instance, it has been estimated that a moderate dressing of about 30 kg of nitrogen per hectare would bring an increase of more than 10 million tons in the annual production of rice. According to FAO experts, food production could be increased by at least 50% in almost all countries of the world, and it could be doubled in many areas, simply by better and more intensive use of fertilizers, manures, and legumes.[8] If chemical fertilizers are to be used widely, however, there must be substantial facilities for producing them and the farmers must be able to afford to buy them. Full benefits are only gained from them by extensive soil testing, demonstration and advisory services.

Combating pests and diseases

Great quantities of food are destroyed each year by pests and diseases which attack either the growing crops and livestock or the food products as they are processed, stored, and transported. It is believed that these losses are equivalent to the annual production of many millions of hectares. Most of them could be prevented at relatively small cost by applying the scientific knowledge which is now available. The gap between what is done and what could be done in this respect has never been wider than it is today, when new weapons for control of pests and diseases that have been produced by scientific research in recent years, for example, fungicides, antibiotics, insecticides, and weed killers are far more efficient than any known in the past. It is scarcely economical, however, to spend much on disease and pest control measures where the yields are very low because of other factors. As yields are improved by other means, plant and livestock protection can play an increasingly important role in food production. More and better refrigeration and storage facilities, where these are lacking or inadequate, can also do much to reduce food losses.

Agricultural implements and machinery

Mechanical equipment has revolutionized farming in some parts of the world, principally North America, Europe and the USSR, and Australia. While it has made possible vastly increased output per worker, its contribution to increasing output per hectare has been much more modest. In many of the under-developed countries, the advantage that could be obtained from increased use of agricultural machinery under present conditions would be limited in view of the existing surpluses of agricultural labour, as well as the difficulties of obtaining fuel, servicing, and spare parts. More important gains in production per hectare, and also in facilitating the extension of cultivated areas, could be won by improvements in simple tools, such as the substitution of a metal hoe for a wooden digging stick, equipping a wooden ploughshare with a steel point, and using a wheeled

8. PAWLEY and others, op. cit.

cart to transport materials and produce which are now being carried laboriously on a man's back.

Greater production of livestock

Domestic animals and fowl are an important source of food in the form of meat, dairy products, and eggs. Better feeding and breeding methods, artificial insemination, and disease and pest control can make possible higher production of these products. Animals are able to convert food resources unsuitable for direct use by man. They supply nutrients that are deficient in the high cereal diets on which much of the world population subsists. However, in several regions of the world, notably India and parts of Africa, there would be little advantage in increasing livestocks in present circumstances; religious and cultural traditions lead to the existence of excessive numbers of poor quality livestock which are competitors with human beings for food rather than being a primary source of food.

Combination of practices

While important gains in agricultural production can often be made through application of one or two simple measures, continued progress in increasing production depends on combining such practices as improved seeds, fertilizers, soil and water management, and pest control into a balanced system of husbandry.

Other sources of food

Fish is an important source of food in many countries, and contributes about 10% of the total animal protein in the current world food supply. It is potentially important particularly for protein-short regions. Cultivation of fish has long been practised in ponds or paddies in China and Japan where it is an important source of animal protein, and the practice has spread to several other countries in the Far East. The world fishery catch before World War II was approximately 20 million tons. It barely recovered in the post-war period, and now stands at about 36 million tons (See table XI). Sizable fisheries are being exploited off Africa and South America.

In recent years a number of altogether untouched sources of food have been discussed as possibilities for expanding world food output. Yeasts and algae with high protein and vitamin content can be used to convert wastes into food and to produce large quantities of material per hectare. At present, these processes may not be economically feasible and their products may not be accepted.

A number of vitamins are now produced synthetically and cheaply. Concentrated foodstuffs can also be manufactured as diet supplements on a mass scale.

Summary of the problem of food production

To sum up, it is clear that the earth's physical resources and man's present technical knowledge are sufficient to multiply the world's production of food many times. But the existence of resources and technical knowledge is not enough in itself to bring about the increase of production which the world desperately needs at present and the further increases which will be needed in the future to feed the growing population according to a satisfactory standard. To be effective, knowledge must be applied in developing resources and increasing productivity. The magnitude of the obstacles that must be overcome in bringing present knowledge into full play throughout the world cannot be over-emphasized.

Farmers must be given the incentive to produce larger quantities of food. Reliable markets, good prices, and facilities for transport, storage, handling, and processing must be developed. Channels of supply for fertilizers, pesticides, and improved seeds must be expanded. Institutional reforms affecting such matters as credit and tenure are often necessary. Advisory services must be supplied to spread the techniques that have proved successful and research programmes to develop successful practices are necessary. Capital must be obtained and invested, not only in the development of land resources and agricultural equipment, but also in the non-agricultural sector of the economy – in industrial plants, railroads, storage facilities, laboratories, and so on – and also in schools, hospitals, and the other essential facilities for social and economic progress.

So the problem of mouths and food is seen as an inseparable part of the whole, vast problem of economic, social, and cultural development of the world's under-developed regions. There is no sure or simple answer. On the relation of population growth to these problems, a survey published by the United Nations Economic Commission for Asia and the Far East [9] stated that "the faster the population grows, the more difficult it be to assure the necessary investment funds for an equivalent increase in agriculture production, and capital is one of the main limiting factors to economic growth in Asian countries. Furthermore, the cumulative nature of changes in population size following from a continued high rate of fertility will increase pressure on effective food supplies unless there is a considerably greater acceleration in such supplies than foreseeable...."

"If Asian agriculture adopted the modernized techniques used in some other parts of the world, food production in most of the countries could probably be made to keep pace with this upsurge in demand for food. In addition, research and technological advancement might make it possible to cultivate land which has been hitherto considered uncultivable."

The solution of the world's food crisis appears to be a matter of having not only the power but also the will to solve it. The total application of

9. *Economic Bulletin for Asia and the Far East*, June 1959.

existing technologies would unquestionably provide enough and for all. But how can this knowledge be put to work? Where will the capital come from to set up this world food production plant? What might be done to redistribute the existing food? At present, 400 million human beings in the western industrial nations consume as much protein as 1,300 million of their fellow men in Asia. A great effort must be made to equalize these disparities.

THE ISSUE OF POPULATION POLICY

In terms of simple arithmetic, it seems evident that the problem of achieving the needed increases in food production during the next decades would be made easier, and the risk of failures would be diminished, if the population were to increase less than is indicated by the projections of present trends for the economically less developed regions of the world. Actually, the mathematics of the problem are not so simple; it is not just a question of addition of a larger or smaller number of consumers to share a certain quantity of food, for people are producers as well as consumers. While population growth adds to requirements, it also contributes, through increasing manpower, to the possibilities of producing food and other goods. It is necessary to consider the *relative* effects on requirements and productive capacity in order to get a correct expression of the equation of food and mouths, and the form of the equation is not the same in regimes where the economic circumstances differ. Still, when these complexities are taken into account, it appears that population growth at the rates now observed in most of the under-developed countries is a major hindrance in solving the problems of food supply and of general economic and social development.

With few exceptions, the experts who have studied this question agree that the outlook would be far more favourable if the present rates of population increase in the under-developed countries could be slowed down by moderation of birth rates. In fact, some experts hold that unless the growth of population becomes slower in the near future, there is little hope of improving the conditions of life in many of these countries or even to hold the present low levels of living may prove to be difficult.

The problem is not the same where the density of population is lower and there are large reserves of unused or little used land suitable for agriculture, as in many countries of Latin America and Africa. But it has been pointed out that even in such circumstances, excessively rapid growth of population is a major hindrance to economic development. The report of a recent United Nations seminar on population problems in Latin America makes the following observations on this score: [10]

"Of course for each new mouth there is also a pair of hands. But the

10. Seminar on Evaluation and Utilization of Population Census Data in Latin America (ST/TAO/SER. C/46; E/CN. 9/CONF. 1/1/Rev. 1). United Nations, New York, 1960, p. 37.

mouth has to be fed now; the hands become useful only some years later. In several Latin American countries as much as 40% of the population is under the age of fifteen. At the same time, Governments must find productive jobs for a rapidly growing and sometimes poorly trained labour force, a task which entails demands on scarce capital resources which would not be made by a population growing less rapidly. From each of these points of view, present rates of population growth are a real handicap to economic development.

"...The majority of the countries in this region are generally believed to be under-populated in the sense that if they had more people, suitably distributed within their territory, they could make more effective use of resources which are now idle, and could benefit from certain economies in the scale of production and distribution of goods and services.... On the other hand, it seems to have been made clear that nearly all countries of the region are suffering from a considerable handicap in their efforts towards economic development because of the rapid rates at which their populations are growing. Those which are under-populated naturally have less reason to be concerned about this matter than the others, but in their case, too, it seems evident that in spite of the advantages which in the long run might accrue to them from a larger population, their economic progress would be more satisfactory if they could arrive at those larger numbers at a more leisurely pace."

These considerations lend force and urgency to the demands for policies in favour of birth regulation which are being pressed upon governments in various parts of the world and upon the United Nations. But the issue of population policy and birth regulation is not purely one of economics. It also involves questions of cultural ideals, moral principles, and social and political philosophy which are seen in different lights by the people and the governments of different countries. Some groups object in principle to birth control in general or to certain forms of it; others hold that the decision to practice it or not should be left strictly to the people without any governmental interference or pressure.

In spite of all the difficulties, it may prove possible within a decade or two to achieve with determined efforts, appreciable reductions of birth rates in the countries where national policies having this aim have been adopted, or where they may be adopted in the near future. But it scarcely seems realistic in view of all the circumstances to expect a radical reduction of births in the under-developed countries generally during the next ten or twenty years. Meanwhile, the population of most of these countries can be expected to go on growing rapidly – quite possibly even more rapidly than it is growing at present. Thus it is absolutely imperative to find adequate solutions for the problems of increasing food production sufficiently during the decades ahead, especially in those countries where the present standards of food consumption are lowest and where the largest increases of population are in store.

Prospects of increasing food production

Experts are convinced that technical knowledge exists to meet the world's present food shortages and to take care of the needs that will result from population growth for some time to come. Similarly, there is enough technical knowledge of the means of controlling births to bring about a decided moderation of the rate of population growth whenever the Governments – and more important, the people – have the will to do so.

If everything possible were done to bring the existing technical knowledge of food production methods to bear fully throughout the world – including, among other things, large-scale programmes for training key personnel, vigorous and imaginative attacks on ignorance and traditional inertia, and massive mobilization of capital on a worldwide scale for investments in agricultural and industrial development of the under-developed regions – the Freedom from Hunger Campaign might achieve its great objective over the course of some decades. But neither the present programmes nor the efforts to implement them are adequate.

In India, for instance, the current large expenditure on agricultural research and development has served to increase food production by about 3% a year, but an 8.2% annual increase is necessary to meet the 1965–66 targets for adequate production.[11]

With reference to the countries of Asia and the Far East, the ECAFE-report previously quoted [12] puts the problem in these terms:

"... If Asian agriculture adopted the modernized techniques used in some parts of the world, food production in most of the countries could probably be made to keep pace with this upsurge in demand for food. In addition, research and technological advance may make it possible to cultivate land which has been hitherto considered uncultivable....

On the assumption that average land productivity in Asia could be raised to Japanese levels, that calorie supplies were increased to 2,500 per person per day and the present low-protein type of diet maintained, many countries could still support a population two or three times as big as their present population. Assumptions, on the other hand, of calorie supplies at the same level as in, say, the western European countries and a diet of a high animal protein content would imply that many countries, even at the very high Japanese levels of land productivity, could support fewer people than their present populations....

All these calculations indicate the need to bring the present divergent trends in mortality and fertility into a closer balance within a not very distant future."

In addition to the programmes for increasing agricultural efficiency

11. *Report on India's Food Crisis and Steps to Meet It.* Government of India. April, 1959, p. 11.
12. *Economic Bulletin for Asia and the Far East.* June, 1959.

through fertilizers, seeds, mechanization and better techniques, there is the technical possibility, although at somewhat higher costs, of producing foods from sources not now exploited: algae, yeasts, fish meals, and hydroponics, and by the use of extractive methods for converting plants directly into proteins and oils instead of raising secondary sources of nutrients such as fish and animals. However, the difficulties must not be underestimated – "the mere fact that it is theoretically possible to increase food production should not blind us to the magnitude of the task. It is immense. Agriculture involves more of the people of the world than any other productive activity. To change its procedures, we must change attitudes." [13]

By 1970, the population of the earth will be increased by over half a billion. Most of this increase can be expected to occur in the under-developed, food-short regions of Asia, Africa and Latin America, where population growth rates in some countries are now higher than any that have been known in the history of the human race.

Time is too precious to be wasted in futile arguments over what steps should be taken first to deal with the problem of population and food supply. Nothing less than an "all out" attack on all major aspects of the problem can bring success. To banish hunger and achieve a minimal diet for all people in the face of rapid population growth will at best take time. To check population growth in those countries where such is the desire of the people and their governments will also take time. And time is of the essence.

13. BROWN, HARRISON, BONNER, JAMES & WEIR, JOHN. *The Next Hundred Years*, The Viking Press. New York, 1957, p. 82.

Research in Biotechnology: A Factor in Advancing the Technically Underdeveloped Countries

by

CARL-GÖRAN HEDÉN

GENERAL ASPECTS
ON THE IMPORTANCE OF LONG-RANGE RESEARCH PLANNING

This century has seen many examples of the powers held by directed research, the most notable illustrations being Man's release of nuclear energy and his flights into space. As we all know there has also, after the Second World War, emerged an international conscience, concerned not only with the preservation of peace but also with the provision of food, housing, clothing, medical care and education to those nations lacking them. Since reaching such ambitious goals involves the solution of extremely difficult and complex problems, there is naturally widespread belief that new efforts of directed research will play a fundamental role in satisfying the needs mentioned. Many instances of success can also be cited to show that such a belief is indeed not unwarranted. However we now also realize that every success, which is not part of an integrated program, may introduce new and bigger problems. Without comparison the most serious so far is the present state of semistarvation caused by the spectacular growth of the human species, essentially a consequence of advances in medicine, hygiene and technology.

Since waste and competition are certainly prerequisites for the genetic development of the species,[1] a biologist might well regard an increase in numbers as an advantage. However he can hardly be called humanitarian if he wishes to stimulate a further increase before control and selection mechanisms,[2] other than starvation and wars, have been put into operation.

Reprinted by kind permission of the United Nations Conference on the Application of Science and Technology for the Benefit of the Less Developed Areas. Geneva, Febr., 1963.
1. HARDIN, G., *Nature and Man's Fate*, Rinehart & Co., 1960. Biology: its Human Implications, Freeman, 1961.
2. MULLER, H. J., *Evolution and Man's Progress*, Darwin Centennial Symposium, Chicago: 1959, Daedalus 1961.

However this seems to call for a transfer of the burden of morality from religion to science, and that is apt to be a very slow process. In a brilliant essay: "A Moral for an Age of Plenty" J. BRONOWSKI has pointed out that there are two things that make up morality: one is the sense that other people matter, the sense of human love, the other is a clear judgement of what is at stake. It is the realization of the truth that Man can hardly be good without being wise which will take a long time to take effect, perhaps even longer than the realization of the obsolescence of sovereign states as adequate units of economic and political organization and the necessity of cooperation, first on a regional, and finally, on a global scale.

Obviously we must buy the time necessary for the transition from the present amoral or at the best uneducated state of mind, in which we for instance oppose birth control, to an understanding that we cannot make up for ignorance and compromise by an appeal to universal goodness. By buying time I understand both a reduction in human misery by giving proper aid to underprivileged areas and the aversion of major losses in the human genetic pool due to the unselective forces of total warfare. By proper aid I mean: 1. improved utilization of such natural resources which will help to feed people during the critical transition period and 2. aid towards industrialization, since this eventually may be a factor in checking the population expansion. I will later try to show that biotechnology may offer contributions in both areas.

I have felt it necessary to give this general introduction to my paper, since expressions of resignation are so common in discussions concerned with the types of aid mentioned. I have for instance often stressed the well-known geographical separation of the need for industrialization on the one hand and the 'know-how" and capital on the other, as being a great obstacle in the development of many underprivileged areas. When saying that a theoretical way around this might be to put off the most expensive parts of the space-race for some ten years, channelizing a portion of the technically advanced countries' growing steelproduction into the building of highly automatized shipboard plants (power production, fertilizer synthesis, fermentation-, canning-, freezing-, milkdrying and mechanical industries etc.), this has as a rule not been denied. However, doubt has been expressed about the morality of such major actions, if there was no guarantee that the final result would not spell an increased total of human misery. My attitude in this connection has been outlined above, and it is the same with regard to the proposal which is the essence of this paper. The aim is obviously not a contribution to the solution of any of the basic problems of the population growth, but rather it is a help in buying the time necessary to solve them.

THE PLANNING
OF THE CONTRIBUTION FROM THE BIOLOGICAL SCIENCES

The first installments on the purchase of time just mentioned are already being paid in the form of already available knowledge, but the need for additional capital, in the shape of new knowledge, is already being felt. This capital will have to come from many of the different branches of biology, and much of the initiative for stimulating desirable activities will have to come from the scientist's own organizations. An awareness of this responsibility is illustrated by the scope of ICSU's International Biological Programme: "The Biological Basis of Productivity and Human Welfare" which is planned because so many problems of vital importance to Man's future welfare can only be solved by means of new scientific information. This Programme will be concerned both with the biological productivity of terrestrial, marine and freshwater communities and with the biological basis of human adaptability, both physiological and genetical.

Frequently an item of information in pure science "pays off" in a practical way only after it has long been in existence and only after it has been combined with other items of pure science. Earlier, when one scientist could cover more than one field, this process of association was no problem, but to-day, when we are in the midst of a virtual explosion of data, where few can master more than a small sector of their basic areas, the progress tends to become sluggish and random. A reaction has been the establishment of the "team" as the most efficient operational unit at the level of the individual and more recently the creation, on a higher administrative level, of chains of laboratories, active in fringe areas bridging the gap between well-established disciplines.

One example of the "chain" type of cooperation is the "International Cell Research Organization (ICRO)", which was recently created to satisfy the need for contacts not only among the present practioneers of Cell Biology but also with those of other disciplines. This Organization may be of great importance to the solution of many of the problems facing Mankind, since the golden era of biological science "will unfold as we gain understanding of the cell as a unit of life. If we can better understand and control the mechanisms and functions of living cells, we will have vastly increased ability to breed more productive, higher quality crops and livestock; to control and eradicate insect pests; to maintain the quality of farmer products during processing and marketing; to find new uses for farm-grown raw materials; and to improve human nutrition.[3]

Besides ICRO one could mention proposals more directly concerned with applying existing knowledge to human welfare. To this category

3 SHAW, B. T., *Prospective world production and distribution of food.* Fed. Proc. Part III, Suppl. 7. p. 373, 1961.

belongs the recommendation of the VII. Pugwash Conference (1961) to set up a network of regional agricultural experimental stations, linked to an international center under the UN, and my own suggestion concerned with the importance of extending the scope of such field-stations to applied biology in general.[4]

THE STRUCTURE OF BIOTECHNOLOGY

Among the fringeareas biotechnology – defined as the study of the establishment and maintenance of artificial environments in which living cells or labile biologicals are produced, preserved, selectively destroyed or modified as desired – should be of particular interest. It is an area which depends for its vitality on contacts with cell biology, molecular biology, microbiology, fermentation technology, chemical engineering and physics, all of which receive a feed-back stimulus in the process. However, this stimulus will not be discussed here, important as it may be. I will rather try to indicate why a consolidation of the area ought to concern those working on the advancement of the technically underdeveloped countries, and I will also try to outline a way to achieve the desired consolidation by establishing a laboratory-chain of the type mentioned earlier.

A CONTRIBUTION TO THE APPLICATION
OF ALREADY AVAILABLE KNOWLEDGE

First the well-known fact must be emphasized that the solution of most of the biological problems which face the underprivileged areas requires a double attack: an application of available knowledge and a search for new knowledge. The former is already in the able hands of the specialized agencies of the UN and other bodies, but biotechnology could still be of some assistance in the attack by devising techniques designed for areas where the resources are limited. As a rule such techniques would involve simplifications, for instance the production of feed supplements by fermentation processes practiced on the farm level,[5] but occasionally they might call for more sophisticated approaches than those common in technically advanced countries. In this connection I could mention large-scale manufacture of certain products, for instance veterinary vaccines.

A CONTRIBUTION TO THE SEARCH FOR NEW KNOWLEDGE

The role of basic and applied studies

The fundamental contribution from biotechnology should be concerned with the search for new information in such fields as nitrogen fixation,

4. HEDÉN, C.-G., *Biological Research Directed Toward the Needs of Underdevel. Areas.* TVF. *32*, 297, 1961. (Paper read at IUBS' Gen. Ass. July 14, 1961).
5. NOVOTNY, K. & HEROLD, M. - ΛHTNONOTNKN *4. 42.* 1960.

photosynthesis and fermentation, a search which must proceed on a broad front involving both basic and applied science.

The relevant basic sciences can be expected to expand at the same rate as biochemistry and microbiology in general, but the cross fertilization with technology, which is most probably essential to a rapid development of the applied sector, seems to require an artificial insemination on the intellectual plane.

Nitrogen fixation

Lord FLECK expressed the view of many scientists when he called the fixation of atmospheric nitrogen one of the least exploited discoveries of all time. The most important aspect is of course the direct synthesis of fertilizers, because this opens attractive possibilities for increasing the food supplies,[6] but the study of the fundamental processes of biological nitrogen fixation may also prove to be greatly rewarding. Some practical results can already be noted, for instance the improvement of some leguminous crops by seeding *Rhizobium* cultures and by adequate control of the trace elements in the soil.

Other findings are still within the domain of basic biology, but may well lead to practical applications. An example is the observation that irradiation of nitrogen can reduce the energy-requirement of bacteria which convert the gas into organic matter.[7], [8] It should be obvious that the application of this observation, originally made in a biotechnological laboratory, requires contributions from physics, chemical engineering, microbial genetics and physiology.

Photosynthesis

The utilization of atmospheric carbon dioxide by photosynthesis is another area which requires the types of horizontal contacts between disciplines, which is characteristic for biotechnology. I have elsewhere [4] illustrated how the minds of a basic scientist and a pure-bred application man might complement each other in this particular field and will here only express the belief that the practical uses will soon be within reach in certain parts of the world. Mass cultivation of algae has been successfully carried out in many countries, notably Japan, but the transformation of the material into food of dependable quality is a difficult problem, where novel methods of biotechnology may be required, for instance the disruption of the cells by decompression and shear or by freeze-pressing.[9] Possibly therefore the

6. RICHARDSON, H. L., *Increasing World Food Supplies Through Greater Crop Production*. Outlook on Agriculture 3. 9. 1960.

7. ZACHARIAS, B. & HEDÉN, C.-G., *Effect on Biological Nitrogen Fixation of Nitrogen Gas treated with Ultraviolet Radiation*. Nature 190. 817. 1961.

8. ZACHARIAS, B. *Effect of UV-Irradiated Nitrogen Gas on Biological Nitrogen Fixation in Batch Cultures of Azotobacter Vinelandii*. Biotech. and Bio-eng. 4, 87. 1962.

9. EDEBO, L., *A New Press for the Disruption of Micro-organisms and Other Cells*. J. Biochem. Microbiol. Tech. and Eng. 2. 453. 1960.

marine biologist will be the first to reap a harvest from algal culture by using higher organisms of the sea to circumvent physical separation techniques on the one hand and to improve the food value on the other. Actually this approach has been tried successfully in Britain where one alga (*Phaeodactylum*) has been grown to high concentrations in fertilized sea water and harvested by shellfish (*Venus mercenaria*).[10] The latter possesses a remarkable filtering capacity (up to 2 liters per hour) and can definitely be characterized as a highvalue food. When it comes to translating a finding of this nature first into field-tests and then into practical use biotechnology will have to enter the picture to answer many questions. How far will sterile or semisterile conditions have to be maintained in the process, and how can they be incorporated into a continuous operation? Which are the limitations in the carbon dioxide and heat content of industrial combustion gases and which are the optimal conditions for aeration and stirring? How far would the carbon dioxide release from a fermentation process like yeast/alcohol-manufacture go to satisfy the algal culture, and how could the products – say clams and yeast extract – be combined in a final product? And finally, how should the culture be contained when handled in different geographical locations: natural water reservoirs, concrete tanks, wooden structures, plastic containers floating in lakes or in the sea etc. etc.?

Anybody who expresses the view that this is "just technology" knows very little about our ignorance with regard to basic phenomena like aeration, interphase transport and many areas of microbial physiology such as the mechanism of photosynthesis, the metabolism of volatile intermediates and the genetic stability in continuous culture. Only when those and similar problems. which are now in the focus of biotechnology, have been solved and the information fused with relevant data of marine biology can one hope for optimization and for a scale-up, which is not just based on "trial and error."

Fermentation

Fermentation is the third sector of biotechnology which might make a notable contribution to the advancement of the technically underdeveloped areas. The control of insects and pests with the aid of bacterial and viral infections is a promising field, and the fermentation microbiologist can already offer numerous processes for the production of vitamine and essential aminoacids, yes even certain anticonceptional steroids like norethynodrel. Yeasts and other microorganisms can be used as food supplements and microbial genetics has still only been scraped on the surface by the industrial microbiologist. We know that relatively small amounts of certain yeasts can satisfy Man's requirement of thiamin, riboflavin and niacin, besides providing ergosterol, phosphorus, sulphur and iron. We also know that a small supplement of the aminoacid lysin,

10. ANSELL, A. D., *An approach to sea farming*, New Scientist No. 288, p. 408, 1962.

which is easily made by fermentation, considerably increases the nutritional value of such staple foods as wheat, rice and corn. Finally we know that chloromycetin is valuable, not only as a fodder supplement and veterinary drug, but also in dipping processes for increasing the storage life of animal protein.

A versatile plant might actually turn out all three types of product (yeast, aminoacids and antibiotics and, perhaps, also vaccines and biological control agents), but it would then be so advanced that I doubt that it could be built anywhere but in the technically most highly developed countries. A natural thought would then be to make it shipbound, but probably one would then have to increase the output per unit of equipment space above the figures attainable in conventional batch processes: It is at this point that basic research in biotechnology comes in, because we have much to learn before we can design a flexible, truly continuous, highly automatized fermentation plant even on dry land.

Studies in bacterial physiology concerned with the ability of certain mixed populations (for instance those residing in the gut of herbivorous animals) to break down cellulose and polysaccharides, other than starch and simple hexose and pentose polymers, might also "pay off" later by offering possibilities for the release of edible proteins and carbohydrates from green leaves, copra, seaweeds etc. So might a study of the microbial breakdown of lignin, a process which might be incorporated in certain fermentation chains.

On the one hand a technically underdeveloped area might thus need a more sophisticated technology than is currently available, on the other hand it may, as pointed out before, need techniques which are so simple that they may fall outside the lines of thought which are normal to the microbiologist and chemical engineer in a technically advanced country. Those individuals may be so concentrated on steamsterilization and stainless steel fermentors, that they forget the possibilities of chemical sterilization of media and equipment [11] and the fact that this might take unconventional forms like drumlinings or floating bags. The true biotechnologist is less likely to forget such possibilities, and he may perhaps even be able to suggest theoretical ways to circumvent the need for expensive separation equipment, for instance by cultivation in media incorporating immiscible aqueous polymers [12].

Three research sectors in fermentation biotechnology merit special attention, because they may prove to have farreaching practical consequences. One is concerned with microbiological ensilage techniques suitable for both plant and animal tissue (cf. R. NILSSON and others), and the second with the fact that hydrocarbons, of which the resources in the

11. TOPLIN, I., *Chemical Sterilization of Liquid Media*. Biotech. and Bio-eng. 4. 331. 1962.
12. HEDÉN, C.-G. & HOLMSTRÖM, B., *A versatile continuous culture apparatus for the study of complex processes*. Abstract. VIIIth Int. Congr. Microbiol. Montreal 1962.

world are still plentiful, can obviously be converted into valuable food-stuffs by microorganisms (cf. J. C. SENEZ and others). The third finally concerns F. D. SISLER's observation that electrical energy can be harnessed with great efficiency via microbial metabolism. At the present time it is impossible to say which of the three pieces of information will be of the greatest practical importance, but one thing is certain, namely that bio-technology will have to play a fundamental role in the development. Anybody who has seen the crude microbiological fuel cell of to-day in operation will appreciate what the application of novel continuous culture principles, involving for instance multiple-stage, pH-controlled units, can do for optimization and scale-up. However it must be realized that this is not "just technology," particularly not when the complex relations in mixed cultures, perhaps incorporating photosynthetic steps, enters the picture.

From the foregoing I hope that a general idea has been formed about some sectors of biotechnology which may have importance to the solution of certain problems facing the underprivileged areas. A brief summary is given in table I.

TABLE I

Biotechnology = the study of the establishment and maintenance of artificial environments in which living cells or labile biologicals are:

produced: from simple rawmaterials (including hydrocarbons) in the form of proteins, carbohydrates, fats, aminoacids, vitamins or antibiotics. Also the preparation of human and veterinary vaccines and of certain agricultural products. Finally the fixation of nitrogen and carbon dioxyde and the release of electrical energy.

selectively destroyed or inhibited: as in the control of insects and pests by bacteria and viruses and in preservation and canning (chemical, heat- and radiation sterilization).

or modified as desired: as in the microbiological synthesis of steroids, in the microbiological treatment of organic waste materials or in some ensilage treatments of plant and animal tissue.

THE PLANNING OF THE CONTRIBUTION FROM BIOTECHNOLOGY

With the potential impact of well-coordinated scientific activities within the field in mind some special measures ought to be considered. This is particularly important since the area – with the exception of the narrow sector yeast and fusel oils (covered by IUPAC's Fermentation Division) has lacked an international foothold until a few months ago, when the Section for Economic and Applied Microbiology was formed within the Inter-national Association of Microbiological Societies. In connection with the establishment of this Section I proposed the creation of a chain of bio-technological laboratories aimed at furthering the area in general but also at giving attention to problems of the type outlined in this paper. Acting upon the recommendation of the new Section the General Meeting of the Association convened in Plenary Session with the participants of the VIIIth International Congress for Microbiology (Montreal, August 24th, 1962) considered this proposal. The administrative bodies of the Section were then charged with giving close attention to the possibility of forming an international body for biotechnology and taking whatever action they might see fit in this connection. It was also felt that support from such international bodies as UNESCO should be sought to create a mechanism or organization to stimulate biotechnology.

My personal feeling is that such an Organization as its backbone should have a number of specialized laboratories selected on the basis of scientific capability rather than geographical location. Their main function would be to stimulate basic research aimed at the problems indicated, for instance by circulating a "needed project catalogue" continually revised in collaboration with the specialized UN agencies and other international bodies. Also the exchange of scientists might be stimulated in cases where the solution of a special problem might benefit from this, but generally speaking the Organization should be uncontaminated by general training programs, at least during its first few years. Such programs might be a natural development, if aimed at students from underprivileged areas, but it might be wise to postpone such activities until a mechanism for coordinated efforts, involving fieldstations, had been developed. At the present time the attack on the basic research problems seems to be the most important, and I would go so far as to advise responsible administrators to think twice before they use scientists, qualified to carry out fundamental studies in biotechnology, for basic training programs and application projects.

THE FUTURE OF BIOTECHNOLOGY

Biotechnology is not a new area, which is now trying to steal fuel from biochemistry, microbiology and chemical engineering. Rather it gives a common heading to specialized groups of biochemists, microbiologists and chemical engineers. Let us hope that this heading will forge a bond between disciplines and help to fill the gap between basic research and practical applications, a gap which may become particularly serious for the peoples in the underprivileged areas of the world.

Like other branches of science biotechnology can be used for destructive as well as constructive purposes, and we were fools if we tried to minimize in our minds the sinister potential that biotechnology has given to biological aerosol warfare.[13] It is in our hands to promote the use of biotech-

13. Nonmilitary Defense; Chemical and Biological Defenses in Perspective, Advances in Chemistry 26, ACS. 1960.

nology to effect human ecology in rather more constructive ways than by wiping out parts of our greatest natural resource: Man's genetic pool.

CARL-GÖRAN HEDÉN, M. D., is a Research Professor of Microbiological Engineering at Karolinska Institutet, Stockholm. He is a Member of the Royal Swedish Academy of Engineering Sciences and Chairman of its Division for Biotechnology (1962). He is an Affiliate Member of the British Royal Society of Medicine and a Fellow of the World Academy of Art and Science. He is Vice-President of the International Association of Microbiological Societies, Chairman of its Advisory Council and Vice-President of its Section for Economic and Applied Microbiology. Professor HEDÉN is an Editor of the J. Biotechnology and Bioengineering.

An Appraisal of the Future of Nuclear Energy

by

Robert C. Axtmann

As the population of our planet climbs inexorably, the energy resources upon which man now relies steadily dwindle. Projections for the year 2063 A.D. of either the total world population or the available supplies of coal, oil and gas are fraught with manifold uncertainties. Nonetheless, if conservative estimates of the rates of population growth and the increase in per capita energy usage are combined with optimistic estimates of the true fossil fuel reserve, it is perfectly clear that gigantic new sources of low-cost energy must be fully developed within the next century.

The disappearance of the world's supply of fossil fuel is not the only factor that may dictate the development of alternative sources of energy. Professor Edward Teller, the nuclear prophet (and bogeyman), has recently emphasized a possible danger in the continued use of coal, oil and gas in combustion processes (1). All of these fuels release carbon dioxide to the atmosphere. As little as 10% additional carbon dioxide in the atmosphere – a possibility within 40 years, according to Teller – could seriously affect the rate at which the earth is able to radiate heat. In a sense carbon dioxide in the atmosphere acts as an insulating blanket. The mean temperature of the earth would rise 4° Fahrenheit, the polar ice cap would melt, sea levels would rise and, to cite one of the gaudier consequences, New York City would disappear beneath the Atlantic Ocean!

One of the brightest candidates to gradually supplant fossil fuel is nuclear fuel. In this article I shall attempt to delineate the extent of nuclear energy resources, the range of their applicability and, where appropriate, comment on the economic aspects of the problem.

There now appear to be only two paths to utilization of the energy locked within the nucleus: (1) fission of heavy nuclei – the controlled "A-Bomb" reaction and (2) fusion of light nuclei – the controlled "H-Bomb" reaction. To state that these are the only possible modes of nuclear energy release risks, of course, the myopia of nineteenth century science.

In its present state, nuclear theory gives no hint that there are more spectacular reactions than fission or fusion to come. Yet it must be admitted that nuclear theory is in an incomplete and unsatisfactory state. Current investigations into the fundamental nature of matter emphasize so-called "high energy physics." The term "high energy" comes from the fact that the experimental techniques involved in the research make use of sub-atomic particles having energies reaching into the billions of volts. So far as is known there is no useful end product of this research other than further understanding of the universe. Nonetheless such research is receiving massive support (i.e., all that high energy physicists ask for – currently at a rate of hundreds of millions of dollars per year) from both the U.S. and U.S.S.R. governments. A study of governmental support of research, particularly that of the U.S.S.R., makes it appear axiomatic that where massive support exists, a potential military application exists. It may be stretching a point, but in the present case the application would seem almost necessarily to involve new sources of energy. If this line of reasoning is correct, the man in the street may well wish to pause and pray that the current search for understanding of the universe is less successful than earlier quests that turned up A-Bombs and H-Bombs as by-products.

It should be made clear that only the first-mentioned path to nuclear power, the controlled fission of heavy nuclei, e.g., uranium isotopes, has been developed sufficiently that application awaits only the correct (economically favorable) times and places. Although the eventual promise of power based on the fusion of light nuclei, e.g., hydrogen isotopes, is far greater, not even its feasibility has yet been established. For this reason fission power and fusion power are discussed separately below.

FISSION POWER

Since 1938, when fission was first discovered, the popular press has contained reports of progress in the utilization of the new power source. Frequently articles on the subject begin with an eye-catching statement (in which EINSTEIN's equation for mass-energy equivalence is inevitably cited) of how, for example, the energy contained in a few ounces of uranium could propel a ship around the world or light a sizeable city for a year. The article may then go on to announce some "breakthrough" in nuclear technology and end with the suggestion that economical nuclear power is in the immediate offing.

The eye-catching example of the potency of uranium normally ignores the fact that the fission process releases less than 0.1% of the energy equivalence of the ounce of uranium or that an ounce of coal (or Scotch whiskey) also "contains" the same amount of energy as does an ounce of uranium. Nor is the fact usually mentioned that a given piece of uranium, in the form of a fuel element for a nuclear reactor, can give up no more than approximately 10% of the 0.1% theoretically available fission energy before the fuel element must be either discarded or reprocessed. The "breakthrough" in nuclear technology may or may not be real, but the corner, around which lurks widespread use of power derived from fission, seems ever to recede.

That uranium *is* a superior fuel is not open to question. In a recent calculation, W. B. LEWIS, a Canadian atomic power expert, shows that a kilogram of purified uranium oxide is capable of giving up as much energy as is 30 tons of coal. The uranium would cost $15 and the coal might cost around $130 (2). The twin advantages of uranium as a fuel – compactness and low cost – are readily apparent in this illustration. Yet even optimistic prophets now concede that not until the late 1970's will as much as 10% of the electricity generated in the U.S. be derived from fission reactors. Further, say the prophets, the next century will have turned before as much as 50% of U.S. electrical power will be generated at nuclear power plants(2). Nor would it be expected that the U.S. will lag behind the rest of the world in applying fission power.

Such prophecies might seem puzzling after LEWIS' illustration and in view of the extensive research and development efforts devoted to nuclear power by the U.S., the U.S.S.R. and the U.K. during the past decade. The main reasons why nuclear power is not yet competitive economically are technological ones that are rather easily understood.

There are two main cost factors which make nuclear power more expensive than fossil fuel power in most regions of the world today. The first, which may be considered an operating cost, arises from the expense of fabricating the uranium into a form suitable for use in the interior of a nuclear reactor. The second factor is the high capital cost of constructing a nuclear reactor for the generation of steam as compared to the cost of a boiler, fired by a fossil fuel, for the same purpose.

Natural gas and oil can be used for the generation of steam substantially as they are received from a vendor. Coal may require a low-cost grinding operation. Uranium on the other hand, must be altered drastically before it is suitable for use in a nuclear reactor.

Fossil fuels are consumed almost completely as soon as they are admitted to a combustion chamber. A given charge of uranium, however, because of its low rate of consumption, must remain in the interior of a nuclear "furnace" for weeks or even months depending upon the design of the reactor.

In a common type of nuclear design – a heterogeneous reactor – the fuel is present as a solid in a matrix of other materials which may include high temperature gases and/or liquids. In such a design, the uranium must be protected from undergoing ordinary chemical reactions which would consume the uranium while giving up relatively microscopic amounts of energy. The protection takes the form of a corrosion-resistant cladding of another metal and the resulting entity is then called a "fuel element." The element must be able to withstand high mechanical and thermal stresses as well as the action of corrosive fluids. "Leaky" fuel elements or ones whose cladding could be ruptured by the drastic conditions existing inside the reactor must be carefully excluded. For this reason elaborate and costly quality control measures must be taken with all the fuel elements.

In other designs, i.e., non-heterogeneous reactors in which the fuel is in any of various fluid forms, comparable problems arise that make the costs attributable to fuel equivalent to those in the heterogeneous reactors.

Even in the most favorable cases the costs of the fuel approach or exceed about one half the cost of fossil fuel for the same production of net electrical power.

The second technological factor that helps raise the cost of nuclear power above that of conventional power is the intrinsic complexity of a nuclear reactor. For a variety of reasons the dimensional tolerances allowable in components for a nuclear reactor often are ten to a hundred times smaller than those tolerable for comparable components in a coal-burning boiler. Machining costs are correspondingly higher. Frequently, too, nuclear considerations dictate the use of rare, expensive materials such as zirconium or hafnium in the construction of the reactor. In addition the control and safety devices for a nuclear reactor need to be appreciably more elaborate than in the case of boilers using chemical fuels.

One important reason for the high complexity of nuclear reactor controls is that the total energy release possible in an *uncontrolled* nuclear reaction far exceeds that in an uncontrolled chemical reaction. This statement is not intended to imply that an uncontrolled nuclear reactor may turn into an atomic bomb. Nonetheless, the consequences of an uncontrolled fission chain reaction – even the relatively tame one possible in a reactor designed for electrical power production – are sufficiently severe that great care and expense must be invoked in the construction of the safety and control system. Not all of the care and expense which have been expended in the past has been completely justified. It is regrettable that emotionalism frequently enters discussions of situations that might lead to exposure of the general population to higher levels of radiation than those to which they are already exposed. Proponents of nuclear power plants sometimes wryly claim that if the same safety standards which must be met in the construction of nuclear power plants were objectively applied to plants which use other fuels, the costs of nuclear power would be much closer to economic competitiveness.

Since amortization of the high capital cost of building a nuclear power plant must be added to the price of power, the net result is that nuclear power is substantially more expensive than conventional power in most regions of the world. In the next two decades we may expect a gradual whittling away at costs as experience is gained in the operation of the nuclear reactors, as designs become standardized, as cheap methods for fabricating fuel elements with reasonable longevity are developed and as research and development expenses recede in importance in the capital cost total.

It is reasonable to expect that when the costs of nuclear power begin to approach those of conventional power those organizations with financial interests in conventional power (e.g., coal miners' unions, railroads, utilities with large investments in conventional power facilities) may attempt to reverse the trend. At best they might become sponsors of large-scale research and development programs aimed at, for example, the improvement of mining techniques, of boiler efficiencies or of turbine bearings; at worst they might become sponsors, or at least supporters, of legislation aimed at placing a premium price on power derived from nuclear sources or of harassing lawsuits protesting the safety or location of nuclear power plants. It is by no means axiomatic that a nation will actually use the cheapest fuel available. In making just this latter point, Professor EDWARD S. MASON cites as one example amongst several the current British choice of expensive British coal instead of more reasonably priced Near Eastern oil(3).

In the long run it is likely that it will be the *real* (as opposed to the *projected* or even the *nearing*) depletion of fossil fuel reserves that will force the widespread adoption of nuclear power. In any case the fossil fuels will not suddenly become depleted. Rather, their short supply will become manifest through a gradual rising of mining and transportation costs as either inferior deposits or ones that are further away from customer power plants must be utilized.

The decisive point of depletion may already have been reached for some regions of the developing world. Dr. H. J. BHABHA, Chairman of the Indian Atomic Energy Commission, has recently called attention to the fact that for certain areas in his country one must add to the installed cost of a coal-burning electrical power generating unit the cost of building a railroad for transporting coal to the unit. The railroad could not be justified on other grounds and it surely would not be necessary to carry the extremely compact fuel for a nuclear power plant(4).

No word has yet been said about the forms in which fission fuel is used. Three different isotopes may be employed as the fuel in fission reactors: Uranium – 235, Uranium – 233 and Plutonium – 239. Only the first of these occurs in nature where it is diluted about 140 – fold by the non-fissionable isotope Uranium – 238. It is possible to build nuclear reactors with either the natural mixture of Uranium – 235 and Uranium – 238 or with the separated isotope U – 235. In this latter case the cost of separation must be added to the natural cost of the fuel. Although considerable controversy exists on this point, it does not appear that reactors which use separated Uranium – 235 can approach the economy of those which use the natural mixture(5).

If the world fission fuel reserve is computed simply on the basis of the amount of Uranium - 235 known to be readily extractable from the earth's crust, the total energy available from this source is only about 15% of that of the remaining fossil fuels. Happily it appears possible to construct reactors which combine a "breeding" function with a power-producing function. In such reactors, the abundant but non-fissionable Uranium - 238 could be converted into Plutonium - 239. In other types of reactors the relatively abundant, non-fissionable Thorium - 232 could be transformed into Uranium - 233.

The technology of reactors that will breed or of reactors that can utilize Plutonium - 239 after it is bred currently lags far behind that for reactors that utilize Uranium - 235. It will be necessary to expand this technology before the energy locked within the known sources of Uranium - 238 and Thorium - 232 – enough to supply the world's electrical power needs for several centuries – can be counted on as truly available.

FUSION POWER

Any discussion of fusion power must be couched in terms of "what if." The feasibility of this second avenue to nuclear power is being explored in many laboratories throughout the world. Research on the problem, which began in the early 1950's, has made but slow progress. It is by no means clear that it will succeed at all. In contrast to the fission reaction which can take place at room temperatures, the fusion reaction requires temperatures of millions of degrees. The construction of a vessel to contain such a reaction is clearly a non-trivial affair. Whereas it was clear from the beginning that both the heating and the containment would be exceedingly difficult matters, it has been appreciated more recently – from 1955 onward – that the stability of the reaction conditions over a long enough period to obtain a useful production of energy may well be the greatest problem. Workers in the field remain cheerful, however, and one of them recently remarked that the technical problems associated with controlled fusion are minuscule compared to the political problems of uncontrolled fusion(6).

One of the most significant aspects to the potential use of controlled fusion reactions for power is the cost of fusion fuel. It is generally conceded that if fusion power becomes a reality, deuterium, the naturally-occurring heavy isotope of hydrogen will be the chief fuel. Tritium, the heavier and man-made isotope of hydrogen may also be needed, but this rare substance would be regenerated by the fusion reactor in a manner analogous to the breeding fission reactor. In other words the inventory of tritium, if it is indeed required, would remain constant for a given fusion reactor while deuterium would have to be supplied continuously.

Deuterium is present in nature as 0.015% of all hydrogen. Even at this extremely low concentration the ocean waters are estimated to contain a million billion tons of deuterium. Known processes are capable of extracting deuterium from the ocean at extremely small cost: the $\frac{1}{8}$ of a gram of deuterium in a gallon of water can be extracted for four cents. The energy available from this tiny amount in a hypothetical fusion reactor is equivalent to that obtainable in ordinary combustion processes from 300 gallons of gasoline(7). Clearly such fuel costs would be negligible in comparison with either fission or fossil fuel costs. In addition the deuterium present in the oceans is essentially inexhaustible – enough for millions of years at the present rate of power consumption.

There would be further advantages of fusion power over fission power. A "runaway accident" wherein the power of a fission reactor might rise arbitrarily (alluded to in the discussion of the safety of fission reactors above) would not be possible in a fusion reactor. Nor would disposal of the waste products of fusion reactors be anywhere near as difficult a problem as it is with fission reactors since comparatively little radioactivity would be produced in the fusion reactors.

The capital costs of a practical fusion reactor are necessarily unknown since no design of such a reactor is at hand. One very preliminary study made a number of years ago indicated that the capital costs per installed kilowatt of capacity might not be radically different from power producing devices now operating(8), but it would seem much too early to make any positive statements until it has been determined what, if any, conditions will permit a fusion reaction to give up more energy than it consumes. Clearly, however, the advantages are such that as long as a reasonable chance exists that fusion power may be feasible, any amount of effort or expense, intelligently directed, is justified in its pursuit.

CONCLUSION

No discussion of the prospects of nuclear power should ignore an extremely grave problem that was clearly pointed out a decade ago by PALMER PUTNAM(9). In analysing the existing pattern of energy consumption, PUTNAM claimed that if that pattern were not drastically altered, only 10–20% of the *total energy input* (to be contrasted with *electrical energy output*) could ever be supplied from nuclear sources. Whether or not this shockingly low percentage can actually be justified or not is not important. The fact is that the great bulk of current energy input goes into transportation, comfort heating and process heating – three energy sinks for which electrical power (whether derived from nuclear sources or others) currently has little application. Nor do fission and fusion appear to offer any great possibilities for the *direct* production of energy for these three sinks, i.e., *not* via the electrical energy route. To cite a single example, there exists nothing in nuclear technology that indicates that a nuclear powered automobile will ever be developed.

No encouraging changes have occurred since PUTNAM's analysis was published. Indeed, a world-wide tendency toward decentralization of industry brought on by the high cost of labor near metropolitan centers and world tensions may have actually decreased the fraction of energy needs that might be supplied by nuclear sources. The economy of a large nuclear reactor is considerably better than that of a small reactor since capital costs account for such a large proportion of the total cost. In a nation with a highly dispersed industrial pattern, the fact that a given large nuclear power plant would not be located reasonably close to a sufficient number of large customers would severely curtail the possibility of wide-spread use of nuclear process heat and likewise effect the applicability of nuclear plants for generating electricity because of power distribution costs.

On the other hand, an encouraging proposal has recently been made for giant electrical power networks using new methods for low-cost, long distance transmission of electric power(10). If such proposals become a reality, a change in the pattern of energy consumption might be considerably easier since large nuclear power plants would not need to be located near an ultimate consumer so long as the latter were near a giant power grid.

In summary, it is clear that nuclear power offers no panacea for the world's energy problems. The adoption of fission power will be slow and its rate will depend ultimately on the exhaustion of fossil fuel reserves. Fusion power, while potentially having many advantages over fission power including an inexhaustible fuel supply of negligible cost, has not yet been established as feasible and its costs cannot be reliably assessed. Both types of nuclear power are uniquely adapted to the generation of electrical power and less so to the production of other forms of energy such as those now used in comfort and process heating or in land transportation. Thus a radical change in existing energy consumption patterns is required before the fossil fuels are finally exhausted.

REFERENCES

1. "Energy and Man," pp. 56–58, Appleton Century – Crofts, Inc. New York (1960).
2. "Nuclear Power-One of the Giants," *Nuclear News*, Vol. 5, No. 7, pp. 3–6 (1962).
3. Ref. 1, pp. 83–5.
4. "Atomic Energy in the Indian Economy," *Nuclear News*, Vol. 4, No. 12, pp. 6–8 (1961).
5. W. B. LEWIS, "A Canadian Views the U.S. Civilian Power Reactor Program," *Nuclear News*, Vol. 5, No. 5, pp. 3–10 (1962).
6. M. N. ROSENBLUTH, *Nucleonics*, Vol. 20, No. 2, p. 55 (1962).
7. A. BISHOP, "Project Sherwood," Addison-Wesley Publishing Co., Inc. (1958).
8. L. SPITZER, *et al.*, "Problems of the Stellarator as a Useful Power Source," U.S. Atomic Energy Commission Report NYO–6047 (1954).
9. "Energy in the Future," D. Van Nostrand Co., Inc. (1953).
10. "Pacific Northwest – Pacific Southwest Extra–High Voltage Common Carrier Interconnection," Report of Task Force, U.S. Department of Interior, December 1961.

ROBERT CLARK AXTMANN, Ph.D., was Research Supervisor in Nuclear Reactor Physics, E.I. du Pont de Nemours and Company from 1953–56, and Senior Research Supervisor in Chemical Physics from 1957–59. He has been Socony Mobil Associate Professor of Nuclear Studies, Princeton University, since 1959.

The Discovery, Development and Constructive Use of World Resources

by

W. TAYLOR THOM, JR.

INTRODUCTION

When the writer was asked to prepare a definitive statement regarding the sizes of presently-known and prospectively-available world resources, he actually was asked three questions, namely:

What are the dimensions of the world's *known* material-resource-reserves?

What expansions of such reserves are reasonably possible and expectable under present exploratory and developmental practices? and

What implications do the answers to (1) and (2) have in terms of the world's capacity to support enlarged populations for an indefinitely-long period? – (this latter question being implicit within the topic "Population Crisis – And the Use of World Resources")?

Insofar as these three questions relate to the world's ability to continue to discover and produce essential-resource materials, the answer can be best and most quickly given by a consideration of:

The Ability of the World's Mineral Industry Organizations to Continue to Discover and Produce Essential Mineral-Resource Substances in the Volumes needed.

Amazing changes have taken place in mineral-industry capacities to discover and produce natural-resource substances – as Man has moved forward from the Horse-drawn Era into the Space Age. Moreover these changes can be most readily made apparent by a brief description of what has taken place in the world's petroleum industry during the past 110 years. To this description will be added brief comments (1) about the reserve situation in one or two other sectors of the material-substances industries; (2) about the spectrum of intangible as well as tangible resources available for human use; and (3) about the ways in which proper and imaginative use of world-resources *may* lead to a sensible, competitive-cooperative coexistence – in place of the present mad rush toward mutual annihilation

SECTION I

The foregoing matters are too important to be allowed to drown in a sea of words. So the writer will put the present mineral-resource discovery-situation in perspective, by giving a table, (Table II – p. 501) indicating the changes in the world's petroleum situation which have been brought about during the past 6 epochs of oilfield exploration. However this synoptic statement needs to be prefaced by definitions which will show what the kinds and varieties of "natural-resource reserves" are supposed to be. Therefore Table I is given, together with the covering definitive extensions.

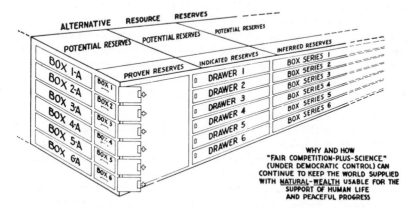

Fig. 1. The Proven Reserve Boxes are open and their contents are available. Th. Contents of the Indicated Reserve boxes have as yet been only partly-determined The inferred Reserve boxes must be drilled, in order to get them open. The key-holes to the Potential Reserve drawers must be reached *through* the "Proven," "Indicated" and "Inferred" boxes.

With reference to the terms used in Table I, the usual definitions run as follows:

Proven Reserves are ones which are commercially available at current prices and under present practices. Wheat stored in a grain elevator or bin is thus a "proven reserve" of wheat.

Indicated Reserves are partly-discovered ones, of commercial grade and of known location. Such "indicated" reserves can be estimated, scientifically, with moderate accuracy – just as fairly accurate "forecasts" for a particular wheat crop can be made a month or so prior to the harvest, by multiplying planted acreages by weighted yield-factors, based on results in previous years.

Inferred Reserves, in the case of wheat, would represent educated guesses as to how much grain could be produced over a considerable period of years to come. Whereas with respect to the size of *inferred reserves* – say of petroleum – the estimates would be made by comparing the quantities of oil previously and prospectively obtainable from a known producing region – say in Oklahoma or Texas – with what might reasonably be expected from other areas of similar geological character, which had not yet been tested.

Latent Reserves. These are contained by deposits which are *not yet* commercial (at current cost and prices). However, greater and greater proportions of *latent* reserves will become "proven" (or available) ones as prices of products rise or as costs of production drop, thus raising outputs from a submarginal to a super-marginal level. (Wheat lands which are too infertile to produce commercial crops of wheat now, would thus be classified as *latent* sources of wheat – such as could become actual sources as soon as the costs of production, including the costs of fertilizers, had dropped below the total of the returns which would be receivable from the sale of crops.)

Alternative-Resource Reserves. Alternative resources are ones from which usable substitute-substances can be gotten, if and when necessary. Maize and millet and rye and barley and potatoes are then alternative sources from which usable flour or meal could be gotten, should wheat flour become unavailable at some future time. Therefore, as will be seen from the foregoing definitions and from Table I, in any consideration of long-term socio-economic problems and plans, competent consideration must be given to *nine* kinds of mineral-resources reserves, any and all of which may serve (eventually) as sources from which particular products, usable for particular purposes may be obtainable – when needed.

However, ordinary trade journal discussions, and normal business plans deal *only* with "proven" or defined reserves (see Fig. 2) despite the fact that mineral-industry writers and executives know that "the Miraculous Pitcher" or "Fifth Dimension" is still working – as "Indicated" reserves and "latent" reserves are gradually being converted to proven ones; as "inferred reserves" gradually shift over into the "indicated" category and as "proven

* "Latent" and "Potential" used as synonyms.

TABLE I

Showing Kinds and Categories of Mineral-Resource Reserves From which Usable Products may be Obtainable.

Categories of Mineral Sources from which particular usable substances are being (or may be) obtained	Kinds of Mineral – Resource Reserves		
	"Proven" (available) reserves, of known location, size and quality	"Indicated" (Available) reserves. Location known but size not fully proven	"Inferred" reserves (Neither exact location nor size yet proven). Estimates of "inferred" reserves based upon *relative sizes of regions* which are roughly of similar character, geologically speaking
Proven or Available Reserves — Category 1 now of usable grade	Proven but economically sub-marginal reserves	Partly-defined and economically sub-marginal reserves	Scientifically Estimated or "Inferred" reserves as yet of sub-marginal character.
Latent Reserves — Category 2 Potentially usable	"Proven" Alternative-source reserves	"Indicated" Alternative-source reserves	"Inferred" reserves of commercial, alternative-source reserves
Potential Reserves — Category 3 Potentially usable	"Latent" Alternative-Resource reserves	"Indicated" Latent Alternative Resource reserves	"Inferred" reserves of sub-marginal alternative-source substances

* The vertical dividing lines thus marked will shift progressively toward the right, as exploration progresses.
* * These bounding horizontal interfaces will move downward progressively – as productive and extractive processes undergo recurrent improvement,

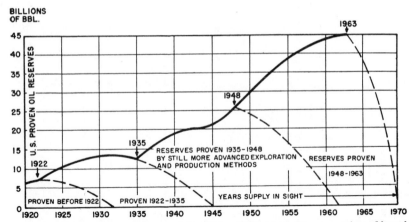

Fig. 2. The important question regarding Fig. 2 is *"How long will* our supplies of liquid fuels and lubricants last? And the answer is "How long will Fair-Competition Enterprise be able to plan ahead with confidence and be able to *re-invest enough, soon enough,* in new research laboratories, exploratory operations and manufacturing plants?"

alternative-source" reserves become gradually transformed into economically super-marginal sources of needed products. (See Table I).

Now in order to set a scale for discussing the world-resource situation in meaningful terms, Table II provides a typical illustration of how geo-exploratory practices have advanced as industrial Engineering Science has progressed from "The Horse-drawn Era," through "The Automobile and Airplane Era" and on into "The Space Era."

The facts (and opinions) set out in the foregoing Table are, of course, in violent contrast with statements which have been repeated and repeated in our economic "folk-lore" – such partly-true statements being to the effect that "our oil reserves are very limited", are "wasting assets" and are "non-renewable resources." Since the writer was a member of the committee of 12 men that prepared the estimates which started this misleading chain-reaction going, it is perhaps in order for him to explain both what started "the oil-famine scare" in 1922, and also what basis of reasoning he has now used in arriving at the putative oil-reserve figures contained in Table II. This story runs as follows:

During 1919 and 1920 there were clear indications that advances in geo-exploratory discovery methods were lagging behind what was needed. Consequently a committee was formed in 1920 (consisting of 6 men each, from the American Association of Petroleum geologists and from the U.S. Geological Survey) and they were asked to prepare estimates of those U.S. petroleum reserves ("Proven, probable and possible") which were believed to be *discoverable and producible, commercially, by methods and techniques then in use.* This latter qualifying clause *was included* when the estimates were published early

TABLE II

The Seven Epochs in Petroleum-Industry Exploration and Development

Epoch	Approxi- mate duration	Degree of Scientific guidance of exploratory work	Petroleum reserves pro- spectively estimated to be available at end of epoch (in billions of barrels)	
			United States	World
1	Prior to 1859	Discovery guided by (essentially) *one*-dimensional, empirical Prospector's Art	Nominal	Nominal
2	1860–1912	Discovery guided by seepages, by em-pirical rules, and by *two*-dimensional semi-scientific geological prospecting	?	?
3	1913–1922	Incipient *three*-dimensional (geological engineering or) quantitative mapping of promising areas	5 proven & 2 probable & 2 possible	20
4	1923–1927	*Four*-dimensional geological engi-neering mapping – using geological, geophysical, geochemical and paleo-biological principles and techniques	18	40
5	1928–1945	Five-dimensional engineering use of science, technology and applied-science research-and-development	75	160
6	1946–1955	Six-dimensional or "Space-Age" em-ployment of science and technology, using (cross-checked) inductive and deductive *team*-research	300	1280
7	1956–	7-dimensional Exploration (= six scientific and technologic dimensions plus another *human* or *ethical* dimension considerate of *global human need*	Both Inexhaustible I F human beings behave responsibly	

in 1922 – because all of the geologists concerned knew that exploratory and extractive (and refining) techniques were being constantly extended and improved – though no one could guess just how fast such improvements would be made, or how great their impact would be – as measured by increases in the *available* crude oil supplies. Therefore the 9 billion barrels of (estimated) oil reserves (5 billion "proven" and four billion "probable" and "possible") set out in the 1922 news release was given as a *base figure* to which new increments should be added as time went on. However headline writers took the 9 billion barrel figure of reserves, available as of 1922, divided it by the 1921 production figure, and came up with the really exciting assertion that the U.S. could look forward to "an oil famine" in less than 14 years. Whereas, as of 1962, it is obvious (see Fig. 2) that the U.S. *"proven"* oil reserves of today are much greater than the 9 billion barrel *total* of all reserves set in 1922, despite the fact that *many* billions of barrels of oil have already been produced in the U.S. since 1922. (Likewise today's estimates of the world's proven crude oil reserves are necessarily relatively much larger than they were in the early 1920's). This contrast between the 1922 and 1962 "oil pictures" has been due to several factors, which will be mentioned in the next few paragraphs.

Thus, in 1922, exploratory geology was just *beginning* to be a quantitative engineering science, though many men on the frontiers of oil exploration were still chiefly practitioners of the prospector's art; an "Art" which was a factual, qualitative, theoretical-and-intuitive one, operated on an empirical and rule-of-thumb-plus-"hunch" basis.

To prepare for the rest of the oil-reserve story, let us then set down here the following two figures.

Estimated total reserves of the United States – *available* (in 1922) *by methods then in use* – approximately............................... 9 billion barrels
Estimated totals of world oil reserves, similarly available (in 1922) something of the order-of-magnitude of .... 20 billion barrels

Advances during Exploratory Epoch 4

By 1925 pertoleum geology had become a fairly well advanced engineering science, which was bringing a Fourth Dimension (Time and Earth History) into its scheme of things, through its use of fossils and of geological history. Also about 1925 geophysical (gravitational, seismic, magnetic and electrical) exploratory methods were beginning to be used and soon made it possible to extend commercial exploration into great regions which formerly had been too hazardous for effective prospecting, (because of water or swamp cover or because of lack of surface outcrops). Also, by about the same time, "subsurface structural mapping" had proven that information yielded by careful study of well records and of well "cuttings" and cores could give effective guidance for new drilling operations. These advances in scientific knowledge and in operational technique resulted in at least a doubling of the oil reserves prospectively discoverable and producible. Consequently, as of the end of 1927, the prospective U.S. and world oil reserves had increased in rough terms, to:

U.S. oil reserves estimate as of 1927 – 18 billion barrels
World ,,   ,,   ,,   ,, ,, 1927 – 40   ,,   ,,
representing an improvement of exploratory effectiveness by a factor of 2.

The Onset of Exploratory Epoch 5

As the 1930's began, petroleum exploration was entering into its Fifth Dimensional phase, as it became an *effective engineering science engaged in cooper-ative-competitive programs of compilation, analysis and interpretation of evidence*, aimed not just at determining *what* had happened; *where* it had happened; and *how* it had happened; as in the Three-Dimensional phase, or of *"what"* had happened and *when"* – as in the Fourth-Dimensional phase – but also at determining *why* critical relationships had developed (areally, chrono-logically, *and* dynamically) during long spans of geologic time. Wherefore, by the end of 1945, these improvements plus the ones which had taken place in oil well drilling-and-production techniques, coupled with a widespread and intensive use of geophysical exploratory methods and with the intro-duction of the above-mentioned Fifth Dimension into geoexploratory work, had provided a further combined improvement-factor for petroleum discovery and production work of at least 4, as of that time. Consequently U.S. oil reserves, as of 1945 (and comparable world-reserves) would reason-ably have been estimated then as follows:

U.S. oil reserves, expectable as of 1945 – 75 billion barrels
World „   „   „   „ „ 1945 – 160   „   „

Epoch 6 in the evolution of oilfield exploratory and developmental practices

Somewhere between 1945 and 1955, petroleum exploration entered its "Sixth Dimensional" or "Limitless" phase – a phase within which a general employment of research teams, (seeking scientific answers while following sub-parallel or convergent – but independent – lines of evidence) were finding it possible to make highly-successful use of *prospective* and *inductive* thinking, while also *continuing* to use *retrospective* and *deductive* methods in their research procedures and practical applications. Therefore by 1956, because of recurrent increases in the proportion of the oil underground, which is now extractable commercially, and because of the introduction of the (Research-and-Development) Sixth Dimensional factor into practical operations, it is reasonable to believe that the prospectively-recoverable oil reserves were subject to improvement-factors of at least 2 × 2 for the United States and of more than 4 × 2 for the world. Therefore, these factors if applied to the 1945 estimates, would give:
Estimated prospective oil resources of U.S. as of 1956 – 4 × 75 –

approximately 300 billion barrels
Estimated prospective oil resources world as of 1956

approximately 1,280 billion barrels
The foregoing (1956) world oil-reserve estimates, just given, are con-servative (rather than optimistic ones), besides which they do not include estimates applying to the large volumes of "natural gas liquids" (propane,

butane, etc.) which are now recoverable as condensates from (marketed) natural gas. Nor do they make any allowance for those "usable liquid *substitutes*" (for gasoline or diesel fuel or fuel oil) that have already been produced in small volume from coal, from "tar sands," from oil shale and from natural gas (by polymerization). But all of these *alternative-source* resources would enter the oil-products picture rapidly – and in great volume – if there were really commercial need for their use. Furthermore these *alternative-source* resources do exist in great volume – and do need only minor changes in cost-versus-price differentials to make them at least locally commercial.

To illustrate: The world's coal resources (particularly of lignitic or low-rank coals) are very large indeed; the energies now available from natural gas are prodigious. And one single deposit of "tar sand" (the one cropping out along the Athabaska River, in Western Canada) contains the equivalent of hundreds of billions of barrels of material from which commercial (oil-like) liquid fuels can be made quite readily. (Indeed commercial production of such liquid-fuel products from these "tar sands" is about to begin).

So one major world-question of today is *not* "*What can we use* when the oil-famine comes?" but is, instead, "Now that we have it found, what are we to do with it?" – with the obvious answer being that great parts of our discovered and discoverable (but as yet unproduced) oil reserves should speedily be supplying motor fuel for fleets of trucks travelling on as yet unbuilt, continentwide farm-to-market road systems in Africa, Latin America and Asia.

What of petroleum discovery and development during Epoch 7, within the Space Era?

The course of petroleum discovery and development in the Space Era can easily be predicted – on an alternative basis. For the peoples of the world, through the UN, will either decide to develop and use the world's resources properly, globally and for human benefit (in which case discovery and development will go forward rapidly and easily). Or the world's governments will continue the stupidities of the Cold-War Arms Race until "we all go away together." (True great care will have to be taken if a non-disastrous transition is to be made from a Cold-War world-economy into a true Peace-Time economy – but for persons *capable of thinking in global terms* this presents neither a terribly large nor terribly difficult problem. For *IF* human well-being and peaceful progress *are* to provide that "ultimate human orientation" toward which all approaches are to be made convergent, then the whole business of discovery, development and use becomes a fairly simple (engineering-style) business capable of providing *earnings* for an almost unlimited number of people.

The Discovery and Development Situation in Resource-Sectors Other Than That of the Petroleum Industry.

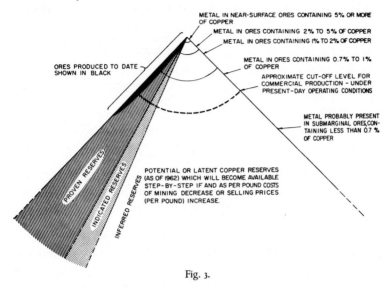

Fig. 3.

The Natural Gas Reserve and Ore Reserve Situations – as of 1963

The reserve-situations applying to other vital material resources are in their essential terms comparable to the petroleum reserve situation, just described. Therefore only a few comments will be made apropos of the world's present natural gas reserve situation – with a slightly longer treatment of the copper reserve picture – as being quite typical of the general ore-reserve conditions.

Natural gas reserves: It will merely be stated here that the world has enormous stores of natural gas – as had been demonstrated for example, by recent discoveries of very large gas reserves along the north-eastern coast of the Netherlands. There are, however, two particular points about natural gas development which deserve emphasis – these points being covered by the two questions:

(1) How can waste of this almost-priceless resource be avoided, (a question which links up with question 2), which is

(2) How can certain groups of nations be brought to realize that if their own legitimate self-interests are to be properly served it will be necessary for them to undertake, cooperatively, the building of major natural gas pipeline systems such as will lead (for example) from the oil-and-gas field areas of the Persian Gulf region, into and across Turkey, and on into the fuel-hungry countries of South-eastern and Central Europe?

The present-day terms of the ore-reserve problem. In dealing with the world's ore-reserve problems it is necessary to use the same qualifying terms as were used in discussing the oil-reserve problem, these terms being (see Table I) "commercially-available," "latent," and "alternative-source reserve" categories, each divisible into "proven," "indicated" and "inferred" sub-totals. And in order to cite a single case-example (which will suffice to show that "Relativity" terms also apply to the general ore-reserve situation) the writer will next discuss briefly the matter of copper reserves.

The World's copper-resource situation. The world's copper-resource situation (which is broadly illustrative of the world's metallic-resource situations in general) is describable as follows:

The world's reserves of rich copper ores (those assaying 5% of metallic copper – or better) are probably relatively limited in amount, and naturally have been the ones which have been more intensively developed – since the discovery (and mining) of such ores, at shallow depths could be carried forward by primitive rule-of-thumb prospecting and mining methods, ever since the beginning of Bronze Age times. But, as Fig. 3 indicates, the quantities of copper available in ores assaying between 2½ and 5% metal, are far greater than the amounts to be had from 5%-and-better ore. Also the quantities of metal to be had from 1 to 2.5% ore are very much greater still. The assay-bracket between 1% ore and 0.7% ore is far larger yet – with huge proven latent reserves of metal, also existent at known locations, in ores of less than 0.70 grade – this 0.70 figure representing the approximate cut-off value for commercial (large-scale open-pit) mining as of today.

It is to be noted that real expansions of now-available and usable supplies of copper have, as a matter of fact, been brought about by improvements in geoexploratory practice; by improving mining and milling techniques, and by improving extractive processes – so that the world's *usable* supplies of the metal have grown notably in the past 50 years despite mine-depletion. Moreover this increase in *usable* supplies will expectably be carried forward for so long a time that it extends far beyond the range of really useful present-day prediction. (This is especially true since the world's supply of "secondary" copper – extractable from scrap and from obsolete equipment – is also growing rapidly).

The essential terms of the copper-reserve problem, are then also really resident in the question as to how wise will the world's peoples be (in their use of – and support of the UN) – in clearing the ways for proper, sensible and constructive use of *all* resources.

*   *
*

However what are probably the world's two greatest material-resource reserves do not even need to be discovered. They merely need to be put to use sensibly and on an adequate (global) scale. And these resources are, respectively, river waters (especially those in rivers flowing northward to the Arctic) which are now of *minimal* human use, plus the water (and the contained "ores and minerals") and the food resources contained by our oceanic areas.

In terms of modern engineering capacities it would not be impossible to turn the water of the north-flowing rivers of Siberia and Canada southward into dry regions crying for moisture. It would not be impossible to move great volumes of "Congo-Ubangi" and Niger River water northward across (or through) their divides into the Sahara. Nor would it be *too* difficult to move water, along contour, from the headwaters of the Amazon into the dry uplands of Brazil. Difficult? Yes. Worthwhile? Yes. Costly? Yes, in immediate money-terms, but *not* in ultimate, economic-growth and human terms.

But the great resource-opportunities and *the* great challenges which are wide open before all of us (– if we can *really* use atomic power *sensibly* and *if* we can *harness* the energies of the H-bomb) are, after all, so large, so simple and so obvious that they have been looked at – and over-looked – for years. And these opportunities and resources are resident in the oceans. For, "where *is* the world's *great* water supply?" It is in the oceans, of course. And where are the world's greatest potential sources of all manner of minerals and chemicals and rare metals? In the oceans of course. And what is needed to make these resources available? Just three things: (1) A combination of common sense and creative imagination; (2) a properly-engineered use of prodigious quantities of atomic or thermonuclear energy; and (3) the employment of large-scale fractionation systems (much like those currently used in oil refining or in the milling, smelting and fractionation of complex ores) whereby the salt waters of the seas would be split up into ten or twenty or more usable (and needed) products, each valuable in its own right and all (taken together) having a *combined* sales value far exceeding the combined costs. Especially if one considers the prodigious expansions of earnings and of employment – (for both unskilled and skilled workers) which would be induced by the ocean-water plus river-water projects. True, these things cannot be done instantaneously – fortunately. Nor will they be done if the nations allow their peoples to smother themselves with their own human increase.

SECTION II

THE CONSTRUCTIVE AND CREATIVE USE OF THE WORLD'S MINERAL (MATERIAL)-RESOURCE SUBSTANCES

As of 1963 the world's geoexploratory engineers and scientists needed to find about 40 billion dollar's worth of new mineral raw materials per year to offset current drains upon the world's proven resource-reserves. And, as Fig. 4 indicates, this total must be at least doubled – at the earliest possible moment – if the present distressing plight of the needy nations is not to

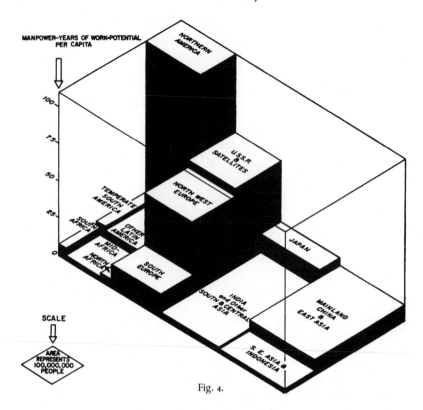

Fig. 4.

become completely desperate. To show why this conclusion is justified let us consider what Fig. 4 shows. For within this Figure the surface *areas* of the several blocks shown are proportionate to the (1960) sizes of the several national or regional populations specified, whereas the vertical *heights* of the several blocks represent the per capita productive energies available to these several populations. (And therefore give a fair quantitative measure of average national living-standards).

However certain facts about the "work-potential" components included in the columns of Fig. 4 need to be mentioned now. For the "work-potentials" upon which possible productive capacities have been based, have been computed by dividing total-population numbers into the sum-total of energies available to the nation – these "total energies" representing the sum of all energies available to the nation from human and animal labor; from the burning of fuels of all sorts; from falling water; from wind power; solar radiation, etc.

Therefore, within hoe-culture and village-economy systems of operation *almost* the whole of the energy available, from animals and from people, must be devoted to the raising of food – with very little energy left for the production of clothing or shoes or manufactures of any sort. Consequently the general standard-of-living within nations having a predominantly agricultural-village or herdsman economy is not only necessarily very low, but tends to move progressively downward toward the Starvation Level (see Fig. 5–A) – unless death-rates from disease or war are suddenly increased – or unless birth-rates become controllable and are greatly reduced.

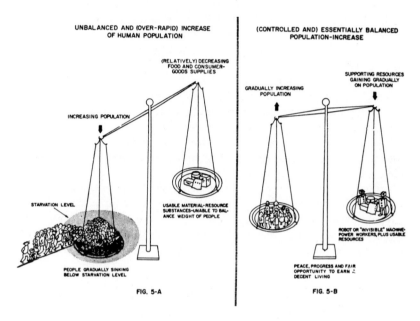

FIG. 5-A

FIG. 5-B

By contrast, where work-potentials run in terms of 15 or more manpower years per capita, much of the work will be done by power machinery and, *one* man, provided with power farm-equipment, may be able to produce enough food to supply hundreds of people; or one man or woman or older child operating suitable power-machinery, may be able to spin or weave more thread or cloth than could have been produced by scores of manual workers; or one coal-mining power-shovel, with a crew of two men may be able to do work which would require 15,000 pick-and-shovel laborers for its accomplishment. Similarly one Diesel-powered train, with a crew of five, can haul more freight than could be transported by thousands of camels or other pack animals, etc. And yet, as can be seen, the relative amounts of food and clothing needed in a highly mechanized civilization are vastly less in proportion to the totals of articles produced, than in a manual-labor, animal-power agricultural economy. Consequently it is the large-scale use of power-machinery that makes possible the creation of the wealth and variety of consumer-goods characteristic of high-standard-of-living areas – if population-increase becomes controllable, as has been accomplished, for example, in Japan.

Therefore the basic problem of the world's (predominantly agricultural) Needy Peoples (see Fig. 4) is stated graphically in Fig. 5-A, shown above. For the imbalances between population-numbers on the one hand, and supporting resources on the other are increasing rapidly as modern health measures are reducing disease-caused death rates (without being balanced by decreases in birth-rates) – with the result that the Scales-of-Nature are sagging down to where General Famine (and revolutionary outbreak) *must* ensue – soon – unless effective measures to limit population-growth are taken *at once*. (Japan has, as indicated, taken such measures, and it is reported that the Peiping Regime has decided to apply them either at once, or very soon, within Mainland China.) By contrast, under the general economic conditions prevailing in Northwestern Europe (where informal population-control has been largely effective for years) the standards-of-living are high (see Figs. 4 and 5–B) and are tending to rise, as the beneficial influences of regional economic integrations are causing per capita productivities to incréase rapidly (see Fig. 5–B).

Again, by contrast it is probable that an "invisible population" crisis is developing in Northern America because of an over-rapid, accelerating (exploitationist) increase taking place in the replacement of human workers by "invisible workers," represented by the work-potentials of *automated* mass-production equipment (see Figs. 5–C and 5–D just below).

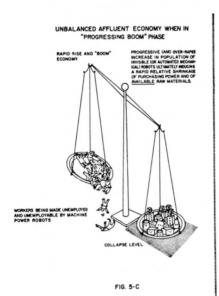

UNBALANCED AFFLUENT ECONOMY WHEN IN "PROGRESSING BOOM" PHASE

RAPID RISE AND "BOOM" ECONOMY

PROGRESSIVE (AND OVER-RAPID) INCREASE IN POPULATION OF INVISIBLE (OR AUTOMATED MECHANICAL) ROBOTS ULTIMATELY INDUCING A RAPID RELATIVE SHRINKAGE OF PURCHASING POWER AND OF AVAILABLE RAW MATERIALS.

WORKERS BEING MADE UNEMPLOYED AND UNEMPLOYABLE BY MACHINE POWER ROBOTS

COLLAPSE LEVEL

FIG. 5-C

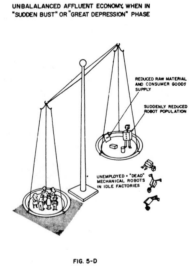

UNBALANCED AFFLUENT ECONOMY, WHEN IN "SUDDEN BUST" OR "GREAT DEPRESSION" PHASE

REDUCED RAW MATERIAL AND CONSUMER GOODS SUPPLY

SUDDENLY REDUCED ROBOT POPULATION

UNEMPLOYED - "DEAD" MECHANICAL ROBOTS IN IDLE FACTORIES

FIG. 5-D

Indeed the expanding use of automated power-machines in Northern America seems to be causing not only a progressive enlargement of the unemployed fraction of the adult working population, but it is also causing a shocking increase both in the numbers of unemployed adolescent (would-be) workers – and in the large (and increasing) numbers of other (uneducated) and (unskilled) adolescents who are not only now un-employed *but are prospectively unemployable, at any foreseeable future time.*

The huge projects and problems mentioned above therefore naturally bring us face to face with the problem of employing and developing another essentially-unused resource of enormous size, namely the ca-pacities of the world's young people – young people who, at this point, are thoroughly dissatisfied with both the timidities, the "fixed-idea" (out-dated) and parochial view-points of various "world-leaders" – and also with the absence of visible opportunities for daring action, for adventure, and for great team-effort such as *should* make youth "the Hope of the World."

Let us now consider what must be done about *developing* resources – if Humanity's dreams are to come true. Is it not necessary to decide that what *should* be done *can* be done? That if something *should* be done that the world *must* be able to *afford to do it?* – Indeed, and more importantly, that the world cannot afford *not* to do it? Money *is* important – but over-emphasis on *money* has bred enormous sorrows in the Divided World of the Past – and it will repeat these sorrows and bring on World-War III – unless it ceases to be the world's prime policy-objective and end-it-inself, becoming, instead, merely an (essential-but-subordinate) element in the building of a peaceful competitive-cooperative Space Age world-society – a society within which people are willing to be "earners" and do not merely aspire to be conspicuously-successful cheats, profiteers and exponents of "con-spicuous consumption and of Megalomaniac Egotism."

SECTION II-A

THE DISCOVERY AND DEVELOPMENT OF LATENT HUMAN CAPACITIES

As shown by Fig. 6, the world's present populations include about 2 billion people who are either unskilled or are illiterate or both. Wherefore they are, at present, capable of only minimal production and are, as of now, probably more of a world-liability than an asset both to themselves and to society. However these people exist. They have needs and deserve the opportunity to prove that they can (and will) earn the "rights" that they are asking for, which can be possible if they accept the responsibility to earn more – by learning to produce more – thus enabling them to earn decent livings for themselves and for their families.

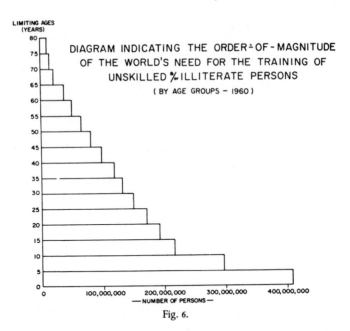

Fig. 6.

The world's unskilled and illiterate persons belong to all age-groups as shown by Fig. 6. And they not only present a developmental problem, which must be dealt with but also constitute a prodigious training problem, that needs to be dealt with quickly, effectively and inexpensively. Obviously this needs to be done by use of a combination of old-style multi-level apprentice-training, coupled with modern "earn-while-learning" and "each-one-teach-two" techniques – such as are being experimentally developed by UN agencies, by various Foundations and by various church groups and comparable units.

The one thing certain about these lacks of literacy and of skill is that no satisfactory (and peaceful) development of the world's under-developed lands – and peoples – can be expected unless a massive and accelerated program for training *is* provided for the individuals included in the groups represented in Figure 6. Wherefore the questions immediately arise "Who can (and will) plan and administer such a huge training and schooling program as is needed?" And how can funds be gotten to carry these programs forward? With respect to the first of these questions (as to who would be able to "carry the ball") the answer can be gotten through a consideration of a series of corollary questions: Thus

1. Can we expect much help with this problem from people of ages of more than 75 years? Answer: No.

2. Can we get much help from persons between 65 and 75 years of age? Answer: Yes – in terms of advice – both as to what to try and what *not* to try.

3. Can we get help from people between 28 and 65 years of age? Answer: Only from relatively rare, thoughtful and dedicated individuals, who are not so wholly absorbed in family, or business, or political or social or church affairs as to be practically irresponsible in terms of *effective* world citizenship.

4. Can help be had from young people between 15 and 20 years of age? Answer: Yes. These adolescents can render *great* help, if allowed to work as junior colleagues or "apprentices," to other persons a few years older.

5. Can children between 7 and 15 years of age help? Answer: Yes. More than many persons would expect – if *they*, too, can assist others in the *15 to 20 age bracket.*

6. Can we expect much help from the world's young people who are between 20 and 28 years of age? And the answer is YES! For it is with this group of young people that the hope of the world rides – because: *They* are the ones who have the ability, the energy, the courage and the vision called for by the present world-crisis;

They are ones whose minds were not already closed before the Nuclear Age began;

They are ones who not only can, but must dare to devise and try out imaginative, new, quick and effective methods for training and teaching (such as can and will make full and expert use of "earn-while-learning" systems and also of radio, and Kinescope and TV methods – so that large numbers of students can be trained by a few adequately prepared teachers, who (like captains) will be helped to carry out their assignments by competent younger "sergeants" and "corporals," performing effectively under qualified and inspiring guidance).

These young people, between 20 and 28 know that they *cannot count on having any future themselves* unless the *whole world* has a future. And the *whole world* will not have a future unless these *young* people *do* decide *what* kind of a world is needed; *how* progress can be made toward the meeting of this need; and *what* persuasions they must use to overcome the inertia of "old-timers" who may be running governments according to outdated patterns-of-thought.

The Self-Development of Personal Capacities. How can talented youngsters, revealed by the foregoing program, be able to use their personal resources – most beneficially? An "earn-while-learning" program for training can be made to generate a chain-reaction – in terms of both the continuation, and the financing, of this kind of a training project – as the writer knows from personal experience. For during the 1930–1939 Depression period he was one of a group of professors who organized and ran such a multi-level training, educational and research program. And it was possible to draw in the money needed for the operation of this project, even during the Depression, because *all* activities were made to yield at least three dollars' worth of results for each dollar spent. This was true because the activities were simultaneously doing four things: (a) training younger students; (b) helping graduate students to learn research methods and also to produce valuable research-results through the conducting of significant research projects; (c) giving faculty members opportunities both for mutual education and for self-education; and (d) providing ideas and data which were of marked practical benefit both to the local communities, and also to mineral-industry organizations engaged in commercial exploration and development.

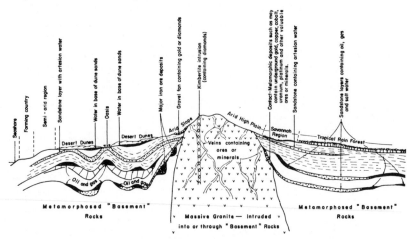

Diagram Showing How Great Mineral Wealth May Lie Undiscovered Beneath the Surface in Many "Underdeveloped" National Areas

Fig. 7.

The world's young persons, engaged in (self) education and training, should also arrange for sound tests of new training methods – in order to see which methods are time-wasting or otherwise overly-expensive. Also in connection with training under the "earn-while-learning" program, four things can usefully be kept in mind: (1) that during the basic initial search for mineral wealth within the national area (see Fig. 7) air-photograph mosaic maps and also aero-topographic maps will almost certainly have been made, covering the whole national territory.

(2) That young people between 10 and 16 years of age can construct (sectionized) topographic relief-*models*, for parts or all of a region covered by such topographic maps – by cutting out and piling up cardboard sheets which have been marked and cut according to pairs of contour lines. The method for making such cardboard relief models is a simple one. For after deciding the horizontal scale at which the model is to be made, then cardboards are used having a thickness that would suitably represent a contour interval. For such work a very small scale is used if a whole national

region is to be shown by one single (dissected) model – of manageable size. Or an intermediate scale would be employed – if a moderate-sized region is to be depicted; and large scales (and thicker topographic-interval) cardboards would be used if small areas, including particular villages or towns, are to be modelled – at such a scale that each house, street or road, garden-plot, spring-and-stream, wood-lot, pasture, etc., could be shown.

(3) It has already been proven that young people 14 years of age or over would find it easy to understand how such model-construction should be done (probably upon background plywood mounting-units about 40 cm square), after which they could guide further construction (by pairs) of picked young people from 10 to 14 years of age. (As can be seen, the accuracy of the model-construction done could be tested, not merely by visual inspection but also by checking how the edges of each model-unit would match those of contiguous units.

All of the young people engaged in such work would by their own efforts not only learn how to read aerial photographs and topographic maps, but they could also learn how to show new houses and roads, etc., both on the (enlarged) map and on the models constructed therefrom. And then, if a group should have made a model of their home-village they could explain what the model showed to their parents and neighbors. After which *all* could compare ideas as to where bridges should be built, or where a village water-supply well should be drilled, or where carpenter shops or saw-mills or garages or other training-centers should be located etc., etc.

SECTION III

THE DEVELOPMENT OF THE RESOURCES OF NEW NATIONS

The writer stresses the construction of such models partly because they make *developmental planning* very simple and very easy. Whereas most people do *not* read topographic maps readily – despite the fact that landforms and rates-of-slope must be considered – properly – if good plans are to be made. He also emphasizes such model-making because duplicate casts of model-units can be readily made, if desired; and because if trainee-groups at each training center do produce models for *their* respective areas, it would not take long to produce unit-sets of models that could be fitted together to portray a whole region. Which would be most helpful if irrigation projects needed to be considered and planned for; if road networks needed to be laid out, or if landing fields or trading centers or garages-and-filling stations needed to be established at strategic localities. In other words the initiation of a model-construction program by children can be made to trigger a whole (expanding) series of nationally-important development projects.

Moreover in this latter connection it may be usefully remembered:

(1) That one of the most educational and useful "earn-while-learning" work-activities *is* the building of simple graded roads and of simple bridges – such as can be done by local unskilled workers, operating under teachers able to give instruction in the use of the tools and equipment needed.

(2) That major oil companies are teaching their local employees, in many lands, how to do more and more skilled work – in connection with these company's exploration and development activities.

(3) That oil company agricultural experts have been showing many people that modern methods and fertilizers will increase crop-yields greatly.

(4) That drillers, formerly employed by oil companies, are in some regions now drilling water wells – as a private business. And are being taught, (by company-made educational movies) how to *conserve* ground-water, as well as to produce it.

(5) That the oil-producing nations – and oil-producing companies – would reasonably give substantial money – and technical support – to road-building activities in new nations for obvious reasons.

(6) That the major companies manufacturing trucks and autos could reasonably be expected to establish local training-and-service centers (employing local citizens) – *if* reasonably-extensive road-systems are being constructed.

(7) That in terms of *effective general education* and of *social awakening* the building of roads, and the use of cheap automobiles, are perhaps even more effective than radio and TV – as has been shown by the results which have accrued from the building of access roads past, or across, the previously-isolated "coves" and "branch water" areas of the Appalachian mountains and across "the wide-open spaces," – which formerly isolated Great Plains hamlets and ranches from the outside world, during "the Horse-drawn Era."

(8) That there are surely many other youth organizations (like The Boy Scouts of America) which have prepared series of educational booklets (for self-educational purposes) that are simply, clear, effective, inexpensive – and undoubtedly obtainable in large numbers.

A great many of the "educational" ideas and systems currently being employed in the United States are *terribly* time-consuming, terribly expensive, and likewise uninteresting – because they are not relevant to those things which will fit young persons to earn their living in The World of Tomorrow. And

(9) That the best teachers will be people who can *show* their pupils what to do and how to do it – rather than ones who try to *tell* their pupils how to do things, despite the fact that they, themselves, do not really know what they are talking about.

THE DEVELOPMENT, AND CONSTRUCTIVE AND CREATIVE EMPLOYMENT, OF THE WORLD'S INDUSTRIAL AND ECONOMIC RESOURCES

The current world-crisis has, of course, two prime causes – unlimited population-increase, and the carryover, into the (uniting) Space-Age World, of the economic thought-and-behavior patterns that were characteristic of an Ages-old, traditional Divided-World, economic exploitationism. This is a vital point. For not only does the world's economic-and-industrial complex constitute the (multiple or single) "body" of world-civilization, but, it has, heretofore, been subject to no sensible control, and has neither been dedicated to meeting human need, ñor has it been dedicated to the advancement of worthy and humane purposes. Its interests have characteristically been materialistic and exploitationist, inhuman and destructive. Thus the older economies have grown like trees which have flourished as long as their roots could exploit their own territory (and such other territories as could be reached) but which exercised no foresight and had no constructive and humane policy. They merely exploited and profiteered – in inhuman or Jungle-Law fashion. And then they gradually died out at the top and rotted out within (until collapse occurred) – as pioneer and frontier conditions ceased to exist and as sustaining nutrients could no longer be wrung from the depleted soil. (Stages in the growth and decay of such an old-fashioned materialistic-exploitationist economy are shown by Figures 8 to 11, inclusive).

The kind of industrial and economic development with which we must be concerned now is, then, that which is guided by worthy and humane purposes – such as animate an intelligent farmer. For such a farmer, though he recognizes the necessity of earning an adequate *cash* income, nevertheless also regards this money-income as a by-product of, and a corollary to, his central purposes which are: (1) to meet the needs of his own family for a home plus adequate material support (which he can do best while also helping, cooperatively) (2) to meet the basic and natural needs of such other members of the modern "economic team" as are constructively busy in non-farming occupations. For a wise farmer does continually build up and increase the productivity of his land and thus, even when he dies, his land passes on to his family – for continued use and for continuing improvement. Which is in complete contrast with the ruin wrought by exploitationists. For the latter first deplete the fertility of their soil, by continued (unfertilized) cropping. Then they over-graze the land – first with cattle, then with sheep and finally with goats. And when the goats have finished, all vegetation is gone. The soil has eroded away or been blown away. And only a desert of stony rubble remains.

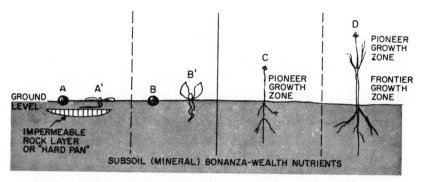

Fig. 8-A and 8-B. Showing "unsprouted seeds" for production of a modern National Economy. (These are Caravan or Pack Animal Hoe Culture Subsistence-Economies).

Fig. 8-A′ and 8-B′. Situation after first growth-season has been started by watering of seeds by "liquid capital" provided from abroad.

The Root of Nascent Economy A′ is blocked off from needed subsoil nutrients by a feudal "Landlordism" condition – or rock-like "hard-pan" layer.

The Root of Nascent Economy B′ has been abundantly nourished by rich subsoil (mineral-resource) wealth.

Fig. 8-C. Shows an immature economy at the end of its first (or Pioneer) growth period.

Fig. 8-D. Shows the same economy after its second (or Frontier) growth-period.

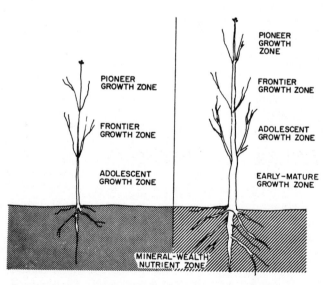

Fig. 9-A. Shows an "unoriented" economy after its third (or Adolescent) growth-period
Fig. 9-B. Shows an "unoriented" economy, after its fourth (or Early Mature) growth-period.

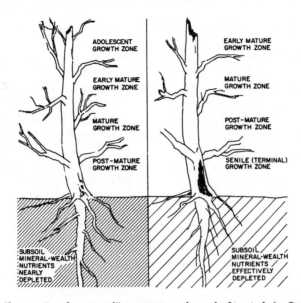

Fig. 10-A. Shows a "profit-oriented" economy at the end of its sixth (or Post-mature) growth-period. This is after Pioneer and Frontier growth-conditions have ceased to exist.

The heart of the economy is decaying, though superficial growth is still being induced, by deficit spending and by installment selling (on more and more unsound terms).

Fig. 10-B. Shows the same economy near the end of its Senile of Moribund growth-period. At this stage the heart of the economy (a satisfactory and all-inclusive human employment) has been largely rotted out partly by proliferation of public-relief parasites; partly by loss of Pioneer-to-Adolescent growth activities and partly by unwise Big Business, Big Labor and Big Government actions, forcing an acceleration of human unemployment, through an over-rapid introduction of automated mass-production machinery.

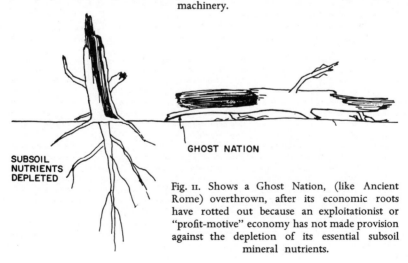

Fig. 11. Shows a Ghost Nation, (like Ancient Rome) overthrown, after its economic roots have rotted out because an exploitationist or "profit-motive" economy has not made provision against the depletion of its essential subsoil mineral nutrients.

Therefore our national and global hopes for survival and progress depend largely upon the development of intelligent plans for making our economies more and more effective in the meeting of normal, (legitimate) and continuing human needs. Because on *this* basis peace can prevail. Adequate *earnings* can be had. And satisfying economic growth will continue. For natural and proper consumer-demands are not only effectively unlimited in their extent but they are also capable of inducing unlimited employment (and earning power) and also a similarly-unlimited economic growth – *provided that resources are available wherewith to support that growth.*

Therefore we need next to consider both the varieties of resource-materials required by modern industry, and the developmental conditions which can cause the world's "economic and industrial body" to do what

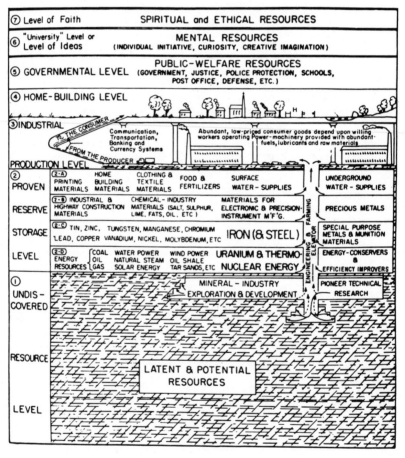

Fig. 12.

needs to be done. A diagram (Fig. 12) has therefore been prepared, in order to show that there is a real spectrum of resources – both tangible and intangible – all of which have parts to play in the operation of a full-fledged properly-organized economy. This diagram also points out the fact that the whole weight of the social structure is supported by the people who mine subsoil resources or cultivate the soil; or transport, transmute, and distribute the manufactures, upon which family-life and world society depend.

Fig. 13 is therefore given just below, in order to emphasize this point – and also to show how various kinds of engineering activities relate to the discovery, storage and use of natural-resource substances – as depicted at levels 1, 2 and 3 of Fig. 12.

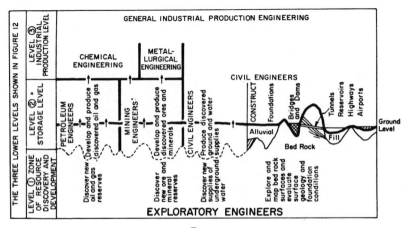

Fig. 13.

THE ROLE OF "THE UNIVERSITY" IN THE SPACE-AGE DEVELOPMENT OF RESOURCES

Diagram 1 has also been prepared to show how, within a properly-integrated "University" different Divisional groupings carry different (but inter-dependent) functional responsibilities: Thus

One group yields information regarding the emotional, aesthetic and spiritual insights and aspirations which have guided the growth of past civilizations;

Another group seeks to discover the Laws of Nature which provide the natural frames-of-reference for human activity; whereas

Engineering *science* seeks to devise and guide operational systems which will conform to proper motivation and to natural law and hence make possible the peaceful progress of Mankind.

DIAGRAM I

A University includes

			Engineering
Religion History Philosophy Other Humani- ties	Which provide	insights into Man's spiritual nature and moral and social responsibilities and into basic human motivations – and normal responses thereto.	
Psychology Social Sciences and Law Geography	Which provide	insights into the objectives, methods and patterns of short-term, constructive, social and political action.	Which employs that combination of Art, Technology and Science, under guidance con- tributed by all other University scholarly and professional groupings, whereby creative imagi- nation, natural re- sources, human capaci- ties, and intellectual and spiritual wisdom can be so integrated and sup- ported as to serve con- structively, the needs and worthy purposes of Mankind.
Biological and Medical Science Earth Sciences Natural Science and Mathematics	Which provide	insights into the basic princi- ples of natural law; into the world-geography of es- sential natural-resource occurrence; into the pro- spective and long-term human significance of recent scientific discoveries; and into the probability of yet further revolutionary scientific dis- covery and invention.	

SECTION IV-A

THE IRREGULAR OCCURRENCE
OF THE WORLD'S IMPORTANT PHYSICAL RESOURCES,
AND WHY DIFFERENT REGIONS HAVE DIFFERENT KINDS
AND DIFFERENT AMOUNTS OF (HIDDEN) MINERAL WEALTH

The world's more important physical resources are of very irregular geographic occurrence. Thus climate, rainfall and water supply are highly irregular in their global distribution – in considerable measure due to irregularities in the size, shape and geographic position of the continents and to irregularities in the shape, height and position of the world's mountain systems and ranges, as these affect climate and the circulation of moisture-laden winds. (The irregularities in the world's climatic, topo- graphic and agricultural situations are depicted by maps appearing on pages 18 and 19 of this volume).

Not only climatic, agricultural, forest and water resources occur ir-regularly, because of topographic and geographic factors, but the world's mineral deposits are at least equally irregular in their occurrence due either to ancient – or – recent mountainbuilding movements and regional elevations or depressions or tiltings which have affected different parts of the earth's crust. (See Fig. 14).

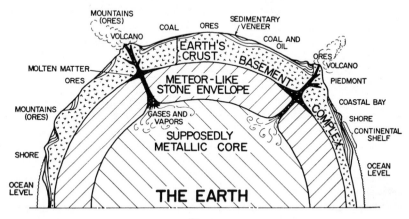

Fig. 14.

The same deformative forces that have caused the elevation of mountain ranges have also caused recurrent deepenings of old basinal depressions and downfolds in the earth's crust, within which thick sea-laid and strand-line deposits may have accumulated, thus providing conditions favorable to the origin and "accumulation" or "trapping" of commercially valuable deposits of oil and gas.

(See Fig. 15).

Thick layers of rock salt, locally associated with potash minerals, also have been developed in ancient lagunal deposits, closely associated, genetically and geographically, with the oilbearing strata. Likewise, old coastal swamps may have become loci for the accumulation of thick peat deposits – to be later metamorphosed into coals of different ranks.

(See Fig. 16).

Furthermore, many metallic ores are found within present-day volcanic or mountainous areas (see Figs. 7, 14 and 17), or they are present where the "roots" of old and deeply-eroded mountain-systems have been laid bare by the stripping off of former sedimentary cover, thus exposing great belts of rich iron ores (developed in ancient times within great trough-fillings of taconite or iron rich flinty rock). By contrast less deformed foothills or

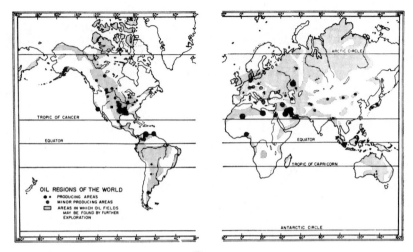

Fig. 15.

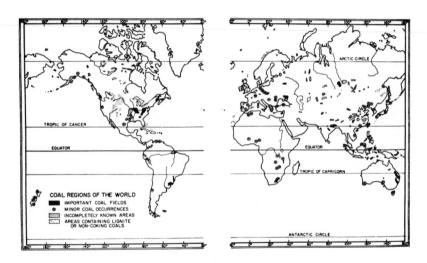

Fig. 16.

plains areas may contain "telemagmatic" lead and zinc ores, or limestones or other useful rocks or minerals.

(See also Fig. 17).

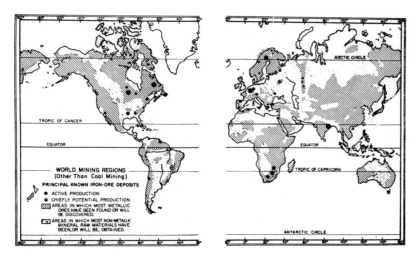

Fig. 17.

THE ABATEMENT OF WORLD CRISIS –
THROUGH THE ADVANCEMENT OF WORLD-RESOURCE DEVELOPMENT,
BY MEANS OF REGIONAL ECONOMIC INTEGRATIONS

The abatement of world-crisis calls not only for the establishment of effective controls over population-increase but also for voluntary regional economic integrations. This is both because of the far-flung and irregular world-occurrence of many of the material resources indispensable to modern productive industry and technology – mentioned just above – and also because two World-Wars (and many lesser ones) have resulted from the fact that voluntary *economic federation* and political *confederation* have not kept pace with scientific discovery and with technologic capacity-to-produce. This fact – that the creation of *regional* United Nations groupings should be agreed to and announced as the prime aim of World-War II, was pointed out by the writer in a 1940 publication – copies of which went to President ROOSEVELT before he and Prime Minister WINSTON CHURCHILL devised their Atlantic Charter and announced their advocacy of the Four Freedoms. In this brochure the writer stated a world-wide United Nations economic (and eventually political) union should be an ultimate. second-step, goal. But that such a *world-wide* organization could not be a really effective one until after *regional* United Nations economic-unions had been built, as piers upon which the total economic-and-political bridge could be supported. Now the member-nations of the UN are trying to hold the "bridge" up with one hand, while going back to start the building of the piers by which that bridge must be supported.

Historical Sidelights Indicating Why Progressive Regional Economic Integrations Are Both Natural – and Necessary – for Satisfactory Economic Growth and for Industrial-Resource Development

Case Illustration 1. About 174 years ago there were, on the Atlantic Seaboard of North America 13 small new Sovereign States – or nations. Each one with high aspirations; each one trying to grow in a relatively small and undeveloped area, and each one incapable of generating enough production (and enough revenue) to support its people, its defense-establishment and a satisfactory standard of living. They were like 13 shrubs planted in 13 small flower pots (see Stage 1 of Fig. 18-A) – pots which were too small to provide the nutrients and the support-bases required for sustained and effective growth. Hence by 1789 all 13 "nations" had become bankrupt. All were moribund, politically, and all were defenseless – to all practical purposes.

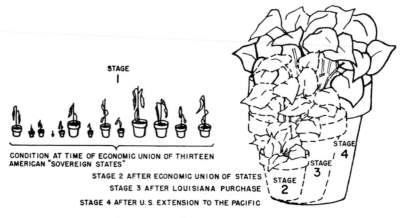

STAGE
1

CONDITION AT TIME OF ECONOMIC UNION OF THIRTEEN
AMERICAN "SOVEREIGN STATES"

STAGE 2 AFTER ECONOMIC UNION OF STATES
STAGE 3 AFTER LOUISIANA PURCHASE
STAGE 4 AFTER U.S. EXTENSION TO THE PACIFIC

STAGE 4
STAGE 3
STAGE 2

Fig. 18–A.

ALEXANDER HAMILTON and others thereupon persuaded the 13 Sovereign States to enter into a full-fledged economic-and-currency union, while retaining their State governments (for local, legislative and administrative purposes) under an ambiguous overall Constitution, which some regarded as Federal and some regarded as Confederative. Howbeit, the new (combined) economy, planted in a new flower pot (which included not just the seaboard areas but all territory east of the Mississippi River (see Stage 2 of Fig. 18-A), flourished and gained such strength that THOMAS JEFFERSON was able to substantially double the size of the flower pot by the Lousiana Purchase – while also establishing (through the Lewis and Clark expedition) a claim upon part of the "Oregon Country". (See Stage 3 of Fig. 18-A). Later on the U.S. economy was again transplanted into a yet bigger flower pot (see Stage 4 of Fig. 18-A) and the pre-1921 growth of the U.S. economy went on apace. But after that, though the growth was continuing, the "national" flower pot was not exchanged for a larger one – with the results that the "national" pot was fractured, (see Figure 18-B) whereafter the roots of the U.S. economy spread widely, and the new "economic growth" (proceeding from these U.S. roots), has been (and is now) taking place in regions far beyond the boundaries of the United States. For in these foreign areas the subsoil nutrients have not been depleted – as they have *within the United States itself*. (And yet Americans seem to be amazed that their *domestic* economy is not growing more robustly!)

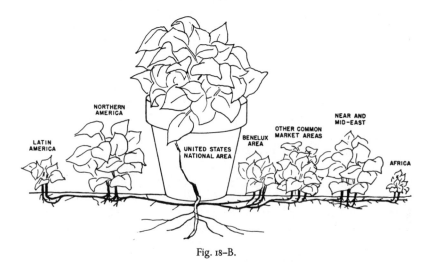

Fig. 18–B.

However the Soviet Union has gained the consent(?) of its satellite countries, to their inclusion in a Soviet economic union – of a sort. So that with the combination of the productive industries of the satellites, with the vast virgin mineral resources of Siberia, the Soviet economic growth is able to go forward with ample growth-space and with a full suite of needed nutrients (see Fig. 18-C, § 3).

Also, with the effective example of the Benelux economic integration to guide them the Inner Six nations (of the European Common Market) and the EFTA (or Outer Seven) groups have been moving in the same direction. But it is clear that a *constructive* development of West European industrial and

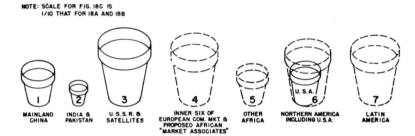

Fig. 18-C.

economic capacity cannot take place (peacefully) within a merely Western European "flower pot," any more than the U.S. economy can *grow*, merely within a U.S.-sized national area. Neither can the economics of the Latin American countries become modern ones, within the limits of their respective *national* areas. Nor can the newly-created African nations hope to be able to support national governments and national populations – *except* through participation in regional *economic* integrations so large that they include not only adequate sources of raw materials but also adequate manufacturing facilities; sources of capital; and goods-exchange (or market) areas.

Wherefore, since the needs of populations grow – as do also the needs of modern productive industry, it seems clear that Regional Economic groupings must be developed within the UN framework – as the Charter permits. Because if this is done each of those six or seven viable regional economic unions which might be so developed, would be able to join, advantageously, in competitive-cooperative global economic cooperation. Whereby all efforts could be directed toward a constructive (and non-exploitationist) meeting of human needs. Moreover if reasonable and mutually-advantageous trade arrangements should be thus developed-across the Iron and Bamboo Curtains – then reasonably the Soviet and Chinese and Indian peoples should be able to join in helping to solve the problems of the peoples of Mainland Asia – while the Pan-Atlantic Countries, plus Japan – and Australia and New Zealand try to solve the problems of the other half of the human race. On this basis the tax money now being poured into the Arms Race would be usable to provide alternative employment for the workers and the factories now producing war material – because of the need for mass-producing the enormous volumes of simple consumer-goods articles which are so essential to the well-being of more than a billion people.

At the maximum the world cannot presently support (peacefully) more than seven economic unions (see Fig. 18-C) and it would probably be far better if four of these units (Units 4, 5, 6 and 7 of Fig. 18-C) were actually to develop as one unit because, for basic reasons of history and culture, it seems probable that direct European cooperation in Latin America will be more acceptable than North American – even though the small guidance committee (for the total evolving mainly "Atlantic" economic union) should be under combined French, German, Japanese and Anglo-American *leadership* – with a proper (democratic) representation of the interests of *all* the component countries, in all legislative phases of the union's operation.

SECTION IV-C

It is the writer's opinion that it is through the development of such regional economic integrations that World-Peace will become possible. (After the several nations have put into operation proper and effective population-control measures – thereby enabling them to cross over the "Population Control River") (see Figure 19).

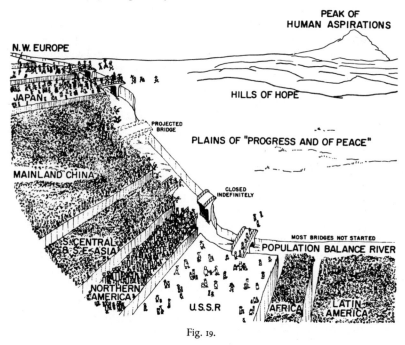

Fig. 19.

For such effective population-control measures must be in operation before the nations will be able to move, together, onto the Plains of Progress and of Peace – where stable, progressive and cooperative conditions will make it possible, for example, to:

(1) Undertake continent-wide water-diversion and irrigation projects;

(2) Undertake the building of great natural-gas pipeline systems – as, for example, from the Persian Gulf area, across Iraq, Turkey and Greece into Southeastern and Central Europe; or from Libya, northward to the coast, and thence eastward to Egyptian ports and industrial areas.

(3) Undertake global (and cooperative) development of the water, minerals and chemicals, and biologic resources of the oceans.

(Whether these things *will* be done will probably depend upon the dedicated efforts of the World's Young People – for the older ones, who grew up in a different world, are mostly too old, too tired and too inflexible in their thinking to make the prodigious efforts that present situations call for.)

Finally – these young people may find it useful to think over certain things (which were quoted by a Boy Scouts of America geological brochure) from an article written by EUGENE HOLMAN, a geologist and a wise and concerned man, (who was – at the time he wrote, the President of the Standard Oil Company of New Jersey – one of the world's largest industrial concerns). As quoted, Mr. HOLMAN said:

"To the Free Man all things are possible. Imagination, controlled and applied, is the wand which can reveal the invisible, change the useless into the useful, waste into raw materials of great value, *exhaustible* resources *into* inexhaustible resources..... Pioneer research is the key that unlocks the greatest energy resource of all – the infinite power of the human individual." And, in concluding his article Mr. HOLMAN pointed out *that industry should, in its own interest – and in the interest of all – be dedicated to the meeting of legitimate human need* – his words being "The longer I live, the more convinced I am that material progress is not only valueless without spiritual progress – it is, in the long term, impossible."

SUMMARY

The rhythms of the political pendulum, recorded in ancient and eo-modern history, and the systole and diastole of cultural and spiritual development (made so strikingly evident by the rise, and decline, of successive civilizations), have been induced by opposing forces, operating within a particular environmental continuum. To re-state the foregoing two propositions more simply and in more specific terms, it can be said that the facts of history show that rapid and continuing upswings in local population-pressures have heretofore been inevitably followed by rapid releases of such pressures (through expansionist war-and-colonization) and that the periods of growing material-resource scarcity (which had characterized the pressure build-up period) were, in turn, succeeded by periods of relative economic abundance, following a war-of-conquest (as the resources of other peoples had become available, through the processes of conquest-plus-massacre.) Hence, stating in economic terms, what has happened so many times, historically, *dynamic demand* for material resources would mount, due to population-increase. But this demand was repressed and kept bottled up for longer or shorter periods of time, during which there was a progressive relative decrease in the available per capita *supply* of needed materials. Therefore, political explosions recurred – when *demands* could no longer be held in check; just as volcanic eruptions and geyser eruptions take place, periodically, because limiting resistances are recurrently overcome by continuously-generated pressures.

It is also worthy of note that whenever a local and rapid build-up in population-pressures *had* resulted in an expansionist *outflow* of soldiers and an *inflow* of captured wealth and captured slaves, a period of cultural and spiritual flowering would take place within the newly-expanded kingdom or empire – a flowering which would occur because it had become possible for unusually-gifted persons (among the elite of the newly-expanded kingdom or empire) to free themselves from the routine chores and cares of life. Wherefore such unusual persons would find it possible to spend time in quiet thought; in a seeking for new stimulation and new insights (through conferences and discussions with others); and in seeking to mature and to make use of their new insights and of their newly-gained capacities. The cultural flowerings thus induced, might, perhaps, be in the field of Revelation and Religion; or in those of Philosophy or Science; or in those of Literature or of the Graphic Arts or Music, etc. – progress in these several fields being jointly expressive of Man's instinctive (and perennial) yearning for the Good, the True and the Beautiful.

Moreover, in time, such a "springtime" flowering of a particular culture would pass on into a summer period – during which there would be a development and maturing of seeds (for some subsequent renewal of cultural and spiritual growth) despite the fact that a progressive and accelerating deterioration of local living conditions was already again in progress – for the simple reason that local populations were again multiplying rapidly and were again beginning to outstrip such supplies of useful material resources as were locally (and technologically) available. This was true because the supplies of such "support resources" would undergo not only *relative* but also *actual* shrinkage, due to the crude and destructively-exploitationist practices then employed. Hence demagoguery and political corruption would be stimulated; social stresses and disruptions would increase and the mental and spiritual elements of the local culture would become formal: then static; and then reactionary and repressive – so that the people, being no longer provided with wise and inspiring leadership, would first become the victims of domestic demagogues and despots and later on would be overwhelmed, either by the eruption of mobs of jobless workers and of frustrated juveniles – or by some new horde of expansionist barbarians, pouring in from a nearby region.

Wherefore it is clear that throughout all ages, up until "yesterday," the accelerating increase of human populations (though temporarily *checked* by famine or by pestilence or by massacre) had, only rarely and locally, been subject to any intelligent human control (despite the facts that a limited infanticide was apparently practiced by some peoples, and that in primitive cultures intertribal war – plus "practical" (or "reasonable") cannibalism held population in check.) Moreover, this progressive, though irregular growth of human populations has, until recently taken place under such circumstances of haste-and-waste that contemporary exploratory and developmental science-and-technology have not been able to gain upon – or even offset – the current rates of soil depletion; of deforestation; or of the exhaustion of (known) deposits of useful minerals. Wherefore, since the ravaging and devastation of natural resources has increased, effectively pari passu with the accelerations of population-increase, it was inevitable that national and imperial economic collapses would recur, leading to economic-and-political downfalls (see Fig. 11) and to local or regional "Dark Ages-periods" of lesser or greater length.

The three forces, then, which gave rise to this ages-long cyclic rhythm of national growth, cultural flowering, and political-and-military collapse, were: (1) The recurrent local build-up of explosive economic demand, induced by population-growth. (2) The inability of the then-existent agricultural and exploratory technologies to keep supply in balance with the accelerating needs of the growing populations, partly because of opportunistic and exploitationist (i.e. "profit-motive") modes of operation, and (3) the fact that population-growth (and contemporaneous economic decline) went on within a socio-economic environment which lacked adequate information as to the elements, principles and characteristics of natural law (as these have been learned about through scientific inquiry); which also was inadequately provided with the technologic experience (and devices) needed to cause sufficiently-rapid increases in the output of usable material substances; and which similarly lacked an adequate awareness of those principles of (modern) Engineering Science which now make it possible for cooperating *teams* of persons to be successful in visualizing, analyzing and solving the enormously-complex problems of today. (This last-mentioned matter is of basic world-importance, because today's problems cannot be either visualized or solved by simple citizens, or by individual legislators or by groups of non-engineer administrators – except with adequate and unbiased advice and guidance). Therefore it is most important to note that modern science, technology and engineering have, in fact, *now* advanced so far that world-society *can* be assured that (under non-exploitationist planning and operation) the world's supplies of *needed*, (usable) substances can be made to increase continually – and also relative to population size – IF medical men and biologists and political leaders can, and do, devise-and-apply proper methods for holding family-size at reasonable, proper and supportable levels. Wherefore, as of today, the transcendent question with respect to human survival is "Are the world's human beings finally reaching a stage where they can (and will) so use their intelligence and also so control their animal instincts that they may be able to assure both their own survival plus a peaceful and satisfying future for their children?" These issues – which are truly ones of Life or Death for all of us – are, today, being balanced on the razor's edge – and national and international (UN) decisions regarding them will soon determine whether the Cold War can be abated and ended, or whether it will instead, soon explode into unimaginable tragedy.

Fortunately the problems involved in establishing plans for setting up and operating a peaceful, progressive and *fair* system for a *competitive* (yet also cooperative) co-existance *are* ones which *can* be solved – if the leaders concerned *really* have the "guts" needed to make – and enforce, the decisions required. For both the information and means exist for the formulation and implementation of the solutions called for. Wherefore, the general questions regarding our ability to survive current and impending population-crises narrow down to two specific ones, namely: "Will the world's leaders *dare* to show the wisdom, the courage and the quickness necessary for devising and applying positive and constructively-remedial measures?" And also "have these leaders been provided with adequate, competent, practical and unbiased information (and suggestions) as to *how* the world's population-problems *can be* solved?" (One nation (Japan) *has* recently solved this problem – *as a nation*. Other peoples have solved it informally, as citizens. Therefore the population-control problem, *is not* an impossible or an insoluble one).

CONCLUSION

The readers of *this volume* may reasonably hope to find within it both a competent and full concensus as to the over-all terms of the world's population-problems, present and prospective. Also they may hope that the conclusion to *this chapter* will similarly present competent and enlightening statements about the nature, usefulness and adequacy of the world's material-substance reserves. Wherefore, in order to cover this total resource-situation quickly and in understandable terms, the writer's conclusions relative to these matters can be best provided through the quotation of a parable, which runs as follows:

"Once upon a time there was a Great Emperor who ruled over many lands and over many peoples. And one day this Emperor summoned before him the Court Jester and spoke to him in this fashion: "I have called you before me, O Fool, in order that you shall answer for me three questions – and I ask *you* these questions, O Fool, for two reasons – first, because a Wise Ruler may ask questions which only a Fool would try to answer; and secondly, because I have already propounded these same

questions to my Seven Court Soothsayers – all mighty interpreters of
auguries and omens – such as are provided by flights of birds and by other
"economic indicators" – and I have received from these Seven Wise Men
twenty-one (21) answers to my *three* questions. Moreover these twenty-one
answers were quite contradictory. Each one was based upon the *theories*
of some particularly great Expounder. And many of them were supported
by massive statistical statements, which had been compiled with great care
(and with equally-great "discretion"). Thus seeming to give confirmation
to that ribald jest which says that "statistics are used by some to provide
mathematically-straight lines – from unwarranted assumptions to foregone conclusions."

"BUT NOW, O Fool, I WANT TO KNOW THE FACTS!! For being a Great Emperor
it is obvious that the more subjects I have the greater Emperor am I.
Hence, my three questions are these:

"*Question 1.* Will the resources of my Empire provide support for an
unlimited number of people for an *unlimited* length of time?

"*Question 2.* Will the resources of my Empire support a gradually-*increasing*
number of people for an *unlimited* length of time? And

"*Question 3.* Will the resources of my Empire provide support for the
present number of my subjects for an unlimited period of time?

Whereupon the Jester made answer as follows:

"The answer to Question 1, O Sire, is certainly – No! For experiments
in unlimited procreation have been tried hundreds and hundreds of times
– each time by a different form of Life – with the same invariable result –
the speedy extinction of each and every such experimenting Life-form.

'The answer to Question 3, is also – No! Both because you cannot move
quickly enough to hold the populations of your Empire at today's level;
and, more importantly, because today's standards of living are already so
low through great parts of your territories that even a brief continuation
of present rates of population-growth will cause various groups to become
completely desperate – wherefore, they will attack their neighbors and seek
to seize their property. Then, as such attacks are pressed, other nations
will be drawn in; the fighting will spread and sooner or later Nuclear War
will result. And Nuclear War, O Sire, does not promise a Bright Future
for anyone."

"Lastly, in answer to your Question 2, I shall need to tell you the story
of the tenderhearted farmer, who gave the weeds of his farm the same
loving care that he lavished on his flowers, vegetables, field-crops and
fruit trees. Whereupon, on this basis, O Sire, the weeds throve and multiplied mightily – while the flowers and vegetables and crops and fruit trees
were gradually choked out – and died. So – presently, Sire – the Jungle
moved in and swallowed all."

"These, O Sire, are my answers. And, since you *are* a Great and Wise
Emperor, you will know what I mean by this, my third, answer. For

verily YOU needs *must decide* whether *you* wish to raise weeds – and more weeds – or, on the contrary whether you wish to raise bigger and bigger crops by using better and better farming methods. For on this latter basis your lands *will* produce ever-larger yields of essential foods and so will be able to support an ever-growing population, so long as this population remains *in balance* with the supplies being produced. *This can be done if you are determined that it shall be done!*

Therefore either YOU *or* the People, must decide which answer to *choose*. But YOU, as the People's Leader, are the one who must take the action needed to enforce the answer chosen. Wherefore I feel very sorry for you! And now – "Selah and Salaam, O Sire."

WILLIAM TAYLOR THOM, Jr., Ph.D., D.Sc., is President of the American Institute of Geonomy and Natural Resources and Chairman, Emeritus, of the Department of Geological Engineering, Princeton University. He was a staff member of the United States Geological Survey from 1913 to 1929. He has served as Chairman of the National Research Council Committee on Studies in Petroleum Geology; also Chairman of the American Geophysical Unions Special Committee for the Geophysical and Geological Study of Continents, 1935–1948. He has been a member of numerous professional associations including the Yellowstone-Bighorn Research Association (Past-President); the American Association of Petroleum Geologists (Honorary Member); the American Institute of Mining, Metallurgical and Petroleum Engineers (Honorary Senior Member); The Geological Society of America, and others. Professor THOM is author of Petroleum and Coal, the Keys to the Future (1929); the Goal of Democracy (1940); National and Regional Work-Potentials, 1790–1938 (1945); Tectonic Sketch Map of North America (1959); Tectonic Team-Research – Key to Social Progress and World Peace (1952); and Science and Engineering and the Future of Man (1961).

APPENDIX

The World Academy of Art and Science

The *second Plenary Session of the World Academy of Art and Science*, held in Stockholm July 29 to August 2, 1963, adopted as a partial statement of immediate objectives, the following resolution:

ANNOUNCEMENT

"The World Academy of Art and Science is not its own end. Its Fellows are no less sensitive to the needs, aspirations, and underdeveloped potentialities of the world's illiterate herdsmen and villagers, than to the perplexities of presidents and directors of international organizations, universities, foundations, and even nations.

Echoing through the turbulent corridors of our century are overused ideas appropriate to times now best dead. Mankind is coming to recognize and wish removed many traditional psychological and sociological barriers. Truly this is a time of transition in which knowledge and wisdom are coming to be regarded as inseparable.

The World Academy of Art and Science has aspired to be a transnational forum in which the problems of mankind can be responsibly discussed and from an objective, scientific, and global point of view. It now stands ready to serve as best it can as an advisory body in the service of human welfare outside of all group interests.

The World Academy of Art and Science is now open to consideration of a limited number of applications from international organizations, universities, foundations, and governments for assistance with non-political problems and programs. Special temporary committees headed by Fellows of the World Academy will be established for working on those problems accepted for study.

It is believed that in some instances the Academy will be of help by formulating and reformulating pertinent questions bringing multi-disciplinary talents and knowledge to bear on situations, pointing-up the mirage and colorations of pre-scientific assumptions, and opening the way to developing a climate of opinion suitable for growth of the scientific and creative spirit.

Applications can be made to the Secretary General

> World Academy of Art and Science
> 1 Ruppin Street
> Rehovot; Israel

Included should be an adequate statement of the problem and help desired. To the extent possible thoughtful consideration will be given to all."

EXECUTIVE COMMITTEE OF WAAS

The Second Plenary Meeting of WAAS in Stockholm confirmed the election of the following Fellows to the Executive Committee for the first period until 1965 (III. Plenary Meeting):

President: Lord JOHN BOYD ORR (U.K.)
Vice Presidents: STUART MUDD (U.S.A.)
HERMANN JOSEPH MULLER (U.S.A.)
HUGO OSVALD (Sweden)
Hon. Sec. General: HUGO BOYKO (Israel)
Hon. Secretary   : LLOYD L. MORAIN (U.S.A.)
Hon. Secretary   : SOLCO W. TROMP (Netherlands)

Chairman, Committee for the Study on Symbols:
ALDOUS HUXLEY (U.S.A.)
(died November 22, 1963)

Bank Accounts: Discount Bank (Overseas) Ltd.,
5, Quai de l'Ile, Genève, Switzerland.

Jacob Japhet & Co., Ltd.,
P.O.B. 289, Jerusalem, Israel.

The membership of the World Academy of Art and Science, as of August 1963, is the following:

List of Fellows

as of August 31, 1963

First Honorary Fellow: H. M. KING GUSTAF VI. ADOLF OF SWEDEN, F.R.S.

Fellows:

			Main International Organizations or Special Activities, etc.
ALVAR H. AALTO	Helsinki, Finland	Architect	Hon. member of Academies of various countries
JOSE MARIA ALBAREDA-HERRERA	Madrid, Spain	Soil Scientist	Rector del Estudio General de Navarra, Hon. Consultant of UNESCO
PIERRE AUGER	Paris, France	Physicist	Advisor and former Director of UNESCO Dept. of Natural Sciences; Director General, European Space Research Org.
FRITZ BAADE	Bonn, Fed. Rep. of Germany	Economist	Dir., Res. Inst., Economy of Developing Countries
MARSTON BATES	Ann Arbor, Michigan	Zoologist	Former Chairm. Cttee on Biol. and Medic. Sciences, National Science Foundation, etc.
M. BATISSE	Paris, France	Science Coordinator	Head, Div. Natural Resources, UNESCO
I. BERENBLUM	Rehovot, Israel	Exp. Biologist Cancer Research	Member, Int. Cancer Research Commission
ERNST D. BERGMANN	Jerusalem, Israel	Chemist	Member, Exec. Council of World University Service
HOMI JEHANGIR BHABHA	Bombay, India	Physicist	Pres., Int. Atomic Energy Conf., 1955; Member, U.N. Scientific Advisory Cttee
HANS BOBEK	Vienna, Austria	Geographer	Consultant to UNESCO, etc.
CATHERINE DRINKER BOWEN	Haverford, Pa.	Biographer	Fellow Royal Society of Literature
LORD J. BOYD ORR	Brechin, U.K.	Nutritionist	President, WAAS; Founder and first Dir. General of FAO; Nobel Laureate

Elisabeth Boyko	Rehovot, Israel	Botanist, Horticulturist	Hon. Secr., International Committee of Ecological Climatography
Hugo N. Boyko	Rehovot, Israel	Ecologist, Science-Coordinator	Sec. General, WAAS; Vice President ISB; Pres. ICE (1947–1961) Hon. Consultant UNESCO
Elisa Braun-Barnett	New York, N.Y.	Professor of Music	Former Head, Music Broadcasting Dept. of India
Jacob Bronowski	London, U.K.	Eng. Scientist, Science-Coordinator	Former Head of Projects, UNESCO
Ralph W. Burhoe	Boston, Mass.	Executive Officer	American Academy of Arts and Sciences
Lyle K. Bush	Boston, Mass.	Professor of Fine Arts	
Julien Cain	Paris, France	Librarian	Pres., Int. Library Commission; Member Exec. Cncl. UNESCO, 1958
Stanley A. Cain	Ann Arbor, Mich.	Plant Ecologist	Form. Pres., Ecological Soc. of America
Ritchie P. Calder	Edinburgh, U.K.	Author, Prof. of Internat. Relations	Pres., Int. Assn. of Science Writers, UNESCO Kalinga Prize
Guido Calogero	Rome, Italy	Prof. of Philosophy	Former Dir. of Italian Inst. London
G. Brock Chisholm	Seawood, Canada	Public Health Research	Founder and first Dir. General of WHO; "Humanist of the Year" Award, 1959
Pierre Chouard	Paris, France	Botanist	Vice President, IUBS; Pres., Bot. Section
Arthur C. Clarke	Colombo, Ceylon	Writer	Pres., Ceylon Astronomical Soc.; UNESCO Kalinga Prize, 1961
J. L. Cloudsley-Thompson	Khartoum, Sudan	Zoologist	
John Cohen	Manchester, U.K.	Psychologist	Consultant to UNESCO, 1948–1950; Tech. Sec., World Congress on Mental Health
Norman Cousins	New York, N.Y.	Writer, Editor	Hon. President, United World Federalists
James F. Crow	Madison, Wis.	Geneticist (Radiation Protection)	Past Pres., Genetics Society of America
Pierre Dansereau	New York, N.Y.	Botanist, Plant Ecologist	Member, Int. Council of Botany
C. D. Darlington	Oxford, U.K.	Geneticist	
Bernard D. Davis	Cambridge, Mass.	Bacteriologist	Professor, Harvard Medical School

JOSUÉ DE CASTRO	São Paulo, Brazil	Physian, Geographer, Sociologist	Former Dir. Gen. of FAO; Ambassador, Head of the Brazilian Permanent Delegation to UN, Geneva
GERHARD J. P. DOMAGK	Elberfeld, Germany	Pathologist, Cancer Research	Nobel Laureate
GERHARD EIS	Heidelberg, Fed. Rep. of Germany	Philologist	.
LOREN C. EISELEY	Philadelphia, Pa.	Anthropologist, Essayist	Chairm. History and Philosophy of Sci., Univ. Penna
JOHN FRANKLIN ENDERS	Boston, Mass.	Microbiologist	Nobel Laureate
LEOPOLD ESCANDE	Toulouse, France	Physicist, Hydraulic Eng.	Vice Pres., Int. Assn. of Hydraulic Research; Secr. Gen. Nat. Res. Cncl. of France
MAURICE EWING	Palisades, N.Y.	Geophysicist	Past Pres., Amer. Geophysical Union; Seismol. Soc. America
PAUL FALLOT (died 1961)	Paris, France		
JULIAN W. FEISS	Washington, D.C.	Geologist	
RICHARD M. FIELD (died 1961)	South Duxbury, Mass.		Co-founder of WAAS
RALPH E. FLANDERS	Washington, D.C.	Mechanical Engineer	Former Chairman, Committee for Economic Development, U.S. Dept. of Commerce.
F. R. FOSBERG	Washington, D.C.	Ecologist	Vice Pres., Int. Assn. for Tropical Ecology; Vice Pres., Nature Conservancy
J. D. FRANK	Baltimore, Md.	Psychiatrist	
GILBERTO DE MELLO FREYRE	Apipucos, Brazil	Social Anthropologist	Dir., Inst. Int. de Civilisations Differentes
H. FRIEDRICH-FREKSA	Tubingen, Germany	Physicist	
CLARENCE J. GAMBLE	Milton, Mass.	Physician	President, Pathfinder Fund
HENRY GAUSSEN	Toulouse, France	Botanist	Dir. Int. Inst. for Mapping of Vegetation
CAROLA GIEDION-WELCKER	Zurich, Switzerland	Writer	
MAX HABICHT	Genève, Switzerland	International Legal Advisor	Hon. Legal Advisor. WAAS; Member, Exec. Committee Union of Int. Org.
J. GEORGE HARRAR	New York, N.Y.	Agriculturist, Plantpatholog.	President, Rockefeller Foundation
CARL-GÖRAN HEDÉN	Stockholm, Sweden	Microbiologist, Biotechnologist	Vice Pres., IAMS

ROGER J. HEIM	Paris, France	Mycologist	Past Pres., IUCN; Pres. Académie des Sciences
J. HEIMANS	Amsterdam, Netherlands	Botanist	
ERICH M. HERING	Berlin, Germany	Entomologist,	Member, Int. Commission on Zoological Nomenclature
WILLIAM BAYARD HEROY	Dallas, Texas	Geologist, Geophysicist	
WALTER R. HESS	Zurich, Switzerland	Physiologist	Nobel Laureate
GEORGE DE HEVESY	Stockholm, Sweden	Biophysicist	Nobel Laureate; Atoms for Peace Award
CORNIELLE J. F. HEYMANS	Ghent, Belgium	Pharmacologist	Nobel Laureate
ROCHI HINGORANI	London, U.K.	Physician	World Chairman, Int. Cultural Exchange World Org.
HUDSON HOAGLAND	Shrewsbury, Mass.	Neurophysiologist	Pres., American Acad. of Arts and Sciences
ALBERT HOFMANN	Basle, Switzerland	Chemist	
F. G. HOUTERMANS	Bern, Switzerland	Physicist	
A. EDWARD A. HUDSON	Jackson, Tenn.	Haematologist, Parasitologist	
ALDOUS L. HUXLEY (died Nov. 22, 1963)	London, U.K. Los Angeles, Calif.	Essayist and Poet	Chairman, Editorial Cttee. of WAAS
HENRYK F. INFIELD	Jerusalem, Israël	Sociologist	Pres., Int. Council Sociology of Cooperation
JOHN D. ISAACS	La Jolla, Cal.	Oceanographer	
WIESLAW JEZIERSKI	Krakow, Poland	Political Scientist	Professor of Legal and Political Philosophy
JOSEPH MARION JONES	Washington, D.C.	Economist, Author	Former Special Assistant, Marshall Plan
ROMAN DE VICENTE JORDANA	Madrid, Spain	Microbiologist	
LOUIS I. KAHN	Philadelphia, Pa.	Architect	Pres., American Soc. of Planners and Architects
THEODORE VON KARMAN (died 1963)	Paris, France	Physicist, Aeronautical Eng.	Dir., Int. Academy of Astronautics; Hon. President, IUTAM; „ „ ICAS
AARON KATCHALSKY-KATZIR	Rehovot, Israel	Chemist (Polymer research)	Pres., Israel Acad. of Sciences
OUAY KETUSINH	Bangkok, Thailand	Physiologist	
JAMES R. KILLIAN, JR.	Cambridge, Mass.	Technologist, Science Coordinator	Former Pres., Mass. Inst. of Technology

O. Klineberg	New York, N.Y.	Psychologist	
Hilary Koprowski	Philadelphia, Pa.	Biologist	Pres., New York Acad. of Sciences; Consultant WHO
Serge A. Korff	New York, N.Y.	Astrophysicist	Vice President, New York Acad. of Sciences
V. A. Kovda	Paris, France	Soil Scientist, Science-Coordinator	Dir. Dept. Natural Sciences, UNESCO
Swan Liat Kwee	Leiden, Netherlands	Philosopher	Hon. Editor, Bulletins of WAAS
Willis E. Lamb, Jr.	New Haven, Conn.	Physicist	Nobel Laureate
Harold D. Lasswell	New Haven, Conn.	Political Scientist	Co-founder of Political Science; Visiting Prof. in various countries, (incl. Univ. of Peking, Tokyo, etc.)
W. C. de Leeuw	Leiden, Netherlands	Plant Sociologist	Pres., Int. Assn. of Plant-Geogr. and Ecology
Sir Ben Lockspeiser	Birchway, U.K.	Physicist, Industrial Res. Science Coordinator	Pres., European Org. for Nuclear Res.
Walter C. Lowdermilk	Berkeley, Cal.	Soil Conservation	Consultant to WHO, FAO and various Gov'ts.
André Lwoff	Paris, France	Biophysicist	President, IAMS
Michel Magat	Orsay, France	Physical Chemist	
P. C. Mahalanobis	Calcutta, India	Statistician	Hon. Pres., Int. Statistical Inst.
P. Maheshvari	Delhi, India	Botanist (Embryology)	Sec., Nat. Inst. of Sciences India
F. Mainx	Vienna, Austria	Physicist	
Ivan Malek	Praha, C.S.R.	Microbiologist	Vice President, Czechoslovakian Academy of Sciences
Sven G. Markelius	Stockholm, Sweden	Architect	Member UNESCO Art Committee, etc.
Gaetano Martino	Messina, Italy	Physiologist	Pres., Academia Pelovitana; Former Minister of Education
Abraham Maslow	Waltham, Mass.	Psychologist	
Guiseppe Medici	Rome, Italy	Agricultural Economist	Pres., Land Reform Agcy.; Former Minister of Agriculture, of Education
Heinrich Meng	Basle, Switzerland	Psychologist, Psychohygienist	Founder of Psychohygiene
Yehudi Menuhin	London, U.K.	Violinist, Writer	

ROBERT K. MERTON	New York, N.Y.	Sociologist	
THEODORE A. MONOD	Dakar, Senegal	Zoologist	Pres., Intergovernmental Scientific Council for Africa (C.S.A.)
HENRY MOORE	Hoglands, U.K.	Sculptor	Hon. member of Academies of various countries
LLOYD L. MORAIN	San Francisco, Cal.	Author, Business Exec.	Hon. Sec. WAAS; Past Pres., Int. Soc. for General Semantics and the American Humanist Association
MARY MORAIN	San Francisco, Cal.	Author, Social Worker	Member, Exec. Com. Int. Humanist and Ethical Union
EMILY H. MUDD	Philadelphia, Pa.	Educator, Social Scientist	Past Pres. American Assn. of Marriage Counselors
STUART MUDD	Philadelphia, Pa.	Microbiologist	Vice-Pres., WAAS; Past President IAMS
HERBERT J. MULLER	Bloomington, Ind.	Historian, Author	
HERMANN JOSEPH MULLER	Bloomington, Ind.	Geneticist	Vice Pres., WAAS; Nobel Laureate
ALVA MYRDAL	Stockholm, Sweden	Sociologist	Former Director, UNESCO Dept. of Social Affairs
K. GUNNAR MYRDAL	Stockholm, Sweden	Economist, Statesman	Prof. of International Economy; former Executive Secr. U.N. Economic Comm. for Europe; former Minister of Trade & Commerce, Sweden
JOSEPH NEEDHAM	Cambridge, U.K.	Zoologist	Co-founder of UNESCO and first Director of its Natural Science Dept.
P. J. NOEL-BAKER	London, U.K.	Statesman	Nobel Laureate
JOHN H. NORTHROP	Berkeley, Cal.	Research Biophysicist	Nobel Laureate
SIR MARK OLIPHANT	Canberra, Australia	Physicist	Past Pres. Australia Academy of Science
SIR ALEXANDER OPPENHEIM	Kuala Lumpur, Malaya	Mathematician	Vice Chancellor Univ. of Malaya; Past Pres. Ass. of Southeast Asian Trustees of Higher Learning
ROBERT OPPENHEIMER	Princeton, N.J.	Physicist	Atoms for Peace Award
D. ORDMAN	Johannesburg, S. Africa	Medical Research	Chairman, Int. Cttee on Biometeorological Aspects of Human Disease, (ISB)
HUMPHREY OSMOND	Princeton, N.J.	Neuro-Psychiatrist, Anthropologist	Dir., N.J. State Bureau of Research in Neurology and Psychiatry

Hugo Osvald	Knivsta, Sweden	Plant ecologist; Agronomist	Vice Pres., WAAS; Member, Exec. Cttee, World Parliament Assn.; Former Senator, Swedish Parliament
Linus Pauling	Pasadena, Cal.	Chemist	Nobel Laureate: Chemistry (1954), Peace (1963)
Francis Perrin	Paris, France	Physicist	
George A. Petrides	E. Lansing, Mich.	Zoologist	
A. de Philippis	Firenze, Italy	Silviculturist	Vice Pres., Int. Union of Forest Research Stations
John F. V. Phillips	Salisbury, S. Rhodesia	Agriculturist	Former Advisor of World Bank on African Problems
Clarence E. Pickett	Philadelphia, Pa.	Educationist	Nobel Laureate (Peace), as Pres., American Friends Service Cttee.
Gerard Piel	New York, N.Y.	Science Editor and Author	
Gregory Pincus	Shrewsbury, Mass.	Experimental Biologist	Co-founder, Worcester Foundation for Experimental Biology
P. H. Plesch	N.Staffordshire, U.K.	Chemist (Polymer Research)	
Amerigo Pomales-Lebron	San Juan, P. R.	Microbiologist	Pres., Assn. of Microbiologists of Latin America
Christian Poulsen	Kobenhavn, Denmark	Paleontologist, Stratigrapher	Past Pres., Int. Paleontological Union
Boris Pregel	New York, N.Y.	Physicist, Engineer	Past Pres., New York Academy of Science
J. A. K. Quartey	Accra, Ghana	Chemist	
Giulio Racah	Jerusalem, Israel	Physicist	Rector, Hebrew University
P. C. Raheja	Jodhpur, India	Soil Scientist	Dir., Central Arid Zone Res. Inst. of India; Sec. Gen., Indian Soc. of Agronomy
L. A. Ramdas	New Delhi, India	Climatologist, Geophysicist	
Krishna Rao	New Delhi, India	Meteorologist	Mem. Executive Cttee., WMO. Dir. Gen. of Observatories, India Met. Dpt.
Lady Rama Rau	Bombay, India	Humanist	Pres., Int. Planned Parenthood Federation
Sir Herbert Read	Stonegrave, U.K.	Poet and Art Critic	Pres. Inst. of Contemporary Arts
Ernesto N. Rogers	Milano, Italy	Architect, Town Planner	UNESCO Committee of Five Architects, etc.
Walter A. Rosenblith	Cambridge, Mass.	Communications Biophysicist	Member, Exec. Cttee., IBRO; Member, Council, IOPAB

JEAN ROSTAND	Ville d'Avray, France	Writer, Biologist	UNESCO Kalinga Prize
J. ROTBLAT	London, U.K.	Physicist	Sec. General of Pugwash Conferences
EARL BERTRAND RUSSELL	Marioneth, U.K.	Philosopher	Nobel Laureate; UNESCO Kalinga Prize
JONAS EDWARD SALK	San Diego, Cal.	Physician Preventive Med.	
VICTOR SALKIND	New York, N.Y.	Hydro-Engineer and Hydrologist	Int. Consultant for Hydr. Eng. Projects
ARTHUR W. SAMPSON	Berkeley, Cal.	Forest Scientist	
FREDERICK SANGER	Cambridge, U.K.	Chemist	Nobel Laureate
FREDERICK SARGENT II	Urbana, Ill.	Physiologist	Pres., Int. Soc. for Bio-meteorology
FREDERICK SEITZ	Washington, D.C.	Physicist	Vice Pres., IUPAP. Pres., Nat. Academy of Sciences U.S.A.
T. SHIPLEY	Miami, Fla.	Experimental Psychologist	
H. L. SILVERMAN	Newark, N.J.	Clinical Psychologist	Sec. General, New Jersey Academy of Sciences
M. J. SIRKS	Haren, Netherlands	Geneticist	Past Pres., IUBS
EDGAR P. SNOW	Vaud, Switzerland	Writer	Expert on Asiatic countries, particularly China
STEPHEN SPENDER	London, U.K.	Writer, Poet & Critic	Counsellor to UNESCO
E. C. STAKMAN	St. Paul, Minnesota	Plant Pathologist	Scientific Advisor, Rocke-feller Foundation
HARLAN T. STETSON	Philadelphia, Pa.	Astronomer	
W. F. G. SWANN (died 1962)	Swarthmore, Pa.	Physicist	
ALBERT SZENT-GYORGYI	Woods Hole, Mass.	Biochemist	Nobel Laureate
LEO SZILARD	Washington, D.C.	Physicist, Microbiologist	Atoms for Peace Award
KENZO TANGE	Tokyo, Japan	Architect	
HAROLD TAYLOR	Bronxville, N.Y.	Educator	
HUGO THEORELL	Stockholm, Sweden	Biochemist	Nobel Laureate
HANS THIRRING	Vienna, Austria	Physicist	
W. TAYLOR THOM, JR.	Princeton, N.J.	Geologist, Geol. Engineer	Pres., American Inst. of Geonomy & Natural Re-sources
ARNE TISELIUS	Uppsala, Sweden	Biochemist	Pres., Nobel Foundation; Nobel Laureate; Past Pres., Int. Union of Pure & Applied Chem.

CARL TROLL	Bonn, Fed. Rep. Germany	Geographer	Past Pres., Int. Geographical Union
SOLCO W. TROMP	Oegstgeest-Leiden, Netherlands	Biometeorologist	Hon. Sec. WAAS; Secretary General, Int. Soc. of Biometeorology
A. C. UKIL	Calcutta, India	Geographer	Pres., The Asiatic Society
HAROLD C. UREY	La Jolla, Cal.	Chemist	Nobel Laureate
J. VAN MIEGHEM	Brussels, Belgium	Meteorologist	Secr. Gen., Int. Council of Scientific Unions (ICSU)
P. VAN OYE	Ghent, Belgium	Hydrobiologist	Vice-Pres., Int. Assn. of Limnology
J. L. VAN SOEST	The Hague, Netherlands	Prof. of Electro-Engineering	
J. UNGAR	Greenford, U.K.	Biochemist	
FRANS VERDOORN	Utrecht, Netherlands	Bio-historian, Botanist	Sec. General, Int. Bio-Historical Comm.
C. H. WADDINGTON	Edinburgh, Scotland	Geneticist	President, IUBS
E. T. S. WALTON	Dublin, Ireland	Physicist	Nobel Laureate
RACHAEL C. WASSERMAN	Montreal, Canada	Prof. of Humanities	
SADAMU WATANABE	Tokyo, Japan	Gerontologist	Chief Dir., Gerontological Assn. of Japan
WALTER W. WEISBACH (died 2 Sept., 1962)	The Hague, Netherlands		Co-founder of WAAS
EUGENE H. WEISSENBERG	Rio Piedras, Puerto Rico	Physician	Pres., Academia de Artes y Ciencias de Puerto Rico
VICTOR WESTHOFF	Driebergen, Netherlands	Botanist, Nature Conservationist	
HAROLD WESTON	New York, N.Y.	Artist and Humanist	Pres., Int. Assoc. of Plastic Arts
GEORGE H. WHIPPLE	Rochester, N.Y.	Pathologist	Nobel Laureate
GILBERT F. WHITE	Chicago, Ill.	Geographer	Past Pres. of A.A.A.S., Hon. Consultant of UNESCO
JOHN TUZO WILSON	Toronto, Canada	Geophysicist	Past Pres., IUGG
GEORGE P. WOOLLARD	Madison, Wis.	Geophysicist	
J. YANNEY–WILSON	Accra, Ghana	Botanist, Cytogeneticist	Secr. General, National Research Council, Ghana
HIDEKI YUKAWA	Kyoto, Japan	Physicist	Nobel Laureate

ABBREVIATIONS

FAO	Food and Agricultural Organization of United Nations Organization
FWA	Fellow, World Academy of Art and Science
Int.	International
IAMS	International Association of Microbiological Societies
IBRO	International Brain Research Organization (UNESCO)
ICAS	International Council of the Aeronautical Sciences
ICE	International Commission for Ecology of IUBS
IOPAB	International Organization for Pure and Applied Biophysics
ISB	International Society of Biometeorology
IUBS	International Union of Biological Sciences
IUCN	International Union for the Conservation of Nature
IUGG	International Union of Geophysics and Geodesy
IUPAP	International Union of Pure and Applied Physics
IUTAM	International Union of Theoretical and Applied Mechanics
UNESCO	United Nations Educational, Scientific and Cultural Organization
WAAS	World Academy of Art and Science
WHO	World Health Organization of United Nations Organization
WMO	World Meteorological Organization of United Nations Organization

Index

Index of Bibliographes and References to: